USING INDUSTRIAL HYDRAULICS

A state of the art textbook from
REXROTH WORLDWIDE HYDRAULICS

Prepared by:
Tom Frankenfield,
Manager, Technical Services Group,
The Rexroth Corporation,
Bethlehem, Pennsylvania

Published by:
HYDRAULICS & PNEUMATICS Magazine
Penton Plaza
1111 Chester Avenue
Cleveland, Ohio 44114

Second Edition 1984

Third Edition
First Printing
1979

Current printing (last digit):

10 9 8 7 6 5

RA 00301

Library of Congress Catalog Card Number: 84-81279

Printed in the United States of America

"Why does this magnificent applied science, which saves work and makes life easier, bring us little happiness? The simple answer runs, because we have not yet learned to make sensible use of it."

Albert Einstein (1879-1955)

PREFACE TO THE SECOND EDITION

Today, hydraulic equipment has become so influential in the design of industrial machinery, that without hydraulic systems automation as we know it would not be possible. If it were not for the ability to transmit and control energy through the use of hydraulics, modern machinery would have to be totally redesigned. Out of necessity, these machines would have to be made larger, they would require more manual supervision, and would cost considerably more to produce. Likewise, we would have to accept the fact that the products manufactured by these machines would have to be produced at a lower daily rate. Still more production processes would have to be completely abandoned without the assistance of hydraulics.

Over the past twenty five years, the rapid technological growth of the hydraulics industry, has caused *pressure drop* in the flow of technical information. Whenever a technology displays a rapid growth, educational tools are not developed until late in the process. Initially, information on new methods and products passes simply by word of mouth. Of course, second, third, or fourth hand information is not very reliable and prohibits a thorough working knowledge of the equipment in question. This can obviously lead to mis-application of the product and frustration with its use.

Since the early 1950's, The Rexroth Corporation has played an influential role in the development of the hydraulic industry. Rexroth has under one roof the most complete line of hydraulic equipment in the world, and therefore, we feel that it is our responsibility to provide the necessary educational tools, for proper application of these products. For this purpose, this text has been written.

During the development of our training program the question most frequently asked was, "What audience will your training material address?", the arbitrary division being placed between service and maintenance technicians and engineering personnel. To this question we can only reply with the following thoughts.

To keep up with the technological growth of the hydraulic industry we must have well trained personnel in *every* facet of the industry. In addition, if hydraulics is to meet the new challenges of energy transmission now being presented by industry, we must continue this growth in technology in the years to come. Components have and will become more sophisticated. Likewise, if these new components are to perform at an optimum level they will require equally sophisticated system designs. The intricacies of this sophistication, out of necessity, influence the maintenance and troubleshooting of the system. The problem of machine downtime can only be solved by maintenance technicians who have a thorough working knowledge of hydraulics. The key words, then, are knowledge of hydraulics and to this end the curriculum is the same for both maintenance and design personnel.

Our First Edition was published in 1979 as a state of the art textbook for use in our customer training courses. Today this text is also being used by colleges, technical schools, and industry for the purpose of either student or employee training. In order to keep up to date with the technology growth in our industry this Second Edition of Using Industrial Hydraulics has been published. The Second Edition includes three new chapters on electronic proportional control of the hydraulic system.

Although electronic control is not new to the hydraulic industry, the hardware which is available today opens up new possibilities for its applications. This new technology is less sensitive to contamination, and more cost effective. Likewise, both design and maintenance are simplified by standardized amplifier cards and more dependable hydraulic components. With the advent of process controllers, and other forms of computerized control both the designer and the maintenance technician must be prepared to deal with the interfacing of these controls with the hydraulic system. For those involved in the design or maintenance of new equipment or for those who wish to modernize an existing system, this Second Edition includes specific application details, and "how to" information.

Chapter 9 covers design consideration which applies Newton's second law of motion to the hydraulic system in order to predict the actual pressure which will be experienced during periods of acceleration (or deceleration). In addition, formulas are developed whereby the designer can determine the *natural* frequency of the hydraulic system. This assures smooth acceleration and stability in the system's operation.

We wish to express our gratitude to our Rexroth employees who have dedicated a good deal of their personal time toward the publication of this text. We would also like to extend our sincere thanks to those individuals who assisted in the technical editing of the material which is presented herein. And finally we wish to express our appreciation to you, the student, for selecting Rexroth as your instructional service.

Tom Frankenfield
Manager, Technical Service Department
Rexroth Corporation

TABLE OF CONTENTS

We have attempted to comply with ISO (International Standards Organization) Recommendation R1219; Entitled "Graphic Symbols for Hydraulic and Pneumatic Equipment and Accessories for Fluid Power Transmission." This Recommendation is published in the United States by The National Fluid Power Association (NFPA) 3333 N. Mayfair Road, Milwaukee, Wisconsin 53222. (414) 259-0990

The cross sections used in this book, generally reference a main poppet of a pilot operated relief valve for comparison of the cross section to the actual hardware.

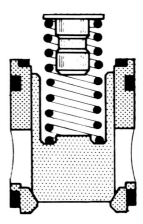

Circuits in this book do not show all components for proper and safe operation. This has been done so as to avoid confusing the control function being explained.

Throughout this manual, operational cross sections and circuit drawings use the following color codes. The color key is not applicable when color is used solely to enhance the graphics.

Tank Return Flow
(Tank Passage)

Intake Flow To Pump
Or Drain Line Flow

Inlet Pressure Or The
Highest Of All Possible
Working Pressures

Intermediate Pressure
(Shades Of Orange May Be
Used To Indicate Different
Pressure Levels)

Controlled Flow By Some
Type Of Metering Device
Or The Lowest Of All
Working Pressure

Inactive Hydraulic Fluid

For easy reference this
sheet can be folded out.

other books may define energy as the capacity to do work. For example coal has the capacity to do work ∴ coal is energy.

CHAPTER 1
HYDRAULIC PRINCIPLES

"Operated, moved, or effected by means of water," according to Webster, means that hydraulics is as ancient as water itself. By strict definition, hydraulics has existed ever since the first stream of water eroded the first section of earth. A more modern definition of hydraulics was first realized in the 17th century when it was discovered that a fluid under pressure could be used to transmit power. Hydrostatics, a contemporary definition of the principles of hydraulics, is a very simple term based on a discovery by Blaise Pascal (1623-1662). He discovered that if a fluid in a closed container receives a force over any area of that container, the *pressure* is then transmitted throughout the system undiminished and equal in all directions. From this simple system (for distribution of power and changes in its direction) an interesting technology has evolved, which is the most versatile means of power transmission known today.

Hydraulics is probably the most unique method to *transmit energy* to do *work*. It is more compact than the line of sight methods which are unavoidable in mechanical transmissions. Likewise, hydraulics is considerably more precise in controlling energy, and has a broader adjustability range than either electrical or mechanical means. It is the purpose of this chapter to study the laws of physics governing fluids.

BASIC PHYSICS OF THE WORLD WE LIVE IN

Before getting into the specifics of hydraulics it would be helpful for us to understand the objectives we are trying to accomplish through its use. We are not trying to rewrite a Physics I course, but only wish to summarize those elements that a hydraulic system must contend with.

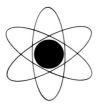

ENERGY

One of the most important topics of today is *energy* and *conservation* thereof. However, most people discuss and debate the use of energy without understanding what energy really is. By simple definition, *energy is the ability to do work.* Although energy shows itself in the form of mechanical, electrical, sound, light, heat or chemical, its origin is usually from our natural resources, namely oil or coal. In physics the law of conservation states that *energy can neither be created nor destroyed*, although it can be converted from one form to another, with some forms more useful to us than others.

In a hydraulic system the energy input is called a *prime mover*. Examples of prime movers are electric motors and internal combustion engines. Prime movers and hydraulic pumps do not create energy, they simply put it in a form that can be utilized by a hydraulic system.

WORK

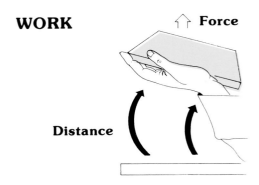

Example of Work

In defining energy we had to use the term *work*. Simply stated, *work is done when something is moved.* If we lift a book from the table we have done work, however, there are two components which must exist to do work on the book. First of all, if we are to move the book we must exert a *force* on it in the form of a push or a pull. This force must be equal in magnitude to the *weight* of the book and opposed in direction. Consequently, a force has the units of pounds (lbs.) and we must know the pounds of force required to do any type of work.

Secondly, if we move the book it must move through some *distance* which can be measured in inches, feet or miles. Thus, we have defined the other unit of work; namely distances represented in inches or feet.

If enough force in pounds (lbs.) is exerted to move the book through a distance (ft.), then work is done.

WORK =

FORCE (lbs.) x DISTANCE (ft.) = (ft. · lbs.)

LOAD AS A RESISTIVE FORCE

In hydraulics, the load is the object we want to do work upon. By definition, *load is resistance to work.* Any force which tends to hinder the movement of an object is resistance. Resistive forces can be frictional, inertial, or forces due to acceleration.

Although frictional forces are well understood, inertial forces are somewhat more complicated. *Inertia is the tendency of a body in motion to stay in motion, or if at rest to stay at rest, unless acted on by an external force.* Inertial forces are directly related to the mass or weight of an object. The heavier an object is, the harder (more force) it is to start that object moving or to stop it once it's in motion.

ACCELERATION FORCE

On high speed equipment it is often necessary to move relatively heavy objects from rest to high speed (or vice versa) in a short amount of time. This requires fast acceleration (or deceleration) rates. We must take into consideration the forces required for this acceleration. Isaac Newton's (1642-1727) second law of motion states that the force required is simply the product of the object's mass times the required acceleration rate. It must be remembered in the English system of units, mass is the weight of an object in pounds divided by the acceleration due to gravity. Consequently:

$$F = ma$$

Where F = **force in (lbs.)**

M = **Mass in (slugs)** = $\dfrac{w}{g}$ = $\dfrac{\text{Weight}}{32.2 \text{ ft/sec}^2}$

g = **acceleration due to gravity** = 32.2 ft/sec^2

a = **acceleration (ft/sec)**

Example: A vertically acting cylinder is to move a 5000 lb. load from rest, and is to achieve a velocity of 30 ft./sec. in 1.5 sec. What force must be exerted by the cylinder?

a. We know that to lift the load we must exert an upward force of at least 5000 lbs. to balance the weight of the object, but we must also add to this a force to accelerate the mass.

b. If we are to achieve 30 ft./sec. in 1.5 sec. we must accelerate at the rate of:

$$a = \frac{\Delta V}{\Delta t} = \frac{V_f - V_i}{t_f - t_i} = \frac{30\frac{ft}{s} - 0\frac{ft}{s}}{1.5s - 0s} = \frac{30\frac{ft}{s}}{1.5s}$$

$$\textbf{acceleration} = \frac{\textbf{required velocity}}{\textbf{time}} = \frac{30 \text{ ft./sec.}}{1.5 \text{ sec.}} = 20 \text{ ft./sec}^2$$

c. From Newton's second law, $F = ma$, where:

$$m = \frac{w}{g} = \frac{5000 \text{ lbs.}}{32.2 \text{ ft/sec}^2}$$

$$\sum Forces = ma$$
$$F_{cyl} - W = ma$$
$$F_{cyl} = ma + W$$

$$F_a = \frac{5000 \text{ lbs.}}{32.2 \text{ ft./sec}^2} (20 \text{ ft./sec}^2) = 3105.6 \text{ lbs.}$$

d. The total force which must be exerted by the cylinder during acceleration is:

$$F_{Total} = 5000 \text{ lbs.} + 3105 \text{ lbs.} = 8105 \text{ lbs.}$$

If, in your engineering you forget to add in the force due to acceleration, the system will still obtain maximum constant speed, but it will take considerably longer to achieve it.

In other words, if the system is designed for a pressure just sufficient to exert the 5000 pound force to move the load, during the acceleration period there will not be enough energy (force) available to reach the required velocity in the allotted time. Since the maximum velocity can't be achieved, the excess oil will be blown over the relief, until the 30 ft./sec. velocity is reached.

POWER $= \dfrac{work}{time}$

Power is defined as the rate of doing work. To better describe this term we will use the example we cited earlier. Assuming the book weighs 1 pound and we lift it 3 feet off the table we have done 3 ft.-lbs. of work. It does not matter if we lift it fast (1 second) or slow (1 hour), we always do the same amount of work. It does, however, take more power to lift the book in a lesser amount of time. Consequently, the units of power are defined as the amount of work (ft.-lbs.) per unit time (seconds) or:

$$POWER = \frac{\text{ft-lbs.}}{\text{sec.}}$$

The common method of measuring power is known as *horsepower.* Horsepower is defined as the amount of weight (lbs.) a horse could lift one *foot* in one *second.* By experiment it was found that the average horse could lift 550 lbs. one foot in one second, consequently:

$$1 \text{ Horsepower} = \frac{550 \text{ ft.-lbs.}}{\text{sec.}}$$

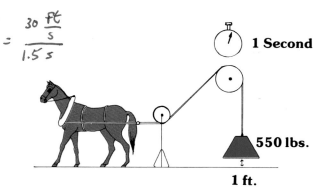

HEAT AND WASTED ENERGY

Energy, which is not used to do useful work, can be considered wasted. Although energy cannot be destroyed it can be converted into heat or noise, which is useless for performing work through hydraulics. As a hydraulics engineer it is your responsibility to calculate the *power to do the work in both directions*. Once you know the power needed you can then design a system which delivers that *power only when needed*. A truly efficient system never generates heat by dumping high pressure oil over a relief valve for long periods of time. We will discuss the effects of heat in a hydraulic system later in this chapter.

UNDERSTANDING PRESSURE AND FLOW

Pressure and flow are the two concepts which are the foundation of modern day hydrostatic technology. Although "pressure" and "flow" are the two most frequently used terms in our industry they also are probably the two most confusing. It is important for those dealing with hydraulics to realize why increasing relief valve setting can sometimes increase system speed, and why this method of speed adjustment should *never be practiced*.

FLOW CAUSES MOTION

For work to be done by a hydraulic system there must be motion. Since motion in itself is mechanical we must have some type of interface between the hydraulic system and the mechanical motion of the load. The simplest form of interface is a linear actuator known as a hydraulic cylinder.

A hydraulic cylinder is nothing more than a closed cylindrical container having a sealed but moveable piston which is connected to a piston rod. The rod protrudes through one end of the cylinder for transmittal of force and motion to the load.

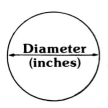

3 **The oil held in the other end returns to tank through this line.**

Piston Rod

Piston

2

The oil pushes the piston upward as it fills the housing.

Cylinder Housing

Pump

1 **The pump creates a flow of oil.**

A pump does not create pressure !! *see pg 1-7*

If we first consider how motion is produced, we can think of the cylinder with the piston rod fully retracted. As oil flows into the blind end of the cylinder, the piston begins moving upward to allow room for the increased oil volume in the cylinder housing. It stands to reason that the faster we fill the cylinder with oil the faster the piston and rod assembly extends.

AREAS

It is well known that the area of a square or rectangular surface is found by multiplying its length times its width dimension. If a rectangular table measures 30 inches by 40 inches then it is said to have a surface area of 1,200 *square inches* (in²).

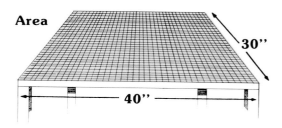

Area

30"

40"

Likewise, to find the area of a circle, you must know its diameter:

Diameter (inches)

The radius of any circle is 1/2 its diameter. Thus, a circle with a diameter of 10 inches has a radius of 5 inches. To find the area of a circle, multiply its radius times its radius times a mathematical constant π, which is always equal to 3.14.

$$\textbf{Area (in)}^2 = \pi \textbf{ x } \textbf{r}^2$$

Example: Circle diameter = 10 inches
Radius is 1/2 x 10 inches = 5 inches
Area = πr^2 = 3.14 x 5 x 5 = 78.5 in²

VOLUME

The volume of a rectangular milk carton is found by multiplying its length dimension times its width dimension times its height dimension.

It is resistance to flow that causes pressure.

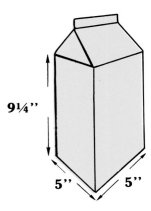

$9\frac{1}{4}''$

$5''$ $5''$

Volume = 5 inches x 5 inches x
9¼ inches = 231 cubic inches (in³)

Volume is also represented in a familiar term; the gallon.

There are 231 in³ in every gallon.

In other terms, the volume of a container is the area of its base times its height. To find the volume of a cylinder which is 10 inches in diameter, we multiply the area of the bottom times the height.

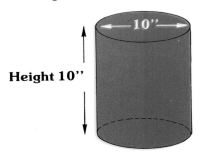

10''

Height 10''

Volume = 78½ in² x 10" = 785 in³

Area is 78½ in² (See area calculation above)

FLOW RATE

We normally represent flow in hydraulics by the number of gallons that can move into a measuring container in a given amount of time.

$$\textbf{FLOW} = \frac{\textbf{Volume}}{\textbf{Time}} \text{ or } \frac{\textbf{Gallons}}{\textbf{Minute}} \text{ or } \frac{\textbf{in}^3}{\textbf{min.}}$$

To expand on what we first said about flow it is important to realize that the speed or the rate of doing work is dependent on flow rate without regard to pressure. Of course, the size of the actuator must also be taken into account, since for a given amount of flow, larger actuators would move slower than smaller ones. (see page 7).

FLOW CALCULATION FOR HYDRAULIC CYLINDERS

$$\begin{matrix} \textbf{Required} \\ \textbf{Flow} \\ \textbf{Rate} \end{matrix} = \begin{matrix} \textbf{Piston} \\ \textbf{Area (in}^2\textbf{)} \text{ x } \textit{Required} \textbf{ Velocity (in/min.)} \end{matrix}$$

$$\textbf{GPM} = \frac{\textbf{AxV}}{\textbf{231}} = \frac{A\,in^2 \times V\frac{in}{min}}{231\,\frac{in^3}{gal}} = \frac{AV}{231}\,\frac{gal}{min}$$

FLOW CALCULATION FOR HYDRAULIC MOTORS

$$\begin{matrix} \textbf{Required} \\ \textbf{Flow} \\ \textbf{Rate} \end{matrix} \quad \textbf{GPM} = \frac{\frac{\textbf{Cubic in.}}{\textbf{rev}} \textbf{ x RPM}}{\textbf{231}} \qquad \frac{\frac{in^3}{rev}\,\frac{rev}{min}}{231\,\frac{in^3}{gal}}$$

SIZING PIPING, TUBING, AND HOSE

In efficient system design it is important to size the fluid conductors properly for the flow rate. Whenever there is a fluid flow there is motion, and we said before that when something moves, work is being done. Since there is work, a force must also exist in the form of pressure. It is this force we want to minimize in efficient system design.

To minimize the force required in the form of pressure we must limit the resistance to flow. Since most of this resistance (as with any dynamic system) is in the form of friction, for any given cross sectional area, the higher the flow rate the more heat that is generated because of friction.

VELOCITY VS. CROSS SECTIONAL AREA

Since fluid conductors are round, their cross sectional area is that of a circle. If we double the diameter (and thus the radius) of that opening we quadruple the area since we mathematically square the radius.

If for example, we take a piece of ½" schedule 40 pipe, we find that it has an inside diameter of .622" which gives us a cross sectional area of .3037 (inches)². It would take 63 feet of this size pipe to hold one gallon of oil. Consequently, to accomplish a flow rate of 1 GPM, we would have to have an oil velocity of:

$$\frac{63\,feet}{1\,gallon} \text{ x } \frac{1\,gallon}{1\,minute} \text{ x } \frac{1\,minute}{60\,sec} = \textbf{1.0 ft/sec}$$

If we do nothing more than use ½" schedule 80 instead of schedule 40 the velocity changes drastically:

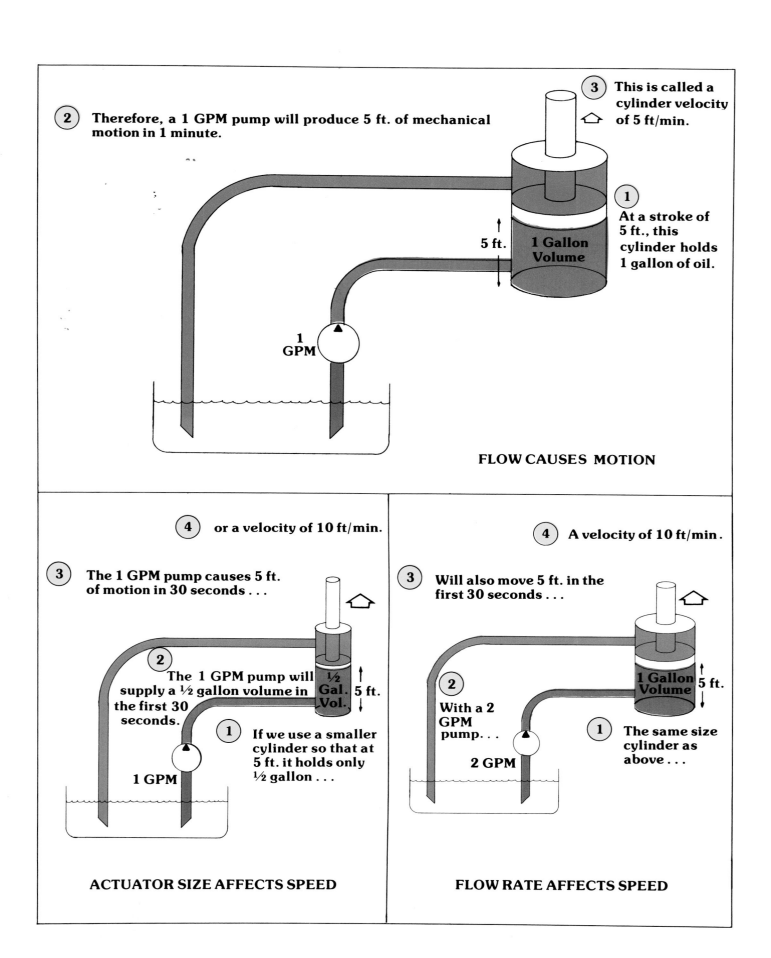

② Therefore, a 1 GPM pump will produce 5 ft. of mechanical motion in 1 minute.

③ This is called a cylinder velocity of 5 ft/min.

① At a stroke of 5 ft., this cylinder holds 1 gallon of oil.

5 ft.

1 Gallon Volume

1 GPM

FLOW CAUSES MOTION

④ or a velocity of 10 ft/min.

③ The 1 GPM pump causes 5 ft. of motion in 30 seconds . . .

② The 1 GPM pump will supply a ½ gallon volume in the first 30 seconds.

① If we use a smaller cylinder so that at 5 ft. it holds only ½ gallon . . .

½ Gal. Vol.

5 ft.

1 GPM

ACTUATOR SIZE AFFECTS SPEED

④ A velocity of 10 ft/min.

③ Will also move 5 ft. in the first 30 seconds . . .

② With a 2 GPM pump . . .

① The same size cylinder as above . . .

1 Gallon Volume

5 ft.

2 GPM

FLOW RATE AFFECTS SPEED

½" schedule 80 has a diameter of .546 which relates to a cross sectional area of .2340 in². It takes 82 feet of schedule 80 pipe to hold a volume of one gallon and to accomplish a 1 GPM flow rate, we have:

$$\frac{82 \text{ feet}}{1 \text{ gallon}} \times \frac{1 \text{ gallon}}{1 \text{ minute}} \times \frac{1 \text{ minute}}{60 \text{ sec}} = 1.37 \text{ feet/sec}$$

In this example a simple change in the schedule of ½" pipe increases the velocity (and thus the heat loss, because of friction) by 37 percent. The following formula can be used to calculate the pressure drop per foot of pipe (assuming laminar flow):

$$P = \frac{V \times F}{18,300 \ D^4}$$

V = viscosity in SSU
F = flow in GPM
D = inside diameter of pipe in inches
P = pressure drop per foot in PSI

If the flow rate in GPM and the desired oil velocity in feet per second (feet/sec.) are known the following formula can be used to calculate the *inside area* required:

$$\text{Area} = \frac{\text{GPM} \times .3208}{\text{velocity}}$$

Because available energy levels in different portions of the circuit vary, we recommend the following velocities to keep the energy loss to a small percentage of the total energy available:

Suction line		Pressure line		Return line
Viscosity υ in SUS	v in ft/sec	Pressure p in PSI	v in ft/sec	v in ft/sec
700	2.0	365	8.2 to 10.0	5.5 to 15.0
465	2.5	725	11.5 to 13.0	
230	4.0	1450	14.5 to 16.5	
140	4.3	2900	16.5 to 20	
		> 2900	20	
		When υ = 140 to 700		

LAMINAR AND TURBULENT FLOW

As oil flows through a pipe, it can be thought of as flowing in hundreds of small streams, each stream with its own velocity. The reason for the different velocities stems from the fact that there is friction among the oil molecules, as one layer of liquid moves over another. Likewise, the outermost layers are made to flow along the inside diameter of the pipe, where the coefficient of kinetic friction between the steel and the oil is higher. The net results are that fluid velocity is highest in the center of the flow stream (where the friction is lowest) and the speed decreases as you move toward the inside diameter of the pipe.

As long as the overall oil velocity is kept within reasonable limits, the relative speed from center to outside of the oil stream is about the same, and the outside stream more or less can keep up with the innermost stream. This results in flow streams that remain parallel. Laminar flow is a flow with parallel streams, resulting in the least loss of energy due to friction.

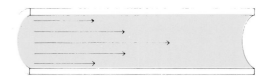

Turbulence, on the other hand, results when too much oil is being forced through a pipe with too small a cross sectional area. Under these conditions, there are big differences in speed between the innermost and outermost flow streams. This results in turbulence in the main flow of oil, where the oil molecules are forced to move in erratical paths, resulting in a high loss of energy.

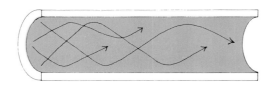

PRESSURE IN HYDRAULIC SYSTEMS TRANSMITS FORCE

By definition, pressure is nothing more than a force, usually represented in pounds, exerted over some area which is normally represented in square inches.

$$P = \frac{F}{A}$$

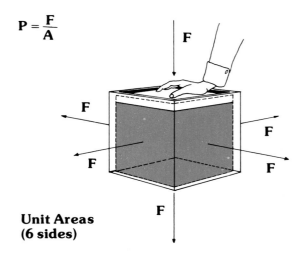

Unit Areas (6 sides)

With consideration to Pascal's Law, if we exert a force over an area of a fluid in a closed container, this pressure is then exerted perpendicular to, and undiminished in all directions,

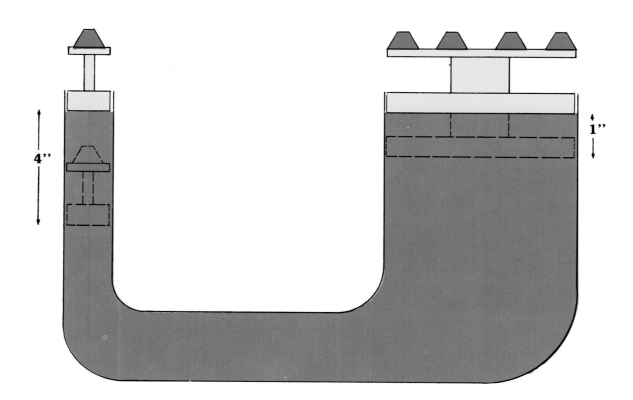

on every unit area of that container. It is exactly this principle which not only lets us transmit energy through a fluid but at the same time get a multiplication of force.

Assuming that we have a closed container of any shape, with two movable but sealed pistons, the output piston having a 4 times larger area than the input piston; for every pound input on the small piston we get a 4 pound *potential* output on the second. Since the pressure in the container is equal in all directions, the input to output force ratio is directly proportional to the input and output area ratios.

It is important to note, however, that to multiply force with a hydraulic system, we must sacrifice speed and distance. You will notice that for every inch of motion of the larger piston, the smaller piston must move 4 inches to displace the same volume of oil.

The input work is 1 lb. moving 4 inches, or 4 in.-lbs., while the output work is 4 lbs. moving 1 in., or 4 in-lbs. Since the input work and output work is the same, we have complied with the fundamental law of physics that says energy can neither be created nor destroyed. The only thing lost is speed for force, or vice versa.

It is the responsibility of any basic hydraulics course to justify the often used myth that hydraulic pumps pump pressure. The only thing a pump does is to create a flow of fluid. Its maximum pressure rating only determines how much resistance to that flow the pump can withstand.

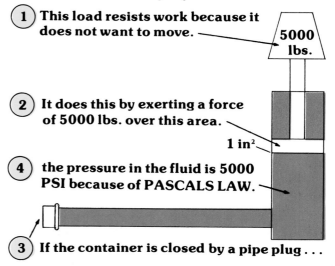

(1) **This load resists work because it does not want to move.**

(2) **It does this by exerting a force of 5000 lbs. over this area.**

1 in²

(4) **the pressure in the fluid is 5000 PSI because of PASCALS LAW.**

5000 lbs.

(3) **If the container is closed by a pipe plug . . .**

We said earlier that a load is resistance to work. If we are to do work on this load with a hydraulic cylinder, then the load is exerting a force which is resisting the motion of the piston in the hydraulic cylinder. Since the load exerts a certain amount of force in pounds, and the piston in the cylinder has a certain area in in², we have force over area or pressure. If the cylinder has a piston area of one square inch, and supports a 5000 pound load on a blocked column of fluid, then you can see that by Pascal's Law we have a pressure in the fluid of 5000 PSI.

If, instead of a blocked column of fluid, we connect the cylinder to a hydraulic pump, then the 5000 PSI would be transmitted back to the inlet of the pump. For the pump to create a flow, it must be able to withstand this 5000 PSI resistance:

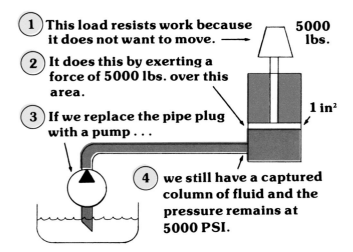

① **This load resists work because it does not want to move.** ⟶ **5000 lbs.**

② **It does this by exerting a force of 5000 lbs. over this area.**

1 in²

③ **If we replace the pipe plug with a pump...**

④ **we still have a captured column of fluid and the pressure remains at 5000 PSI.**

PRESSURE IS NOTHING MORE THAN A RESISTANCE TO FLOW

A load is resistance to work and in turn a resistance to flow in the hydraulic system, but there are two other forms of resistance. These forms of resistance to flow are:

1. Those found in friction in moving oil through pipes, hoses, tubing, and valves.

2. Those which are induced by *orifices* in the stream of fluid, by flow controls.

ORIFICES & PRESSURE

Orifices in hydraulic systems are much like doorways in crowded hallways. The higher the flow rate in people/min. or the smaller the doorway, the more crowded it becomes at the entrance.

With hydraulics when oil *moves* through a restriction (orifice) there is work being done to the oil. In doing this work, pressure is lost because it creates the force required to push the oil through the restriction. For a given orifice, an *increase in pressure drop* from inlet to outlet *is always accompanied by an increase in flow*. The pressure drop across an orifice can be affected by three variables (assuming constant viscosity):

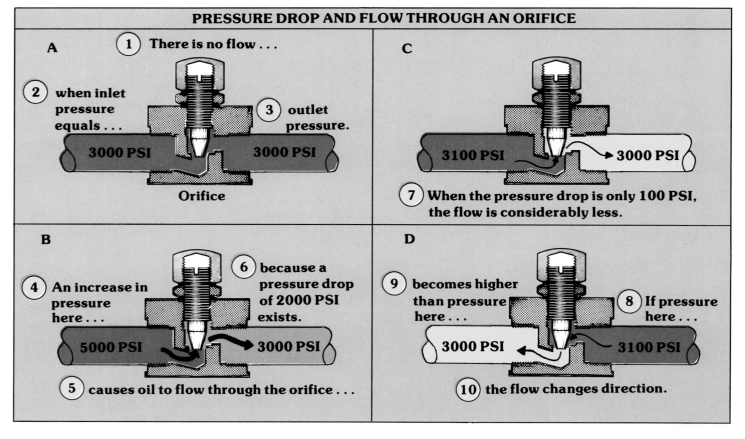

PRESSURE DROP AND FLOW THROUGH AN ORIFICE

A

① **There is no flow...**

② **when inlet pressure equals...**

③ **outlet pressure.**

3000 PSI   **3000 PSI**

Orifice

B

④ **An increase in pressure here...**

⑥ **because a pressure drop of 2000 PSI exists.**

5000 PSI   **3000 PSI**

⑤ **causes oil to flow through the orifice...**

C

3100 PSI   **3000 PSI**

⑦ **When the pressure drop is only 100 PSI, the flow is considerably less.**

D

⑨ **becomes higher than pressure here...**

⑧ **If pressure here...**

3000 PSI   **3100 PSI**

⑩ **the flow changes direction.**

1. An increase in load pressure at the outlet increases downstream pressure, and assuming inlet pressure remains at relief valve setting, has the effect of decreasing pressure difference from inlet to outlet. This means less flow, so that the system slows down with increased load.

2. An increase in the inlet pressure, by raising the relief valve setting, has the effect of increasing the pressure drop across the orifice. Assuming constant load pressure, the system speeds up. For this reason many think that to adjust speed in a hydraulic system, you adjust system pressure. The higher the number of restrictions a system has the better this method works. This, however, is the most ineffective and highly inefficient means of trying to adjust speed.

3. By opening and closing the restriction we change the resistance to flow. The lesser the resistance, the less the pressure loss from inlet to outlet. This is the most efficient way to tune system speed when the system has a fixed displacement pump (see page 10).

SETTING THE RELIEF VALVE

First, the relief valve setting is set so that the system does its work on the load at a load pressure, with the flow control wide open. Then, by closing the orifice we allow some of the energy that was needed to move the load at full speed, to be dumped over the relief valve in the form of heat. This happens at the instant the orifice adds enough resistance to flow, to increase the system pressure at the relief valve, to a value just slightly more than load pressure. The relief valve cracks, and begins allowing some of the pressurized fluid to flow to tank. The more the orifice is closed, the more it tries to increase the inlet pressure, and the more the relief valve opens to pass the excess oil to tank. The outlet pressure at the orifice is always load induced pressure:

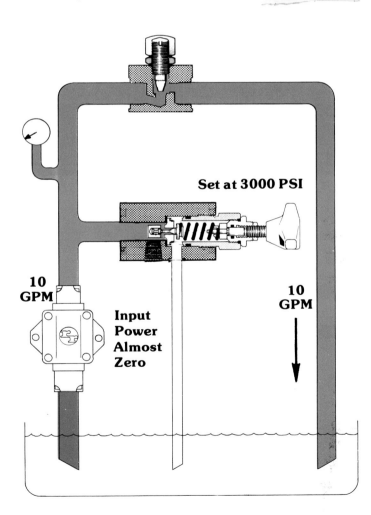

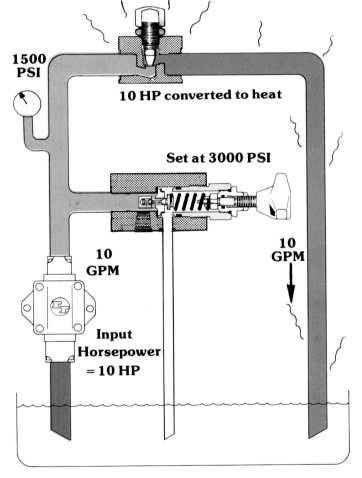

When the restriction is wide open there is virtually no resistance to flow, therefore, no pressure.

As the needle valve is closed, pressure builds up in the system and energy is converted to heat (since no useful work is being done). All the flow is still across the restriction since pressure isn't high enough to open the relief.

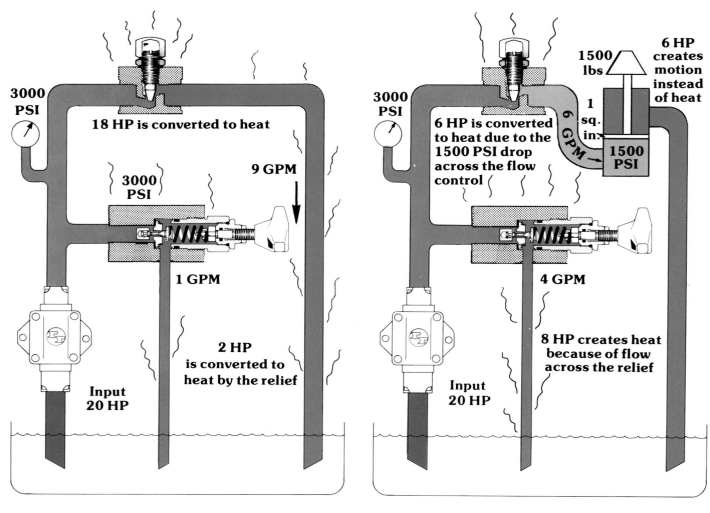

When the restriction is closed sufficiently to increase the inlet pressure to relief valve setting, some of the flow is diverted to tank via the relief valve. Notice that the horsepower which is converted into heat by the two valves, equals the input horsepower.

When a load is added to the circuit without changing the setting of the needle valve, more flow is diverted to tank over the relief because less flow can be pushed through the needle valve, due to the decrease in pressure drop. If the load is increased, the speed drops even further.

PHYSICAL TO HYDRAULIC COMPARISON

PHYSICAL	HYDRAULIC
ENERGY IS THE ABILITY TO DO WORK	
Force (Pounds)	Pressure (Pounds/sq. inch)
Distance (Inches)	Displacement (Gallons or Cubic Inches)
Work = Force (lbs) x Distance (in) (in-lbs or ft-lbs)	Work = Pressure x Displacement $= \dfrac{\text{Pounds}}{(\text{in}^2)}$ x (in³) (in-lbs or ft-lbs)
Power $= \dfrac{\text{Work}}{\text{Time}}$ $\dfrac{(\text{in-lbs})}{(\text{sec})}$	Power $= \dfrac{\text{Pressure x Displacement}}{\text{Time}}$ or $=$ Pressure x Flow Rate $\dfrac{\text{in}^3}{\text{min}}$ $\dfrac{(\text{in-lbs})}{(\text{min})}$

In converting the units of hydraulic power:

$$\text{Theoretical Hydraulic Horsepower} = \frac{\text{Flow (GPM) x Pressure (PSI)}}{1714}$$

ROTARY MOTION WITH HYDRAULIC MOTORS

We have described that with hydraulic cylinders, the pressure required is nothing more than the total output force in lbs. (including acceleration), divided by the net surface area of the piston in square inches. However, in the design of hydraulic systems involving rotary motion, we must also be able to determine the pressure required at the hydraulic motor.

To relate back to hydraulic cylinders, the output force was given the unit of lbs. and, if we did work with the cylinder we assigned the units of work in in-lbs or ft-lbs. We now want to cover a different subject entirely.

First, we must define what we mean by torque. Simply stated, torque is the twisting effort of a rotational device. In general, we are interested in torque capabilities of devices such as internal combustion engines, electric motors, and hydraulic motors. To give us a starting point anyone who has ever played on a seesaw has dealt with the elements of torque.

If, for example you and your childhood sweetheart were to play on a seesaw it would have been necessary to give her the longest side. Even though she may have been 20 or 30 pounds lighter than you, her weight could effectively balance yours, as long as she had the longer side. If the situation were reversed and she had the short side, the moment you got on, she went up and you stayed down.

Let's look closer at the physical elements which are coming into play.

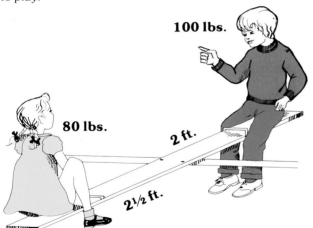

With reference to the above diagram, if you weighed 100 lbs. and were sitting two feet from the balancing point (fulcrum) then you created a *torque capability* of 100 pounds x 2 ft or 200 lb-ft which tends to cause a clockwise rotation around the fulcrum. Now, if your girlfriend weighed only 80 lbs. then she had to sit 2½ feet from the fulcrum (80 lbs x 2½ ft = 200 lb.-ft) in order to obtain an equal balancing torque in the counterclockwise direction.

Consequently, torque is equal to the load multiplied by its distance from the center of rotation.

T = force x radius

Notice that the units of torque are written in lb-ft or lb-in, whereas the units of work (described earlier) are written in reverse, as ft-lbs or in-lbs. This is done purposely so as not to confuse two totally different concepts. The torque of a hydraulic motor is synonymous to the thrust of a hydraulic cylinder. Consequently both a torque and a force can exist without causing motion (doing work). Likewise, the pressure at the inlet of the hydraulic motor only builds to a sufficient level to cause a torque which will produce motion. In other words, the torque load is resisting rotary motion, thus determining the torque produced by the hydraulic motor.

With hydraulic cylinders, we said the pressure level was determined by the load, and the square inch area of the piston in the cylinder. Likewise, with hydraulic motors, the pressure level is determined by the torque load, and the size of the hydraulic motor.

The size of a hydraulic motor is determined by its geometric displacement in in³/rev. The *displacement* is the amount of oil the motor consumes in making one complete revolution. As with hydraulic cylinders, a larger motor will produce more torque at a given pressure level than will a smaller one. The following formulas are necessary for relating torque pressure and displacement:

Formulas for applying Hydraulic motors

$$\text{Displacement} = \frac{2\pi \times \text{Torque}}{\text{Pressure}} \qquad \boxed{D = \frac{2\pi T}{P}}$$

$$P = \frac{2\pi T}{D}$$

or

$$T = \frac{P \times D}{2\pi}$$

Where:

D = displacement in in³
T = Torque in lb-ins
P = Pressure in PSI
π = 3.14

Sometimes it is necessary to determine the power level of the rotary motion. If the torque for a given hydraulic motor is determined by pressure, and the speed (RPM) of the same motor is determined by the flow rate, we now know the horsepower level of the motor.

$$\text{HP output} = \frac{\text{Flow} \times \text{PSI} \times (e_t)}{1714}$$

e_t Enters into the equation because hydraulic motors by nature are not 100% efficient. The total efficiency (e_t) is the product of the motor's mechanical efficiency (e_m) (losses because of friction and inertia) and its volumetric efficiency (e_v). The volumetric efficiency is determined by the percentage of the inlet oil leaked to the case drain, and/or to the low pressure outlet of the motor. Basically, the following facts hold true for most hydraulic motors:

WITH HYDRAULIC MOTORS:

— Volumetric efficiency is higher at low pressures and falls off as you approach the maximum pressure capability of the motor.
— Volumetric efficiency is highest at maximum speed. This is true because leakage is mostly pressure dependent and consequently is a small percentage of the larger flow rate supplied at higher speeds.
— Mechanical efficiency is higher at lower speeds because of less friction.
— Mechanical efficiency is higher at higher pressure because of better lubrication.
— Dependent on motor design the starting torque may be as low as 60% of the motors running torque capabilities. The starting torque capabilities must always be considered when the motor must start under load.

In designing the actual machinery it will be helpful to know the following mechanical relationships between HP, Torque, and Speed (RPM).

Torque in lb-ins	Torque in lb-ft
— Values are Theoretical —	
$HP = \dfrac{T \times RPM}{63025}$	$HP = \dfrac{T \times RPM}{5252}$
or	or
$T = \dfrac{HP\,(63025)}{RPM}$	$T = \dfrac{HP \times 5252}{RPM}$
or	or
$RPM = \dfrac{HP\,(63025)}{T}$	$RPM = \dfrac{HP\,(5252)}{T}$

The formulas as listed in the chart are theoretical values without consideration of mechanical inefficiencies. Of particular interest the formulas clearly show that with a constant input torque the horsepower levels vary directly proportional to the speed. Likewise, for constant horsepower installations the speed must drop with increasing torque.

These formulas are also useful in calculating gear box application. That is, assuming we get out of the gear box the same horsepower we put in (100% efficiency) we can write the following formula:

$$T_{in} \times RPM_{in} = T_{out} \times RPM_{out}$$

For example if we have a 2:1 reduction with a 100 lb-ft torque input at 1000 RPM our output torque would be

$$100 \text{ ft-lb} \times 1000 \text{ RPM} = T_{out} \times 500 \text{ RPM}$$

$$T_{out} = \frac{100 \times 1000}{500} = 200 \text{ lb-ft}$$

SERIES AND PARALLEL CIRCUITS

SERIES CIRCUITS

Resistances in series are additive. In any hydraulic circuit, as we work our way from the load to the pump, each length of pipe, every fitting and valve, adds its part to the total resistance to flow. We said before that resistance to flow results in pressure. Therefore, pressure required at the pump, is the sum of load induced pressure, plus all the individual pressure drops created by piping, fittings and valves.

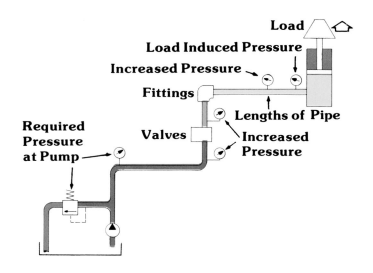

It should be noted that when the system becomes static, pressure will equalize at relief valve setting (in accordance with Pascal's Law).

PARALLEL CIRCUITS

Fluid flows through the path of least resistance when there is more than one possible flow path in the system.

In the following circuit, the 1000 pound load will move first, because it requires the least amount of force. Pressure will build up only to the point where the 1000 pound load begins to move. The system will reach no higher pressure until the cylinder reaches the end of its stroke, and no more oil can flow into that cylinder. Then, the system becomes static instaneously, as the pressure builds up the 5000 PSI to move the 5000 pound load.

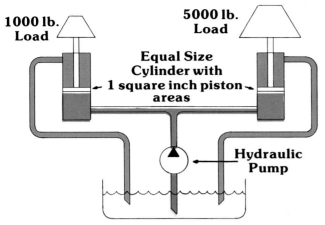

1000 lb. Load

5000 lb. Load

Equal Size Cylinder with 1 square inch piston areas

Hydraulic Pump

Fluid takes the path of least resistance.

HEAD PRESSURE

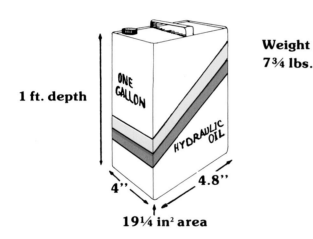

Weight 7¾ lbs.

1 ft. depth

ONE GALLON

HYDRAULIC OIL

4"　**4.8"**

19¼ in² area

Static head pressure is a force over an area created by the weight of the fluid itself. If we were to weigh a one gallon volume of a typical hydraulic oil, we would find that it weighs approximately 7¾ lbs. Likewise, a container which holds one gallon of fluid at a one foot depth, has a bottom with a surface area of 19¼ square inches (approximately 4.8" x 4"). Consequently, we have a pressure on the bottom of the container of 7¾ lbs. over 19¼ square inches or:

$$\frac{7.75 \text{ lbs.}}{19.25 \text{ sq ins}} = 0.4 \text{ PSI per ft}$$

It does not matter how big the bottom of the container is, we are only concerned, that for every one foot of depth, *oil creates a static head pressure of 0.4 PSI.*

The weight of oil in a large reservoir which holds oil at a 10 foot depth, creates a pressure in the fluid at the bottom of the reservoir of 4 PSI:

$$10 \text{ ft. depth} \times .4 \frac{\text{psi}}{\text{ft}} = 4 \text{ PSI}$$

ATMOSPHERIC PRESSURE AND VACUUMS

As with oil, air also has weight. It is a well known fact that atmospheric pressure at sea level averages 14.7 pounds per square inch. Therefore if we were able to weigh our earth's atmosphere, and then divide this weight by the surface area of the earth, we would find that the pressure due to the weight of air above us is equal to 14.7 PSI. In working backwards we find some interesting trivia:

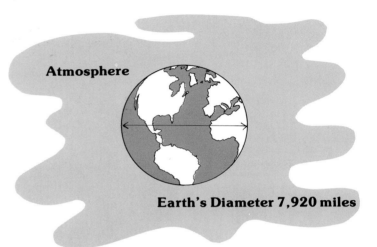

Atmosphere

Earth's Diameter 7,920 miles

The earth has a diameter of 7920 miles or a radius of 3960 miles. Consequently, its surface area is:

$A = 4\pi r^2 = 197,060,790$ square miles
　or　$791,098,480,000,000,000$ sq. inches

Our Atmosphere weighs $= 7.91 \times 10^{17}$ ~~sq. ins.~~ $\times 14.5 \frac{\text{lbs.}}{\text{~~sq. ins.~~}} =$

$11,470,927,000,000,000,000$ lbs. OR 5.73×10^{15} tons.

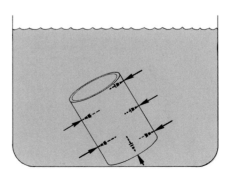

Force due to head pressure is normally equal in all directions.

As with any object immersed in a fluid (either air or oil), we live in an *atmosphere* which exerts 14.7 pounds on every square inch of our body. Because we breathe, the pressure is also exposed internally so we don't feel the effect of this pressure. We do, however, feel the effects of static head pressure when we dive into the deep end of a swimming pool. This happens because we can't breath in the higher pressure water to equalize internal and external forces. Under normal conditions, the forces created by head pressure are *equal in all directions*, and cancel the effects of each other.

VACUUM

A perfect vacuum is a volume which is totally evacuated. In a perfect vacuum all air molecules are removed. Although a perfect vacuum is virtually impossible to achieve, partial vacuums can be used so that the static head pressure of our atmosphere can exert a force to do work.

In comparison with a mechanical system, a vacuum and atmospheric pressure work together much like two people pushing on opposite sides of a door:

Equal force on both sides of the door cancel the effects of each other, and the door cannot move.

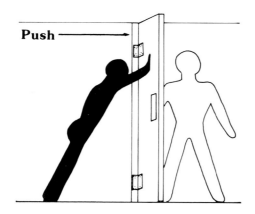

When one person stops pushing the door moves in his direction.

BAROMETER

A barometer is a device used to measure the effects of the static head pressure of our atmosphere. Barometers measure the *absolute pressure* of the atmosphere and are usually calibrated in inches of mercury. A mercury barometer can be made by immersing a long test tube in a pool of liquid mercury. When all air is expelled, the tube is turned vertically with the open end still suspended in the pool. In doing this, the mercury drops in the tube, leaving a near perfect vacuum in the top of the tube. The mercury is simply the media separating the atmospheric pressure from the vacuum. The gauge is read by measuring how high the ambient pressure pushes the mercury up the tube. Hence, the calibration in inches of mercury. Water could also be used in place of mercury. However, 29.92 inches of mercury is equivalent to 34 feet of water which would require an extremely long test tube.

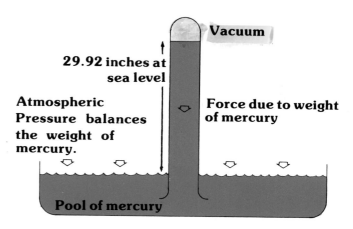

ABSOLUTE AND GAUGE PRESSURE

There are two basic methods of measuring pressure. Namely those readings which take into account the atmospheric pressure we live in and secondly, readings which ignore atmospheric pressure and start the scale at zero when the ambient pressure is actually 14.7 PSI.

Absolute pressure readings use a vacuum as their zero base. Atmospheric pressure on this scale would be 14.7 PSI or 30 in-hg (29.92 in-hg).

Gauge pressure readings are always 14.7 PSI lower than absolute pressure, since a standard pressure gauge will read 0 PSI at sea level.

Therefore:

**Gauge Pressure + 14.7 PSI =
Absolute Pressure**

SUCTION CONDITIONS FOR HYDRAULIC PUMPS

With hydraulics, we concern ourselves only with absolute pressures when calculating the inlet conditions of the hydraulic pump. Dependent on the type of pump, and the specific conditions under which it must operate, the pump can be mounted either above or below the oil level in the reservoir. To assure proper pump operation, we should always check the pressure available to push the oil into the pump, and the pressure drop per foot of suction line. For the pressure drop per foot calculations, the viscosity at cold start up should be used.

PUMPS MOUNTED ABOVE THE OIL RESERVOIR

Most hydraulic pumps available today are capable of creating at least a partial vacuum. Air pressure on the oil in the reservoir pushes oil up the suction line, identical to the way mercury is supported in the tube of a mercury barometer. Since hydraulic pumps are not capable of approaching the perfect vacuum of the barometer, the height of the pump above the oil level must be severely restricted:

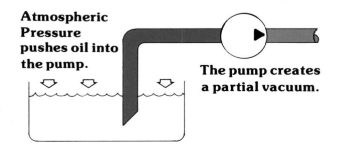

Atmospheric Pressure pushes oil into the pump.

The pump creates a partial vacuum.

Pumps available today, can normally create a vacuum condition equivalent to six inches of mercury (3 PSI under atmospheric pressure, or 11 PSI absolute). Since 6 in-Hg is equivalent to 7.4 feet of oil (29.92 in-Hg = 37 ft-oil) the height of the inlet above the oil has a definite limit. Although 7.4 feet would be the absolute maximum height of the inlet above the oil level, we must reduce this dimension even further when considering the pressure drop encountered in moving oil through the suction lines and strainers.

Let us, for a minute, consider a 15 GPM pump capable of "lifting" 6 in-Hg that has a schedule 40 1¼" pipe 48" long. First, schedule 40 1¼" pipe has an inside diameter of 1.38 inches. It we were to use this pump with Mobil DTE 24 (a 150 SUS fluid) at 100°F, we would have to calculate the pressure drop under the worst cold start up conditions.

Assuming the pump would have to start in a 30°F ambient this same fluid would display a viscosity of approximately 1200 SUS.

Thus, we can calculate the pressure drop per foot as follows (assuming laminar flow):

$$\Delta P_{ft} = \frac{V \times F}{18300\, D^4} = \frac{1200 \times 15}{18300\, (1.38)^4} = .27 \text{ PSI/ft}$$

For a 4 foot straight in suction line (not considering suction strainers or elbows) we would have an overall drop of:

$$4 \times .27 = 1.08 \text{ PSI}$$
1.08 PSI is equivalent to 2.19 in-hg or 2.7 ft. of oil

The maximum height of the pump above the oil level is now limited to 4.7 feet:

$$7.4 \text{ ft} - 2.7 \text{ ft} = 4.7 \text{ feet}$$

Likewise an adequately sized suction strainer will add ½ to 1 PSI (assuming the best):

$$.5 \text{ PSI} = 1.01 \text{ in-Hg or 1.25 ft of oil}$$

The maximum height, again, drops to 3.4 feet:

$$4.7 \text{ ft.} - 1.25 \text{ ft.} = 3.4 \text{ feet}$$

Although the suction characteristics vary from pump to pump, and must be checked for each application, a good rule of thumb is:

A hydraulic pump with adequately sized inlet pipe and strainer should never be mounted higher than 3 feet above the oil level.

PUMPS MOUNTED BELOW THE OIL LEVEL

For pumps with inadequate suction characteristics, or where fine inlet filtration is required, additional force can be made available for pushing oil into the inlet by utilizing the static head pressure of the oil. We said before that for every foot of depth, oil creates a static head pressure of 0.4 PSI. All that needs to be done to take advantage of this positive pressure (above atmospheric) is to locate the inlet at some depth with respect to the oil level in the reservoir. Of course, the deeper the better.

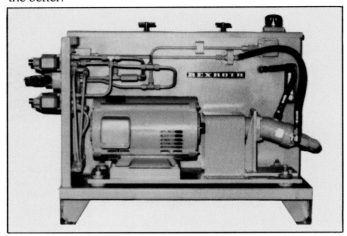

Under these conditions, strainer, suction line, and fittings still subtract from the total pressure available at the inlet under a flow condition. Therefore, the total pressure available is considerably higher because we are starting at a level above atmospheric pressure.

PUMP INLET CONDITIONS AFFECT NOISE AND HEAT GENERATION

Usually, a mineral based hydraulic fluid, when exposed to atmospheric pressure at room temperature, contains 8-9% (by volume) of dissolved air. If we reduce the pressure to this oil, to something less than atmospheric pressure, the air expands and becomes a higher percentage of the volume. Consequently, if a pump is pulling a vacuum of 6 in-Hg at its inlet, more air and less oil is filling the pumping chambers than when we have a positive pressure of 1 PSI at the same inlet. The expanded gas bubbles at the inlet collapse with considerable force as the pumping chamber is exposed to system pressure. This rapid collapsing of air bubbles results in rapid energy losses in the form of heat and noise. Of course, the larger the air bubble the higher the noise level, and the more heat is generated. In high pressure pumps, the heat given off by this phenomenon is actually high enough to cause carbonization of the oil. This formation of carbon particles can be a continual source of contamination in the system, and should be avoided.

UNITS FOR MEASURING PRESSURE AND VACUUMS

Through the years, several standards have been used for measuring pressures and vacuums. We wish to mention those standards that are commonly used in our industry:

1. **Pounds per square inch** — Pressure, by definition, is force over area, and in our English system of units, force is represented in pounds and area in square inches. Pounds per square inch is usually represented by PSI, and can be used to call out absolute pressure (PSIA), or gauge pressure (PSIG).

2. **The standard atmosphere** is defined as the pressure that corresponds to a mercury height of exactly 76 centimeters in a mercury barometer at sea level and 0°C. In consideration of the mass density of mercury (ρ) the acceleration due to gravity (g) (remember F=ma) and the 76 cm height.

1 standard atmosphere = $\rho g h$ =

mass density	acceleration due to gravity	height
$13.595 \times 10^3 \frac{kg}{m^3}$ ×	$9.80665 \frac{m}{sec^2}$ ×	$0.76m$ =

$$1.01325 \times 10^5 \text{ N/m}^2 \quad \boxed{1 \text{ N} = \frac{1 \text{kg-m}}{sec^2}}$$

In the metric system, force is represented in newtons (N), and area is represented in square meters. In converting the units from newtons to pounds and square meters to square inches, we find that:

1 standard atmosphere = 14.7 PSI

By definition, the atmosphere uses a vacuum as its base, so that pressure ratings in atmospheres are absolute pressures.

3. **The Bar** is another system of measuring pressure in the metric system of units. The bar has been defined as the pressure equal to one million dynes force over an area of one square centimeter. In converting 1 million dynes force to pounds force, and one square centimeter to square inches, we come up with the conversion factor of:

1 bar = 14.5 PSI

Since 0 bar is equivalent to a perfect vacuum, bar readings are also absolute. Likewise, the bar is quite close to the atmosphere in magnitude so that 1 bar can be thought of as atmospheric pressure at sea level. In actual practice, however, bar ratings are assumed to be "gauge" unless otherwise noted; i.e., 315 bar is usually 315 bar gauge.

Work = Force × distance only when the force and distance are in the same direction
Weight is a downward force

4. **Pascals** are units of pressure measurement and have been defined as one newton per square meter or:

$$1 \text{ Pa} = N/m^2$$

Since this unit of measurement is quite small in magnitude (1 pa = 10^{-5} bar or 6897 Pa = 1 PSI) this method of pressure measurement is usually represented in kpa (kilo pascals). Hence:

6.89 kpa = 1 PSI or
100 kpa = 1 bar

The pa and kpa are SI units accepted for pressure measurement by ISO (International Standards Organization). While the bar, most utilized by our industry, is a non SI unit, it will be a matter of time until we see which units of pressure measurements will be adopted by the fluid power industry.

WHAT YOU SHOULD KNOW ABOUT HEAT

A shortcoming in many basic hydraulics courses is that not enough emphasis is placed on heat and its adverse affects on hydraulic systems. The tendency is to discuss how heat is generated in hydraulic systems, with no association as to how much. Since, hydraulic systems are the most compact means of transmitting energy, it is difficult to get a physical relationship to the huge amount of power which can be converted into heat, in a short period of time. Let us now take a look at what happens with too much or too little heat in hydraulic systems.

TOO MUCH HEAT
See bottom of pg 110

Unfortunately, the newcomer to hydraulics, until he gets burnt, so to speak, with his first system, really has no way of realizing just how efficient a heater a hydraulic system can be. We must remember that flow multiplied by pressure is the hydraulic equivalent to horsepower. Wherever we have flow from point A to point B in a system, with any loss in pressure, there is an equivalent loss of horsepower between points A and B. Since, a pressure loss occurs without doing useful work (causing mechanical motion), a percentage of the input horsepower is wasted. This wasted horsepower shows up in the hydraulic system in the form of heat. Of course, the higher the pressure loss and the higher the flow, the more we waste horsepower. Some typical examples where pressure is lost without doing useful work are summarized as follows:

For flow to occur P_1 must be greater than P_2

Heat is generated when there is a drop in pressure as oil flows:
— **through pipes & fittings**
— **through flow controls**
— **over relief valves**
— **across counter balance valves**
— **internal leakage of pumps and motors**

If we know the flow rate (GPM), and the loss in pressure (PSI), across any device which does not produce mechanical motion, we can calculate the heat generated.

Since the hydraulic system either does work, or creates heat, the units of heat may be expressed in any units of work or energy. However, we more often see heat expressed in *BTU (British Thermal Units)* than we do in ft-lbs of heat.

1 BTU = 778 ft-lbs

In effect, this shows that one BTU contains enough energy to move a one pound object 778 feet. *upward, since Weight is a downward force.*
In hydraulic systems we are more concerned with the *rate of doing work* or the *power* level of the system. We said earlier that one horsepower is, *by definition*

$$550 \frac{\text{ft-lb}}{\text{sec}}$$

So that the relationship between mechanical power and the rate of generating heat would be:

$$1 \text{ HP} = \frac{550 \text{ ft-lbs}}{\text{sec}} \times \frac{1 \text{ BTU}}{778 \text{ ft-lbs}} = \frac{.707 \text{ BTU}}{\text{sec}}$$

OR

$$\frac{.707 \text{ BTU}}{\text{sec}} \times \frac{60 \text{ sec}}{1 \text{ min}} = \frac{42.4 \text{ BTU}}{\text{min}} \times \frac{60 \text{ min}}{1 \text{ hr}} = \frac{2545 \text{ BTU}}{\text{hr}}$$

Therefore,

$$1 \text{ HP} = \frac{42.4 \text{ BTU}}{\text{min}} = \frac{2545 \text{ BTU}}{\text{hr}}$$

To make this more useful for those calculating the heat generated by a hydraulic system, we can write the following expression:

$$\frac{\text{BTU}}{\text{HR}} = 1.5 \times \text{GPM} \times \text{PSI}$$

where PSI is the loss in pressure for a given flow rate which does no useful work.

Let us now consider the following hydraulic lift circuit as an example:

Lift circuit parameters:
Constant load variation,
Duty cycle 50% full speed,
50% half speed,
Maximum pump flow 20 GPM,
Maximum pressure 3000 PSI

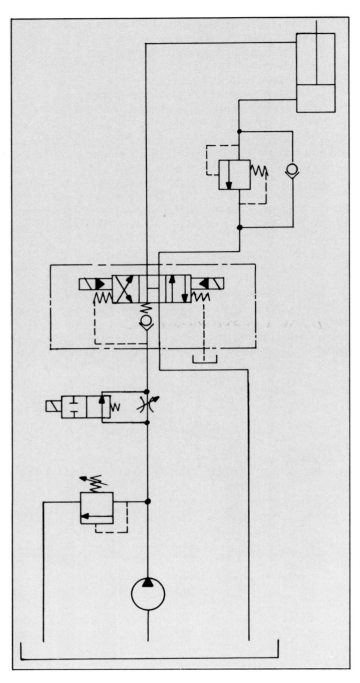

If we assume that at full speed and full load the horsepower required for upward motion is:

$$HP = \frac{20 \text{ GPM x } 3000 \text{ PSI}}{1714} = 35 \text{ HP}$$

Since all the flow is required for full speed, and all the pressure is required to overcome the load, the relief valve stays closed and no heat is created. (Assuming a totally efficient system with no pressure drop between the pump and the load).

Let us now look at the 1/2 speed, 1/2 load - up condition.

For 1/2 speed we have only to supply 1/2 the flow, or 10 GPM, at 1/2 the pressure, or 1500 PSI, to do the required work. With a fixed displacement pump, this means that the other 50 percent of the flow has to go over the relief valve to tank at the full 3000 PSI set pressure. Consequently, we develop a significant amount of heat:

BTU/hr = 1.5 x 3000 x 10 = 45000 BTU/hr

only because of flow across the relief.

The second heat generator under these conditions exists because of pressure drop across the flow control.

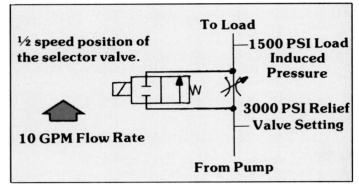

This creates:

BTU/hr = 1.5 (10 GPM x 1500 PSI) = 22,500 BTU/hr

The total power which goes toward generating heat is:

$$\frac{45,000 \text{ BTU}}{\text{hr}} + \frac{22,500 \text{ BTU}}{\text{hr}} = \frac{67,500 \text{ BTU}}{\text{hr}}$$

By converting 67,500 BTU/hr to horsepower we obtain:

$$67,500 \text{ BTU/hr x } \frac{1 \text{ HP}}{2545 \text{ BTU/hr}} = 26.50 \text{ HP}$$

which is the same value we get by comparing input power and horsepower required to do useful work in the following chart, at the top of the next page.

Let us now find out how much heat we really generate if we were to run the lift up and down for 1 hour with a 50% load, at 50% speed.

$$UP = \frac{67,500 \text{ BTU}}{\text{hr}} \text{ x .5 hr} = 33,750 \text{ BTU}$$

$$DOWN = \frac{89,075 \text{ BTU}}{\text{hr}} \text{ x .5 hr} = 44,538 \text{ BTU}$$

Total heat in one hour = 78,288 BTU

In generating heat at the rate of 78,288 BTU/hr this hydraulic

DIRECTION OF CYLINDER	SPEED	LOAD	HP REQUIRED FOR USEFUL WORK	HP INPUT TO PUMP NOT INCLUDING EFFICIENCY	WASTED HEAT ENERGY	
					HP	BTU/hr
UP	FULL	FULL	35 hp	35 hp	NONE	0
	FULL	HALF	17½	17½	NONE	0
	FULL	NONE	0	0+	NONE	0
	HALF	FULL	17½	35 hp	17½	44,538
	HALF	HALF	8¾	35hp	26½	67,500
	HALF	NONE	0	35 hp	35 hp	89,075
DOWN	FULL	FULL	"O"	10 hp To override counterbalance	10	25,450
	FULL	HALF	POTENTIAL	27½	27½	69,987
	FULL	NONE	ENERGY OF	35+hp	35+hp	89,075
	HALF	FULL	LOAD DOES	35+hp	35+hp	89,075
	HALF	HALF	WORK	35+hp	35+hp	89,075
	HALF	NONE		35+hp	35+hp	89,075

system could maintain a 70°F room temperature in an average 3 bedroom home on a 0°F winter day.

Referring to our circuit example, a 20 GPM pump in a good industrial hydraulic system would, more than likely, be mounted on a 60 gallon reservoir. Assuming that the 78,288 BTU/hr would be total transferred to the 60 gallons of oil, and that the maximum recommended temperature for mineral oil is approximately 140°F, you can readily see that the system would severely overheat in a matter of minutes.

GUIDELINES FOR ESTIMATING HEAT GENERATION:

1. **Calculate the flow rate and pressure levels required to move the load. This will give you the ability to calculate the actual horsepower** HP = $\dfrac{(GPM \times PSI)}{1714}$ **necessary to do the work at the prescribed rate. Remember, you must do this for each motion (forward and reverse) in the cycle.**
2. **For each motion, calculate the input horsepower to the pump:** HP = $\dfrac{GPM \times PSI}{1714\,(e_t)}$ e_t = (overall pump efficiency)
3. **Subtract the results from step 1 from the respective results in step 2. This will give you the horsepower wasted in each portion of the cycle.**
4. **Multiply this HP figure by 2545 BTU/hr to obtain BTU/hr heat generation, for each portion of the cycle.**
5. **Multiply the BTU/hr figure in step 4 by the portion of the hour during which it occurs.**

6. **Add the BTU figures of step 5 and determine the average heat generated during a one hour period.**

HEAT DISSIPATION

Hydraulic reservoirs, pipes, hoses, and components radiate heat into the ambient air. Assuming that the heat generation rate from your system is low, it is possible that there is enough radiating surface to maintain stable oil temperature within the prescribed limits. Remember, *for maximum oil life, the system should never be allowed to operate above 140°F.*

With free air convection, a steel surface can radiate heat in an amount that can be calculated by using the following formula:

$$BTU/hr = 2.54 \times area \times \triangle T$$

where:
- BTU/hr = the heat radiated.
- Area = the surface area of the steel that is in contact with the oil in square feet.
- $\triangle T$ = Desired oil temperature minus ambient air temperature in degrees Fahrenheit.

The problem with using the formula accurately is estimating the steel surface area that is in contact with the oil. Also, since the top plate of the reservoir has an air space between it and the oil, and the bottom is less efficient in its ability to radiate heat than the sides (remember heat rises), we can only estimate the radiation ability for a given system. A good guideline is to use only the vertical surface areas of the reservoir in your calculations. The heat radiated from piping, components, and the top and bottom surface areas of the reservoir allows a safety factor for minor changes in ambient temperatures, and inefficiencies overlooked in your estimation of heat generation.

Once we know the rate of heat generation, and the approximate radiating ability of our reservoir, we can determine the extra cooling ability we will have to provide with either an air/oil, or water/oil, heat exchanger.

Getting back to our example, a 60 gallon reservoir which is 3 ft. long and 2 feet wide holds 60 gallons at a depth of 16 inches (1 1/3 ft.). Therefore, the vertical surface area is 13 square feet. If the system is operating in an ambient which does not exceed 80°F we have:

$$\text{BTU/hr} = 2.54 \times 13 \times (140 - 80) = 1981 \text{ BTU/hr}$$

This means that we must provide additional coiling in the amount of

$$\frac{78,288 \text{ BTU}}{\text{hr}} - \frac{1981 \text{ BTU}}{\text{hr}} = 76,307 \text{ BTU/hr}$$

when operating at 50% speed and load.

In actual practice, we would not want to design a system which creates this much heat. We only intended to show how a seemingly innocent circuit design can be nothing but a heat problem.

Before going to a heat exchanger manufacturer you will need the following information:

1. **The heat in BTU/hr you wish to dissipate.**

2. **The amount of oil flow you will be passing through the heat exchanger.**

3. **The flow rate of water (GPM) you have available (assuming you are selecting a water/oil model).**

4. **The inlet temperature of the water (or the ambient air temperature for air/oil models) in °F.**

In actual application, you will need to know the pressure rating of the selected model, and you probably will be interested in the pressure drop for the flow rate you prescribed.

In plumbing the unit, follow the recommendations of the manufacturer, but remember that *it will do no good at all if hot oil can return to the reservoir without passing through the heat exchanger.* Also, if you are piping case drain lines of pumps and motors through the heat exchanger, the model selected must have a low pressure drop for the total combined return flow, since most *case drains cannot exceed 15 PSIG.*

TOO LITTLE HEAT

A well designed system with proper cooling can still be a problem if we fail to consider (in the engineering stage) what the minimum temperature of the oil will be. On cold morning start-ups the oil may not be fluid enough to fill the expanding chambers in the pump. With inadequate filling the pump can not pump its rated volume, and serious cavitation problems may be imposed.

The critical minimum temperature at which you can start your system will be affected by several factors. On the mechanical side, the capability of the pump to pump viscous fluids, and its ability to create a vacuum are important. Likewise, the inlet conditions (as already discussed) are a critical consideration. The maximum viscosity at cold start-up can vary from approximately 4500 SUS for bent-axis design piston equipment, to 4000 SUS for gear and vane pumps, to as low as 1000 SUS for inexpensive in-line piston designs. The optimum viscosity range for most equipment is between 80 to 250 SUS at operating temperature. *The viscosity levels given here are only average values, it is important that you check the exact recommendations for the pump and motors you are using.*

The second determining factor on the minimum cold start-up temperature of your system is the type of oil used. The two oil ratings you must concern yourself with at this point is the overall viscosity at operating temperature, and its viscosity index.

VISCOSITY

RELATIVE VISCOSITY IS MEASURED IN SUS

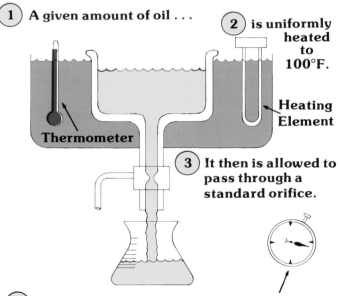

1 A given amount of oil . . .

2 is uniformly heated to 100°F.

Heating Element

Thermometer

3 It then is allowed to pass through a standard orifice.

4 The elapsed time in seconds equals the viscosity in SUS at 100°F.

A fluid's viscosity is a measurement of its resistance to flow. For the purposes of this chapter we need only concern ourselves with the most practical way of measuring *relative viscosity*; that being measuring the SUS viscosity of the fluid. Relative viscosity is nothing more than the measurement of time necessary for passing a given amount of the selected fluid through a standard orifice at a prescribed temperature. The SUS (saybolt universal second), a name derived from the type of viscometer used, is the time measurement of fluid passing through an orifice (usually at 100°F). Since thicker fluids will take more time to flow through this orifice than thinner ones, thicker fluids have the higher SUS number.

VISCOSITY INDEX

It's a well known fact that heated viscous fluids become thinner. With mineral oils, the viscosity varies drastically with relatively small temperature changes. The resistance of an oil to change viscosity with a change in temperature is denoted by an arbitrary measurement called the viscosity index. A fluid which is quite thick when cold and very thin when hot, has a low resistance to viscosity change, thus it is assigned a low viscosity index number. A fluid that has a relatively stable viscosity for a given change in temperature has a high resistance to a change in its viscosity, and would be given a high viscosity index number. High VI oils have a Viscosity Index number over 80, medium VI fluids between 40 and 80, while low Viscosity Index fluids are given a number less than 40. The graph shows a comparison of fluids with both high and low V.I. numbers.

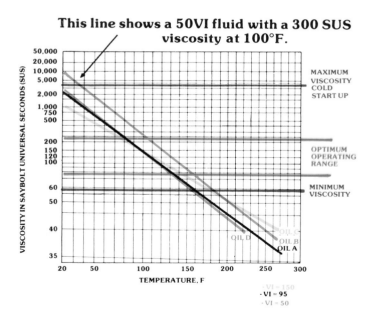

This line shows a 50VI fluid with a 300 SUS viscosity at 100°F.

DETERMINING TEMPERATURE RANGE

You will notice in the above viscosity temperature graph, we have indicated the viscosity parameters for a typical

hydraulic pump. We now wish to point out the *temperature limits for a 50 VI, 95 VI and a 150 VI oil*, all of which display a 150 SUS at 100°F viscosity.

	50 VI	**95 VI**	**150 VI**
Min. Temp. Start-Up	18°F	5°F	0°F
Optimum Temp. Range	85 - 130°F	80 - 135°F	70 - 140°F
Max. Operating Temp. *	155°F	160°F	175°F

*Although the viscosity is acceptable, the maximum operating temperature should be held to 140°F, so that maximum oil life can be maintained. Also, most industrial hydraulic pumps, for mechanical reasons, are not allowed to operate above 160°F.

If, in a system, the start-up temperature could allow the oil to approach the maximum viscosity limit of the pump, a provision should be made for heating or pre-heating of the fluid.

HEATING A HYDRAULIC SYSTEM

As long as the viscosity is within the maximum pump limits, a system can be started and brought up to temperature by its own heat generating abilities. With an extremely efficient hydraulic system, the rate of heat generation may be close to the dissipation rate of the reservoir. Therefore, precautions should be taken so that you may be assured of optimum operating viscosities being reached in a reasonable period of time. To speed-up the warming period it is possible, in some systems, to make use of the most inefficient mode of operation, since this will generate the most amount of heat. For example, by deadheading a flow against a "bottomed-out" cylinder, the pump is forced to pump all of its flow over the relief valve. Although this is not desirable under normal operating conditions, it makes good use of the hydraulic heating capabilities for system warm-up. In initial system design it is possible to build-into the circuit a warm-up stage, so that the pump intentionally pumps its full output over a relief.

Precautions: The above recommendations are viable only if the following considerations have been taken into account:
1. Fluids are within the maximum viscosity limits of the pump.
2. Optimum temperatures can be achieved within a reasonable time period.
3. Proper safe guards have been provided, so that the

system only operates in the warm-up mode until satisfactory temperatures have been reached.

PRE-HEATING

If the ambient temperature allows the oil to cool to a point where the oil viscosity exceeds the limits of the pump, it will be necessary to provide some means of pre-heating the oil. The usual method of pre-heating is to install one or more immersion type electric heating elements in the lower part of the reservoir. Immersion heaters are normally controlled with a built-in thermostatic switch to avoid the possibility of accidental overheating of the oil.

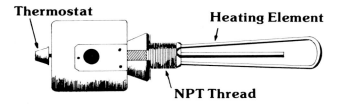

HEAT DENSITY AND OIL CARBONIZATION

Standard immersion heaters, as purchased at a local electric supply store, are normally intended as water heaters and have a heat density of approximately 40 watts per square inch. For normal convection heating of oils this heat density is too high and will burn (or carbonize) the oil in contact with the element. To avoid burning of the oil, the heat density must be limited to 10 watts per square inch.

Although heating elements are available which are designed for heating non circulating hydraulic oil, you can make use of locally available inventories by purchasing a unit which is rated for a higher voltage than you intend to use. *By operating an immersion heater at 1/2 its rated voltage its KW output, and its heat density is reduced to 25% of the name plate ratings.*

Example :
A 480 volt, 4 kw heater with a heat density of 20 watts/in², produces 1 kw at a heat density of 5 watts per square inch when operated on 240 volts.

SIZING IMMERSION HEATERS

If all we had to do, is to heat a volume of oil from a low to a high temperature, then by supplying "x" number of BTU's, we would have put enough energy into the fluid to raise its temperature to the desired level. Unfortunately, the calculations are not that simple. What happens is that the heat dissipating capabilities of the reservoir (as discussed earlier) start working as soon as we heat the oil above the ambient temperature. Of course the higher the desired temperature, the higher the temperature difference, and the more heat we radiate to the ambient. To avoid complicated thermodynamic calculations, the total wattage required can be estimated accurately enough, for our purposes, from the following equation :

$$KW = \frac{\text{Tank capacity (gallons)} \times (\text{temp}°F - \text{temp}°F)}{800 \times \text{allowable time (hours)}}$$

The above formula estimates the kilowatts (kw) required to achieve the desired temperature in a given amount of time. The time allotted for heating should be at least 1 hour, however, if possible, 3 hours is preferred :

The following conversion factors may be helpful in your calculations :

$$1 \text{ HP} = \frac{2545 \text{ BTU}}{hr} = 746 \text{ WATTS} = .746 \text{ kw}$$

or

$$1 \text{ WATT} = 3.4 \text{ BTU/hr}$$

CONCLUSION

In this chapter we have attempted to cover the physical elements which must be understood to properly apply hydraulics. It will be important for you to gain a basic understanding of the following terms:

Energy
Force
Torque
Motion
Velocity
Load
Resistance
Inertia
Acceleration
Power
Pressure
Orifices and Pressure Drop
Flow
Series and Parallel Circuits
Head Pressure
Vacuum
Absolute Pressure
Gauge Pressure
Viscosity
Viscosity Index
Heat

With a solid foundation of the concepts presented in this chapter, it will be relatively simple to understand the operation and proper application of the various hydraulic components, which will be covered, in detail, in subsequent chapters.

USEFUL MECHANICAL FORMULAS

WORK:

$W = F \times D$
F = force in lbs
D = Distance in inches or feet
units are expressed in
(in - lbs) or (ft - lbs)

FORCE REQUIRED FOR LINEAR ACCELERATION:

$F = Ma$
F = force in lbs
M = mass in slugs = $\dfrac{\text{weight (lbs)}}{32.2 \text{ ft/sec}^2}$
a = acceleration = ft/sec²

LINEAR ACCELERATION:

$a = \dfrac{V}{T}$
a = acceleration ft/sec²
v = velocity ft/sec
T = time in seconds

ACCELERATION DUE TO GRAVITY:

$g = 32.2 \text{ ft/sec}^2$

HORSEPOWER:

$1 \text{ HP} = \dfrac{550 \text{ ft -lbs}}{\text{sec.}}$

TORQUE:

$T = F \times r$
T = torque in lb - in:
F = force in lbs
r = radius in inches

HORSEPOWER & TORQUE RELATIONSHIP:

$T = HP \times 63025 \div RPM$
$HP = T \times RPM \div 63025$
T = torque in (lb - in)
$T = HP \times 5252 \div RPM$
$HP = T \times RPM \div 5252$
T = torque in (lb - ft)

HEAT:

$1 \text{ BTU} = 778 \text{ ft - lbs.}$

HP & HEAT RELATIONSHIPS:

$1 \text{ HP} = \dfrac{42.4 \text{ BTU}}{\text{min}} = \dfrac{2545 \text{ BTU}}{\text{hr.}}$
$= 746 \text{ Watts} = .746 \text{ KW.}$

AREA OF A CIRCLE:

$A = \pi r^2$
A = area (in²)
r = radius in (in)
π = 3.14

USEFUL HYDRAULIC FORMULAS

REQUIRED FLOW RATE:

a) For cylinders:

$$GPM = \frac{A \times V}{231}$$

A = area in (in²)
V = Velocity in (in/min.)

b) For motors:

$$GPM = \frac{D \times RPM}{231}$$

D = displacement in (in³/rev)

VELOCITY OF FLOW THROUGH PIPES:

$$V = \frac{GPM \times 0.3208}{A}$$

V = Velocity in feet per second
A = inside opening area in (in²)

REQUIRED PRESSURE:

a) Cylinders:

$$PSI = \frac{F}{A} \text{ or } F = PSI \times A$$

F = force in (lbs)
A = Area in (in²)

b) Motors:

$$PSI = \frac{2\pi T}{D}$$

T = torque in (lb - in.)
D = displacement (in³/rev)

PRESSURE DROP THRU PIPE
(assuming laminar flow):

$$P = \frac{V \times F}{18300 \, D^4}$$

P = pressure drop per foot
V = viscosity in SUS
D = inside diameter (in)
F = flow in GPM

HYDRAULIC HORSEPOWER:

a) $$HP_T = \frac{GPM \times PSI}{1714}$$

HP_T = Theoretical HP

b) Input to pump:

$$HP_{in} = \frac{GPM \times PSI}{1714 \times (e_t)}$$

e_t = overall pump efficiency

c) output of Hydraulic Motor:

$$HP_{out} = \frac{GPM \times PSI \times (e_t)}{1714}$$

e_t = overall motor efficiency

HEAT GENERATION:

$$BTU/hr = 1.5 \times GPM \times PSI$$

PSI=Pressure loss which does not produce work

HEAT RADIATION OF A HYDRAULIC RESERVOIR:

$$BTU/hr = 2.54 \, (Av) \, (\triangle T)$$

BTU/hr = Heat radiated
Av = Vertical tank area in contact with oil
$\triangle$T = Desired oil temp minus ambient air temperature in degrees Fahrenheit

ESTIMATING IMMERSION HEATERS:

$$KW = \frac{V \times \triangle T}{800 \, T}$$

V = Tank capacity gallons
$\triangle$T = (desired - ambient) temperature in degrees Fahrenheit
T = Time in hours
KW = Input heat required.

USEFUL CONVERSION FACTORS

The equivalents given can be used per the following example:

12 in. = 1 ft.

a) to convert 36 in into feet :

$$36(in) \times \frac{1 (ft)}{12 (in)} = 3 \text{ feet}$$

b) To convert 4 ft into inches :

$$4 (ft) \times \frac{12 (in)}{1 (ft)} = 48 \text{ inches}$$

VOLUME:
1 gallon = 231 in.³
1 gallon = 3.785 liters
1 liter = 61.02 in.³

PRESSURE:
1 bar = 14.5 PSI
1 atmosphere = 14.7 PSI
1 kg/cm² = 14.2 PSI
1 in-hg = .4912 PSI
1 bar = 100 kpa
1 PSI = 6.89 kpa

SPEED:
1 ft/sec = 0.3048 M/sec

LENGTH:
1 inch = 25.4 mm
1 meter = 39.37 inches
1 micron = .000039 inches

POWER:
1 HP = 1.014 metric HP
1 HP = .7457 KW
1 HP = 42.4 BTU/min
1 HP = 2545 BTU/Hr.
1 HP = 550 ft - lb/sec

FORCE:
1 N (newton) = 0.2248 lbs.

USEFUL DATA

HORSEPOWER INPUT TO PUMP:
1 HP = 1 GPM at 1500 PSI

ENTRAINED AIR:
At room temperature standard hydraulic oil contains 8-9% air by volume

FLOW VELOCITIES:
See table on Page 1-6

HEAD PRESSURE:
Oil creates a pressure due to its weight of 0.4 PSI per foot of depth.

OIL COMPRESSIBILITY :
For every 1000 PSI there is a reduction in oil volume of ½%.

OIL TEMPERATURE :
Oil temperature should never be allowed to exceed 140°F.

PUMP MOUNTING :
Hydraulic pumps should never be mounted higher than 3 ft above the minimum oil level in the reservoir.

PUMP & MOTOR CASE DRAINS :
Most pump or motor case drains cannot exceed 15 PSIG.

VISCOSITY AT START-UP :
Maximum viscosity at start-up ranges from 1000 for inline piston pumps to 4000 SUS for gear and vane equipment.

NOTES:

CHAPTER 2
PRESSURE CONTROL VALVES

The sheer existence of the world in which we live, depends on the interaction and the balancing of forces. From baby's first breath, to the complex network of forces holding our solar system together, forces are constantly acting and reacting to keep energy in equilibrium. From the beginning of time, man's unyielding quest to understand and to manipulate the interaction of forces has made our world a better place. In Chapter 1, we have shown how *pressure relates to force* in a hydraulic system. This chapter will be devoted to an understanding of various pressure controls, and of how we can manipulate forces through the use of hydraulics.

In general, there are five basic functions which can be performed by pressure control valves, namely:

Relief Valves: First, limit the maximum system pressure which, in turn, protects system components, piping and tubing; and second, *limit the maximum output force* of the hydraulic system.

Reducing Valves: are used to limit a certain branch of the hydraulic circuit to a pressure *lower* than the relief valve setting for the rest of the system. By reducing pressure in the secondary circuit, we can *independently limit the output force to that in the primary circuit.*

Sequence Valves: are used to assure that one operation has been completed before another function is performed. They operate by *isolating the secondary circuit* from the primary circuit until the set pressure is achieved. The flow of fluid is then sequenced from the first to the second circuit. Primary pressure must be maintained for the secondary function to be performed. Sequence valves *establish an order for the interaction of forces.*

Counterbalance, overcenter or brake valves: are a broad range of pressure valves which control a load induced pressure to hold and control the motion of a load. This group of valves *provides balancing forces which prevent the load from running away* because of its own weight or because of inertia.

Unloading Valves: are usually used in circuits with two or more pumps or in circuits incorporating accumulators. The valve operates by sensing pressure in the system downstream of a check valve. Once a certain pressure level is obtained, the unloading valve unloads its pumps to tank. The check valve isolates the unloaded pump from the rest of the system. System pressure is then maintained by the accumulator or by a smaller volume higher pressure pump.

BASIC PRESSURE VALVE OPERATION

All types of pressure valves function by balancing a hydraulic force with a spring force. You will notice that from the simplest direct operated design to the most sophisticated pilot operated model, the spool, poppet, or ball is held in position by an adjustable spring. Opposite this spring force is an area which is exposed to system pressure.

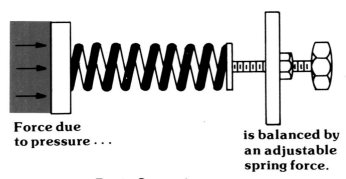

Force due to pressure . . .

is balanced by an adjustable spring force.

Basic Operation

We know that force due to pressure is:

$$\text{Force} = \text{Pressure} \frac{\textbf{(lbs)}}{\textbf{(in)}^2} \times \text{Area (in)}^2 = \text{lbs.}$$

To balance this force, we use a spring which can be compressed by some adjustable mechanical means. Compression springs exert a force proportional to the amount they are compressed. Depending on the stiffness of the spring, the increase in force can be very high per inch of compression, or it can be very low. For any given spring, a numerical value is assigned which indicates the spring stiffness. This value is called the spring constant and has the units (lbs / in). Consequently,

$$\textbf{Spring Force} = \textbf{kX}$$

Where: k = Spring Constant
X = Compression length (in.)

PRESSURE CONTROLS MUST MODULATE

Since any pressure control must handle a dynamic flow of fluid, it must modulate to maintain the balance between the spring and the hydraulic force. When functioning, these valves are in constant motion (internally) at one of the many positions between fully open and fully closed. In this way, they pass just enough fluid to keep the system pressure at valve setting.

With the understanding that all pressure valves balance a hydraulic force by a spring force in a dynamic condition, we now wish to discuss, in detail, the various valve types.

PRESSURE RELIEF VALVES

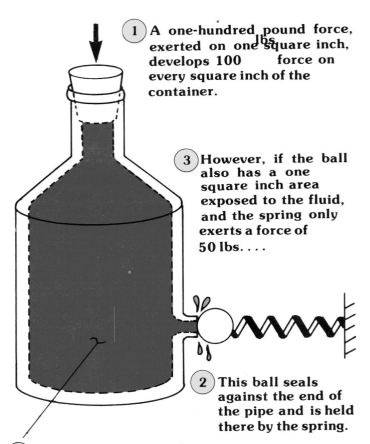

1. A one-hundred pound force, exerted on one square inch, develops 100 lbs force on every square inch of the container.

3. However, if the ball also has a one square inch area exposed to the fluid, and the spring only exerts a force of 50 lbs. . . .

2. This ball seals against the end of the pipe and is held there by the spring.

4. the pressure in this fluid cannot get higher than 50 PSI, because the ball will be pushed away from the end of the pipe, allowing the oil to escape.

The purpose of a relief valve is to limit the maximum pressure in the system to which it is connected. Although pressure is generated by the load, the hydraulic pump is the

energy input. Since we want to limit the energy source, the inlet of the pressure relief is usually piped into the hydraulic circuit as close to the outlet of the pump as possible. The valve is piped in *parallel* to the pump, which gives the output of the pump two possible flow paths, either to the system or over the relief, depending on which is the path of least resistance.

The relief is a *normally closed valve* which keeps the flow of fluid in the system until its pressure setting is reached. Once the valve opens and oil flows through it, energy in the pressurized fluid is expelled in the form of heat. Pressureless fluid from the relief valve's outlet is then returned to the reservoir through the tank port connection.

To System

1. The inlet of the relief valve is positioned as close to the outlet of the pump as possible.

2. The valve being normally closed, keeps the flow of fluid in the system until the pressure setting has been reached.

3. When the path of least resistance is through the relief, heat is created as pressure is expelled from the fluid.

Normal Location of a Pressure Relief

A second source of energy input which often must be limited by the relief is that generated by the inertia of the load.

As shown in the two examples, the load can also be an energy source which must be limited to prevent damage to the system components or piping. The system can be protected from shock loading or inertia overloading by using either a *port* or *crossport* relief between the actuator and the rest of the hydraulic circuit.

Port reliefs are piped into the hydraulic system at the actuator the same way main system reliefs are piped into the

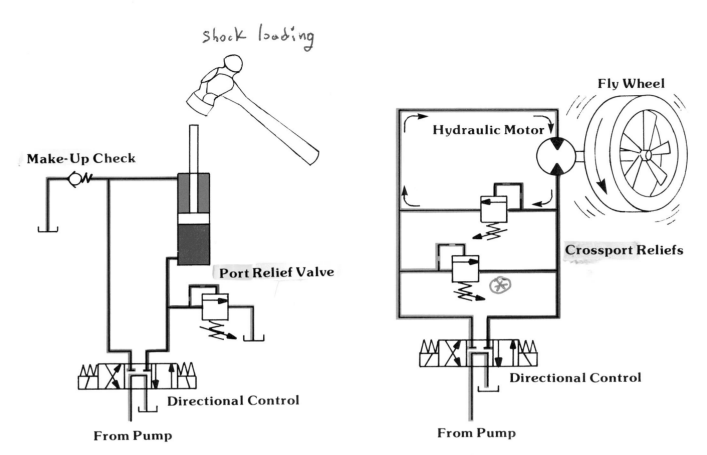

Shock loading

Make-Up Check

Port Relief Valve

Directional Control

From Pump

Fly Wheel

Hydraulic Motor

Crossport Reliefs

Directional Control

From Pump

Other Uses for Pressure Relief Valves

system at the pump. Any pressure overload in the service line to which they are connected is simply relieved to tank at valve setting. In some applications, other circuit precautions must be taken to prevent cavitation in the low pressure side of the actuator. As shown in the example, a make-up check allows the actuator to draw oil from the reservoir as the piston is displaced downward.

A second way of preventing cavitation in the actuator is simply to relieve its outlet port to its inlet. During the overrunning load condition, the actuator actually becomes a pump, drawing oil into its inlet and pumping pressurized fluid out of its outlet. A *crossport relief valve* simply adds resistance to flow as it short circuits the outlet and inlet of the actuator. Although this works satisfactorily only with actuators which have equal displacements in both directions of operation (double rod cylinders, motors, and rotary actuators), cross port reliefs are almost mandatory when the rotary motion of a hydraulic motor is blocked by a closed center directional control. almost ?

In selecting a valve to be used as a port or crossport relief, choose one which responds quickly and has little or no leakage when seated. Reliefs used in these applications should be set at least 150 PSI higher than maximum load induced pressure. This assures that the relief will not influence normal operation of the system, while, at the same time, it will provide relief protection the moment pressure rises above that induced by the load. One last precaution for

crossport applications: a relief must be chosen which can withstand full system pressure on its tank port. By studying the previous example, you can see that under normal system conditions the "tank port" is exposed to full load induced pressure.

TERMS

In discussions involving relief valves, the following terms are used to describe their operating characteristics. A basic understanding of these terms is essential in understanding the features of various relief valve designs.

Cracking Pressure is the pressure at which the valve just begins to let oil escape from the system.

Full Flow Pressure is the pressure needed to pass all of the output flow of the pump through the relief.

Pressure Override is the difference between full flow pressure and cracking pressure for any particular valve. Pressure override is higher than cracking pressure for several reasons. First, the valve itself is a restriction (orifice), and the higher the flow across an orifice, the higher the pressure drop. Since the outlet of the relief is exposed to atmospheric pressure, the increase in pressure drop, with increased flow, is solely an increase in pressure at the valve's inlet.

Second, in any pressure control the ball, poppet, or spool is directly supported by a spring. If the spring tension is adjusted so that the valve just "cracks" at, say 3000 PSI, then the poppet moves just far enough from the seat to let the first drops of oil out of the system at this pressure.

When a bigger opening is required to pass more of the output of the pump, the poppet must be moved further from its seat. In moving the poppet, the spring must be compressed more, which in turn increases spring force and hydraulic system pressure.

A less obvious reason for pressure override is that a loss of effective area occurs as the poppet moves away from the seat. When the relief is closed, the effective area can be calculated by using the full inside diameter of the seat. However, when the poppet moves away from the seat, the theoretical point of pressure loss occurs along the perpendicular line between the poppet and the seat. As shown in the diagram, this can cause a substantial reduction in the effective area.

Hysteresis is pressure variation between pressure increase and pressure decrease as related to flow.

Reseat Pressure is the pressure at which the valve closes again.

Stability is the fluctuation in pressure at any given setting.

Overshoot is the pressure rise above set pressure during the short time period when the valve is responding.

HOW IMPORTANT ARE THE VALVE'S PRESSURE OVERRIDE CHARACTERISTICS?

In general, hysteresis, reseat pressure, and overshoot are values which are not detectable on a pressure gauge. Minor instability also has little influence on the satisfactory operation of the system. Therefore, unless you are looking for very precise control, you need not be too concerned with those items which need electronic equipment to detect. But,

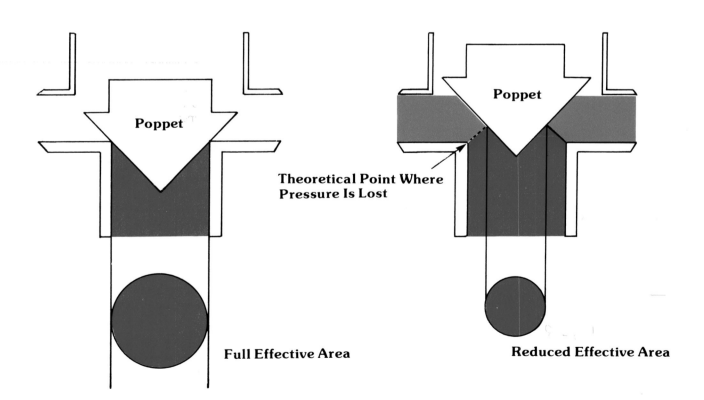

Full Effective Area   Reduced Effective Area

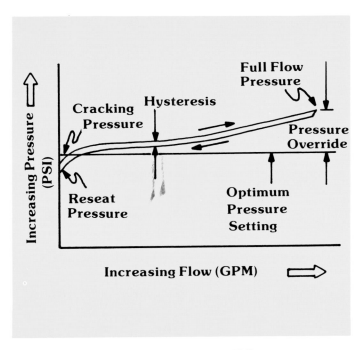

**TYPICAL PRESSURE
VS.
FLOW CHARACTERISTICS**

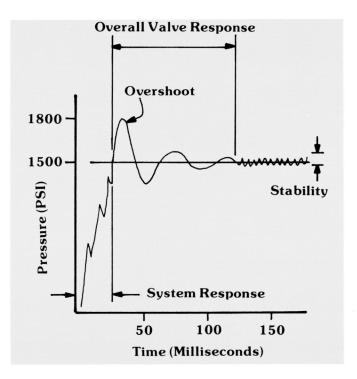

TYPICAL PRESSURE VS. TIME GRAPH

how does pressure override affect the operation of a system? Let us now consider a 10 GPM pump operating with a relief valve which displays a 500 PSI override between cracking and full flow pressure. Although override characteristics are not perfectly linear, our example is intended only to show the effect of pressure override on the system. For convenience sake, we will eliminate all circuitry except for the pump, relief valve, cylinder and load.

First, if we are looking for maximum efficiency, we would want to set the relief valve at 1000 PSI since this is all the pressure that is needed to obtain the required force. We find, however, that when the cylinder bottoms out, our pump flow is relieved to tank at 1500 PSI rather than at the initial setting of 1000 PSI. Although all flow across a relief turns energy into heat, a 500 PSI override increases our energy loss by 33%, or a net increase of 3½hp for this particular example.

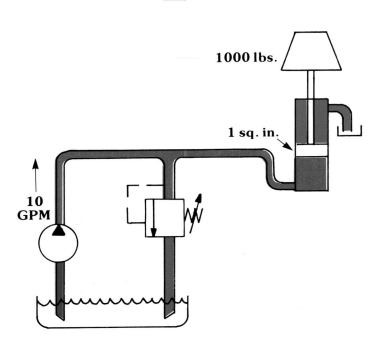

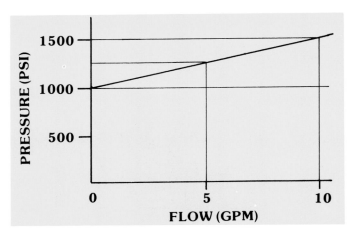

Second, if the cylinder encounters a slight increase in load, say 250 pounds, ideally, we would want our system to stall since it was our original intent to limit the output force to 1000 lbs. In actual practice, however, we find that the system will do the work at approximately half speed, while wasting the other 50% of our power input in the form of heat, as oil flows across the relief. When the load is mechanically stalled, our pressure again rises to 1500 PSI creating 500 lbs. more thrust than originally intended.

DIRECT ACTING RELIEFS

Direct acting (operated) reliefs are valves in which the spring force directly opposes the hydraulic pressure force. It stands to reason that a given spring constant can only be optimum for a given pressure level. Therefore, most direct operated valves have several spring options to cover the different operating pressure ranges. The spring constant has varying effects on the valve's operating characteristics, which are more or less related directly to the actual valve design. Under the worst conditions, the relief can have a very narrow adjustability range due to the spring constant's influence on pressure versus flow characteristics, hysteresis, and stability. With other designs, the only real effect is on sensitivity of adjustment. In the family of direct operated valves, several designs are offered by various manufacturers. We now wish to study the intended use and operation of the most popular designs.

BALL TYPE RELIEF

Although this is the simplest in design, the ball relief valve is probably the least desirable. Its disadvantage is that it can only handle small flows (usually less than 3 GPM) before it becomes noisy. The noise is developed when the ball lifts from its seat and begins to chatter in the flow stream. Of course, the higher the flow, the more unstable the ball becomes. The instability of the ball shows up in bad pressure fluctuations in the valve's performance characteristics. Therefore, its use should be limited to infrequent duty safety relief, thermal expansion relief, or remote pilot for a pilot operated pressure control.

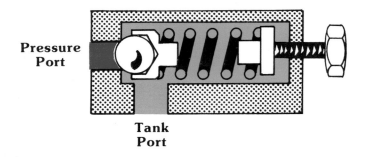

POPPET STYLE RELIEFS

The simple poppet design has operating characteristics similar to those of the ball design. This design, however, is somewhat more stable, since the cone has a tendency to center itself in the flow stream, where the ball is more likely to roll on top of the stream of fluid. Because it is somewhat more stable, it can handle slightly larger flows without excessive noise. Pressure override with a poppet style relief is as undesirable as it is with the ball style relief. Its use should, therefore, be limited to infrequent duty or for remote piloting in low flow applications.

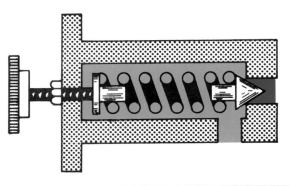

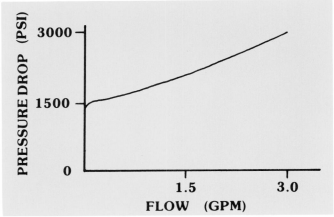

Typical Pressure vs. Flow Characteristics for a Simple Poppet or Ball Style Relief.

GUIDED POPPET DESIGN

By guiding the poppet with a close tolerance fit, direct operated reliefs can technically be made to pass considerably more fluid without the instability problems associated with unguided models. A problem arises in mechanically guiding the poppet because the poppet guide blocks the free flow of fluid to tank once the valve opens. To overcome this problem, with most designs, the oil flows to tank through cross drillings in the poppet. This, of course, is a restriction which limits the maximum flow capacity of the valve. Although stability and noise are improved, this design still has a problem in overcoming pressure override with increased flow. In general, precautions must be taken not to exceed the recommended flow, since high velocities through the cross drillings in the poppet can cause a severe whistle.

Although this design is basically intended for use as a remote pilot control, it can also be used as a main system relief in low powered systems. Before selecting this design, however, you should consider the effects pressure override will have on satisfactory system operations.

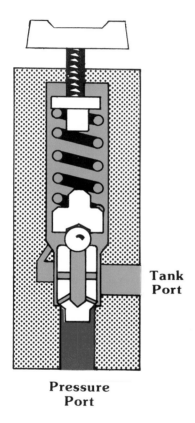

Tank Port

Pressure Port

DIFFERENTIAL PISTON

We said before that the poppet area exposed to system pressure creates a force which is opposed by a spring. If we were able to design a valve in which the exposed poppet area was only a small percentage of the final open flow area, we could have a direct operated relief capable of handling larger flows with a relatively lighter spring than a basic poppet design. This is exactly the principle used in the differential piston design. The lighter spring has a lower spring constant. Hence, pressure override due to length of compression can be reduced.

You will notice in the cross-sectional illustration, that by locating the pressure port on the same side of the seat as the poppet, the nose of the poppet, which extends through the seat, is exposed to atmospheric tank pressure rather than to

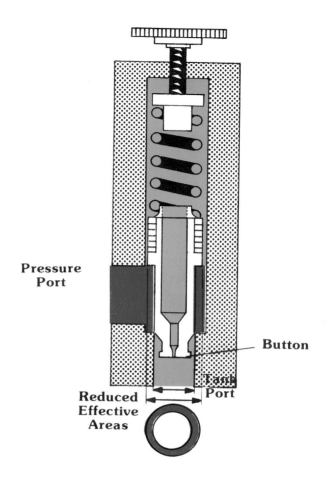

Pressure Port

Button

Reduced Effective Areas

Tank Port

system pressure. The only effective area for system pressure to act upon is the ring area, which has an ID of the seat, and the OD of the sliding fit of the poppet guide. As you can see in the figure, the area can be easily changed by proper poppet design to optimize the required spring force to balance the smaller hydraulic force.

The only major problem with most differential piston designs is that once they open, the nose of the poppet enters the pressurized flow stream. A drastic increase in the effective area can occur, and the spring can no longer close the valve. To overcome this problem, the nose of the poppet has a button machined on it, which disturbs the flow path to the tank. This captures the velocity head of the fluid, which assists in *closing* the valve. Unfortunately, the poppet nose restricts the effective flow area to tank. This orificing can have a detrimental effect on the pressure override characteristics of the valve. Nevertheless, the advantages offered by the differential piston are in some way incorporated in most high pressure, high flow, direct operated designs.

THE GUIDED POPPET WITH DYNAMIC ASSIST

This direct operated relief valve overcomes the typical performance problems which are normally associated with direct operated designs. As mentioned, the problems include

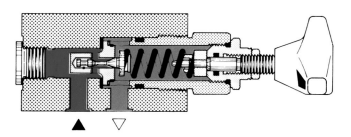

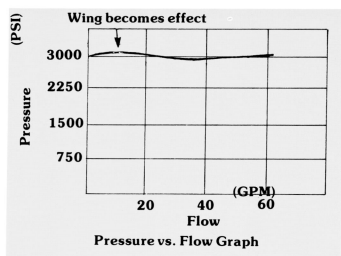

Pressure vs. Flow Graph

bad pressure override, noise, instability and a narrow range of adjustability. Let us now consider each problem individually, and the design feature incorporated to overcome this problem.

Pressure Override

We know that with direct operated reliefs, pressure override occurs because of increased spring force with additional compression, loss of effective area with poppet opening, and additional pressure drop due to increasing flows. All of these are physical facts which exist, and, therefore, must be dealt with to give good performance specification. With this guided poppet design, a wing is incorporated on the poppet just above the seat. The advantage of the wing is that a hydrodynamic lifting force, similar to the aerodynamic force which lifts an airplane wing, helps open the poppet after cracking pressure has been reached. The wing area and shape can be optimized so that the valve uses the kinetic energy, or momentum of the fluid at high velocity, to counteract exactly the increased spring force and the loss of area. This results in a perfectly flat pressure vs. flow curve.

Noise

Two basic noise generators in relief valves are poppet and spring chatter and high velocity oil. As mentioned previously, we can mechanically guide the poppet. However, when this is done, the mechanical means incorporated can cause obstructions in the free flow path to tank. By placing a "nose guide" on the high pressure side of the seat, we take the guiding mechanism out of the oil path to tank, allowing a 360° divergent flow path as formed by the wing. High velocity through cross drillings is overcome, eliminating the whistle. Since the poppet is not allowed to move laterally, spring and poppet chatter is also eliminated. Consequently, the relieving function is quiet at any flow rate.

Stability

If you ever tried to hold your thumb over the stream of water coming from the end of a garden hose, you can understand how erratic the poppet position can be in the stream of oil. Each lateral or vertical motion of the poppet, no matter how small, compresses or relaxes the spring. This rapid changing of spring position shows up in instability on the pressure gauge. Guiding the poppet eliminates the possibility of lateral movement and helps the stability of the relief. However, we must also concern ourselves with erratic axial movement.

The nose guide not only guides the poppet, but also serves as a shock absorber. System pressure fills the can in which the nose guide rides. Small metering notches on the guiding lands restricts the oil transfer from one side of the land to the other. Since the oil must transfer for poppet motion to occur, erratic axial motion of the poppet is dampened.

Adjustability Range

Although the guided poppet with dynamic assist does not conform to the basic design of differential piston relief

valves, you can see from the diagram that a hydrostatic balancing force exists which greatly reduces the effective area which is exposed to pressure.

Since system pressure works only on a small area, the spring can be much lighter than that needed to balance the force created by the full area of the poppet. A lighter spring means fewer pounds per inch compression (spring constant k), and, therefore, a larger adjustability range. In actual practice, the higher pressure relief valves can be adjusted quite low without adversely effecting performance. A 3000 PSI spring can easily be adjusted from 300 to 400 PSI with only an expected loss of adjustment accuracy.

SYMBOLS

The direct acting relief valve is represented by a square. The pressure sensing line (pilot line) is represented by the dash line, and is directly opposed by the spring force. The arrow position shows that the valve remains closed until the pressure force overcomes the spring force and pushes the arrow over so that the flow is directed to tank.

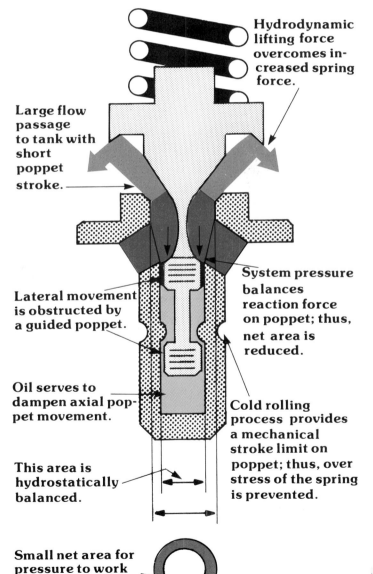

Hydrodynamic lifting force overcomes increased spring force.

Large flow passage to tank with short poppet stroke.

Lateral movement is obstructed by a guided poppet.

Oil serves to dampen axial poppet movement.

This area is hydrostatically balanced.

Small net area for pressure to work against.

System pressure balances reaction force on poppet; thus, net area is reduced.

Cold rolling process provides a mechanical stroke limit on poppet; thus, over stress of the spring is prevented.

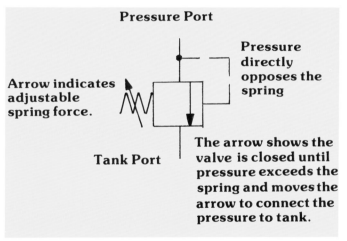

Pressure Port

Arrow indicates adjustable spring force.

Pressure directly opposes the spring

Tank Port

The arrow shows the valve is closed until pressure exceeds the spring and moves the arrow to connect the pressure to tank.

PILOT OPERATED PRESSURE RELIEF VALVES

The pilot operated relief performs the same function as the direct operated design in that it serves to protect the system components from over pressure, and it limits the maximum output force. This model, however, offers advantages in both versatility and performance which make it more desirable than direct operated valves.

As already discussed, direct operated valves are limited in their capability to handle large flows at high pressures. Although some designs are more capable than others, the pilot operated design is really the only way to relieve flows of more than 75 GPM. The major disadvantage is that large valves have larger poppet areas exposed to system pressure. This larger area multiplied by high pressure creates a need for an undesirably large spring. For this reason, pilot operated valves use the principle of the "hydraulic level" to multiply the force of a smaller spring.

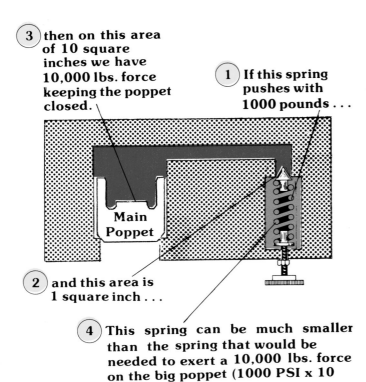

③ then on this area of 10 square inches we have 10,000 lbs. force keeping the poppet closed.

① If this spring pushes with 1000 pounds . . .

Main Poppet

② and this area is 1 square inch . . .

④ This spring can be much smaller than the spring that would be needed to exert a 10,000 lbs. force on the big poppet (1000 PSI x 10 sq. in. = 10,000 lbs.).

BASIC PILOT OPERATED CONSTRUCTION

The pilot operated relief is nothing more than two separate direct operated reliefs combined into one unit. One section is a relief designed to handle high flow at low pressure, while the pilot relief handles high pressure at very low flows. Let us consider the low pressure high flow portion.

The main valve consists of a housing with a pressure inlet and a tank outlet. Like a simple direct operated relief, pressure is blocked from tank by the main poppet or spool. The poppet is held against its seat (or the spool is held in the closed position) by a light spring force. Since this portion of the relief must handle large flows, the main poppet has a relatively large poppet area exposed to the system pressure. The combination of a large area being supported by a light spring makes the valve capable of handling large flows at low pressures. Since this portion uses a weak spring, it has a low spring constant which does not result in a high pressure override.

The pilot valve is also a simple direct operated relief. However, this valve incorporates a stiff spring used in con-

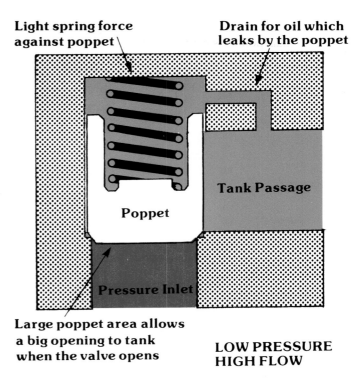

Light spring force against poppet

Drain for oil which leaks by the poppet

Tank Passage

Poppet

Pressure Inlet

Large poppet area allows a big opening to tank when the valve opens

LOW PRESSURE HIGH FLOW

junction with a small area exposed to system pressure. This makes the pilot valve capable of handling high pressures but very little flow. Should this section have to handle large flows, the stiff spring constant and small seat area would result in objectional pressure override.

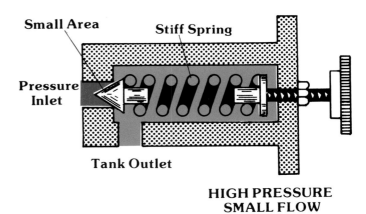

Small Area

Stiff Spring

Pressure Inlet

Tank Outlet

HIGH PRESSURE SMALL FLOW

By using these two components to accomplish a single function, we obtain the ability to handle large flows at high pressures. Let us now take a closer look at the static and dynamic interaction of the two sub-assemblies.

THE STATIC OR CLOSED CONDITION

Pilot operated reliefs stay closed because of the principle of

Pascal's Law. In reference to the figure, the fluid above and below the main poppet is captive in a closed container. Since the area on top of the main poppet is somewhat larger than that on the bottom, there is a larger closing force than opening force, and the valve remains closed. A light spring force is incorporated above the poppet which not only keeps the valve closed during start-up, but also provides an additional unbalancing force when pressures are equal above and below the poppet. Under these conditions, you can see that the valve is closed no matter whether there is 100 PSI or 10,000 PSI in the system.

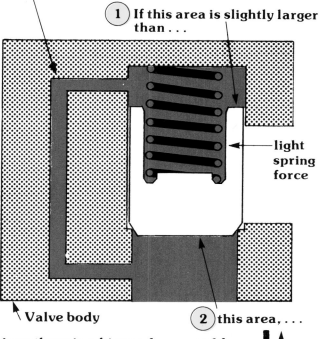

③ the *equal* pressure on both sides would keep the poppet closed against the seat . . .

① If this area is slightly larger than . . .

light spring force

Valve body

② this area, . . .

④ since there is a bigger downward force ⬇⬆ than upward force.

THE DYNAMIC OPENING OF THE RELIEF

By adding the high pressure low flow relief to the chamber above the main poppet, we can limit the pressure and thus the closing force. The pressure in the oil above the main poppet is regulated as follows:

In reference to the diagram, system pressure is exposed to areas A1, A2 and A3. As pressure increases, it increases *equally* on all areas. As long as area A3 remains closed, there is *no flow,* and the pilot circuit conforms with the principles of Pascal's Law. Under these conditions, we have a larger closing force than opening force; thus, the valve remains closed. Nevertheless, when pressure over area A3 exceeds the spring force, oil escapes from the previously closed container, which establishes a flow in the pilot circuit.

It is this flow which allows the valve to open.

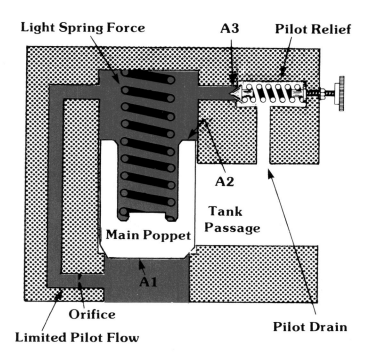

Light Spring Force **A3** **Pilot Relief**

A2

Tank Passage

Main Poppet

A1

Orifice

Limited Pilot Flow

Pilot Drain

Closed Condition

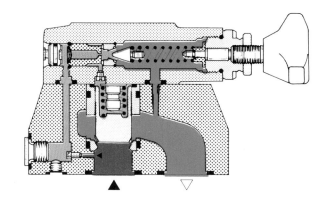

Dynamic Condition

When pressure is sufficient to overcome the spring of the high pressure pilot relief, we immediately see a decay in pressure above the main poppet. This establishes a pressure imbalance across the orifice in the pilot circuit which necessitates a flow of oil across that orifice. This flow of oil tries to replenish the oil lost over the piloting relief. However, in trying to reestablish a static condition, this flow causes a pressure differential which is sufficient to open the main poppet. This, in effect, relieves oil to tank at the pressure setting of the piloting relief. If, on the other hand, system pressure decays, the pilot relief will close. Equal pressure is re-established on both sides of the main poppet due to the principles of Pascal's Law. When pressures above and below the main poppet are equal, the main poppet closes because of the larger downward force. Remember, some of the closing force is created by the light spring above the main poppet.

REMOTE PILOTING

Another reason the pilot operated relief valve is often required is that with it, the pressure can be adjusted at the operator's station, while the main valve can be located elsewhere in the system. This feature is referred to as remote piloting.

Since the force on the main poppet is controlled by pressure in the pilot circuit, it is possible to connect other small piloting relief valves in this piloting circuit. The maximum pressure of the main system is governed by the pilot relief with the lowest pressure setting.

If the main pilot relief is set for the highest possible system pressure, then the small direct operated relief, which can be mounted remotely in the operator's control console, can be used to adjust system pressure to anything lower than that set on the main valve.

MULTIPLE PRESSURE SELECTION

Multiple pressure settings can be set on any number of small piloting relief valves. By using isolating directional control valves, individual pressures can be selected via electrical signals. This offers the ability to quickly recall set pressures by selecting the relief valve with the proper preset pressure. When the solenoid valve is in its closed position, its respective relief valve is blocked from the main relief valve's pilot circuit, and does not effect main system pressure. Under this condition, the small pipe from the main relief to the isolating directional control is only an extension of the "Pascal" closed container.

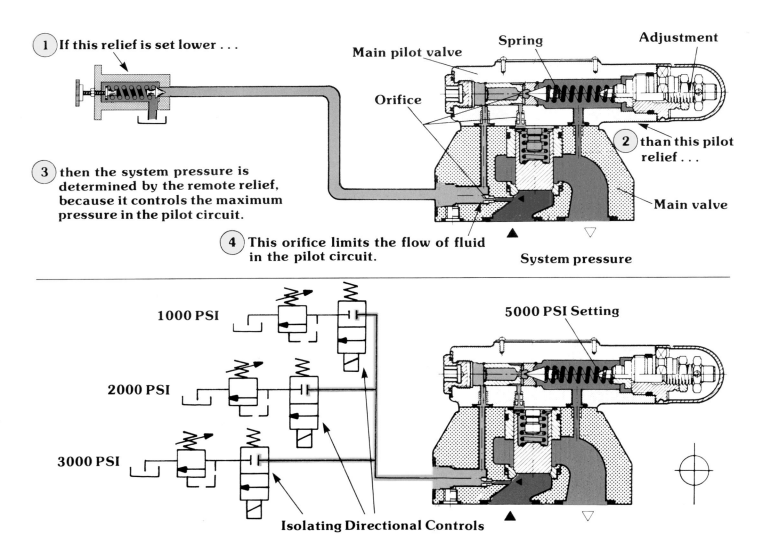

1) If this relief is set lower . . .

Main pilot valve

Spring

Adjustment

Orifice

2) than this pilot relief . . .

3) then the system pressure is determined by the remote relief, because it controls the maximum pressure in the pilot circuit.

Main valve

4) This orifice limits the flow of fluid in the pilot circuit.

System pressure

1000 PSI

2000 PSI

3000 PSI

5000 PSI Setting

Isolating Directional Controls

VENTING THE PILOT OPERATED RELIEF

One of the most important features a pilot operated relief provides is a capability to *vent* the main system. The terminology "venting main system" means allowing all pump output to flow pressureless to the tank. This is quite important because it takes very little horsepower to circulate oil at little or no pressure. If the hydraulic system is not being required to do work, then by venting the system, the full hydraulic horsepower capability of the pump is not turned into heat and wasted, as it would be if the pump had to push the oil over the relief at full system pressure. It allows the hydraulic system to *idle*. The venting feature is such an important feature to industrial hydraulic systems that most manufacturers offer this feature as a standard option in the pilot operated relief line of components. By mounting a small directional control directly on top of the pilot valve of the main relief, the pilot circuit can either be blocked from or connected to the internal tank chamber.

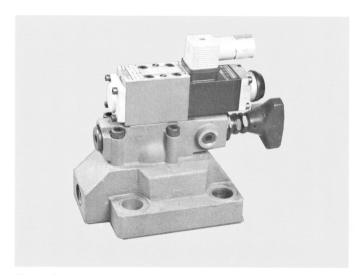

Normally open solenoid vented reliefs are those which allow the oil to flow pressureless to tank when no electricity is being supplied to the solenoid (de-energized). Energizing the solenoid *loads* the system by reestablishing the pilot circuit to that of a standard pilot operated relief.

Normally closed valves, on the other hand, function in just the opposite manner. When de-energized, the relief functions as a standard pilot operated relief. The system is vented by energizing the solenoid.

In hydraulic circuits, it is more common to find normally open valves than it is to find those which are normally closed. The logic behind this is that a normally open valve is *fail-safe* in the event of a power failure in the control circuit. If something goes wrong in the control circuit of a normally closed valve, system pressure is at its highest rather than being vented as it would be with a normally opened valve.

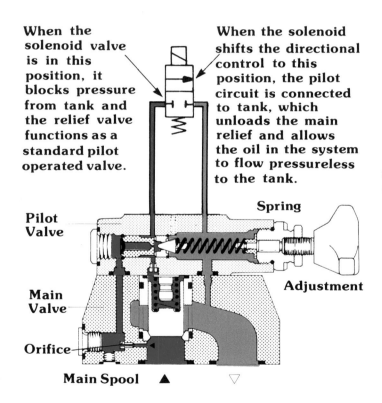

When the solenoid valve is in this position, it blocks pressure from tank and the relief valve functions as a standard pilot operated valve.

When the solenoid shifts the directional control to this position, the pilot circuit is connected to tank, which unloads the main relief and allows the oil in the system to flow pressureless to the tank.

Spring

Pilot Valve

Main Valve

Orifice

Adjustment

Main Spool ▲ ▽

This type of valve is commonly referred to as a *solenoid vented relief.* More often than not, the directional control is shifted from the blocked to the open position, or vice versa, by means of a solenoid. For purposes of this chapter, a solenoid is defined as a component which takes an electric current (the same that is used to light an ordinary household light bulb), and transforms that electrical energy into a linear force. This force is then used to change the position of (*shifts*) the directional control. In talking about solenoid vented relief valves, two terms are often encountered:

HIGH VENT OPTION

We said earlier that the main section of the pilot operated relief is nothing more than a low pressure, high flow, direct operated relief. When the pilot circuit is vented, the pump is actually vented to tank at a pressure determined by this low pressure relief.

To obtain maximum efficiency in the vented condition, the light spring force on the main poppet is usually designed to relieve the pump flow to tank at a pressure of less than 50 PSI. Nevertheless, it is sometimes necessary for proper system operation to maintain a residual pressure of higher than 50 PSI. If this is the case, a higher vent pressure can be achieved by selecting the *high vent option.*

The high vent option is nothing more than a stronger spring holding the main poppet or spool in the closed position. With the high vent spring, approximately 75 PSI is required to open the main poppet. The high vent option is particularly helpful in systems in which we must maintain pilot pressure for pilot operated directional controls, or in situations in which it is necessary to push oil through heat exchangers or filters while the system is idling.

EXTERNAL PILOT DRAIN

In standard pilot operated relief valves, the spring chamber of the pilot valve is drained to the valve's tank port through internal passages. A problem may arise in some applications when the pressure in the tank port varies during different parts of the cycle. This happens when resistances downstream of the "T" port are subjected to different flow rates as the relief valve relieves more or less flow. Remember, it takes more pressure to push a large flow of oil back to tank through filters and heat exchangers than it does when there is little flow. With internally drained valves, tank pressure is exposed on the back side of the pilot poppet, and adds a force of pressure multiplied by area, to the force of the spring. If tank pressure varies, so does the pressure in the main system, since there is a varying force holding the pilot poppet against the seat.

If fluctuations in the main system pressure cannot be tolerated, the spring chamber of the pilot can be isolated and drained through a separate port. This is known as an *external drain* option.

In valves in which the drain port has been designed to withstand full system pressure, a second use of the drain port is often desirable. We can make use of the fact that back pressure in the spring chamber adds to valve setting and use this as the remote pressure adjustment. As will be shown in our discussion of reducing valves, this has a particular advantage when it is necessary to adjust two pilot operated valves from the same adjustment while maintaining a fixed differential between these pressure settings.

As shown in the cross-sectional illustration, the *lowest* pressure is set on the main valve when we remotely adjust by using the "Y" port, as opposed to the *highest* pressure setting on the main valve when using the "X" port. Precaution must be taken in using the "Y" port because there is no inherent safeguard preventing the operator from exceeding the maximum pressure rating of the valve. If, for example, both the pilot valve and the remote adjustment were to have spring settings of 3000 PSI, then the main relief would relieve at 6000 PSI, which is in excess of its pressure rating. Nevertheless, if this method of adjustment offers advantages to the system design, then adequate safeguards can be provided by proper component selection. Being aware of the possibility of overpressure, the designer can select a lockable pressure adjustment on the main pilot valve. In this manner, the resistance of the pilot valve's spring can be locked at its absolute minimum value (100 PSI). Then, by selecting a remote relief with the proper spring, you can be assured that the operator cannot exceed the maximum pressure rating.

USING THE "Y" PORT FOR LOAD SENSING

Although a complete discussion of speed control and energy loss will be covered in Chapter 3, it is relatively simple for us to design a circuit which makes the pressure setting of a pilot operated relief sensitive to changes in load induced pressure. The major advantage here is that the pressure of the relief valve self regulates when circuits are operating over a broad load range. Because the load pressure can be sensed, the pump flow can always be relieved to tank at a pressure slightly higher than that induced by the load. This not only saves energy, but it gives a constant pressure drop across the fixed resistances to flow in the system, resulting in constant actuator speed (see Chapter 3 for full description). To further explain this concept, let us consider a typical circuit with and without the load sensing feature.

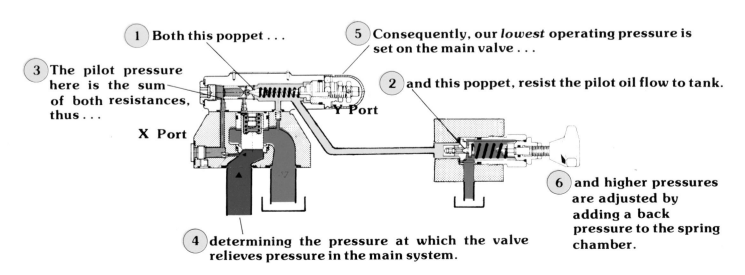

1) Both this poppet . . .

5) Consequently, our *lowest* operating pressure is set on the main valve . . .

3) The pilot pressure here is the sum of both resistances, thus . . .

2) and this poppet, resist the pilot oil flow to tank.

X Port

Y Port

6) and higher pressures are adjusted by adding a back pressure to the spring chamber.

4) determining the pressure at which the valve relieves pressure in the main system.

"Y" Port Pressure Adjustment

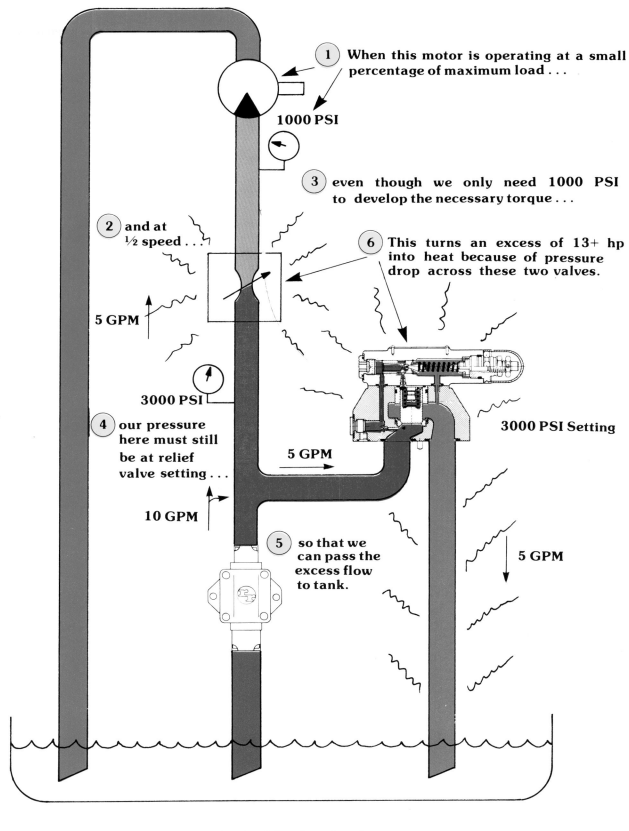

1 When this motor is operating at a small percentage of maximum load . . .

1000 PSI

3 even though we only need 1000 PSI to develop the necessary torque . . .

2 and at ½ speed . . .

6 This turns an excess of 13+ hp into heat because of pressure drop across these two valves.

5 GPM

3000 PSI

4 our pressure here must still be at relief valve setting . . .

5 GPM

3000 PSI Setting

10 GPM

5 so that we can pass the excess flow to tank.

5 GPM

WITHOUT LOAD SENSING

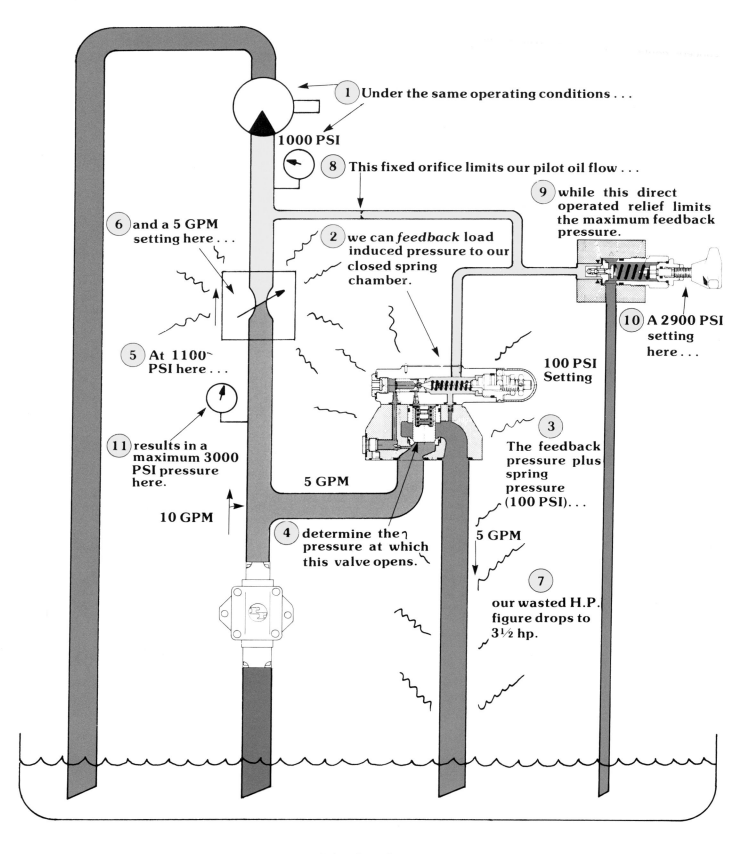

1 Under the same operating conditions . . .

1000 PSI

8 This fixed orifice limits our pilot oil flow . . .

9 while this direct operated relief limits the maximum feedback pressure.

6 and a 5 GPM setting here . . .

2 we can *feedback* load induced pressure to our closed spring chamber.

5 At 1100 PSI here . . .

10 A 2900 PSI setting here . . .

100 PSI Setting

11 results in a maximum 3000 PSI pressure here.

3 The feedback pressure plus spring pressure (100 PSI). . .

5 GPM

10 GPM

4 determine the pressure at which this valve opens.

5 GPM

7 our wasted H.P. figure drops to 3½ hp.

WITH LOAD SENSING RELIEF

The example only introduces the possibility of energy saving by load sensing with the relief. With a little imagination, this concept could result in considerable energy savings in a multitude of applications. Our only warning is that the size of the fixed orifice limiting pilot oil feedback is extremely important to the proper operation of the system. Also, the pilot feedback lines should be rigid tubing (not hose), with lengths kept as short as possible.

OPERATING PRINCIPLES OF VARIOUS MAIN POPPET DESIGNS

Pilot operated relief valves do not always display similar operating characteristics. Although all valves open and close in the same basic manner, the actual design of the main control section has an influence on the operating characteristics of the valve. Pressure override, response, overshoot, stability and sensitivity to contamination are characteristics related to the basic relief valve design. We now will discuss these characteristics individually as related to spool, balanced piston and cartridge poppet designs.

SPOOL TYPE MAIN SECTIONS

Although the spool type relief has been obsoleted by most manufacturers in favor of the superior performance offered by either of the basic poppet designs, we wish to mention its operating characteristics for reasons of comparison. The three major factors which led to its obsolescense were poor response, inherently bad overshoot, and sensitivity to contaminants in the oil.

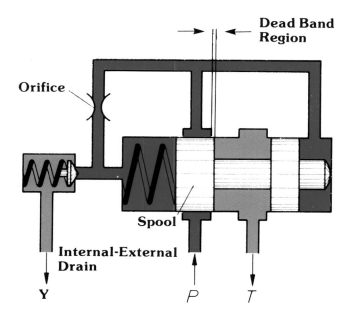

In reference to the operational cross section, the spool must first move through the deadband region before pressure opens to tank. This makes the spool design considerably slower than the poppet, since a poppet begins opening with the first increment of motion. Another detriment to the response time of a spool design is the high mass of the spool as compared to the poppet. Since all reliefs respond to pressure in a small portion of a second, the poppet or spool must undergo drastic acceleration and deceleration forces. Acceleration and deceleration occur as the moving member goes from rest, in the closed position, to a stable opening in the dynamic position. Of course, any reduction in mass greatly improves the response characteristics of the valve. Consequently, with spool reliefs, if the pilot circuit is orificed large enough to give good opening response, the physical overshoot of the spool during deceleration to the dynamic open position requires a longer time period to achieve stability. The optimal compromise is an overall response time of approximately 150 milliseconds.

Likewise, the overshoot characteristics of a relief valve are related to spool (or poppet) stroke as compared to valve opening. When it comes time to relieve oil, pressure can build to very high values almost instantaneously if the oil has nowhere to go. With spool designs, the pressure builds to the point where the pilot valve opens and creates the imbalance on the spool. Also, this imbalance must be high enough to achieve acceleration of the spool mass. The problem is that during the first moments of acceleration, the spool movement provides no opening. Since there is nowhere for the pump supply to go, pressure builds instantaneously to a high value. In other words, even if the spool mechanically responds quickly to increasing pressure, little or no opening during the initial response period shows up as a poor overshoot characteristic of the valve.

Finally, the life expectancy of spool type reliefs is very susceptible to contamination. In any relief, oil passes to tank at extremely high velocities. Contaminants in the oil, traveling at these high velocities, have a sandblasting effect on the exposed steel surfaces. The close tolerances on the large land areas of a spool design are more susceptible to damage and subsequent seizure than is the line contact area of a poppet. When exposed to systems with the same level of contaminants, the spool relief will either seize or leak excessively much sooner than a poppet design.

BALANCE PISTON—POPPET DESIGN

As shown in the cross-sectional drawing, you will notice that pressure is blocked from tank much like a check valve checks reverse free flow. In other words, when the valve opens, the flow of oil is around the poppet towards the seat. The term "balanced piston" comes from the fact that, when the valve is closed, there are equal areas exposed above and below the control piston. The differential force holding the piston closed in the static condition is only that of the light spring. The advantage this design offers over the spool type relief is that flow to tank is established immediately upon

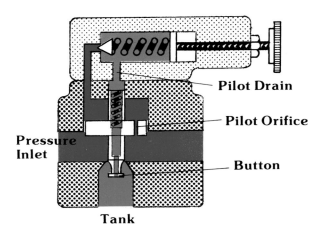

Pilot Drain

Pilot Orifice

Pressure Inlet

Button

Tank

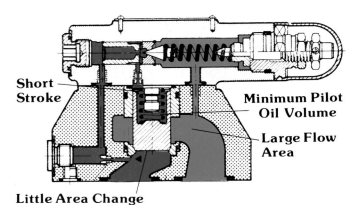

Short Stroke

Minimum Pilot Oil Volume

Large Flow Area

Little Area Change

piston movement. Consequently, overshoot is limited to an average of 350 to 450 PSI.

Although the response of a balance piston-poppet relief is better than that of a spool type relief, the mass of the relatively large piston and poppet assembly is not much less than that of a spool. Consequently, the response time, from the time the valve first cracks to the time it reaches a stable opening, is more or less limited by the same factors that limit the spool design. Typical response characteristics for these designs range between 95 and 135 milliseconds.

One of the major disadvantages of a balanced piston-poppet relief is that it displays relatively bad pressure override characteristics. In this design, the poppet is inherently unstable, since a larger area is exposed to pressure when the poppet opens. As in the direct operated differential piston, a button is machined on the nose of the poppet. This button captures the hydrodynamic force as a force tending to close the valve. Of course, the higher the flow to tank, the higher the closing force; hence, the higher the pressure required to keep the valve open.

Of final concern is the fact that valves of this design can often generate noise in their tank port. The reason for this is the convergent flow to tank. These high velocities in a convergent path create an enormous amount of turbulence. This is especially true when you consider that the button is immersed in this flow stream creating even more of a disturbance.

CARTRIDGE POPPET DESIGN

The operational cross section shows that the cartridge unit consists of a small low mass poppet which offers a large flow area with minimum stroke. These design features allow the relief function to be performed quickly and quietly. Forces on the poppet are always in balance at any flow rate. Because of this, the valve is not only inherently stable, but it also operates with minimal pressure override. Likewise, the cartridge design offers better serviceability and flexibility in mounting style that is not possible with parts and body construction.

In consideration of the cartridge's response characteristics, we said earlier that response is directly related to stroke vs. opening area. The short stroke means that very little oil has to be relieved by the pilot as the poppet moves upwards from its fully closed to its fully open position. Also, the low poppet mass means that movement occurs with a very minute decay in pressure in the pilot section. Low poppet mass, short poppet stroke, and minimum oil displacement in the pilot section, allow the cartridge poppet to respond in the 50 or 60 millisecond range. This is actually faster than most direct operated valves.

Since the poppet provides a large flow path with its first increment of motion, overshoot is very low and of very short duration. Although overshoot is higher at lower operating pressures, the average overshoot is only 8 per cent of set pressure. This means that at 3000 PSI, the maximum pressure spike is in the neighborhood of 3250 PSI.

Another advantage to this design is that there is an insignificant change in effective area between the open and closed position of the valve. Consequently, the forces tending to open and close the poppet are always in balance and not affected by flow. The typical valve reseats within 30 PSI of its cracking pressure, and is inherently stable throughout the entire flow range. Likewise, minimum compression of the light spring force, and a poppet design which is virtually unaffected by flow, result in a minimum pressure override.

Finally, the cartridge poppet is extremely quiet in performing its relief function. This is a result of the fact that the flow passage to tank is not only large, but it also creates a 360° divergent flow stream. The potential energy in the pressurized fluid is disipated quickly and quietly.

DIFFERENT MOUNTING CONFIGURATIONS

Although the mounting conveniences are as numerous as the number of valves themselves, there are six basic mounting options each with its own advantages and disadvantages. The options range from two types of line mounting to subplate and sandwich mounting, to two types of cartridges for custom manifolding. In chosing the mounting style for your system, you should consider adjustment accessability, serviceability, location and its effect on system protection and overall space requirements.

SUBPLATE MOUNTED VALVES

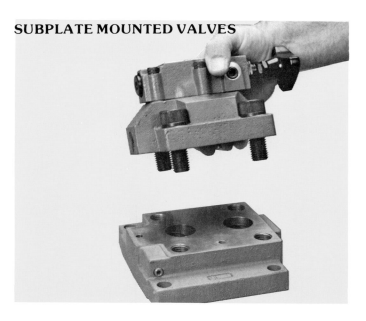

Advantages

The subplate mounted valves, by far, offer the best serviceability. Since the rigid piping is made to the subplate and not to the valve, valve replacement is simply achieved by bolting a new valve to the subplate. Most subplate mounted valves conform to national and international standards, so retrofits are not a problem. In addition, the valve and its subplate can be mounted away from the bulk of the system piping for easy operator access.

Disadvantages

The major disadvantages of subplate mounting show up in initial system cost and in space requirements. Not only is the subplate an additional purchase item, which also requires ad-

ditional piping hardware, it also must be structurally supported by some type of valve panel. This additional cost must be weighed against future service costs in your consideration.

SANDWICH MOUNTING

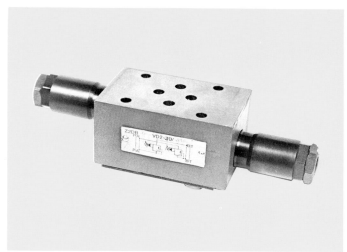

Advantages

Sandwich mounted valves are through ported and mounted between the directional control valve and its subplate. Their porting configuration is accomplished through passages in the block, and they can relieve either the pump supply or the service lines to the actuator. Either crossport or relief to tank can be compactly accomplished in a single block. Serviceability is equal to that of a subplate mounted valve with a smaller space requirement.

Disadvantages

Because of the compact nature of these valves, their performance characteristics are sometimes compromised. Likewise, because the valve is mounted close to the directional valve rather than to the pump or actuator, the relief's ability to protect the system is somewhat reduced.

TWO PORT LINE MOUNTED

Advantages

This type of mounting reduces initial installation cost by eliminating the cost of a separate subplate. Also, except for very large valves, the piping itself can serve as the valve's mounting structure. Since the valve must be teed to the pressure line, it is a relatively simple procedure to locate the valve for the operator's convenience.

The through ported relief is the most economical relief when you consider initial system costs. With three ports, you simply have to pipe to the inlet from the pump, an outlet to the system, and a tank return. Since the number of fittings is reduced, so are the possible points for leakage.

Disadvantages

Since the valve's physical location in the system is determined by the piping, adjustment access for the operator is not always easy to achieve. For serviceability, this valve more than any other, should be of cartridge construction, since the housing is located in the main artery of the system. More often than not, servicing requires a major system disassembly.

CARTRIDGE UNITS

Disadvantages

Care must be taken in "making-up" the fitting for this valve, as in the case with any line mounted valve. Over tightening of a tapered pipe thread can distort the valve housing, causing the valve to malfunction. Serviceability is also complicated because the system has to be partially disassembled to remove the valve. With a cartridge style line mounted valve, these problems are somewhat alleviated, because servicing can be accomplished simply by removing the cartridges. Likewise, even if a valve housing is distorted by over tightening a pipe connection, the chances are that this distortion will be isolated from the critical clearance in the cartridge.

THROUGH PORTED RELIEF VALVES

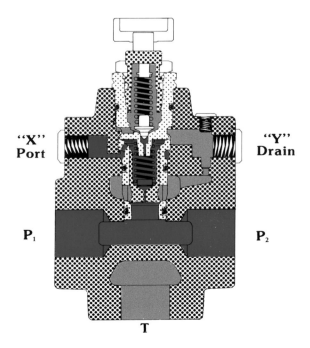

"X" Port

"Y" Drain

P₁

P₂

T

Cartridge units are available today in two basic versions: the threaded insert, and the slip-in cartridge. Since both types offer the same advantages and disadvantages, we will discuss their merits as one.

Advantages

Although cartridges can be mounted in either a subplate mount, or a thread valve housing, they are basically intended for custom manifolding. The cartridge greatly improves the serviceability of the relief function no matter whether it is mounted in a custom manifold or in a standard valve housing.

Disadvantages

The cartridge in itself cannot function. Consequently, it must be used in conjunction with a standard valve housing, or with some type of custom manifold. Of course, due to the high cost of both engineering and low quantity machining, the cartridge is often not an economical consideration.

SYMBOLS FOR PILOT OPERATED RELIEFS

Because of the complexity of the pilot circuit and its many optional uses, the symbol representation of a pilot operated relief can become quite complicated. The following symbol for a pilot operated relief with a normally open solenoid venting feature is a typical example.

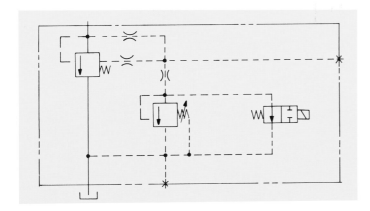

This symbol is complete in showing the main poppet (low pressure, high volume relief), the pilot relief (high pressure, low volume), the orifices which establish pressure decay in the pilot circuit, and the solenoid valve for venting. In common practice, the industry does not use symbols of this complexity. Over the years, it has become standard practice to represent both pilot operated and direct operated reliefs with the simpler direct operated relief valve symbol. This, however, often leads to confusion, since the total function

cannot be represented in this manner. Rexroth has developed and will be promoting the use of a new simplified symbol for representing pilot operated reliefs.

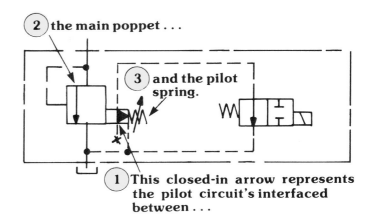

The following are variations showing this simplified symbol with various uses of the pilot circuit:

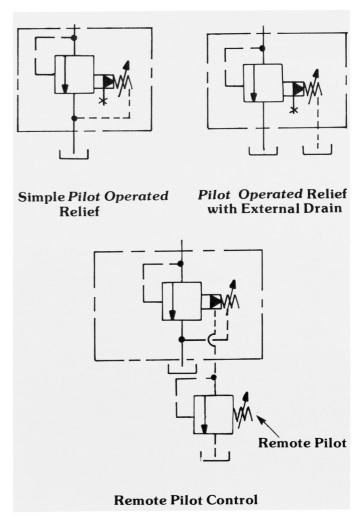

Simple *Pilot Operated* Relief

***Pilot Operated* Relief with External Drain**

Remote Pilot Control

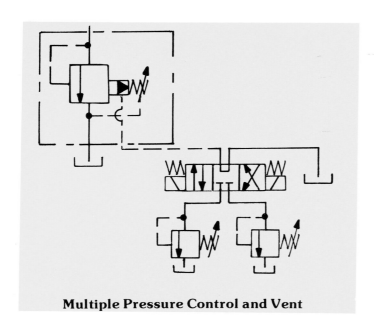

Multiple Pressure Control and Vent

REDUCING VALVES

As previously stated, reducing valves are used to limit a *branch* circuit to a pressure *lower* than the main relief valve setting. Consequently, output force can be regulated in the secondary circuit independent of (at a lower pressure level than) the rest of the system. Reducing valves are always supplied with an external drain on the spring chamber, since there is always pressure at the inlet and outlet working ports during valve operation.

Reducing valves, like relief valves, function by balancing a hydraulic force with a spring force. Consequently, they display similar operating characteristics to those of direct operated or pilot operated reliefs. Unlike relief valves, however, reducing valves are normally open, allowing oil entry to the secondary system. The valve senses the pressure level in the secondary system and tends to close, orificing the oil entering from the primary system, assuming that it is at a higher pressure level. Should the primary system be at a lower pressure level than the setting on the reducing valve, then the reducing valve would remain fully open, and both primary and secondary circuits would be at the pressure level of the primary system.

Reducing valves, more than any other type of pressure control, modulate between fully open and fully closed positions to keep the outlet pressure constant. Once downstream pressure reaches the reducing valve setting, the valve begins functioning as a self regulating orifice. The valve opens or closes its orifice which reduces or increases resistance to flow from inlet to outlet.

Since a reducing valve is nothing more than a self regulating resistance to flow, energy is expelled in the form of heat as inlet pressure is reduced to a lower outlet pressure. The

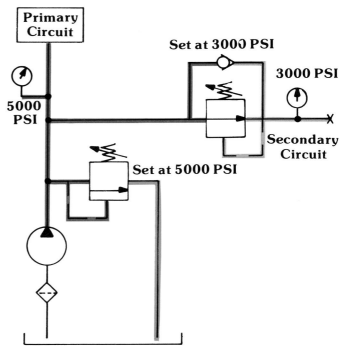

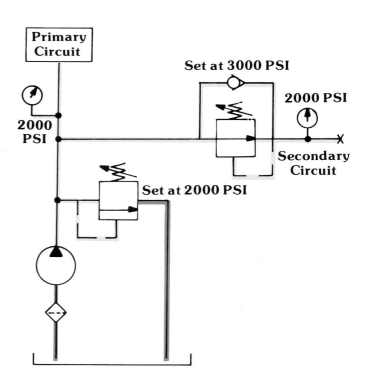

Reducing valves can take only a higher primary pressure and lower it for the secondary circuit.

higher the pressure level difference, the higher is the energy level difference and, therefore, the more energy is wasted in the form of heat. Large pressure differentials, especially with high flow rates, should be avoided through the use of a two pump system.

DIRECT OPERATED VALVES

For the same reasons, direct operated relief valves normally experience bad pressure override characteristics. With respect to increasing flow, direct operated pressure reducing valves show a drop in outlet pressure. To explain this phenomenon, we can consider the operation of a direct acting reducing valve.

spring setting. Because the orifice can be relatively large for high flows, the spring has to be only slightly compressed. However, to establish an identical pressure drop for low flow, the spring must be compressed further to create a smaller passage through the valve. Consequently, higher downstream pressure results with a decreased flow due to increased spring force.

Since pressure vs. flow characteristics can only be kept within acceptable limits with low variations in flow, Rexroth only manufactures direct operated reducing valves up to 1/2" line sizes for flow capabilities up to 12 1/2 GPM. For higher flows, a pilot operated valve is used because of its performance advantages.

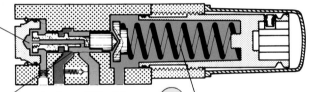

1 Outlet pressure is sensed on this area of the spool . . .

3 When the pressure is high enough to push the spool . . .

4 this orifice is made smaller, which adds resistance to flow . . .

2 and works against this spring.

5 which reduces the pressure in the secondary system.

Because reducing valves are variable orifices, their basic design is usually a tapered (metering) spool, held in the open position in the valve housing by an adjustable spring force. For direct operated valves, outlet pressure is exposed to the spool end opposite the spring, and moves the spool toward a more closed position as downstream pressure exceeds the

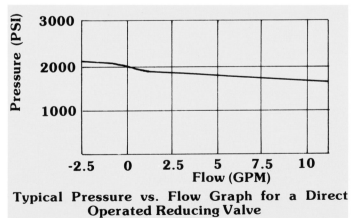

Typical Pressure vs. Flow Graph for a Direct Operated Reducing Valve

THREE-WAY CHARACTERISTICS OF DIRECT OPERATED VALVES

Another thing to consider about reducing valves is their ability to maintain reduced pressure in a fully static condition. During actuator motion in the secondary circuit, we have explained how the reducing valve modulates between open and closed to maintain downstream pressure at the desired setting. A problem arises, however, when the secondary circuit becomes static, and the reducing valve fully closes to separate the primary and secondary system pressures.

Under these conditions, an increase in load, or leakage across the reducing valve control spool, could increase the pressure in the secondary circuit higher than is desired. Since the valve has an inlet at high pressure, and an outlet at reduced pressure, a third port must be provided to rid the secondary circuit of leakage oil and/or reverse flow from the actuator. Most reducing valve designs in some way vent this oil, which tends to increase pressure to the spring chamber, where the oil can be externally drained.

STATIC VENTING AND
REVERSE FLOW CAPABILITY

The easiest method of venting oil, which tends to build pressure in the secondary circuit, is to have a bleed oil passage from the secondary port to the spring chamber. This leakage path, however, adds to the amount of flow out the drain port, which decreases the efficiency of the valve.

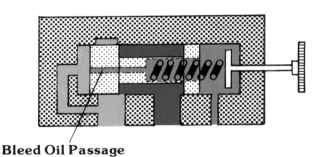

Bleed Oil Passage

Simple Direct Operated Reducing Valve

Some direct operated reducing valves have a three-way spool configuration. We previously stated that the reducing valve is normally open, and that it opposes the spring force with a hydraulic force from the secondary circuit. Depending on the pressure and flow potential at the valve inlet, the valve self-adjusts its orifice to obtain the required pressure loss. The valve closes only when the secondary circuit becomes static. A slight increase in outlet pressure above pressure setting shifts the spool further against the spring into a third position where the outlet is connected to the spring chamber, thus relieving the secondary circuit to tank. The flow capability of this three-way feature is approximately 20% of the maximum flow capacity of the Rexroth valve. When the secondary circuit is stalled, and there is no increase in pressure due to leakage, thermal expansion, or increased load, the valve is closed without leaking excessive oil to tank.

③ **when secondary system pressure shifts the spool to this position.**

② **is relieved to tank through the spring chamber . . .**

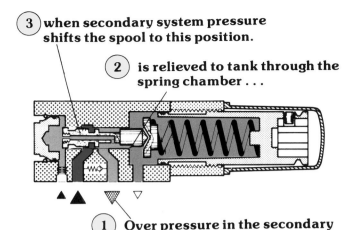

① **Over pressure in the secondary circuit . . .**

3-Way Reducing Valve

SANDWICH MOUNTED REDUCING VALVES

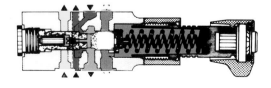

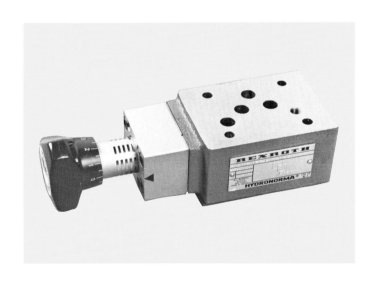

Sandwich Mounted Reducing Valve

In many hydraulic systems, the reducing function is only needed for one particular actuator. For instance, we may want to limit the torque output of a hydraulic motor, or to limit the thrust of a cylinder in one or both directions. For plumbing convenience in these types of circuits, reducing valves are available for sandwich mounting. These valves are simply mounted between the subplate and the directional control for that particular circuit function.

Depending on the model selected, the pressure reduction can be in the pressure supply to the directional valve, or in one of the service lines from the directional control to the actuator. A "P" port sandwich reducer would offer reduced pressure to either direction of operation. Since the flow is always from the pump supply, through the reducing valve to the pressure port of the directional control, a reverse free flow check is not required.

On the other hand, if the model selected reduces pressure in one of the service lines to the actuator, pressure control is achieved only in one direction of operation. Full system pressure operates the actuator in the reverse direction. Of course, since flow must pass through this type of valve in both directions, a reverse free flow check valve must be included. This allows the flow to by-pass the reducing valve mechanism in the reverse direction of actuator operation.

Due to their compact design, sandwich mounted reducing valves normally drain their spring chambers to the tank port connection of the directional valve. Since pressure in the tank return line can influence the pressure setting, precautions should be taken to keep tank line pressure as low as possible in these systems.

PILOT OPERATED REDUCING VALVES

Like pilot operated relief valves, pilot operated reducing valves perform the same function as their direct operated counterparts. Consequently, pilot operated reducing valves must be used for higher flow rates, since increased spring force, with increased displacement, has adverse effects on the performance characteristics of direct operated models. Today pilot operated pressure reducing valves are designed with both *primary* and *secondary* controls. We now wish to study the operation and characteristics of both of these types.

We will discuss the operation of the secondary control first, since this valve is really nothing more than a mirror image, so to speak, of a pilot operated relief valve. First of all, you will notice that the pilot section senses pressure in the secondary (outlet) port rather than the inlet, as with relief valves. As long as the pilot relief remains closed, pressures are equal above and below the main control spool. You will notice that the light spring force holds the main control spool in the fully *open* position, while, in contrast, the relief valve is held closed in the static pressure balanced condition. The valve

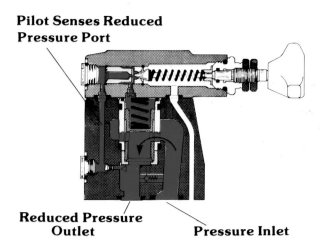

Pilot Senses Reduced Pressure Port

Reduced Pressure Outlet

Pressure Inlet

SECONDARY CONTROL

remains fully open, connecting the primary port to the secondary system until secondary system pressure overcomes the spring setting of the pilot valve.

When the piloting relief opens, a decay in pressure occurs above the main control spool, since a flow is created across the orifices in the pilot circuit. This causes an imbalance of forces on the main spool, which tends to move it vertically upward. An upward motion of the spool orients the center line of the radial drilling in the spool higher than the center line of the radial drilling in the stationary sleeve, in which it slides. The open area for flow is, thus, reduced, creating an orifice through which oil must flow in passing from the primary to the secondary port. Hence, a self-regulating pressure drop is imposed, in concert with the pressure levels dictated by the pilot circuit. Likewise, a full shut-off occurs when the secondary circuit becomes static.

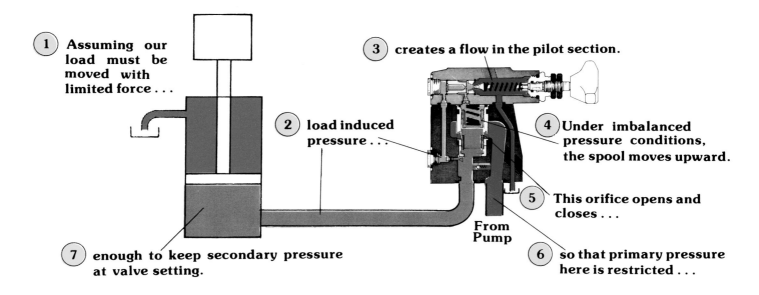

① Assuming our load must be moved with limited force . . .

③ creates a flow in the pilot section.

② load induced pressure . . .

④ Under imbalanced pressure conditions, the spool moves upward.

⑤ This orifice opens and closes . . .

From Pump

⑥ so that primary pressure here is restricted . . .

⑦ enough to keep secondary pressure at valve setting.

In the dynamic closed position of the pilot operated reducing valve, the spool moves completely upward so that, theoretically, there is no flow area through the radial cross-drillings. This position occurs, though only in theory, since there must be a flow of fluid in the pilot circuit to maintain the imbalance on the main spool. To better explain the dynamic closing we will consider a vertical acting, "bottomed out" cylinder.

RELIEVING ABILITY OF PILOT OPERATED REDUCING VALVES

Unfortunately, as you can see in the diagram, the pilot operated reducing valve has little ability to rapidly relieve a pressure build-up due to increased load. When the secondary circuit becomes static, the main spool is nearly closed, which

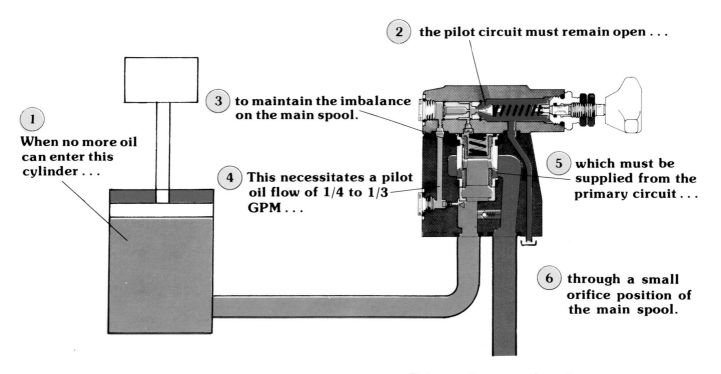

② the pilot circuit must remain open . . .

③ to maintain the imbalance on the main spool.

① When no more oil can enter this cylinder . . .

④ This necessitates a pilot oil flow of 1/4 to 1/3 GPM . . .

⑤ which must be supplied from the primary circuit . . .

⑥ through a small orifice position of the main spool.

Primary Pressure from Pump

except for a small pilot flow, captures a column of fluid between the main spool and actuator. If, for some reason, the actuator encounters an increased load, the pressure downstream of the reducing valve will also increase. Since pilot operated reducing valves, in general, cannot relieve much more than a 1/2 GPM flow rate through their pilot circuits, a separate relief valve should be considered if an increase in load could occur after the secondary system becomes static.

THREE-WAY PRESSURE REDUCING CIRCUIT

When it is necessary for the actuator to "give way" to an excessive load, a separate relief valve can be incorporated to relieve the reverse displacement from the actuator. Actually, this relief valve need be nothing more than a direct operated model, teed into the line between the reducing valve and the actuator. However, a pilot operated model offers better per-

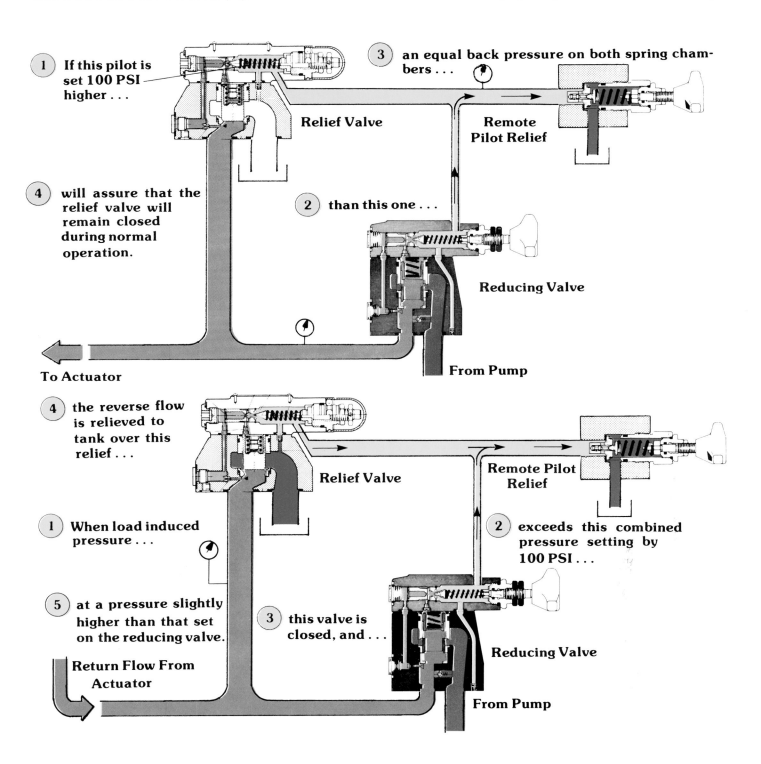

① If this pilot is set 100 PSI higher . . .

③ an equal back pressure on both spring chambers . . .

Relief Valve

Remote Pilot Relief

④ will assure that the relief valve will remain closed during normal operation.

② than this one . . .

Reducing Valve

To Actuator

From Pump

④ the reverse flow is relieved to tank over this relief . . .

Relief Valve

Remote Pilot Relief

① When load induced pressure . . .

② exceeds this combined pressure setting by 100 PSI . . .

⑤ at a pressure slightly higher than that set on the reducing valve.

③ this valve is closed, and . . .

Reducing Valve

Return Flow From Actuator

From Pump

formance characteristics, and the possibility of a fail-proof pressure setting. With this type of circuitry, it is important, from an efficiency standpoint always to adjust the relief valve to a pressure slightly higher than that set on the reducing valve. By setting the relief so that it will crack at a pressure of 100 to 200 PSI higher, you can be assured that under normal operation, all the output flow of the reducing valve produces work. If the relief valve setting is too close to that of the reducing valve, you can easily see that the flow bypassed by the relief not only affects performance, but that, at the same time, it generates excessive heat. The circuit provides a single pressure adjustment, while at the same time it maintains a constant differential between the relief and reducing valve setting.

REVERSE FREE FLOW

Since reducing valves are often used in the working lines supplying the actuator, the reducing valve must be able to allow a free flow in the reverse direction. Since the reducing valve is normally open, one would think that there would be no problem in passing a reverse flow through the valve. Unfortunately, with some circuits, you cannot safely assume that the valve will always remain open.

It is possible that high flow forces (hydrodynamic forces) could cause the main spool to close. This consideration is particularly important when you are using cylinder actuators with large rods. Under these conditions, a 2:1 ratio can double the normal flow rate.

In the illustrated circuit, once the reducing valve closes, pressure can build in the fluid which is captured between the actuator and the closed spool. If this pressure builds to the point where the reducing valve pilot opens, the main spool will remain closed. Since we cannot safely assume that the spool will remain open under all circumstances, most reducing valves include a reverse free flow check as a standard feature.

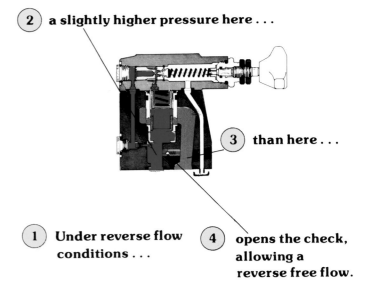

② a slightly higher pressure here . . .

③ than here . . .

① Under reverse flow conditions . . .

④ opens the check, allowing a reverse free flow.

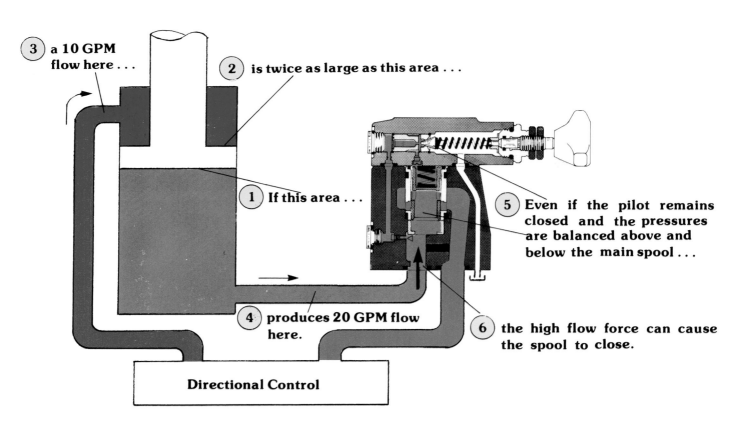

③ a 10 GPM flow here . . .

② is twice as large as this area . . .

① If this area . . .

④ produces 20 GPM flow here.

⑤ Even if the pilot remains closed and the pressures are balanced above and below the main spool . . .

⑥ the high flow force can cause the spool to close.

Directional Control

As shown in the cross-sectional drawing, the check valve simply bypasses the reducing valve mechanism under reverse flow conditions. During normal operation, the higher pressure at the valve's inlet keeps the check valve closed.

REDUCING VALVE WITH PRIMARY CONTROL

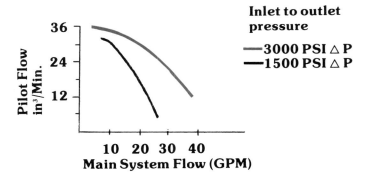

Before we discuss the operation of a reducing valve with primary control, let us first consider the reason for this design. It is a known fact that when an orifice is introduced into a flow stream, turbulence is also introduced, downstream of the orifice. Of course, the higher the flow rate, the more turbulence downstream of any given orifice.

With high flow, high pressure reducing valves, the turbulence downstream of the main control spool causes a loss in pressure at that point in the flow stream (Venturi effect). This loss in pressure reduces the pressure drop across the pilot circuit orifices, which lessens the pilot oil flow. Under these conditions, a reducing valve with secondary control becomes ineffective in maintaining a constant downstream pressure.

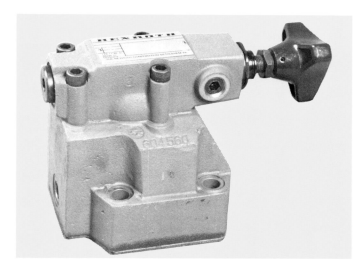

Typical Graph Comparing Loss of Pilot Oil Flow With Main System Flow

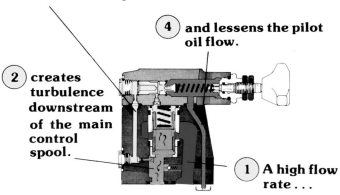

③ This feeds back an inaccurate downstream pressure . . .

④ and lessens the pilot oil flow.

② creates turbulence downstream of the main control spool.

① A high flow rate . . .

Secondary Control Is Not Effective in High Flow Rate Valves

A reducing valve with primary control can be used, to achieve higher flow rates with better stability. With this design, the pilot oil is supplied from the high pressure inlet of the valve. The pilot head incorporates a pressure compensated flow control which maintains a pilot flow of approximately 40 in³/min flow stream. Since the top of the main control spool is exposed to this pilot flow, the force holding the valve open is determined by the pressure setting of the pilot relief. Let us now consider the operation of this design.

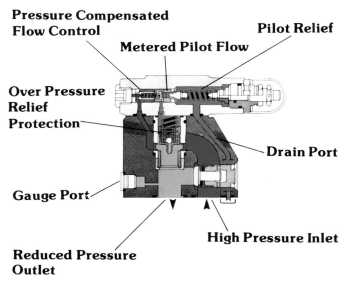

As long as the inlet pressure is lower than the setting of the pilot relief, the pressure on top of the main spool is equal to the pressure at the inlet of the valve. This pressure force, along with the spring force, holds the main spool in the wide open position, allowing free flow to the secondary circuit. As load induced pressure increases, so does the inlet pressure and the force holding the main spool open.

closed position. Under these conditions, the secondary outlet is totally isolated from the primary circuit and the pilot circuit of the valve. Of course, leakage across the sliding fits of the main control spool could cause the secondary system

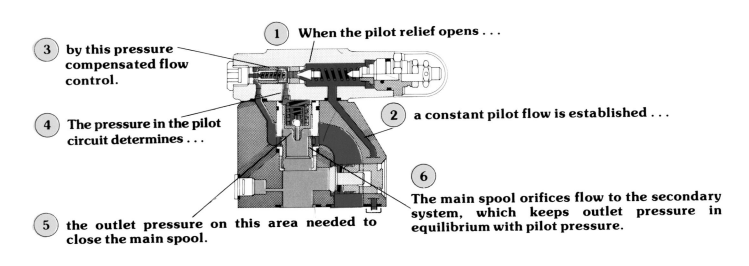

2 the pressure above the control spool is the same . . .

1 When this pilot relief is closed . . .

5 Consequently, the main control spool is held in the WIDE OPEN POSITION, since there is a larger opening force than closing force.

3 as the pressure at the inlet, since the pilot system is static.

4 The pressure at the outlet is only slightly lower than that at the inlet because of pressure drop due to flow.

The moment the inlet pressure exceeds the setting of the pilot relief, a constant pilot flow is established. The pressure determined by the pilot relief regulates the maximum pressure, holding the reducing valve in the open position. As load induced pressure increases on the opposite area of the main control spool, so does the force trying to close the valve. The moment the closing force exceeds the forces holding the valve open, the main spool moves upward, orificing the flow to the secondary circuit. Hence, secondary system pressure is maintained at a level which balances the pressure in the pilot circuit.

pressure to equalize with that of the primary system.

To avoid the possibility of pressure build-up in a static secondary circuit, a small relief valve is incorporated in the main spool. This relief valve has its pressure port exposed to the secondary outlet, and relieves oil to the pilot circuit. The relief valve is nothing more than a ball held on its seat by a light spring force. To open this relief, the pressure in the secondary circuit must overcome the spring force (45 PSI) and the pressure in the pilot circuit working against the back side of the ball. However, since outlet pressure is equal to

3 by this pressure compensated flow control.

1 When the pilot relief opens . . .

4 The pressure in the pilot circuit determines . . .

2 a constant pilot flow is established . . .

6

The main spool orifices flow to the secondary system, which keeps outlet pressure in equilibrium with pilot pressure.

5 the outlet pressure on this area needed to close the main spool.

When the actuator on the reducing valve's outlet stalls, a slight increase in outlet pressure overcomes the forces holding the valve open, and moves the main spool to the fully

pilot pressure, the net result is that the relief valve opens when the secondary system reaches a pressure 45 PSI higher than setting. Since the relief valve relieves oil to the pilot circuit, its maximum flow capability is limited to approximately 60 cubic inches per minute. Although this is satisfactory for relieving leakage oil, it cannot relieve a reverse flow from the actuator.

destroyed, the loss of energy shows up as heat in the hydraulic system. Of course, the lower the pressure in the secondary system, the more heat is generated. Remember:

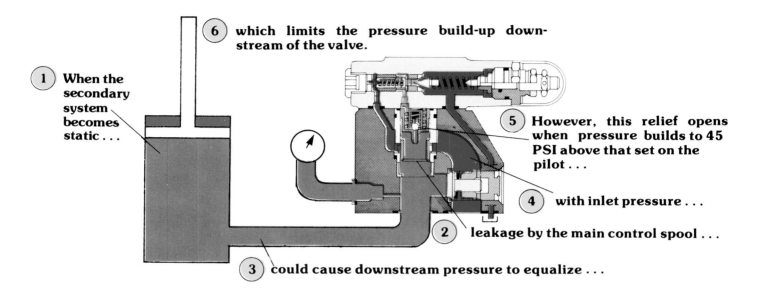

6 which limits the pressure build-up downstream of the valve.

1 When the secondary system becomes static...

5 However, this relief opens when pressure builds to 45 PSI above that set on the pilot...

4 with inlet pressure...

2 leakage by the main control spool...

3 could cause downstream pressure to equalize...

REMOTE PRESSURE ADJUSTMENT FOR PRIMARY CONTROL REDUCING VALVES

As shown, this design does not modulate the pressure above and below the spool (or poppet) in the conventional pilot operated manner. Since there is no "X" port where we can remotely modulate the pressure above the main control spool, we must use the "Y" port to create this function. A complete description of the use of the "Y" port for remote adjustment, and of the precautions to be taken in its use, has been given in the section of this manual which deals with pilot operated relief valves.

HEAT GENERATION WITH PRESSURE REDUCING VALVES

Reducing valves, in general, are unique in their ability to independently adjust force in a secondary system. Likewise, they are the only valves which can be used to isolate components with low pressure ratings from the rest of the higher pressure system. However, we caution the designer to be discrete in his selection of a reducing valve function. We must always weigh the design flexibility offered by reducing valves against their undesirable heating capability.

The pressurized fluid at a reducing valve's outlet has less potential for doing work than the fluid which was exposed at its inlet. This is true since a loss in pressure shows up downstream as a loss of *force potential*. Since energy cannot be

$$BTU/hr = 1.5 \times GPM \times PSI \text{ (Lost)}$$

Consequently, it is left to the designer to keep the secondary system pressure as close to that in the primary system as possible. You can see that this becomes even more important in high flow systems. In these, if the pressure differential is too great, it is worthwhile to consider a separate pump for the lower energy secondary system.

SYMBOLS

Like pressure relief valve symbols, reducing valve symbols can represent either direct or pilot operated valves. You will notice that symbols for reducing valves are similar to those of relief valves, except for two major changes.

First, since the reducing valve is normally open, the flow arrow is in line with the inlet and outlet ports to the square box. This shows that the valve passes fluid freely until pilot pressure overcomes the spring force. At this point, the flow arrow is pushed out of alignment with the inlet and outlet, which closes off the flow.

Second, since the reducing valve is sensing pressure at its outlet, the pilot line differs from that of the relief. In the reducing valve symbol, the pilot line works against its control spool by sensing outlet pressure. Also, since a reducing valve must always have a drain connection to its spring chamber, the "Y" port external drain is always shown.

Various reducing valve symbols are shown below:

SYMBOL	DESCRIPTION
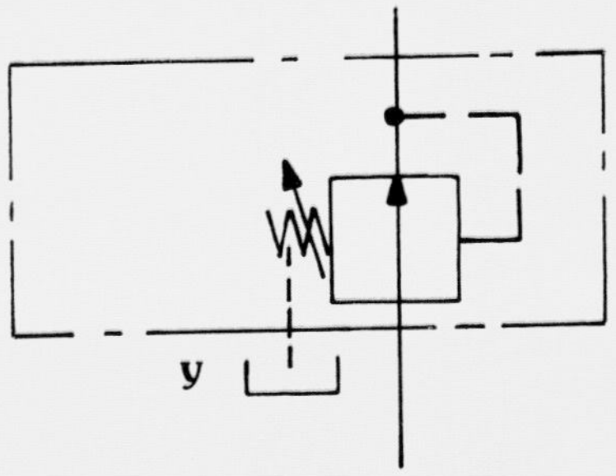	Standard graphic symbol for a direct operated reducing valve, without a reverse free flow check.
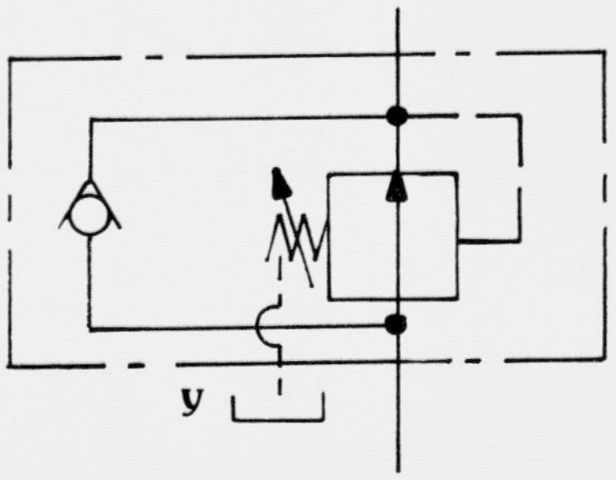	Graphic symbol for a direct operated reducing valve with integral reverse free flow check.
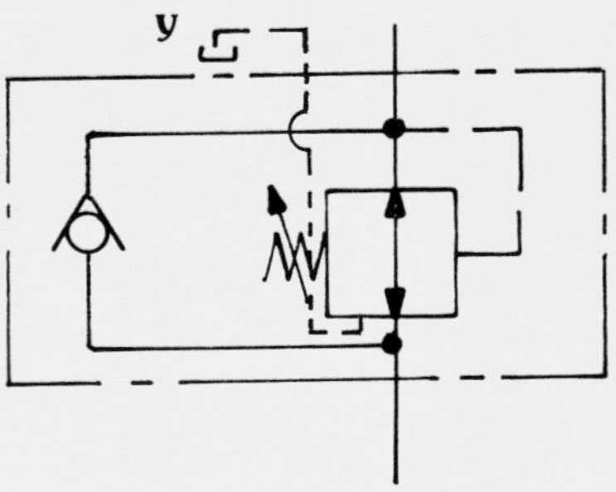	Graphic symbol for a direct operated reducing valve with a three-way relieving capability and integral reverse free flow check.
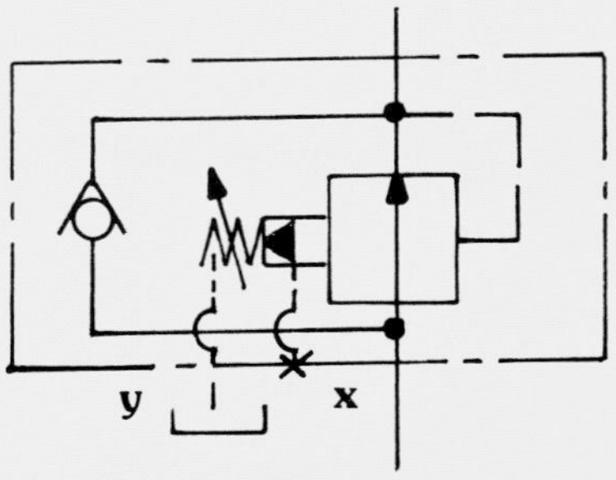	Pilot operated pressure reducing valve with integral reverse free flow check. The remote adjustment connection "X" shows that this valve has secondary pilot control.

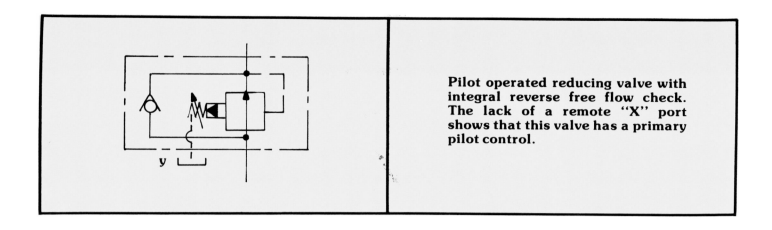

Pilot operated reducing valve with integral reverse free flow check. The lack of a remote "X" port shows that this valve has a primary pilot control.

MULTIPLE FUNCTION PRESSURE CONTROLS

In industrial hydraulics there are basically three general purpose valve types available for pressure controls. We have already covered two of these types, namely, relief and reducing valves. This leaves us with the multi-function family of valves.

Depending on the arrangement of pilot lines, drain lines, and the inclusion of an optional built-in reverse free flow check, these valves can perform various functions. The functions include: sequence, counterbalance, unloading, overcenter and braking. To complicate the selection even further, the valves are offered in both direct and pilot operated versions. We will first discuss the construction and variations of each and then will discuss their operation in various types of applications.

DIRECT OPERATED MULTI-FUNCTION VALVES

Multi-function valves are quite similar to relief valves in that the spring holds the spool or poppet in the closed position. Internal or external pilot pressure, from various sources, works against the spring, and causes the valve to open when the pressure setting has been reached. The working direction of flow is from the valve's inlet to outlet, with both valve ports capable of withstanding full system pressure. Since these valves are often mounted in the service lines to the actuator, their housing is designed to accept an optional reverse free flow check. To better understand the various assembly possibilities, let us consider the following cross-sectional illustration.

Essentially, the valve consists of a spool which slides in a close fitting bore in the valve housing. The spool blocks the inlet from outlet, until the pressure on the right hand area of the spool overcomes the spring force. The small pilot spool serves to reduce the effective area on which pressure can work. You will notice that, with the spool installed, the net area is the same as the diameter of the pilot spool. Since the pilot spool slides in a clearance fit, oil leakage past this spool is connected to the drain passage.

For lower pressure operation, the spool is removed, and the chamber on the right of the main spool is blocked from the drain passage with an internal plug. The valve will now shift at a considerably lower pressure, since the effective area is now the full diameter of the main spool.

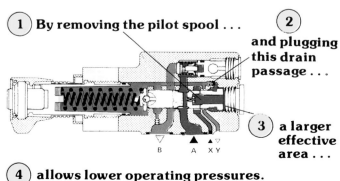

1) **By removing the pilot spool . . .**   2)
and plugging this drain passage . . .
3) **a larger effective area . . .**
4) **allows lower operating pressures.**

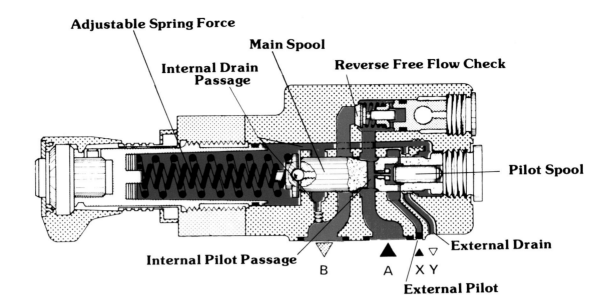

Adjustable Spring Force

Main Spool

Internal Drain Passage

Reverse Free Flow Check

Pilot Spool

External Drain

Internal Pilot Passage

External Pilot

B   A   X Y

"X" PORT PILOT PRESSURE CONNECTION

As shown in the illustration, the pilot pressure can be taken internally from the valve's inlet through axial and radial drillings in the spool. For internally piloted valves, the external "X" connection is plugged in the valve housing. With this assembly, the valve works much like a relief valve, in that pressure at the valve's inlet shifts the spool to an open position once the pressure setting has been reached. As will be shown, internally piloted valves are normally used in sequence and some counterbalance applications.

verted to some external source. In this assembly, the pressure at the valve's inlet can build to the pressure setting of the main system relief, even if the pressure required to shift this valve is set quite low. The valve will not open until it is signaled to do so by the external source. As will be shown, this assembly is generally used for unloading and overcenter type counterbalancing applications.

(1) **By removing this plug . . .**

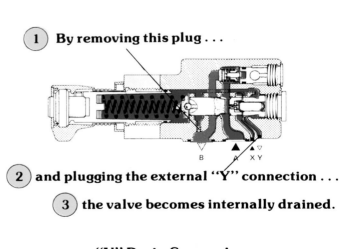

(2) **and plugging the external "Y" connection . . .**

(3) **the valve becomes internally drained.**

(2) **and replacing the orifice with a plug here . . .**

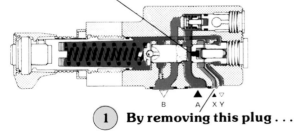

(1) **By removing this plug . . .**

(3) **the valve is converted to an externally piloted version.**

"X" Pilot Conversion

For other applications, it is usually necessary to have the valve shift in relationship to a pressure in another part of the circuit. By opening the external connection and replacing the orifice in the spool with a plug, the pressure signal is con-

"Y" Drain Conversion

Back pressure in the spring chamber is additive to the pressure setting of the valve, as it is in any type of pressure control. Generally speaking, multi-function valves can be internally drained whenever the valve's outlet is connected to tank during the period when the valve is functioning. If an operating system pressure is developed in the valve's outlet, it must be externally drained. With some counterbalance and most unloading applications, the valve can be internally drained. The effects of internal or external draining are shown in the following examples of multi-pressure valves, connected in series:

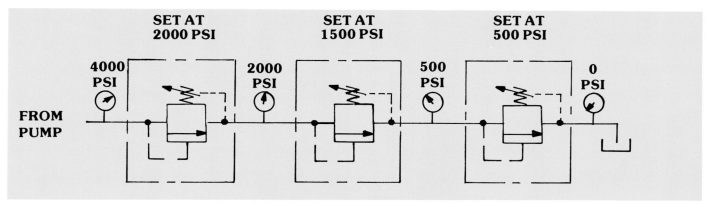

Internally Drained Valves Function Like Resistances in Series

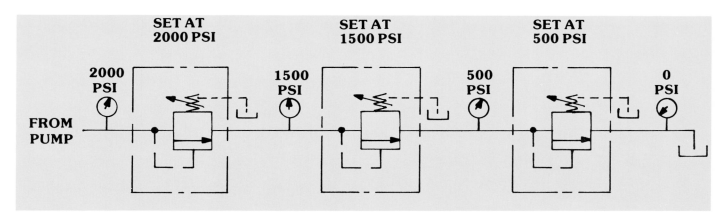

Externally Drained Valves Are Not Affected By Downstream Pressure

PILOT OPERATED MULTI-FUNCTION VALVES

The pilot operated version of the multi-function pressure control can handle larger flow rates, generally with less pressure override than direct operated models. However, in most applications of the multi-function valve, pressure override is not nearly as critical as pressure override in relief applications. In fact, high pressure override characteristics can be desirable in some counterbalance applications. We will, however, postpone this discussion until we discuss applications of the multi-function valves.

The cross-sectional illustration shows that the pilot section functions much like the direct operated valve. The only difference is that a high flow cartridge poppet is installed in series with the inlet of the pilot valve. Let us now consider the operation of this valve.

STATIC CLOSED CONDITION

In the closed condition, pressure in the pilot supply passage ("X") cannot create a force large enough to overcome the setting of the adjustable pilot spring. The pilot spring holds the pilot spool in the farthest left position, which closes the chamber above the main poppet. Through the orifice in the center of the main poppet, inlet pressure is exposed equally above and below the poppet. The slightly larger area, and the light spring force above the main poppet, keep the poppet

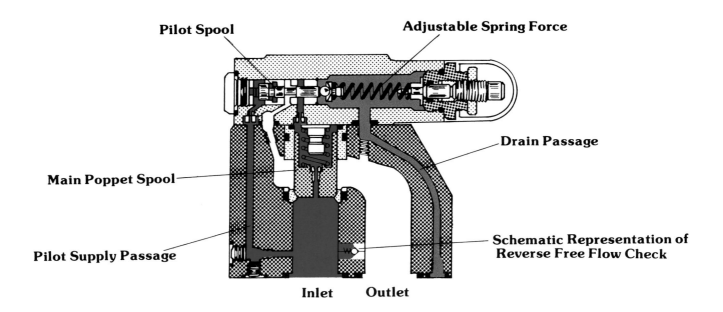

Pilot Spool

Adjustable Spring Force

Main Poppet Spool

Drain Passage

Pilot Supply Passage

Schematic Representation of Reverse Free Flow Check

Inlet   **Outlet**

closed as long as the pilot spool is held in position by the adjustable spring force.

DYNAMIC VALVE OPENING

When pilot pressure is high enough to shift the pilot spool against the spring, the top side of the poppet is vented to System II pressure. Under these conditions, the main poppet functions like a simple in-line check valve (Chapter 4). The valve allows flow from inlet to outlet as long as System I pressure is slightly higher (45 PSI) than that in System II. This pressure is needed to move the main poppet against the spring.

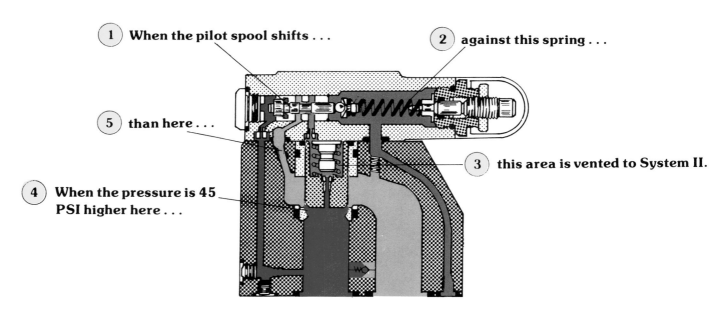

1. **When the pilot spool shifts . . .**

2. **against this spring . . .**

5. **than here . . .**

3. **this area is vented to System II.**

4. **When the pressure is 45 PSI higher here . . .**

6. **the main poppet opens like an in-line check valve.**

PILOT SPOOL DESIGN

Unlike the relief valve, it is desirable to have the multi-function valve open and close more gradually. Since the purpose of this valve is not to protect the system from over-pressure, a slower opening provides smooth transitions between the static and dynamic positions of the valve. In unloading and sequencing application, this minimizes the compression shocks normally referred to as *water hammer*. In counterbalance and braking applications, a cushioning is imposed on the movement of the load. Let us now look at the design of the pilot section to see how this gradual opening is achieved.

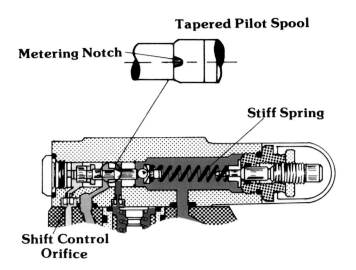

Pilot Section Detail

If we want the main poppet to open slowly, we must provide a gradual decay in pressure above it. Likewise, in closing, the reestablishment of the static condition must be achieved gradually. This function is easily achieved by using a properly designed spool working in conjunction with a relatively stiff spring.

The pilot spool is designed with a slight taper on its sealing land. The edge of the land is also provided with 'V' grooved metering notches. The combination of "V" grooves and tapered land provides for a gradual opening of the top of the main poppet to System II.

Although the pilot spool only strokes approximately 1/8", the stiff spring also aids in gradual valve opening. That is, pilot pressure, which is sufficient to provide initial opening of the spool, may not be high enough to move it to the fully opened position. The net result is that, as pilot pressure builds on the left hand area of the pilot spool, the spool steadily strokes to the right against the spring. The top area of the poppet is vented through a gradually increasing orifice, which allows a smooth opening to System II. This opening, although related

to set pressure for a given pilot spring, optimally occurs over a 100 to 150 PSI change in pilot pressure.

In some higher pressure applications, a high flow potential exists in the "X" pilot line. This high energy potential could adversely affect proper operation by causing the pilot spool to shift too quickly. To avoid this possibility, an orifice is installed in the supply line to the pilot spool end. This limits the flow potential to or from the pilot spool, which, in turn, restricts its shifting speed.

"X" and "Y" PORT CONNECTIONS

(1) **This valve is internally piloted and internally drained.**

(7) **the spring chamber becomes externally drained.**

(6) **and plugging this internal passage . . .**

(5) **By removing this plug . . .**

(2) **By removing one of these plugs . . .**

(3) **and plugging this internal passage . . .**

(4) **our pilot supply is from an external source.**

Note: Illustration is to show operating principles only. It does not depict the true port locations of NFPA standard mounting interfaces or access locations for internal plugs.

We have already discussed the possibility of converting internal and external pilot supplies and drains for the direct operated multi-function pressure controls. The cross-sectional illustration shows that the same possibilities exist for the pilot operated versions. The use of these various arrangements will be discussed in the application descriptions which follow.

REMOTE PRESSURE ADJUSTMENT

One precaution which should be considered is that multi-function valves are not easily adjustable from an external source. First, we do not have an "X" port connection which can be used to modulate the pressure on top of the main poppet to a value lower than that set on the pilot valve. As already explained, the "X" port for multi-function valves serves an entirely different purpose.

Second, we cannot use the "Y" port method of remote adjustment. The problem here is that the only *flow* of oil into the spring chamber is leakage by the pilot spool. We do not have a positive oil supply as we did in the pilot section on either the pilot operated relief or the reducing valve. Consequently, if remote adjustment is absolutely necessary, we must select an externally drained valve, and then supply the spring chamber with a positive pressure source. As shown in the following example, this method can be quite cumbersome.

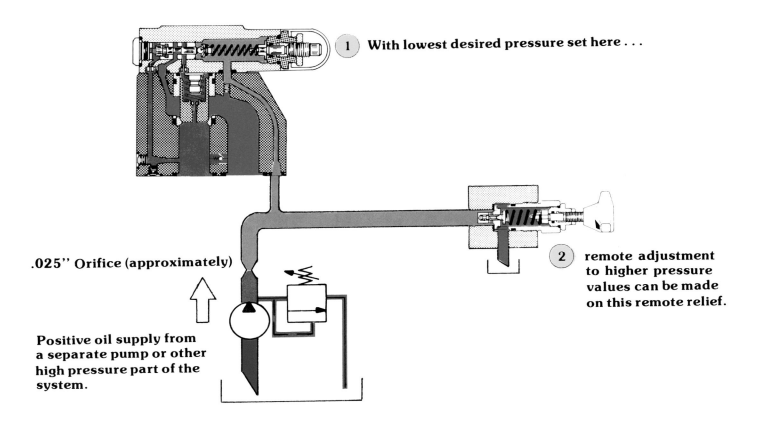

1 With lowest desired pressure set here . . .

.025" Orifice (approximately)

2 remote adjustment to higher pressure values can be made on this remote relief.

Positive oil supply from a separate pump or other high pressure part of the system.

SEQUENCE APPLICATIONS FOR MULTI-FUNCTION VALVES

The *clamp and work circuit* is the classical example of a sequence application. There is good reason for this, since there is no other method which solves this problem as simply. A pressure sequence valve assures a constant holding force in System I, while permitting System II to operate at any load induced pressure up to the pressure value of System I. If System II requires a higher pressure level than that needed to do the preliminary work in System I, the System will still perform satisfactorily up to the pressure level set on the main system relief. It is important to note, however, that when System II achieves a pressure level higher than that set on the sequence valve, System I will also be exposed to this higher pressure. If the work piece or machinery in System I could be damaged by this higher

pressure, other precautions must be taken. These precautions could include sizing the actuators differently to obtain the desired force, or using a reducing valve in series with the System I actuator.

The circuit shows a typical installation of a pressure sequence valve. A close look at the cross section will show you that most sequence valves are assembled with an internal pilot supply, but that they must always have an external drain. Upon actuation of the advance solenoid, the circuit automatically functions as follows:

When the advance solenoid is energized, pump flow is directed to the blind end of the clamp cylinder, and to the inlet port of the sequence valve. Initially, the pressure in the line supplying the clamping cylinder is not high enough to open the sequence valve; hence, the full pump flow is available for cylinder extention. Upon reaching the work piece, the clamp

Typical Sequence Valve Application

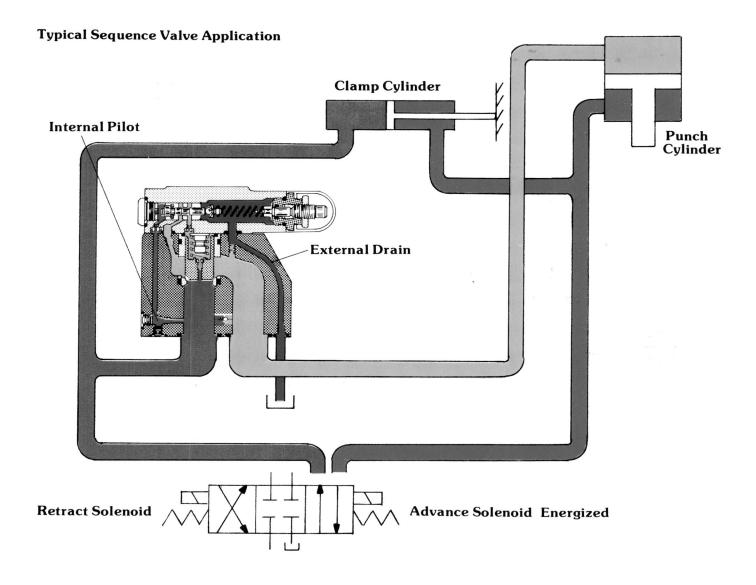

Internal Pilot

Clamp Cylinder

Punch Cylinder

External Drain

Retract Solenoid

Advance Solenoid Energized

cylinder stalls. Since the oil being supplied has nowhere to go, the pressure rises to the level which opens the sequence valve. The oil is then directed to the blind end of the punch cylinder.

During extension of the punch, there is little or no resistance to flow, as the punch is traveling through free air. Without the sequence valve in the circuit, the tendency would be for the pressure to equalize in both the clamp and the punch circuit, at the pressure level needed to extend the punch.

The sequence valve, however, will not allow this equalization of pressure to occur. The moment too much flow is allowed to enter the punch circuit, pressure drops slightly in the clamping circuit. This drop in pressure results in a relaxation of force holding the pilot spool in the original wide open position. The main poppet closes against the flow stream until an orifice is created which will pass the full output of the pump at a pressure drop sufficient to maintain clamping pressure at valve setting.

When the punch reaches the work piece, pressure rises to whatever level is necessary to pierce the material. This pressure can be less than, equal to, or greater than the minimum pressure required for the clamp circuit.

If the punch operates at any pressure lower than that required for the clamping circuit, the sequence valve modulates its orifice to maintain its inlet pressure at valve setting. At the same time, as load induced pressure increases in the punch circuit, the pressure drop across its main control spool decreases. Since the flow across an orifice is related to pressure drop, the sequence valve progressively moves its main poppet to a more open position, so that it can pass the full output flow of the pump.

When punch pressure is equal to, or greater than, sequence valve setting, sufficient pilot pressure exists to hold the valve in the wide open position. Pressure in both the clamp and punch circuits equalizes at the higher pressure needed for the punching operation.

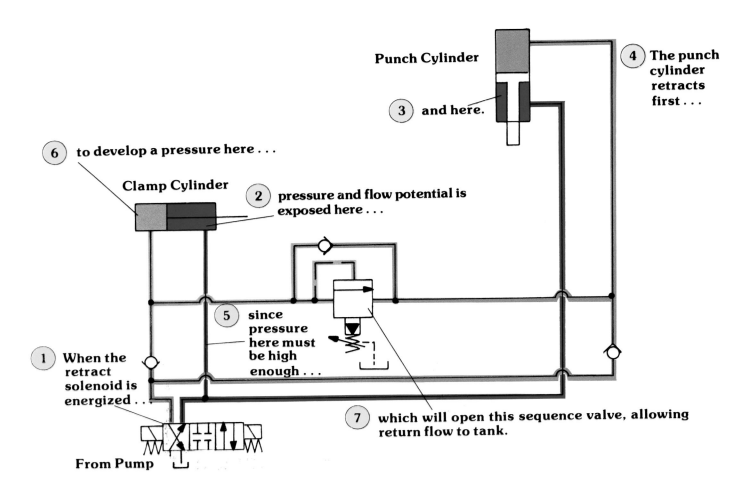

Punch Cylinder

(4) **The punch cylinder retracts first . . .**

(3) **and here.**

(6) **to develop a pressure here . . .**

Clamp Cylinder

(2) **pressure and flow potential is exposed here . . .**

(5) **since pressure here must be high enough . . .**

(1) **When the retract solenoid is energized . . .**

(7) **which will open this sequence valve, allowing return flow to tank.**

From Pump

Depending on the mechanical design of the clamping mechanism, and the punch operation being performed, this example circuit may or may not provide satisfactory operation. That is, when the cycle is reversed, there is no assurance as to which cylinder will retract first. This will depend on which circuit has the path of least resistance to flow. Our example is given only to highlight the operating principle of a sequence application.

The example is but one of many sequence variations which could be used to solve the particular problem at hand. By the simple addition of two check valves in the circuit, we assure that during reversal of the circuit, the punch cylinder will always be the first to retract.

This circuit assures a specific order to the interaction of the clamp and punch circuits in both operating directions. It does not, however, assure a positive pre-determined clamping force in the retract mode. You will notice that the rod end of the clamp cylinder is also exposed to the pressure needed to retract the punch cylinder. Even though there is a captured column of fluid between the blind end of the clamp cylinder piston, the check valve, and the closed sequence valve, any leakage would create a tendency for the retraction of the clamping cylinder. Nevertheless, this circuit could provide sufficient clamping force for the withdrawal of the punch,

especially on very tight systems with fast cycle rates.

USING A RELIEF VALVE IN A SEQUENCE APPLICATION

It is often possible to use a relief in a sequence operation, provided that the selected model can:

1. Be externally drained.
2. Withstand an operating system pressure on its outlet (tank) port. The only problem is that during valve operation, a continuous flow in the "Y" drain port exists.

In comparing the pilot section of the relief valve with that of the multi-function valve, you will notice one important difference. To keep the relief valve open, the pilot relief must be relieving fluid from the chamber on top of the main poppet. Depending on valve design and size, this pilot flow can be in the neighborhood of 3/4 to 1 1/2 GPM. At 3000 PSI, this can result in an efficiency loss of two or three horsepower. This heat generation and loss of speed in System II are not a problem with a multi-function valve used in a sequence operation.

One important advantage of the multi-function valve's pilot head is that it opens and closes the main valve poppet with an insignificant amount of pilot flow. The actual flow required is only that which is displaced during stroking of the pilot spool. Likewise, the "Y" drain connection is only to rid the spring chamber of the oil which leaks by the pilot spool. Consequently, we can add to the overall efficiency of the total system by selecting the proper valve for sequence applications.

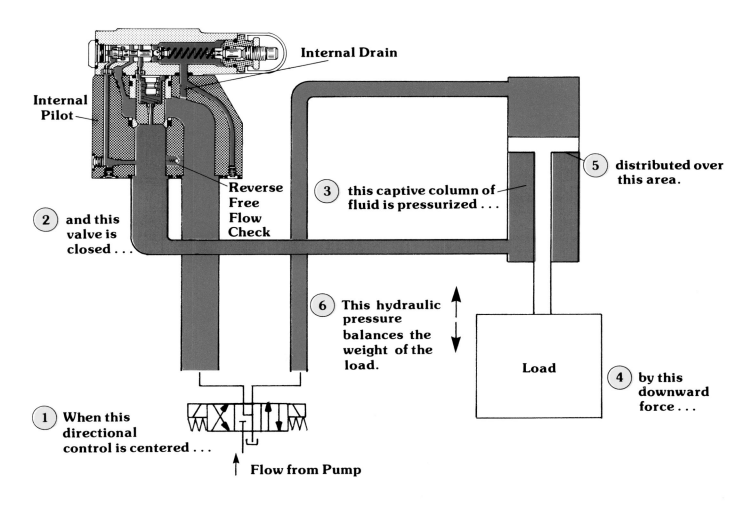

Internal Drain

Internal Pilot

Reverse Free Flow Check

② and this valve is closed . . .

③ this captive column of fluid is pressurized . . .

⑤ distributed over this area.

⑥ This hydraulic pressure balances the weight of the load.

Load

④ by this downward force . . .

① When this directional control is centered . . .

Flow from Pump

COUNTERBALANCE APPLICATIONS OF MULTI-FUNCTION VALVES

Counterbalancing is an often-used term which actually covers several distinctly different valve applications. Unfortunately, this generality of meaning came about because all operations are related to the mass or inertia of the load rather than to the different valve applications. To aid in understanding this, we will discuss the individual applications and valve variation requirements. We will take a look at the different load conditions which determine whether the application is one of counterbalancing, overcenter, or braking. But first let us consider the simplest definition of counterbalancing.

A *counterbalance valve* develops a pressure force in its actuator, which equally counteracts the force of the load.

Counterbalancing is required whenever gravity can move the load faster than the speed intended by the hydraulic system. One criteria for the energy conscious designer is that the load conditions causing motion should always be the same. Let us now take a closer look at a simple counterbalance valve in application.

In this circuit, the basic counterbalance configuration of the multi-function valve is internally piloted and drained. In actuality, the valve is quite similar to a relief valve. The major difference is that a reverse free flow check valve is usually a necessity. The check valve permits a free flow of fluid towards the actuator in the reverse direction of operation.

Counterbalance valves can usually be internally drained, since the outlet of the valve is connected to tank through the directional valve whenever the valve is functioning. However, there is nothing preventing the use of the external drain in systems with high or fluctuating return line pressures.

In this example, when the directional control valve is centered, both the rod end of the cylinder, and the outlet of the multi-function valve, are connected to tank. It is important to choose a directional valve with this center configuration for two reasons.

The first reason is that directional controls shift in a small fraction of a second. If the valve were to block the outlet of the counterbalance valve rapidly, even if the counterbalance were to remain open, the oil coming from the rod end of the cylinder would have nowhere to go. This would eliminate the cushion stopping of the cylinder, which is one of the main advantages of a counterbalance valve in the first place. If we allowed the outlet of the counterbalance to be connected to tank when the directional control is centered, a cushioned stopping of the load would occur.

The second reason for using a directional control as shown is that it is important to preclude the possibility of a pressure build up on the top side of the cylinder. If the directional valve blocks all ports in center condition, high pressure from the pump could leak across the close tolerances of the spool and build on the blind end of the cylinder. As we will show, if the pressure builds high enough, the counterbalance valve will open, allowing the load to drift.

For a better understanding, let us assign some arbitrary values to the previous circuits. Assume that the load is pulling on the cylinder rod with enough force to generate a pressure over the rod end area of the piston of 3000 PSI. Under these conditions, the counterbalance valve would be set slightly higher (3100 PSI) so that it would remain closed, supporting the load on a captured column of fluid.

At this point, it is important to note that although the load is supported by the counterbalance valves, it is not safe to assume that it is positively locked into position. Most industrial counterbalance valves are in some way related to a spool design. Leakage, although minimal, could allow the load to drift, especially if the load was held for extended time periods. As will be shown in Chapter 4, the line contact sealing of a pilot operated check valve is the only way to assure positive holding of the load.

When the directional control is energized, pump flow is directed to the blind end of the cylinder. Since the piston can not move against the blocked column of fluid on its opposite side, a resistance to flow causes the pressure to rise on the top side of the piston. This increases the downward force, which in turn increases the pressure on the block column of fluid at the rod end of the cylinder. Assuming proper setting of the counterbalance, a minimal pressure on the top of the piston opens the valve, allowing downward movement of the load.

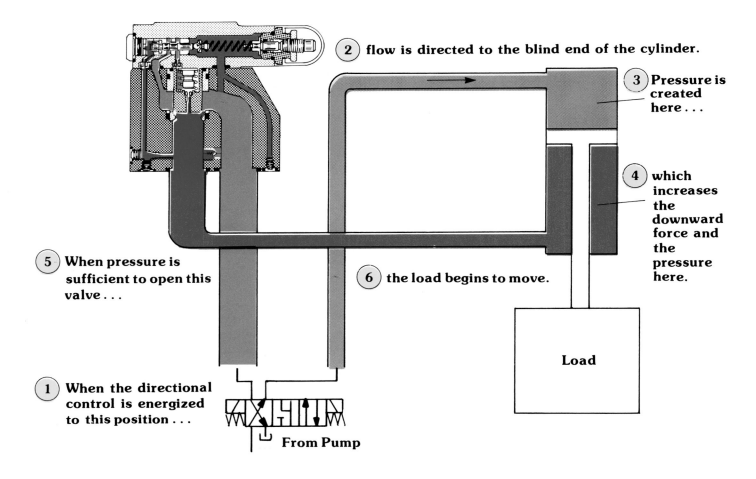

2 flow is directed to the blind end of the cylinder.

3 Pressure is created here . . .

4 which increases the downward force and the pressure here.

5 When pressure is sufficient to open this valve . . .

6 the load begins to move.

Load

1 When the directional control is energized to this position . . .

From Pump

The pressure override characteristics of the multifunction valve allow it to open gradually over a 100 to 150 PSI pressure increase on the top side of the piston. Since pressure must be maintained in the blind end of the cylinder to keep the load in motion, the counterbalance modulates to pass just enough fluid to keep the cylinder from running away from the pump supply. The gradual opening and closing of the counterbalance valve causes smooth acceleration and deceleration of the load.

In our initial description of the counterbalance valve, we said that load conditions should be more or less constant. Any suspended weight has potential energy, or, better still, a potential for doing work. Ideally, since potential energy is available for doing the work, no additional energy should have to be supplied by the hydraulic system. In actual practice, however, we have shown that some energy is necessary to override the counterbalance. Of course, the closer the counterbalance is set to the actual load induced pressure, the more efficient the system becomes.

In our previous example, if we were to remove the load, all of the downward force would have to come from the hydraulic system. Assuming that we did not alter the setting of the counterbalance, all this hydraulic energy would be unnecessarily converted into heat as the pressurized fluid was forced over the counterbalance valve.

OVERCENTER COUNTERBALANCE VALVES

There are three specific load conditions which make a simple counterbalance valve application undesirable. They are;

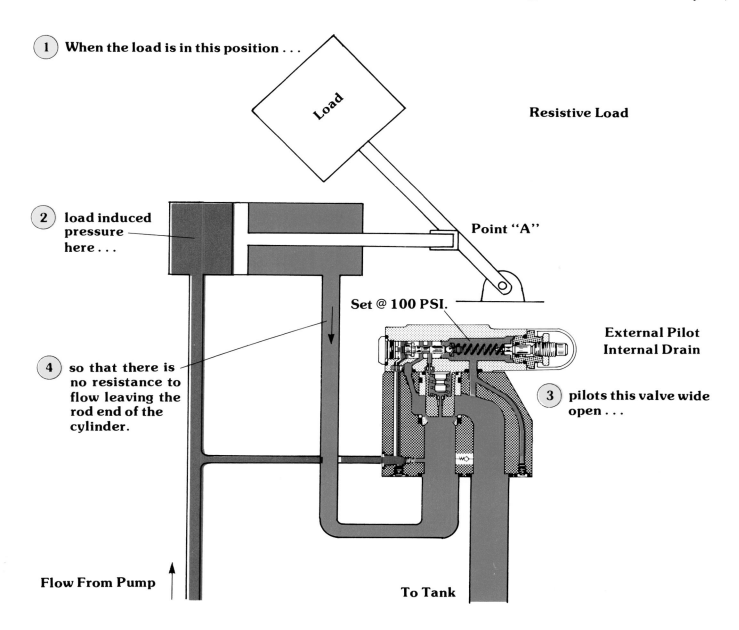

1 **When the load is in this position . . .**

Resistive Load

2 **load induced pressure here . . .**

Point "A"

Set @ 100 PSI.

External Pilot Internal Drain

4 **so that there is no resistance to flow leaving the rod end of the cylinder.**

3 **pilots this valve wide open . . .**

Flow From Pump

To Tank

over center loads, varying loads, and press applications where maximum tonnage is required. However, by externally piloting the counterbalance valve from the opposite supply line to the actuator, the overcenter counterbalance valve improves both system performance and efficiency.

OVERCENTER LOADS

The term *overcenter* comes from the fact that, in many applications, the machinery's geometry causes the load conditions to change from resistive to overrunning. This principle is represented in the example.

In the position shown, you can see that the load is resisting the extension of the cylinder. If a 3000 lbs. force is required at point A to move the load, and the cylinder has a piston area of one square inch, then 3000 PSI pressure is created in the fluid being supplied by the pump. At any pressure over 100 to 200 PSI, the overcenter counterbalance valve is piloted wide open, offering little resistance to flow from the rod end of the cylinder.

After the load moves past the center line, the geometry of the load forces now pulls on the cylinder rod. When the load is at the same angle on the other side of center, a 3000 lb. load force is trying to extend the cylinder. Since the effective area on the rod end of the cylinder is slightly less than one square inch, a pressure slightly higher than 3000 PSI is needed to keep the load from free falling.

Because the overcenter type counterbalance is externally piloted, its opening and closing is not affected by pressure conditions in the rod end of the cylinder. It only responds to a pressure signal in its external pilot line, or, in this case, in the

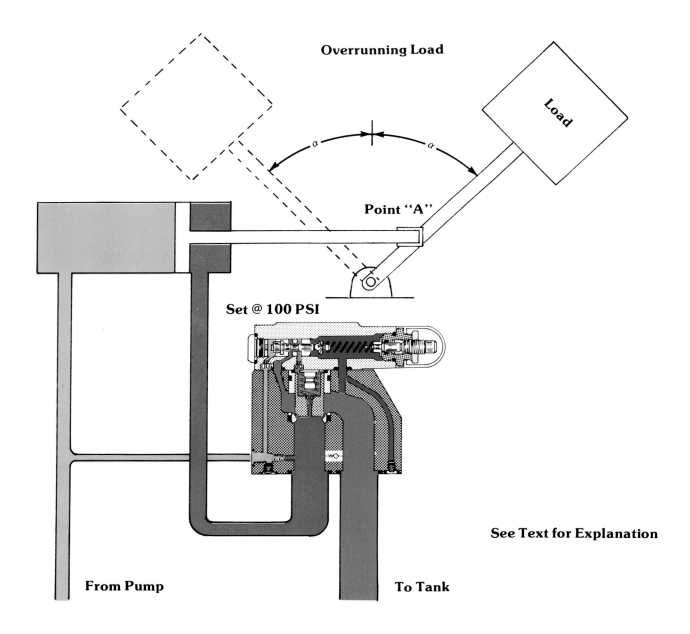

Overrunning Load

Load

Point "A"

Set @ 100 PSI

See Text for Explanation

From Pump

To Tank

blind end of the cylinder.

When the load goes overcenter, the load forces try to pull the cylinder's piston ahead of the oil supply from the pump. Under these conditions, there is no resistance to flow from the pump. In fact, the moment the piston gets ahead of the oil stream, a vacuum condition is created on the blind end of the cylinder.

We said earlier that, because of the pressure override characteristics of the multifunction valve, a change in pressure was necessary to fully open the valve. In our example, if the valve is set at 100 PSI cracking pressure, the full open position does not occur until a pilot pressure of 200 PSI is reached.

As the load moves overcenter, pressure is lost in the blind end of the cylinder. Consequently, a tendency for the closing of the counterbalance valve exists. The counterbalance valve resists the motion of the load with whatever pressure is necessary to maintain a 100 to 200 PSI pressure in the fluid being supplied by the pump.

You will notice that we have explained the operation of our overcenter counterbalance valve in only one direction of operation. For reverse motion of the load, a similar valve would have to be used on the blind end of the cylinder.

OVERCENTER VALVES WITH VARYING LOAD CONDITIONS

The major advantage of using an externally piloted overcenter type counterbalance valve, with varying load, is that it greatly improves system efficiency. We said earlier, in our discussion of the simple counterbalance valve, that the pressure setting of the valve should be set slightly higher than the maximum load induced pressure. We also mentioned that any reduction in load meant that a higher pressure had to be supplied to the opposite end of the actuator to compensate for the loss in load induced pressure. In turn, this unnecessarily high pressure is converted into heat as flow is forced across the counterbalance.

When the externally piloted counterbalance is used, the valve becomes insensitive to the load induced pressure. The valve allows movement of the overhung load as long as a minimum pressure (approximately 100 PSI, depending on valve setting) is maintained in the opposite end of the actuator. You can see that, under these conditions, the hydraulic system never substantially adds to the heat generated in lowering the load. Of course, there is no way to prevent the potential energy of the load from being converted into heat, since the energy must be expelled as the load lowers. This must be taken into consideration when you are calculating the heat generated in the hydraulic system.

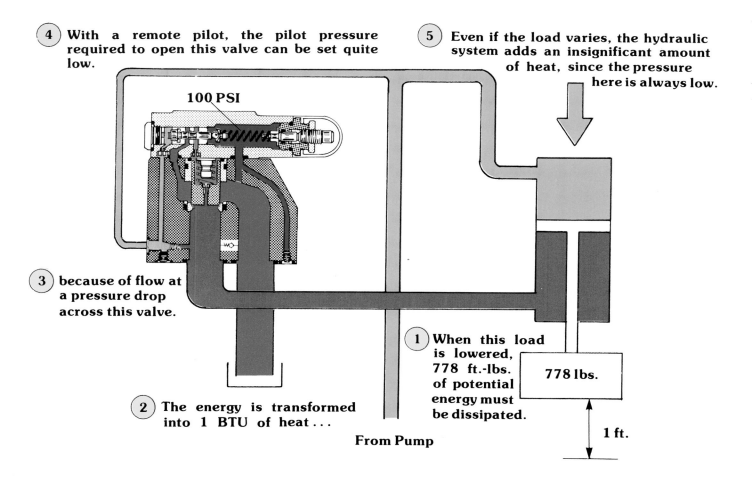

④ With a remote pilot, the pilot pressure required to open this valve can be set quite low.

100 PSI

⑤ Even if the load varies, the hydraulic system adds an insignificant amount of heat, since the pressure here is always low.

③ because of flow at a pressure drop across this valve.

① When this load is lowered, 778 ft.-lbs. of potential energy must be dissipated.

778 lbs.

② The energy is transformed into 1 BTU of heat . . .

From Pump

1 ft.

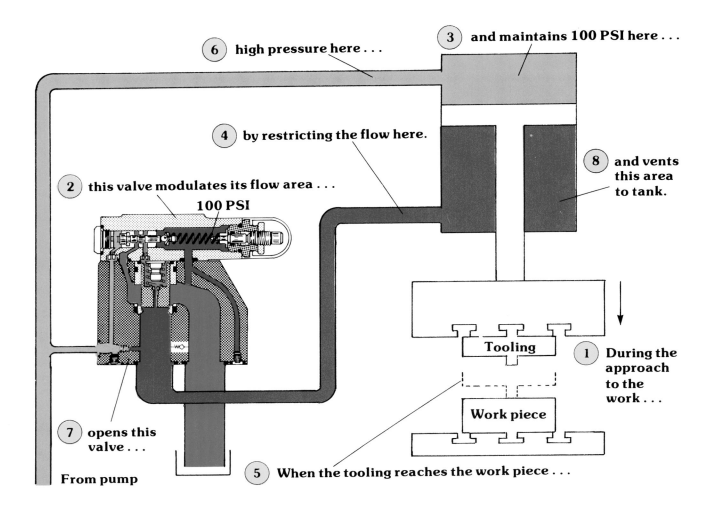

(6) **high pressure here . . .**

(3) **and maintains 100 PSI here . . .**

(4) **by restricting the flow here.**

(2) **this valve modulates its flow area . . .**

100 PSI

(8) **and vents this area to tank.**

(7) **opens this valve . . .**

From pump

Tooling

Work piece

(1) **During the approach to the work . . .**

(5) **When the tooling reaches the work piece . . .**

OVERCENTER VALVES ALLOW HIGHER PRESSING FORCE

The third major advantage of using a remotely piloted over-center type counterbalance valve is that full tonnage can be produced after the load has come into contact with a mechanical stop. Let us consider a down acting press with a relatively heavy upper platen.

In the example, as the platen moves through free air, its weight must be counterbalanced to prevent it from falling. If a simple internal pilot valve were to be used in this application, during the final pressing operation, the rod end of the piston would also be exposed to the pressure needed to counterbalance the weight of the platen during approach. This would be undesirable in this application, since the up acting counterbalancing force would, in effect, subtract the weight of the platen from the available pressing force. On the other hand, an externally piloted valve is wide open the moment pressure on the top of the cylinder's piston exceeds the setting of the valve. This vents all pressure from the rod

end of the cylinder. Under these conditions, the total pressing force available is calculated by adding the weight of the platen to the force due to system pressure over the top area of the piston.

BRAKING WITH AN EXTERNALLY PILOTED COUNTERBALANCE VALVE

A problem sometimes arises when using an externally piloted counterbalance valve with fast moving, high inertia loads. If, for instance, we wanted to stop an inertia load in some mid position, the "x" port of the counterbalance would be vented when the directional control is centered. In losing pilot pressure, the counterbalance valve would slam closed, immediately stopping the motion of the load. If such a load, moving at a high speed, were to be brought to a stop quickly, damaging pressure peaks could develop in the service line between the actuator and the counterbalance valve. Therefore, in systems with high inertia loads, a port or crossport relief should be used in conjunction with the externally piloted counterbalance valve.

UNLOADING VALVES

Unloading valves are used in hydraulic circuits to offer high speeds up to a predetermined pressure level. At valve setting, a remote pressure signal unloads part of the original flow source to tank. A prime example of an unloading application is a two pump "hi-low" unloading circuit.

In many applications, where high speed and high force are not needed simultaneously, you can achieve a considerable savings of installed horsepower by selecting a two pump system. The first pump supplies high flow at lower operating pressures, and the second pump offers higher pressures, but at a lower flow. Remember that:

$$\frac{Flow \times Pressure}{1714} = HP$$

You can see that, at low pressure and high flow, the calculated horsepower can be the same as it would be if the system were operating at high pressure and low flow. Let us now take a look at a circuit which accomplishes this task.

As shown in the example, a multifunction valve with external pilot and internal drain can be used to unload the high volume pump. As long as the system is operating at a pressure lower than that set on the unloading valve, the valve remains closed. Under these conditions, the output of the high volume pump supplements the output of the small pump, and the system operates at full speed. As the system offers an increased resistance to flow, pressure builds on the outlet of both pumps, and on the pilot spool in the unloading valve. When the pressure is high enough to move the pilot spool against the spring setting, the output of the high volume pump is connected to tank. Whenever the main system is operating at a pressure of approximately 100 PSI over the setting of the unloading valve, the output of the high volume pump is circulated back to tank at minimum pressure. If, for some reason, the system pressure drops

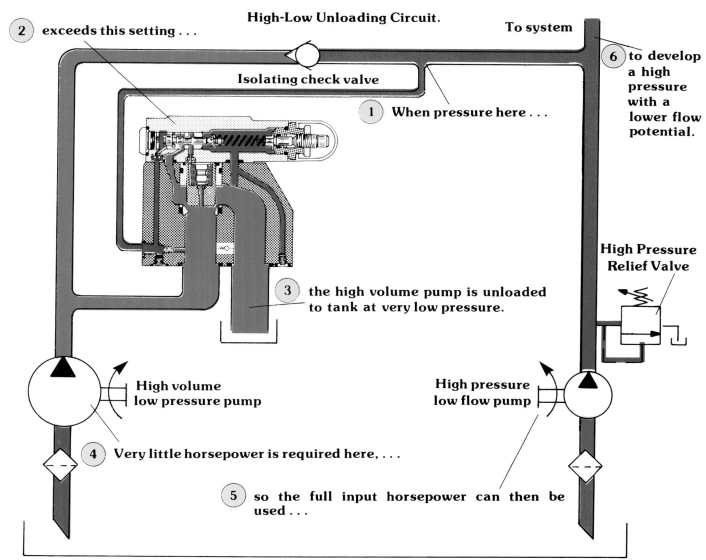

High-Low Unloading Circuit.

② exceeds this setting . . .

Isolating check valve

To system

① When pressure here . . .

⑥ to develop a high pressure with a lower flow potential.

③ the high volume pump is unloaded to tank at very low pressure.

High Pressure Relief Valve

High volume low pressure pump

High pressure low flow pump

④ Very little horsepower is required here, . . .

⑤ so the full input horsepower can then be used . . .

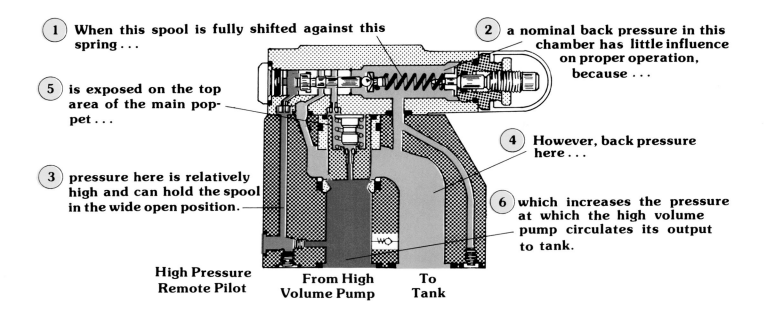

1 When this spool is fully shifted against this spring . . .

5 is exposed on the top area of the main poppet . . .

3 pressure here is relatively high and can hold the spool in the wide open position.

2 a nominal back pressure in this chamber has little influence on proper operation, because . . .

4 However, back pressure here . . .

6 which increases the pressure at which the high volume pump circulates its output to tank.

High Pressure Remote Pilot   From High Volume Pump   To Tank

below the setting of the unloading valve, the circuit automatically shifts itself into high speed operation.

REMOTE DRAIN OPTION FOR PILOT OPERATED UNLOADING VALVES

Since the outlet of the unloading valve is connected to tank, satisfactory operation can normally be achieved by internally draining the valve. However, if it becomes desirable to circulate the output of the high volume pump through filters and heat exchangers, the resistance to flow added by these components can adversely affect the efficiency of the system. Let us now take a closer look at a pilot operated

unloading valve, and how it is affected by back pressure at its outlet.

In unloading applications, the efficiency of the system depends on the minimum pressure at which the high volume pump circulates oil. If, for instance, we were to unload a 100 GPM pump at 50 PSI, our horsepower to drive the pump would be a little less than 3 HP. The same pump, with a 200 PSI resistance to flow in the unloaded condition, would require almost 12 HP to circulate the oil. This not only draws unnecessary power from the prime mover, but, in turn, it generates an equal amount of heat. A slight modification to the pilot spool of a standard multifunction pressure control optimizes the minimum pressure at which the valve unloads its pump.

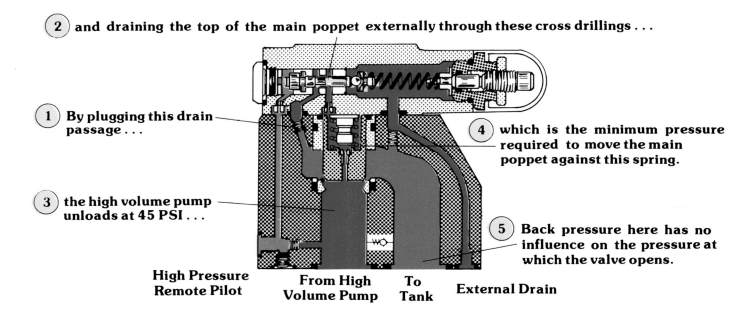

2 and draining the top of the main poppet externally through these cross drillings . . .

1 By plugging this drain passage . . .

3 the high volume pump unloads at 45 PSI . . .

4 which is the minimum pressure required to move the main poppet against this spring.

5 Back pressure here has no influence on the pressure at which the valve opens.

High Pressure Remote Pilot   From High Volume Pump   To Tank   External Drain

THE HI-LOW UNLOADING VALVE

We have just shown how an unloading valve can be piped into a system to provide unloading of the high volume pump. To complete this *hi-low circuit*, it was necessary to incorporate two separate components, namely, an isolating check valve and a high pressure low flow relief.

Assuming that the selected pumps and system requirements fall within the performance capabilities of the valve, multiple components and related piping can be replaced by a single component. As shown in the cross-sectional illustration, this valve package consists of a direct operated unloading valve, a high pressure relief, and an isolating check valve. Pipe connections to the valve include high volume pump, high pressure pump, system and tank return.

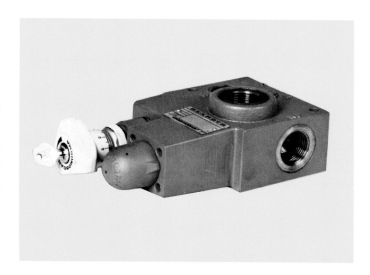

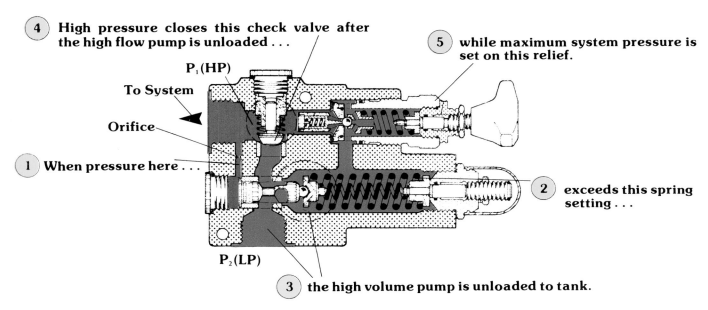

4 High pressure closes this check valve after the high flow pump is unloaded . . .

5 while maximum system pressure is set on this relief.

P_1(HP)

To System

Orifice

1 When pressure here . . .

2 exceeds this spring setting . . .

P_2(LP)

3 the high volume pump is unloaded to tank.

ACCUMULATOR UNLOADING VALVES

The accumulator unloading valve has been designed specifically for use in accumulator circuits. Its design provides three functions. It limits maximum system pressure, unloads the pump to tank when the accumulator reaches the desired pressure, and it reloads the pump to bring the accumulator up to full charge after a predetermined minimum pressure has been reached. (To better understand the operation of this valve, see also Chapter 8, "Accumulators".)

It is sufficient, for purposes of this chapter, to say that an accumulator stores a given volume of oil under pressure. Likewise, at a relatively low pressure, the accumulator stores less fluid than it does at full system pressure. Actually, the oil volume available from an accumulator is determined by subtracting the oil volume held at minimum operating pressure from the quantity of oil stored at maximum system pressure. This differential volume is discharged by the accumulator as system pressure drops from maximum to minimum. Of course, the time period during which the drop in pressure occurs establishes the flow rate available from the accumulator.

Remember:

$$\text{Flow} = \frac{\text{Volume}}{\text{Time}}$$

When used with a fixed displacement pump, the accumulator unloading valve performs both a relief and an unloading function. The valve consists of a cartridge poppet pilot operated relief valve, an isolating full flow check valve, and an unloading piston, which overrides the pilot relief function. Let us now consider the various operating conditions of this valve.

CHARGING THE ACCUMULATOR

The operational crosssection shows that this valve has three working ports: a pump inlet, a system connection, and a tank return.

The pump's outlet is connected directly to the pressure port of this valve, so that all the pump flow must pass through the valve before entering the system. Of course, the tank port is connected directly to the hydraulic reservoir. If you want to pass the return flow through filters or heat exchangers, you should use an external drain for the spring chamber of the pilot.

Assuming that the pilot spring seats the pilot poppet, the main poppet is also closed, due to the hydraulic pressure balance and the light spring force. The valve delivers flow to the system over the isolating check valve, which in turn charges the accumulator as pressure in the system increases. You will notice that as long as there is flow, a higher pressure exists on the right hand area of the unloading piston than on the left, due to the pressure drop across the isolating check valve. The unloading piston is held in the left most position, and has no effect on the relieving function.

RELIEVING AND UNLOADING OF THE PUMP

When the accumulator has reached its desired charge, system pressure unseats the pilot relief, which causes a decay in pressure above the main poppet. At the same time, pressure is lost on the right hand area of the unloading piston, so that pressure in the system from the accumulator holds the unloading piston against the nose of the pilot poppet, keeping it unseated. The moment the main poppet opens, a pressure loss at the inlet of the check valve causes it to close, thus isolating the pump from the rest of the system.

Charging the Accumulator

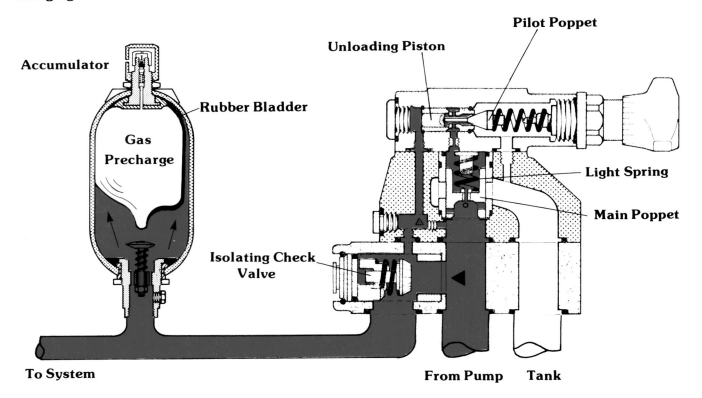

Relieving and Unloading of the Pump

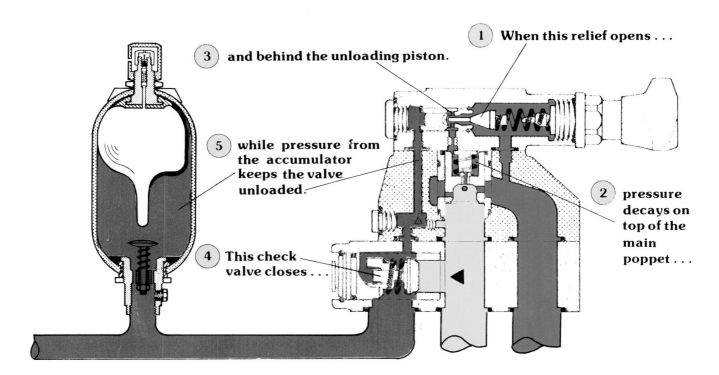

③ and behind the unloading piston.

① When this relief opens . . .

⑤ while pressure from the accumulator keeps the valve unloaded.

② pressure decays on top of the main poppet . . .

④ This check valve closes . . .

Under these conditions, the pump circulates oil freely to tank while pressure in the system is maintained by the accumulator.

RELOADING OF THE PUMP

The whole purpose of an accumulator unloading valve is to prevent the pump from being reloaded the moment a slight decay in system pressure occurs. This is exactly the reason a standard unloading valve cannot be used in an accumulator application. That is, with a standard unloading valve, the small pressure differential between open and closed positions would set up a rapid cycling of the pump between the loaded and unloaded conditions. To overcome this problem, the pilot head of an accumulator unloading valve is designed with differential effective areas between the pilot relief and the unloading piston.

The illustration shows how the accumulator unloading valve allows system pressure to fall to a predetermined minimum value before reloading the pump. Since the effective area of the pilot poppet is smaller than that of the unloading piston, a higher pressure is needed to initially move the pilot poppet against the spring force. Once the right hand area of the

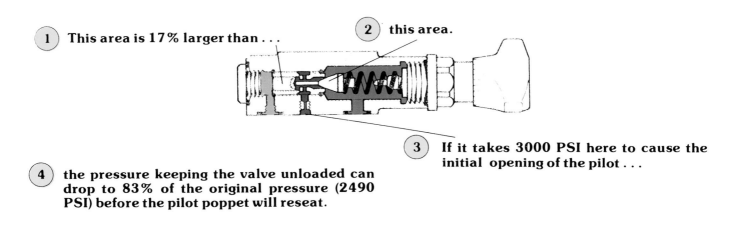

① This area is 17% larger than . . .

② this area.

③ If it takes 3000 PSI here to cause the initial opening of the pilot . . .

④ the pressure keeping the valve unloaded can drop to 83% of the original pressure (2490 PSI) before the pilot poppet will reseat.

unloading piston is vented over the opened pilot poppet, system pressure becomes effective on the larger area of the unloading piston. Of course, the larger area means more available force, so that we can keep the pilot poppet unseated with a somewhat lower pressure. The area ratio is usually in the neighborhood of 17%.

PRECAUTIONS

The function of the accumulator unloading valve should not be confused with that of an accumulator safety valve. Once the accumulator is charged, the unloading valve has no means of bleeding the accumulator charge to tank if the system is shut down. Likewise, a fully charged accumulator is not protected from over pressure due to increased load or thermal expansion. The accumulator unloading valve only provides pressure protection in regard to the pump's capability to pressurize the system.

SOLENOID VENTING OPTION

Like the solenoid venting feature for pilot operated reliefs, a directional control can be added to the pilot section of the accumulator charging valve. An electrical signal can override the unloading of the pump, as was already shown in the discussion of pilot operated reliefs.

Accumulator Unloading Valve with Solenoid Venting

SYMBOLS

Since the function of a multifunction valve so closely resembles that of a relief valve, you will notice that the symbols are quite similar. Of course, most multifunction valves include a reverse free flow check, which must also be represented in symbolic form. In the following examples, you will understand the specific valve function being represented by paying strict attention to the arrangement of pilot lines.

MULTI-FUNCTION VALVE SYMBOLS

Symbol		Description
Direct Operated	**Pilot Operated**	
A ... B	A ... X B	Internal pilot and internal drain, with built-in reverse free flow check. Probable use: counterbalance.
A ... Y B	A ... X Y B	Internal pilot and external drain, with built-in reverse free flow check. Probable uses: sequence, counterbalance.

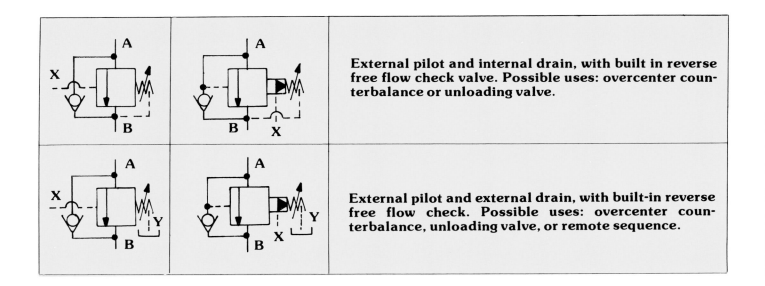

		External pilot and internal drain, with built in reverse free flow check valve. Possible uses: overcenter counterbalance or unloading valve.
		External pilot and external drain, with built-in reverse free flow check. Possible uses: overcenter counterbalance, unloading valve, or remote sequence.

SPECIALTY VALVE SYMBOLS

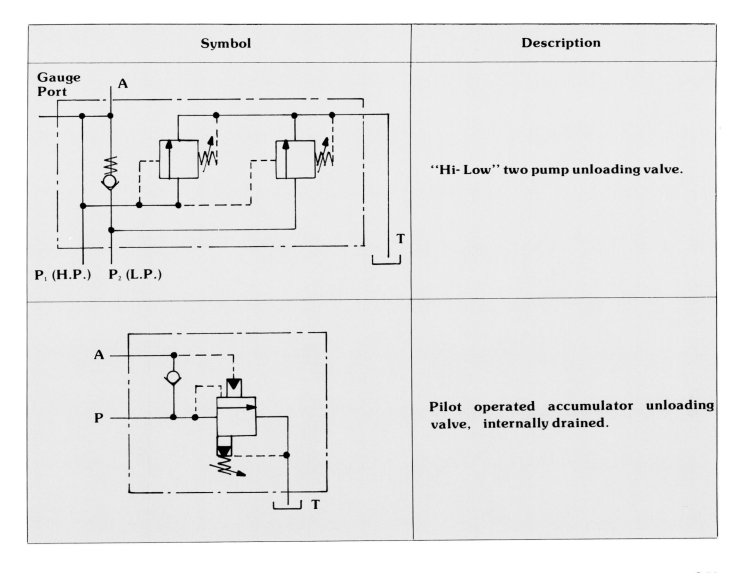

Symbol	Description
	"Hi-Low" two pump unloading valve.
	Pilot operated accumulator unloading valve, internally drained.

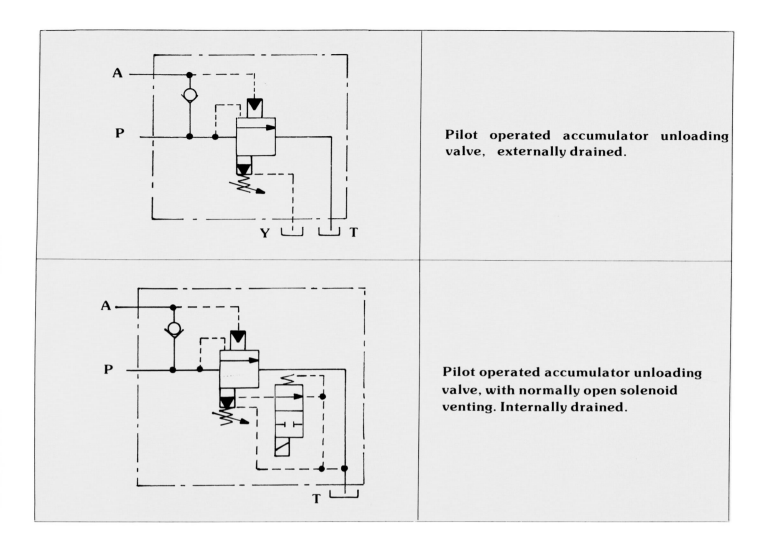

Pilot operated accumulator unloading valve, externally drained.

Pilot operated accumulator unloading valve, with normally open solenoid venting. Internally drained.

CONCLUSION

This chapter has been devoted to an in-depth study of how to manipulate forces by controlling pressure. With a thorough understanding of the five basic pressure valve functions, the design engineer's ability to control the interaction of forces is limited only by his imagination. Hydraulic systems, when properly designed, put tons of force under precise, finger-tip control.

In reviewing your knowledge of pressure control, you should be able to differentiate between the five basic control functions, namely: relieving, reducing, sequencing, counterbalancing, and unloading. Likewise, you should understand that, no matter how complex the function, all pressure controls operate by balancing a hydraulic force with a spring. This spring balancing is readily apparent in direct operated valve designs, but it is also the key operating principle in pilot operated versions.

In reviewing the different pilot operated functions, you will

discover that no matter what the design or desired function, pilot operation always works on the principle of creating either balanced or unbalanced pressure conditions across the main control element.

More specifically, in relation to pilot operated pressure reliefs, you should know what is meant by the terms remote piloting, venting, and high vent option. You should also understand the three uses of the external pilot drain: for more stable pressure adjustments, for remote pressure control, and for load sensing.

The important points covered in our discussion of pressure reducing valves were: first, the relieving ability of a pressure reducing valve, and, second, the differences between pilot operated versions with either primary or secondary control. We also mentioned the inherent ability of the reducing valves to generate heat in the hydraulic system.

In addition to your knowledge of relief and reducing functions, you should also have a good understanding of the versatility offered by the multi-function family of direct and pilot operated valves. You should know the assembly variations and application requirements in using the valve in sequence, counterbalance, overcenter counterbalance, or unloading functions. In addition, you should realize the special requirements of accumulator circuits.

The hydraulic specialist, who understands pressure and how to control it, knows just about half of everything there is to know in his field. When he combines this knowledge with the principles of flow, the designer has the world of hydraulics at his fingertips. Chapter 3 will deal with flow and its relation to speed in the hydraulic system.

CHAPTER 3
FLOW CONTROLS

By controlling the volume of oil supplied to the hydraulic actuator, we control its speed. In order to further develop the concept of flow control as previously introduced, this chapter will cover, in detail, the construction and application of various flow control components. Flow, although it is functionally independent of pressure, is influenced in many ways by the existing pressure conditions. For this reason, it is important that you have a solid understanding of the fact that *pressure is a resistance to flow*. We now wish to cover the construction, performance, and applications of both non-compensated and pressure compensated flow controls.

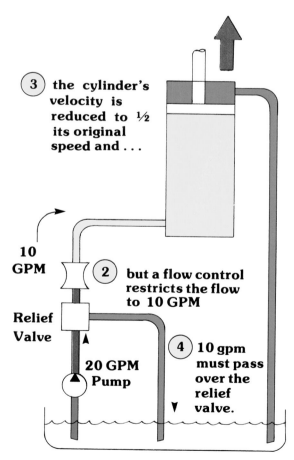

3 the cylinder's velocity is reduced to ½ its original speed and . . .

10 GPM

2 but a flow control restricts the flow to 10 GPM

Relief Valve

20 GPM Pump

4 10 gpm must pass over the relief valve.

1 If the pump delivers 20 gallons per minute . . .

NON-COMPENSATED FLOW CONTROLS

We said earlier that orifices in hydraulic circuits are much like doorways in crowded halls. The higher the flow rate in people per minute, or the smaller the doorway, the more crowded it becomes at the entrance. If we think of a large auditorium, full of people, and the back wall of this auditorium being equipped with doorways the length of the wall, the following conditions could occur:

If, after the performance, the attendants open all the doors, there is almost no resistance to the flow of people, and everyone can exit in a short amount of time. Under the same conditions, if more and more doorways are left locked, the time it will take for the people to exit the room will become longer and longer. That is, the flow rate of people/minute to the outside is reduced as more and more of the exits are closed. If the flow of people is restricted severely enough, the patience of the people who would be last to leave becomes so short, that they elect to sneak out the fire exits. The inlet conditions of a flow control can be thought of as a short tempered crowd, where pushing and shoving is forcing the maximum number of people out the main exit (orifice), while the others elect to exit via the fire exits (relief valve).

As shown in the above example, orifices in hydraulic circuits are nothing more than restrictions, which offer an increased resistance to flow. Since pressure is required to push the oil through the orifice, work (force + motion) is being done on the oil. For a given orifice, an increase in *pressure drop* from inlet to outlet is always accompanied by an increase in flow.

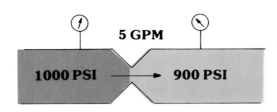

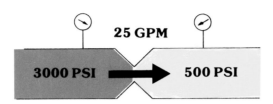

In-Line Needle Valve

The actual flow can be calculated from:

$$GPM = 24.12\,A\,\sqrt{\Delta P}$$
$$A = orifice\ area\ in^2$$

Actually, the use of non-compensated flow controls are limited to applications where feed rates are not critical and where load induced pressure is relatively constant. This is true because the pressure drop across an orifice, and thus the flow, can be affected by four variables:

1. *An increase in load pressure at the outlet increases downstream pressure, and, assuming inlet pressure remains at relief valve setting, has the effect of decreasing the pressure difference from inlet to outlet. This means less flow, and the system slows down with increased load.*

2. *An increase in the inlet pressure, by raising the relief valve setting, has the effect of increasing the pressure drop across the orifice, assuming constant load induced pressure. Therefore, the system speeds up.*

3. *By opening and closing the orifice, we change the resistance to flow. The lower the resistance, the less pressure drop we need from inlet to outlet for any particular flow.*

4. *The temperature of a fluid affects its viscosity, and in turn, the fluid's resistance to flow. It is well known that hot oil is more "fluid" than cold oil. Consequently, like water and molasses, hot oil flows more easily through a given restriction than does cold oil. This is the reason why some systems are sluggish on cold morning start ups, and may not achieve full speed for several hours.*

NEEDLE VALVES

Although a flow control can be nothing more than a pipe plug with a hole drilled through it, it is usually desirable to be able to make an adjustment of the size of the opening.

The needle valve, as shown in the cross-sectional illustration, is the simplest and least expensive way to create a variable orifice.

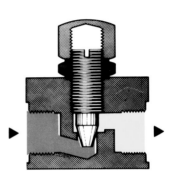

Typical Needle Valve Cross Section

With this valve, the size of the opening, and, consequently, the size of the resulting orifice, are changed by adjusting the position of the cone (needle) with relation to its seat. As we go from the fully closed position (needle in contact with the seat) to the fully open position, you can see that we increase the ring area through which the oil flows. Although this valve will control the flow in either direction, it is advisable to cause the flow to pass first through the seat, then past the needle to the outlet. By flowing in this direction, the metered flow enters the outlet in a divergent flow path, resulting in less turbulence. This means maximum efficiency, less noise generation, and lowest possible variation in metering with changing flow, due to increasing and decreasing pressure drop. This is true because back pressure due to turbulence is minimized.

NON-COMPENSATED FLOW CONTROLS WITH REVERSE FREE FLOW CHECK VALVES

In most hydraulic circuits, it is usually a requirement to have an independently adjustable speed setting for each direction of motion. If, for example, we wanted a cylinder to extend and to retract at the same, but adjustable, speed, we would have to use two flow controls, since more flow is required to extend the cylinder than is necessary to retract it at an equal velocity.

① To achieve equal advance and retract speeds . . .

④ because this cylinder end holds more oil than the rod end.

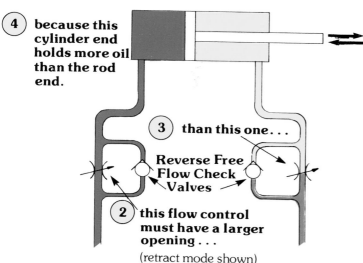

③ than this one . . .

Reverse Free Flow Check Valves

② this flow control must have a larger opening . . .

(retract mode shown)

In this circuit, we need to have flow controls that control flow in only one direction. If we had needle valves without reverse free flow checks., the setting of the flow control on the rod end of the cylinder would also control the speed of the cylinder in the extend mode, because it would be metering the oil being forced out the rod end. Likewise, in retracting, both flow controls would have a part in influencing the cylinder's speed.

① In the extend mode . . .

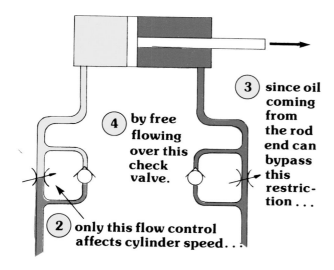

③ since oil coming from the rod end can bypass this restriction . . .

④ by free flowing over this check valve.

② only this flow control affects cylinder speed . . .

The cross-sectional illustration shows a typical flow control with reverse free flow check. In this model, by rotating the outside sleeve, more or less of the radial drilling flow areas can be exposed. As you can see, flow in the opposite direction opens the check valve, thus by-passing the metering area in the valve.

Free Flow Check Poppet   **Outside Sleeve**

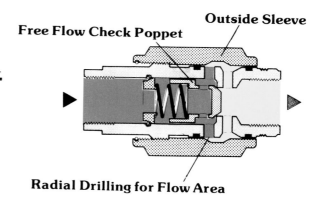

Radial Drilling for Flow Area

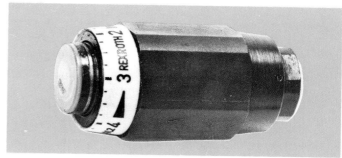

In-Line Flow Control With Reverse Free Flow Check

ADJUSTMENT SENSITIVITY

Normally, when selecting a non-compensated flow control, you simply have to choose one that will pass the full flow with very little pressure drop when it is wide open. Of course, you must also consider its maximum pressure rating. Although mounting convenience, type of adjustment, and aesthetics will have an influence on your decision, you must also consider the accuracy of adjustment for any particular model. With some valve designs, it is virtually impossible to make fine tuning speed adjustments. A valve using coarse threads and a low angle cone has very few turns between the full closed and the full open position. This valve quality is exaggerated in the following cross sections:

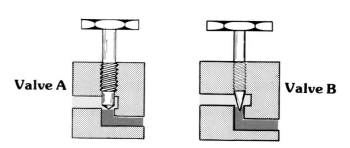

Valve A   **Valve B**

As shown, valve "A" would be almost completely open in two turns of the adjustment, while with valve "B" a very minute change occurs during two revolutions of the hand-knob. As shown in the graph, valve "B" requires many more turns from fully closed to fully open. Consequently, it has the more sensitive adjustment.

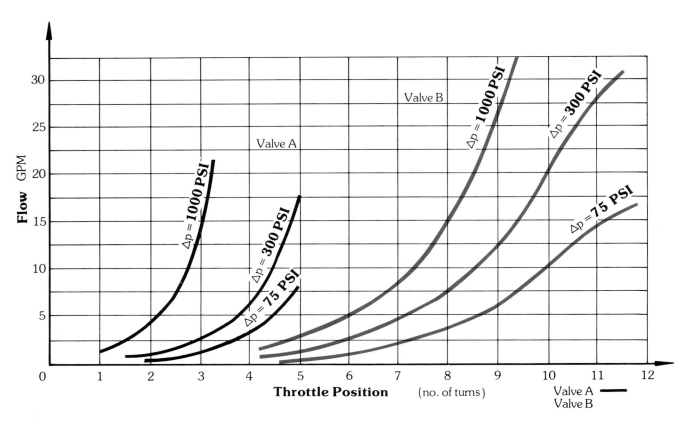

SANDWICH MOUNTED VALVES

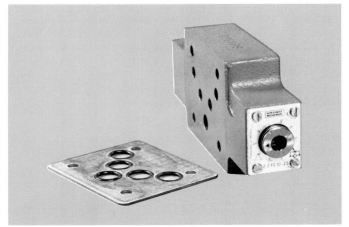

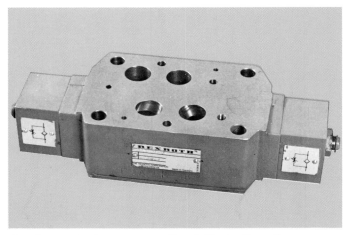

Since, in most applications, we want to control the speed of the actuator in both directions, the logical place to install the flow controls is in the lines supplying the actuator from the directional control. For piping convenience, dual flow controls with *reverse free flow checks* are available for *sandwich mounting* between the directional control and its subplate. These valves are usually non-pressure compensated.

As shown in the cross-sectional illustration, the pressure supply (red) and the tank return (blue) from the directional valve are allowed to pass through the valve unrestricted. In the illustration of the top view of the valve, you can see that flow control is achieved when the poppet's position is adjusted laterally to cause a partial blockage of the "A" and "B" cylinder lines.

Spool Type Directional Control

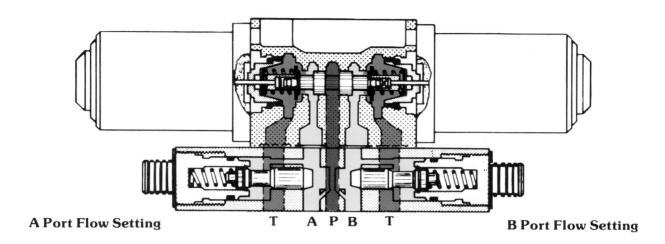

A Port Flow Setting   T   A P B   T   **B Port Flow Setting**

To Actuator

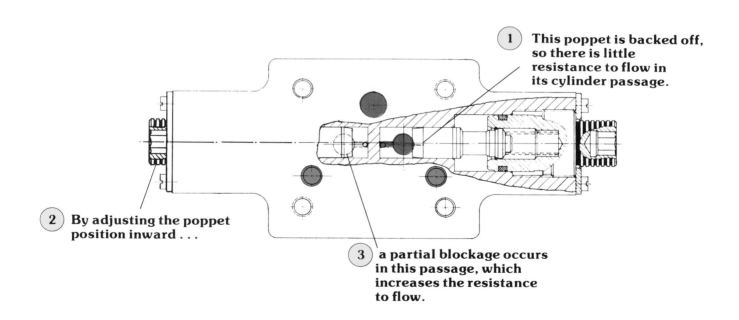

1 This poppet is backed off, so there is little resistance to flow in its cylinder passage.

2 By adjusting the poppet position inward . . .

3 a partial blockage occurs in this passage, which increases the resistance to flow.

Top View of Sandwich Valve

Since space is at a premium with sandwich mounted valves, the poppet which controls flow in one direction also serves as the reverse free flow check in the opposite direction of flow.

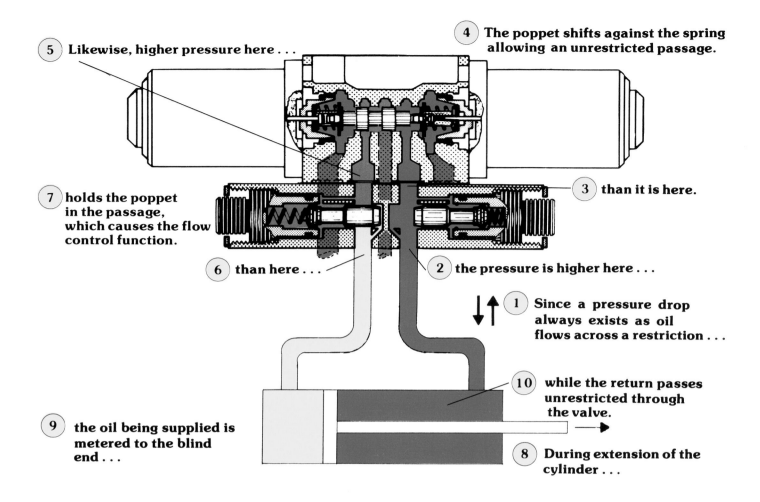

⑤ Likewise, higher pressure here . . .

④ The poppet shifts against the spring allowing an unrestricted passage.

⑦ holds the poppet in the passage, which causes the flow control function.

③ than it is here.

⑥ than here . . .

② the pressure is higher here . . .

① Since a pressure drop always exists as oil flows across a restriction . . .

⑩ while the return passes unrestricted through the valve.

⑨ the oil being supplied is metered to the blind end . . .

⑧ During extension of the cylinder . . .

You will notice that, when the directional control is shifted to cause the cylinder to retract, the conditions of pressure on the flow control poppets are reversed. This allows an independent speed adjustment in the retract mode. As shown, we are metering the oil being supplied to the cylinder. This is commonly referred to as meter-in. For directional controls with symmetrical porting patterns, the position of the flow control can be reversed by 180°, so that the oil returning from the actuator is controlled, while the supply oil enters unrestricted. Meter-in and meter-out circuits will be covered in detail later in the chapter.

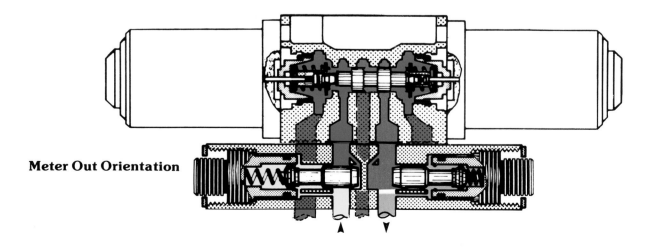

Meter Out Orientation

ACCURACY OF SPEED CONTROL

We have already discussed adjustment sensitivity, and how it is influenced by valve design. We now wish to consider the accuracy of any given flow control setting as load conditions change. The accuracy of a given circuit is determined by measuring the percentage of speed change during operation of the actuator. In actual application, there are four variables which can influence the accuracy of any given speed setting. The first two of these variables are determined by the valve design selected, while the second two are circuit oriented. Let us now look at the variables which determine accuracy.

PRESSURE CONDITIONS AFFECT SPEED ACCURACY

First of all, if our circuit incorporates a non-pressure compensated orifice, the speed will vary as we change the pressure drop across this orifice. Without an alteration in either the setting of the flow control or the relief, the speed will always drop as the load pressure increases. It is virtually impossible to overcome this variable without adding pressure compensation to the valve. Consequently, the accuracy of speed regulation is determined by the valve selected.

TEMPERATURE CONDITIONS AFFECT SPEED ACCURACY

The second cause of inaccuracy in speed setting is related to temperature and its effect on fluid viscosity. We said before that hot oil is more fluid than cold oil. Therefore, the colder the oil, the more resistance there is to flow. The percentage of accuracy in terms of temperature corresponds to the rate of speed increase as the system warms up from cold morning start-up to operation temperature. Temperature compensation and its effect on accuracy of adjustment are determined by the valve design.

ACTUATOR EFFICIENCY AFFECTS SPEED ACCURACY

The third cause of speed loss is related to the efficiency of the actuator. With most cylinder circuits, the volumetric efficiency approaches 100%, which results in very minute speed losses because of leakage in the acutator. We must, however, take into account the volumetric efficiency when we are dealing with hydraulic motors as our actuators. The motors volumetric efficiency can add to the overall speed variation with increased load. This is true because, as load induced pressure increases, we have a higher pressure drop across the clearance fits in the motor, resulting in a higher case drain flow. Since actuator leakage can be isolated so as not to affect adjusted speed, this variable is circuit dependent.

PUMP EFFICIENCY AFFECTS SPEED ACCURACY

The fourth concern is the effect of pump efficiency on speed variation. It is a well known fact that pump leakage increases with increased pressure at its outlet. In some flow control installations, it is possible that the decrease in output flow of the pump will show up as an additional decrease in speed with increasing load. Like motor leakage, pump leakage can be isolated so that it will not affect adjusted output speed. Consequently, this variable is also circuit dependent.

We now want to take a closer look at ways to eliminate the variables in order to obtain the highest accuracy and/or best efficiency in speed control circuits. Since component selection plays only one part in overall efficiency or accuracy, a trade-off of accuracy for efficiency or vice versa is left to the designer.

PRESSURE COMPENSATION

To maintain a constant flow, we need only to keep the pressure drop across the orifice at a constant. Assuming that the load induced pressure is constantly changing with changing loads, we would have constant flow if we could vary the inlet pressure of the orifice at the same rate. This is exactly what a pressure compensated control does.

In the most primitive form, pressure compensation is nothing more than a needle valve with a pressure regulating valve (normally, a reducing valve) in series with it. Between 0 load pressure and stall, we would have a pressure compensated flow as long as the machine operator readjusted the inlet pressure to the orifice each time a change in load occured.

To obtain a flow across the orifice, however, the operator would have to be sure to set the inlet at some constant pressure, higher than load pressure, so that the necessary pressure differential would occur. That is, if load induced pressure were 500 PSI, he would have to adjust the reducing valve to obtain an inlet pressure of, 600 PSI. The moment the load changed to 750 PSI, he would have to readjust the reducing valve to 850 PSI, and so on. In actual application, it would be impractical to regulate the reducing valve manually with each load change. There are, however, valves available which do this function automatically.

2-WAY RESTRICTOR TYPE PRESSURE COMPENSATED FLOW CONTROLS

The two way pressure compensated flow control consists of an adjustable control orifice which is mounted downstream and in series with a pressure reducing valve spool, called a hydrostat. You will notice in the operational cross-section, the *hydrostat* is a spool type reducing valve, which is normally open, allowing the inlet of the valve to be directly connected to the inlet of the main control orifice. The spool is held in the open position by a light spring force, which,

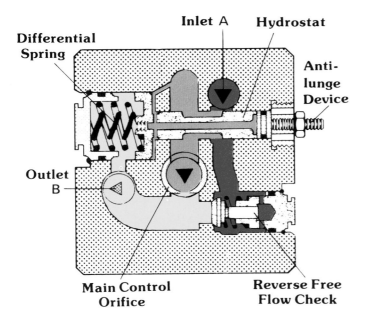

Cross Section Pressure Compensated Flow Control

depending on the size of the valve, opposes a hydraulic force (45 to 170 PSI) on the opposite end of the spool. Assuming that the outlet of the valve is connected to tank, you can easily see how the pressure working on the right-hand area of the spool meters the oil supply so that the main control orifice is never exposed to a higher pressure than is determined by the spring. It does not matter whether the main system relief is set at 300 PSI or 5000 PSI. The hydrostat will position itself so that the pressure downstream of its control land is always equal to the spring force.

SENSING PRESSURE DROP

The hydrostat is nothing more than a reducing valve spool with a piston of larger diameter machined on one end. The piston rides in a close fitting bore in the valve housing, which is cored to expose outlet pressure on the spring side of the piston, while inlet pressure is exposed on the opposite side due to the radial and axial cross drilling through the hydrostat. You will notice that, inlet pressure works on the same effective piston area as the outlet pressure sensed on the opposite side.

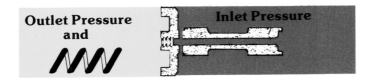

Pressure sensing on inlet and outlet of main control orifice.

Assuming that inlet pressure is equal to outlet pressure, there would be no net differential force on the spool. However, by adding to the outlet pressure a supplemental spring force of 60 PSI, the spool would be in equilibrium when inlet pressure is 60 PSI higher than outlet pressure.

Let us look at a situation in which a cylinder is moving a load at the rate set on the main control orifice, which has a 60 PSI differential pressure from inlet to outlet, as established by the hydrostat. The moment some of the load was taken from the cylinder, a tendency to increase speed would exist because of increased pressure drop across the main control orifice. However, the loss in outlet pressure would also be sensed on the outlet side of the hydrostat. This loss in pressure would mean a loss in force holding it in the previous equilibrium condition. Consequently, inlet pressure exerting the higher force would move the hydrostat against the spring. A movement to the left would close the flow area between the spool land and the valve housing, which would cause a higher pressure drop from valve inlet to control orifice inlet. The inlet pressure at the control orifice would be reduced only to the point at which equilibrium on the hydrostat were reestablished. The net result would be that cylinder speed remains constant, since the pressure drop across the control orifice is automatically adjusted.

On the other hand, if we were to increase the load on the cylinder, the outlet pressure on the flow control would also increase. This would cause the hydrostat to move to the right, which would open the flow area between its spool land, and the valve housing. This would subtract from the original resistance to flow that was being imposed by the hydrostat until inlet pressure increased to the equilibrium condition, when inlet pressure is 60 PSI higher than outlet pressure.

ANTI-LUNGE DEVICE

An undesirable operating characteristic of pressure compensated flow controls often occurs when the flow control is mounted in the actuator supply lines from the directional control. Under these conditions, when the directional control is centered, it is possible that the inlet and outlet of the flow control could be at zero pressure. In a static no-flow condition, the spring would hold the hydrostat in the fully open position.

If the directional valve were energized for a short time period, too much flow and pressure potential would be exposed at the inlet of the control orifice, since the hydrostat could not respond fast enough from its wide open position. The net result would be that the cylinder lunged forward uncontrolled during the time period necessary to establish equilibrium on the hydrostat. The response of the hydrostat is dependent on the oil volume downstream of the flow control and can range from 60 ms to over a second. This characteristic is plotted on the velocity time graph below:

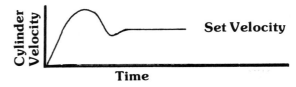

Also, in actual application, the condition is more severe when a low flow setting is adjusted on a relatively large valve. This is true because, under these conditions, the hydrostat has to be displaced further to achieve its equilibrium condition for a low flow state.

To eliminate or drastically reduce the lunge, pressure compensated flow controls can be supplied with stroke limiters on the hydrostat, which are commonly referred to as anti-lunge adjustments. The theory behind their function is that if we limit the stroke of the hydrostat to its maximum open position during dynamic operation, when the flow control goes from no flow to dynamic operation the initial pressure drop will exist because of mechanical positioning of the spool. Likewise, the spool displacement to achieve equilibrium, under any slower operating condition, is shortened. This reduces the response time of the valve.

Pressure and Temperature Compensated Flow Control

SETTING THE ANTI-LUNGE ADJUSTMENT

Since spool positioning can only be optimum for one flow setting, the best lunge control is achieved by setting the adjustment according to the following procedure, each time the main control setting is changed. If this is inconvenient, the anti-lunge control can be set for the maximum operating speed of the machine. The compromise is that at a lower speed setting, the lunge characteristics although reduced, are not completely eliminated.

1. Be sure anti-lunge adjustment is backed off all the way.
2. Operate actuator at full load and set the desired speed on the main control orifice.
3. While cycling in the speed control mode *under full load*, turn the anti-lunge adjustment inward until a noticeable decrease in speed occurs.
4. Back off on the adjustment until the desired speed is

just reestablished.
5. Turn adjustment out one full turn.
6. Recycle the system from static to dynamic condition. The lunge should be almost completely eliminated.

REVERSE FREE FLOW CHECK

Since a pressure compensated valve can only operate in one direction, it is usually supplied with a standard reverse free flow check, which by-passes the main orifice and hydrostat during return flow conditions. Since the check valve is held closed by high inlet pressure during the controlled flow direction, it does not influence applications when there can only be one direction of flow through the valve.

LOCKING ADJUSTMENT

On complicated machinery, machine set-up can be a multi-step procedure. Likewise, since each step in the set-up sequence is dependent on the previous setting, it is desirable to preclude the possibility of unauthorized adjustments of an intermediate speed setting. On the other hand, even simple machinery, if allowed to operate at too high a speed, could endanger the operator, the final product, or the equipment itself. For these reasons, most flow control manufacturers offer some type of locking mechanism for their flow control adjustments.

HOW FOOLPROOF IS THE LOCK

Unfortunately, a lock has never been made that cannot be opened by someone intent on doing so. Similarly, a flow control has not been developed whose setting cannot be by-passed in any one of many possible ways. We do not intend to discuss all these methods, which, in a sense, would be like teaching the lock-picker how to be better at his job. We only want you to understand which lock would be best for your situation. Basically, there are three methods of isolating an adjustment so that it cannot be manipulated by an unauthorized operator.

The first method is simply to hide the adjustment knob in some type of strong box, which must be unlocked and opened to get access to the adjustment. Although this is a deterent to the casual knob twister, it is nothing more than a challenge, so to speak, to the operator who can make more money, if his machine produces more pieces.

Another method is to leave the adjustment in full view, but to prevent the setting from being changed by some mechanical means. The problem with this is that the culprit will soon find out that when he supplies enough torque, the locking mechanisms will break. Even though a 36" pipe wrench would scratch up the hand knob, by using it, he would eventually crack the lock.

The most foolproof method of locking the adjustment is to allow the knob to *free wheel* when locked. The unauthorized operator would then have to pick the lock in order to reach the adjustment.

Since a key is needed to engage the adjustment mechanism, pipe wrenches, hack saws, and bolt cutters can be left out of the criminals tool kit.

RECTIFIER SANDWICH

Any given flow setting can be achieved in both directions by using a rectifier sandwich plate, which mounts between the flow control and its subplate.

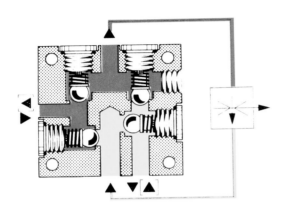

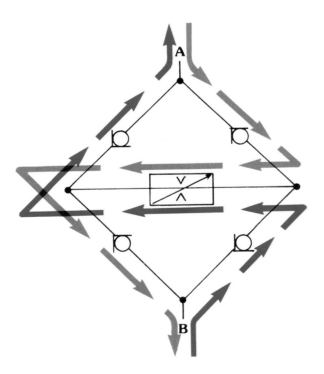

With this assembly, flow being supplied to either the A or B port in the subplate is rectified by the check valve arrangement, so that it always passes through the flow control in the same direction.

TEMPERATURE COMPENSATION

Going back for a moment, we said that the second cause of inaccuracy of speed setting is related to fluid temperature and its effect on fluid viscosity. Hot oil, being more fluid than cold oil, will pass the same flow rate through a considerably smaller orifice, with a pressure drop identical to that of colder oil with a larger orifice. Today's flow controls use two methods to achieve temperature compensation. We will now discuss the operation and merits of both.

TEMPERATURE COMPENSATION USING A BIMETALLIC ROD

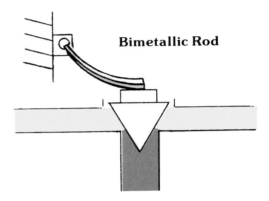

Although the illustration is only a theoretical representation of this type of temperature compensation, you can see that the orifice must offer more of a resistance to a low viscosity fluid than it does to a colder fluid, at a higher viscosity. Temperature compensation is accomplished because the bimetallic rod tends to close the orifice when it is heated and to open it as it cools.

The problem with this type of temperature compensation is that the flow control is used with fluids of different viscosity indexes (see Hydraulic Principles Chapter). Although the orifice and bimetal rod could be designed for optimum performance with any given fluid, it would be impractical to design a different valve for all the different fluids available. The result is that a compromise is incorporated, and the valve is designed for the average fluid, which makes its accuracy fluid dependent.

TEMPERATURE COMPENSATION THROUGH A SHARP EDGED ORIFICE

A totally different concept of temperature compensation has been developed based on the laws of fluid dynamics. Let us consider for a moment how the shape of an orifice affects its sensitivity to viscosity. If we take a long and narrow orifice

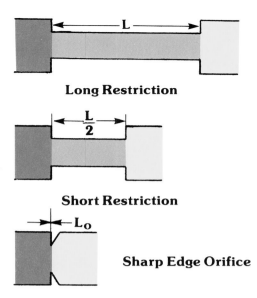

Long Restriction

Short Restriction

L_0

Sharp Edge Orifice

pressure drop for a given amount of flow than would water. But since friction is related to length, each time we cut the length in half, the less sensitive it becomes to viscosity changes. In theory, as we approach an orifice with a length dimension of *zero*, we become immune to changes in viscosity. Unfortunately, it is impossible to manufacture an orifice with a length dimension of zero. We must, therefore, accept the fact that an orifice with a very sharp edge will display flow characteristics which are somewhat dependent on viscosity. In actual practice, though, we find that as we vary the temperature between 65° and 160°F., the maximum variation in flow because of viscosity changes is between 1 and 1.5%. This accuracy is more than acceptable for even the most sophisticated hydraulic circuits.

ACCURACY OF PRESSURE/ TEMPERATURE COMPENSATED FLOW CONTROLS

In discussing the capability of the circuit to maintain speed, we have covered the two component oriented variables, namely, pressure, and temperature compensation. We have shown how the use of sharp edged orifices can be considerably more accurate for temperature compensation, than is the use of a bimetallic rod. However, we have not assigned a number value to pressure compensation accuracy. The accuracy of a valve's pressure compensating ability is largely dependent on the machining accuracy put into the hydrostat during manufacture. This is of utmost importance, particularly for a low flow rate, because leakage from the inlet to the metered port across the hydrostat piston has a definite effect on overall accuracy in speed control.

In the pressure/temperature compensated valves available today, speed variation can be anywhere between ± 2% to ± 20% of maximum flow, depending on design and quality control. These figures represent both the valve's pressure and temperature compensating accuracy combined.

When accuracy is important, care should be exercised in valve selection, since all pressure compensated valves are not necessarily temperature compensated, and vice versa.

with a length dimension "L", we see, through experimentation, that high viscosity fluids resist flowing through this orifice much more than do lower viscosity ones. This is true because of the high kinetic friction between the fluid molecules themselves, and the pipe, as they are forced through the reduced diameter for the given length. It stands to reason that if we cut the length of the orifice in half, we considerably reduce the friction and thus make the orifice less sensitive to viscosity. Of course, since we still have friction involved, a fluid like molasses would still require more

Up to this point, we have discussed and shown the flow control metering the output flow of the pump to the hydraulic actuator. In the hydraulic industry, we refer to this as a *meter-in* circuit. Since the application of the flow control can have as much or more effect on the accuracy of speed regulation, we now want to discuss the merits of different types of speed control circuits.

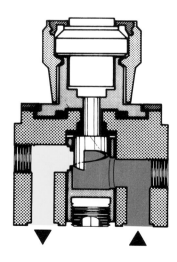

Sharp Edged Orifice

METER-IN CIRCUITS

Meter-in circuits are limited to applications where the load always *offers a resistive force.* In these circuits, the piston in the hydraulic cylinder (or rotary group in a hydraulic motor) is held captive between the pressurized fluid and the load. If for some reason the load conditions change, there is nothing to prevent the load and piston from *running away* from the fluid being supplied to the actuator.

ABILITY TO MAINTAIN SET SPEED

In analyzing our meter-in circuit, we find that variations in pump leakage have no affect on the set speed of our actuator. The fact that we are restricting the pump supply tells us that

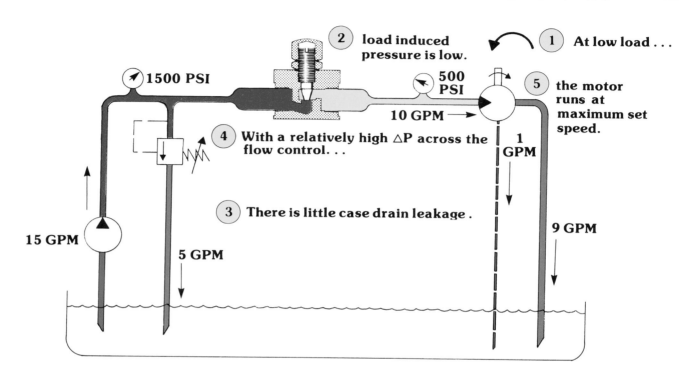

1 At low load . . .

2 load induced pressure is low.

5 the motor runs at maximum set speed.

4 With a relatively high △P across the flow control. . .

3 There is little case drain leakage.

1500 PSI

500 PSI

10 GPM

1 GPM

9 GPM

15 GPM

5 GPM

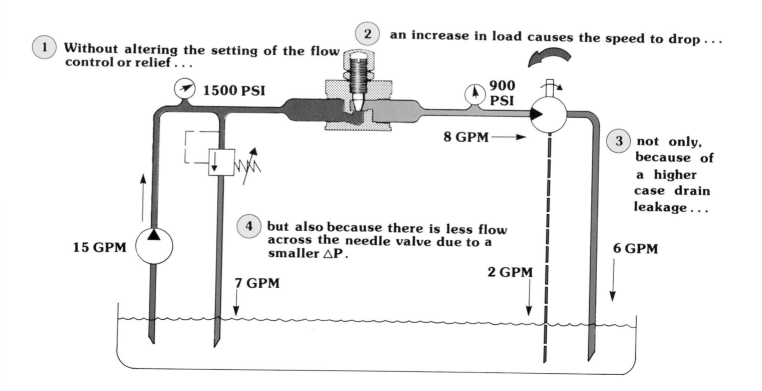

1 Without altering the setting of the flow control or relief . . .

2 an increase in load causes the speed to drop . . .

3 not only, because of a higher case drain leakage . . .

4 but also because there is less flow across the needle valve due to a smaller △P.

1500 PSI

900 PSI

8 GPM

2 GPM

6 GPM

15 GPM

7 GPM

we did not need all of its output flow in the first place. It does not matter whether we force the excess oil over the relief valve or cause it to be leaked out the case drain of the pump. Our output speed is only influenced by the oil which passes through the flow control.

On the other hand, meter-in circuits have no means of supplying more oil to make up for increased actuator leakage with increased load. For this reason, meter-in circuits are considerably more accurate on cylinder circuits than they are with hydraulic motors.

In meter-in motor circuits, the volumetric efficiency has a definite influence on the overall speed variation with increased load. As load pressure increases, a higher pressure drop across the clearance fits in the motor exists. This in turn, creates a higher case drain flow. Even if we use a very accurate pressure and temperature compensated flow control on our meter-in circuit, we can see a considerable decrease in speed because of motor leakage. Remember, flow which leaks out of the case drain cannot create revolution of the motor. If a non-compensated flow control is used, the speed accuracy is considerably worse.

In circuits without actuator leakage, meter-in control is as accurate as any type of flow control circuit. Likewise, when extremely fine feed rates are required, as found in machine tool drives, the meter-in circuit has definite advantages. Since we are talking about extremely fine control, we must discuss these circuits on the assumption that we are using a high quality pressure and temperature compensated flow control.

SURGE DAMPENING IN BRANCH CIRCUITS

An inherent advantage of meter-in circuits is that several operations can be performed simultaneously by the same pump. The only precaution necessary is that, in the design stage, the maximum flow for all simultaneous operations be determined. We can then size the pump (or pump with accumulator) so that adequate flow is provided during all portions of the cycle. Assuming we are metering-in on a number of operations, as long as the sum total of all the controlled flows is less than the output of the pump, the pressure at the inlet of all flow controls will be at relief valve setting. This allows different functions to occur at different pressure levels, without interaction.

The advantage of meter-in pressure compensated flow controls becomes apparent when we begin starting and stopping different branch circuits while the others are in operation. As branch circuits start and stop, more or less oil, respectively, must be supplied. This change in flow rates in the primary supply sets up pressure transients in the circuit, which could affect smooth operation in other branches. The beauty of meter-in circuits is that these transients are dampened by the hydrostat in the pressure compensated flow control, so that a

steady state flow is maintained to the actuator. This would not be the case with meter-out control, since pressure surges would have to pass through the actuator before they would be taken out by the hydrostat.

METER-IN CIRCUITS AND OIL COMPRESSIBILITY

In critical operations, such as those found in machine tool drives, we often must extend the cylinders smoothly and at very constant velocity. If there is a possibility of changes in load, the compressibility of the oil has a negative influence on our constant velocity.

The bulk modulus of a fluid describes its change in volume (ΔV) when it is pressurized. From the bulk modulus formula we have:

$$\Delta V = \frac{V \times \Delta P}{\beta}$$

where: ΔV = change in volume (in³)
           V = original volume (in³)
           ΔP = pressure change (PSI)
           β = bulk modulus of the fluid

Since we are more concerned with the lunge characteristic (ΔS), we can write the above formula as follows:

$$\Delta S = \frac{\Delta V}{A}$$

where: ΔS = change in stroke (in)
           ΔV = change in volume (in³)
           A = net area of piston (in²)

By substitution we have:

$$\Delta S = \frac{V \times \Delta P}{A\beta}$$

where: $V = Vp + (A \times S)$
and: $\Delta P = \frac{\Delta L}{A}$

Consequently, the formula for change in stroke (lunge) can be written as follows:

$$\Delta S = \frac{(Vp + (A \times S)) \times \Delta L}{A^2 \beta}$$

ΔS = lunge (in)
Vp = volume in pipe (in³)
A = net piston area (in²)
S = stroke (in)
ΔL = load change (lbs)
β = bulk modulus of the fluid

Assuming we can calculate the change in stroke, we can also determine the change in velocity (ΔV), if we know how long it takes for the load to change.

$$\Delta V = \frac{\Delta S \cdot 60}{\Delta T}$$

ΔV = velocity change (in/min.)
ΔS = lunge (in)
ΔT = time for load change (seconds)

Let us now apply these formulas to the meter-in and meter-out circuits at different stroke lengths, under the following operating conditions.

Parameters:
a) Cylinder
    2½" Bore x 1-3/4" Rod x 36" Stroke

A_1 = Area of the blind end = 4.9 in²
A_2 = Net area of the rod end = 2.5 in²
S = Stroke
ΔS = Lunge (which can be positive or negative, depending on the direction of the load change)
b) Load Change
    L_1 = Full load = 3000 lbs.
    L_2 = Reduced load = 1000 lbs.
    ΔL = Load change = 2000 lbs.
c) Time for load change:
    ΔT = 1 second
d) Volume of oil in lines:
    3/4" tubing × .049" wall × 9' length
    V_p = 36 in³
e) Bulk modulus of the oil:
    β = 2.0 x 10⁵ lb/in²

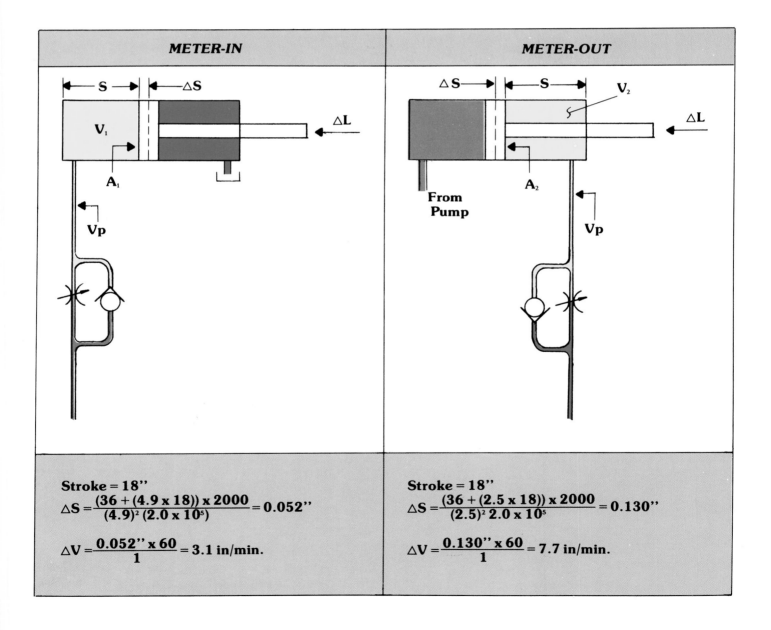

METER-IN	METER-OUT

Stroke = 18"

$$\Delta S = \frac{(36 + (4.9 \times 18)) \times 2000}{(4.9)^2 (2.0 \times 10^5)} = 0.052"$$

$$\Delta V = \frac{0.052" \times 60}{1} = 3.1 \text{ in/min.}$$

Stroke = 18"

$$\Delta S = \frac{(36 + (2.5 \times 18)) \times 2000}{(2.5)^2 \, 2.0 \times 10^5} = 0.130"$$

$$\Delta V = \frac{0.130" \times 60}{1} = 7.7 \text{ in/min.}$$

Stroke = 24" $\triangle S = \dfrac{(36 + (4.9 \times 24)) \times 2000}{(4.9)^2 (2.0 \times 10)^5} = 0.064"$ $\triangle V = \dfrac{0.064" \times 60}{1} = 3.8 \text{ in/min.}$	**Stroke = 36" - 24" = 12"** $\triangle S = \dfrac{(36 + (2.5 \times 12)) \times 2000}{(2.5)^2 \times 2.0 \times 10^5} = 0.106"$ $\triangle V = \dfrac{0.106" \times 60}{1} = 6.3 \text{ in/min.}$
Stroke = 12" $\triangle S = \dfrac{(36 + (4.9 \times 12)) \times 2000}{(4.9)^2 \times 2.0 \times 10^5} = 0.039"$ $\triangle V = \dfrac{0.039" \times 60}{1} = 2.4 \text{ in/min.}$	**Stroke = 36" - 12" = 24"** $\triangle S = \dfrac{(36 + (2.5 \times 24)) \times 2000}{(2.5)^2 \times 2.0 \times 10^5} = 0.154"$ $\triangle V = \dfrac{0.154" \times 60}{1} = 9.2 \text{ in/min.}$

The above calculations show that when we are *extending* cylinders with very precise control, *metering-in to the larger volume* on the blind end of the cylinder, we considerably reduce lunge (or hesitation) as the load changes.

HEAT GENERATION WITH METER-IN CIRCUITS

Whenever a restriction is put in series with the load, the additional resistance to flow is additive to the load induced pressure. Since the pump and relief valve have no way of determining whether the increased pressure is load induced or orifice induced, the pump draws more and more horsepower from the prime mover, so that it can pump its rated flow against the increased resistance. The relief valve limits the maximum pressure in the system, and begins dumping high pressure fluid to tank when the restriction adds sufficient resistance to flow. The sum total of load induced pressure and back pressure of the orifice equals relief valve setting. Flow which is not needed to produce cylinder speed is dumped to tank at maximum pressure, or in other words, when input horsepower is at its highest. With meter-in series circuits, heat generation is highest at lower actuator speeds, and it becomes lower and lower as we approach full speed of the actuator. (Calculation of heat generated has been covered in detail in the Hydraulic Principles Chapter.) Although it may sometimes be necessary, we should try to avoid using meter-in series circuits when we are operating at low speeds a high percentage of the time.

METER-OUT CIRCUITS

A long standing rule-of-thumb in the hydraulic industry states, *"When in doubt, meter-out"*. Unfortunately, meter-out circuits frequently created problems with cylinder damage or leakage because of rod end pressure intensification.

A meter-out circuit is a series circuit much like a meter-in

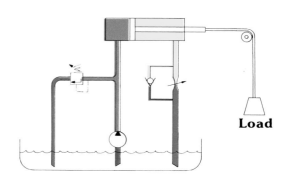

Meter-out circuits prevent run-away but can also create problems with excessive rod end pressure.

control, as shown in the above illustration. The only difference is that with meter-out circuits, the flow control is mounted in series after the actuator. The back pressure created by the flow control is exposed on the annulus area of the rod end side of the piston, which captures the piston, so that it can move only at the rate which the flow control will allow.

As in meter-in circuits, the load affects the differential pressure across the flow control in meter-out installations. With meter-out circuits, however, the outlet of the flow control is more or less at constant pressure (atmospheric), while the inlet pressure varies with changes in loads. Let us now take a closer look at how the load affects the inlet pressure of the flow control on meter-out applications.

When the flow control is in the wide open position, it offers little or no resistance to the flow leaving the opposite end of the cylinder. The cylinder will extend at maximum speed, assuming that load induced pressure is less than the relief valve setting. Under these conditions, it would be possible for a negative load to run ahead of the pump.

When the load induced pressure approaches relief valve setting, it causes speed control to begin the moment the flow

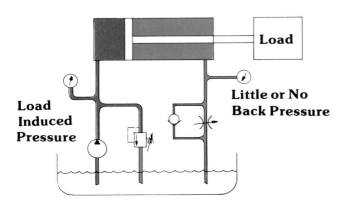

Load Induced Pressure

Little or No Back Pressure

Full Speed Operation

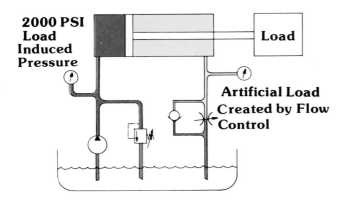

2000 PSI Load Induced Pressure

Artificial Load Created by Flow Control

Controlled Speed

control back pressures the annulus area on the rod end. The total force required to extend the cylinder is the force needed to move the load, plus the artifical force created by the back pressure offered by the flow control, over the net piston area of the rod end. If we reduce the load, a non-compensated flow control would allow the cylinder to increase its speed. This happens with reduced loads, since more of the resistance to flow has to be provided by the flow control. The higher the back pressure the meter-out flow control must offer, the higher the pressure drop across it to tank. This differential pressure is amplified by the area ratio (pressure intensification) of the cylinder. As the load decreases the speed increases more than it would with a meter-in circuit. Likewise, for a given speed, we must see an increase in back pressure when a pressure compensated valve is used.

PRESSURE COMPENSATED METER-OUT CONTROL

Pressure compensated controls in meter-out installations very accurately maintain a set speed, because they have the ability to self regulate the back pressure on the actuator when a change in load occurs. We said in the first chapter that it takes more power to move a given load faster than it does to move it more slowly. As you can see from the following example, the pressure compensated flow control always makes the actuator look as if it were operating at maximum load for any given speed setting. The potential power, which is not required, is changed into heat as the excess flow passes over the relief valve.

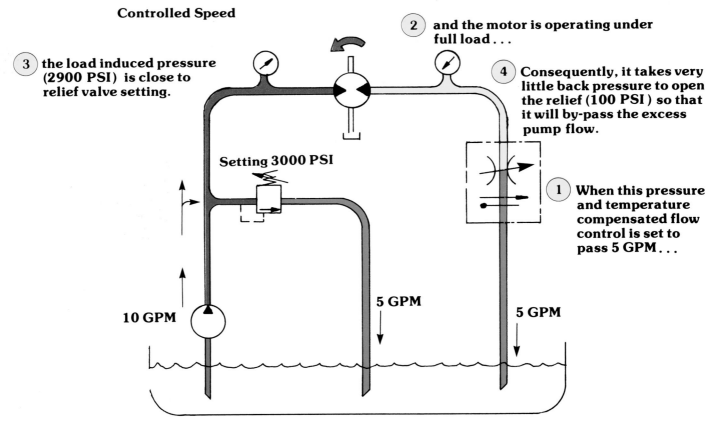

② **and the motor is operating under full load . . .**

③ **the load induced pressure (2900 PSI) is close to relief valve setting.**

④ **Consequently, it takes very little back pressure to open the relief (100 PSI) so that it will by-pass the excess pump flow.**

Setting 3000 PSI

① **When this pressure and temperature compensated flow control is set to pass 5 GPM . . .**

10 GPM

5 GPM

5 GPM

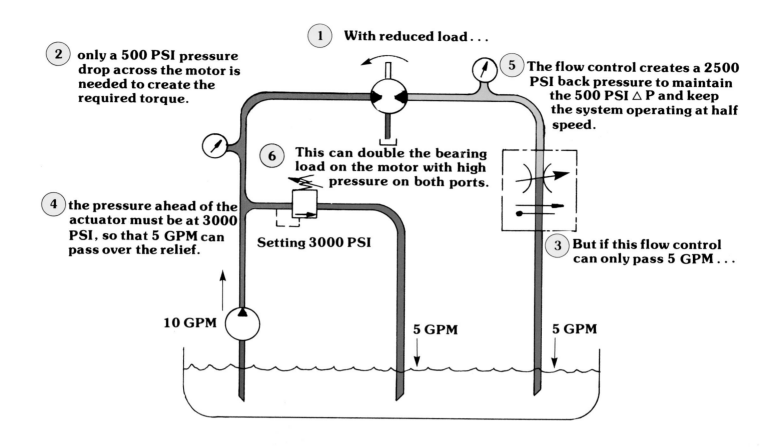

① With reduced load . . .

② only a 500 PSI pressure drop across the motor is needed to create the required torque.

⑤ The flow control creates a 2500 PSI back pressure to maintain the 500 PSI △P and keep the system operating at half speed.

⑥ This can double the bearing load on the motor with high pressure on both ports.

④ the pressure ahead of the actuator must be at 3000 PSI, so that 5 GPM can pass over the relief.

Setting 3000 PSI

③ But if this flow control can only pass 5 GPM . . .

10 GPM

5 GPM

5 GPM

PRESSURE INTENSIFICATION WITH METER-OUT CIRCUITS

With the motor actuator cited in the previous example, it was safe to assume that back pressure created by the flow control would simply be relief valve pressure, minus load induced pressure. We could do this because pressure on the motor's outlet creates an artificial negative torque, which is equal in magnitude to the positive torque that would be created by a similar pressure at the motor's inlet. An often overlooked, but potentially dangerous application of meter-out circuits occurs when we use cylinders with different input and output areas of the main piston.

For instance, if we take a cylinder with a 2:1 ratio, we find that output force equilibrium occurs when we have different pressures in the rod and blind ends of the cylinder.

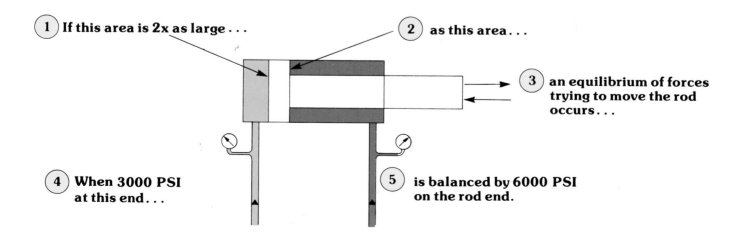

① If this area is 2x as large . . .

② as this area . . .

③ an equilibrium of forces trying to move the rod occurs . . .

④ When 3000 PSI at this end . . .

⑤ is balanced by 6000 PSI on the rod end.

By applying a differential cylinder to our pressure compensated meter-out circuit, we find that pressure levels in the system can become dangerously high. With overrunning load the intensified "push of the pump" is added to the "pull of the load" to create extremely high rod end pressures.

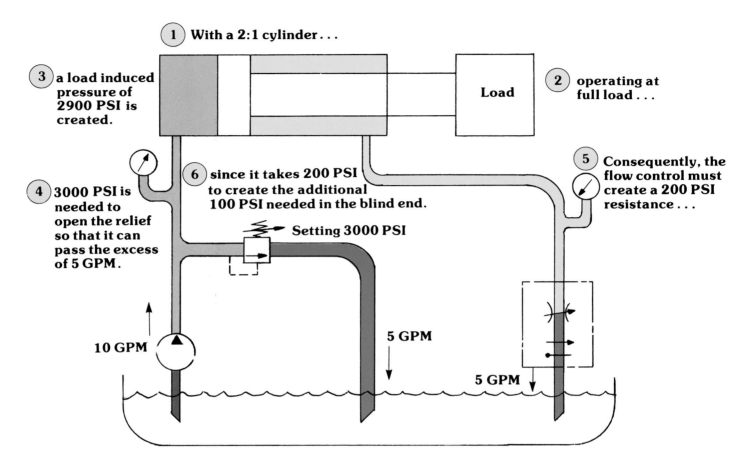

1 With a 2:1 cylinder...

3 a load induced pressure of 2900 PSI is created.

2 operating at full load . . .

Load

6 since it takes 200 PSI to create the additional 100 PSI needed in the blind end.

5 Consequently, the flow control must create a 200 PSI resistance . . .

4 3000 PSI is needed to open the relief so that it can pass the excess of 5 GPM.

Setting 3000 PSI

10 GPM

5 GPM

5 GPM

Under the above conditions, you can see that pressure levels are acceptable, and the system will operate satisfactorily and safely. If the load is removed, our seemingly innocent 3000 PSI system, turns into a 6000 PSI hazard.

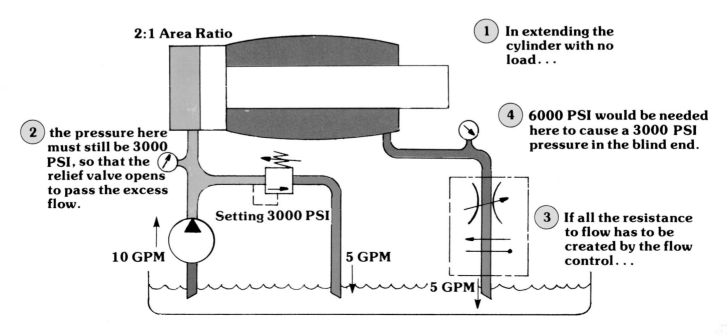

2:1 Area Ratio

1 In extending the cylinder with no load. . .

2 the pressure here must still be 3000 PSI, so that the relief valve opens to pass the excess flow.

4 6000 PSI would be needed here to cause a 3000 PSI pressure in the blind end.

Setting 3000 PSI

3 If all the resistance to flow has to be created by the flow control. . .

10 GPM

5 GPM

5 GPM

As seen in the previous example, pressure intensification can become a serious problem, with pressure compensated meter-out circuits used on large rod cylinders. This *does not preclude* non-compensated circuits, or smaller rod cylinders. A non-compensated flow control would not allow the potential energy, in the form of pressure, to build as high, since some of the excess energy would show up as an increase in speed, due to a higher pressure drop across the orifice. Needless to say, the rod end pressure can still become dangerously high with non-compensated valves.

On the other hand, we do not have to isolate meter-out circuits from cylinders, since the effects of pressure intensification are considerably reduced when using cylinders with small rod diameters. Nevertheless, since the most readily available cylinders are rated at 3000 to 5000 PSI, the possibility of pressure intensification must always be considered.

HEAT GENERATION WITH METER-OUT CONTROL

As in meter-in circuits, the actuator is mounted in series with the flow control and the pump. Flow, which is determined to be needed by the flow control, must be dumped over the relief valve, turning its potential energy into heat. The rate of heat generation is highest at low actuator speeds, and lessens as we approach full system speed (see calculations of heat generation in Chapter One).

METER-OUT CIRCUITS AND THEIR ABILITY TO MAINTAIN SET SPEED

The accuracy of a meter-out circuit, or its ability to maintain

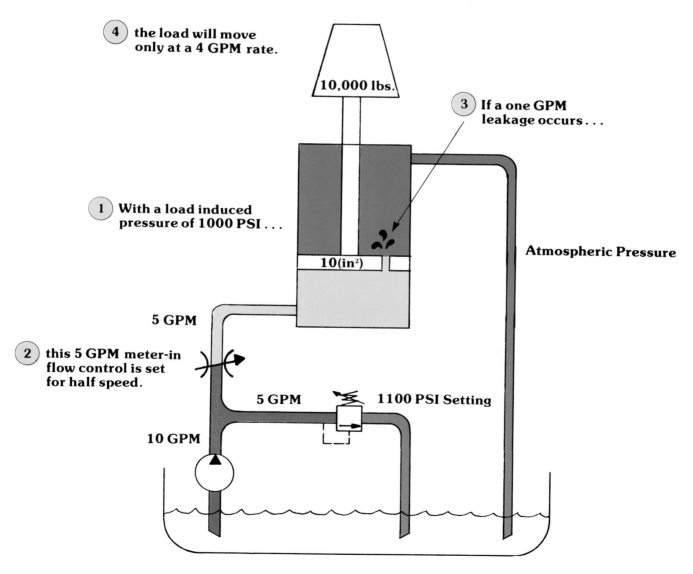

4 the load will move only at a 4 GPM rate.

10,000 lbs.

3 If a one GPM leakage occurs . . .

1 With a load induced pressure of 1000 PSI . . .

Atmospheric Pressure

10(in²)

5 GPM

2 this 5 GPM meter-in flow control is set for half speed.

5 GPM   1100 PSI Setting

10 GPM

Cross Port Leakage Meter-In Circuits

set speed, is influenced by the same factors which cause speed fluctuations in meter-in circuits, namely: change in pressure drop, changes in viscosity, and changes in actuator leakage. On the other hand, both types of circuits are relatively unaffected by pump leakage. However, meter-out circuits usually experience greater speed variation when considering actuator leakage with variable loads.

CROSS PORT LEAKAGE

Cross port leakage can be defined as the oil which passes from the high pressure side of the actuator to its low pressure side. In cylinders, this would be the oil which leaks past the piston packing, while in hydraulic motors, it is the oil which passes through the clearances between the high and low

pressure sides of the rotary group. To avoid a lengthy explanation of the various types of motors, at this point, we will consider cross port leakage of cylinders only. We can safely assume that cross port leakage would have the same influence on the output speed of a hydraulic motor. For purposes of clarity, our cross port leakage will be allowed via a hole drill in the piston.

To explain the effects of cross port leakage with meter-out control, the flow control and the leakage path by the piston can be thought of as two orifices in series. The meter-out flow control back pressures the leakage path, thus influencing the pressure drop across it. Initially as we reduce the load, cross port leakage reduces towards zero since increasing rod end pressure lowers the pressure drop on the leakage path. However, during low loads, no load, and overrunning load operations, the actuator leakage will cause an increase in actuator speed. Because oil would be regenerated to the blind end,

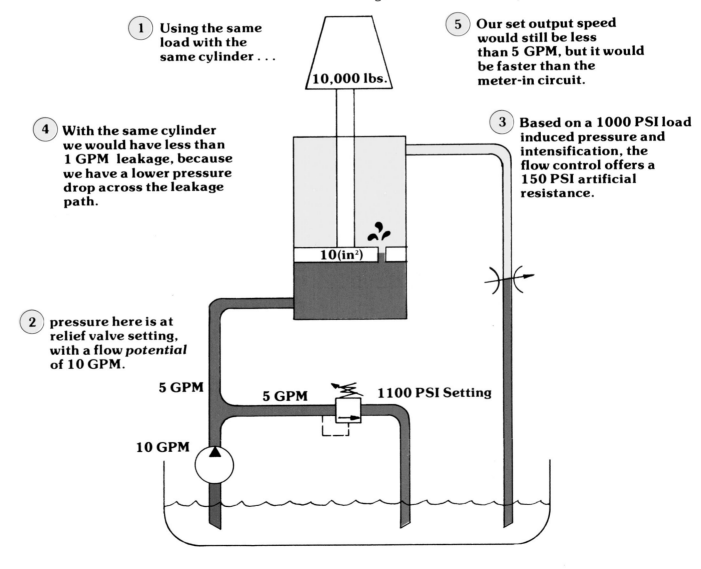

① Using the same load with the same cylinder . . .

④ With the same cylinder we would have less than 1 GPM leakage, because we have a lower pressure drop across the leakage path.

② pressure here is at relief valve setting, with a flow *potential* of 10 GPM.

⑤ Our set output speed would still be less than 5 GPM, but it would be faster than the meter-in circuit.

③ Based on a 1000 PSI load induced pressure and intensification, the flow control offers a 150 PSI artificial resistance.

10,000 lbs.

10(in²)

5 GPM

5 GPM

1100 PSI Setting

10 GPM

Cross Port Leakage Meter-Out Circuits

the speed would increase when the leak occured. This happens when pressure intensification causes higher pressure on the rod end than the blind end, thus causing leakage to the blind end. This supplements the supply which causes an increase in speed.

Hydraulic motors are always affected by cross port leakage to a greater or lesser extent, determined by their efficiency. As a motor goes from no load to its full torque capability, cross port leakage causes a decrease in speed. However, since we are back pressuring the motor's outlet, the ΔP across the clearance fits is less and we get less cross port leakage than we would with a meter-in circuit.

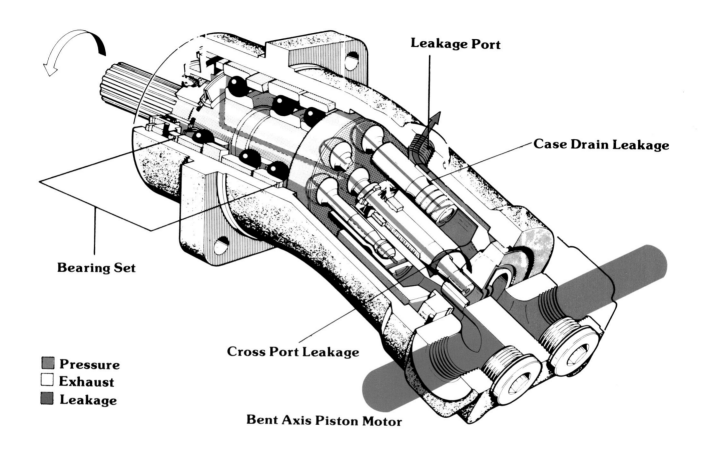

Leakage Port

Case Drain Leakage

Bearing Set

■ **Pressure**
□ **Exhaust**
■ **Leakage**

Cross Port Leakage

Bent Axis Piston Motor

CASE DRAIN LEAKAGE

Case drain leakage has meaning only when we talk about the motor actuator. This type of leakage is that oil which slips by pistons, port plates, bearings, and lubrication passages, and enters the housing (case) of the motor. To rid the housing of oil, hydraulic motors are usually supplied with leakage port connections, which allow this leakage to flow back to the tank unrestricted. This type of leakage has the same effect on speed variation as would a leak in a hose or fitting in supply to the motor, for meter-in circuits, or the motors outlet port for meter-out control.

METER-IN CIRCUITS CANNOT COMPENSATE FOR ACTUATOR LEAKAGE

As shown in the following schematic, the meter-in circuit cannot

compensate for any type of speed variation which occurs due to leakage downstream. In this example, if the 1 GPM leak were occurring at 50% load, the speed would drop off considerably as load induced pressure increased the ΔP across the leakage path. It is even possible that a highly inefficient motor would stall, because there would be less resistance to flow through the case drain leakage path than would exist in trying to cause rotation of the motor.

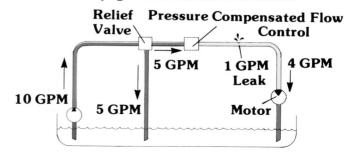

Relief Valve **Pressure Compensated Flow Control**

5 GPM

1 GPM Leak **4 GPM**

10 GPM **5 GPM** **Motor**

With meter-out circuits leakage from the motors outlet port side to the case drain causes the speed to increase above the desired. An increase in leakage occurs at low loads because a higher resistance to flow must be created by the flow control. Since the speed is determined by how much oil leaves the motors outlet, the speed increases with decreasing loads.

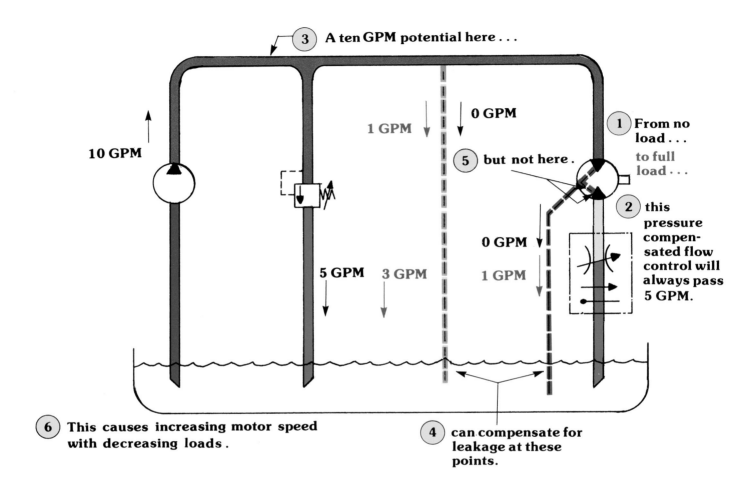

To summarize, meter-in circuits run at nearly ideal speed at no load but experience a decrease in speed with increasing load. Meter-out circuits, on the other hand, are closer to ideal speed at full load but increase their speed with decreasing loads. Under the same condition the amount of speed variation is nearly the same for meter-in or meter-out control. Since speed variation is not improved with meter-out control, meter-in circuits are more often desired since this circuitry does not create additional bearing load on the motor.

BY-PASS SPEED CONTROL CIRCUITS

Up to this point, we have discussed flow controls before and after the actuator, but always in *series*. A third method of speed control can be obtained by mounting the flow control in *parallel* with the actuator. The principle of this type of control is that flow which is not required to produce speed is shunted to tank over the flow control. This says that when the flow control is fully closed we have maximum speed, while a fully open flow control produces minimum or no speed. As discussed in Chapter 1, by-pass flow control circuits work on the principle that flow will always take the path of least resistance.

HEAT GENERATION WITH BY-PASS CIRCUITS

The advantage by-pass circuits have over series circuits is that system pressure is never higher than that induced by the load. In the following schematic we are shown that the relief valve only determines the maximum force which can be produced by the system. Up to relief valve setting, the full flow of the pump is split between the flow control and the actuator. Although the system is shown in the half speed condition, you can see that, by closing the flow control, we increase the resistance to flow across it. The flow, which no

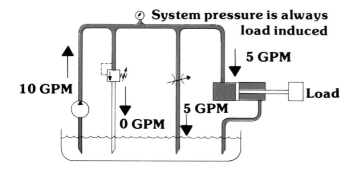

System pressure is always load induced

10 GPM

0 GPM

5 GPM

5 GPM

Load

$$\text{Total heat generation in by-pass circuits} \left(\frac{\text{BTU}}{\text{HR}}\right) =$$

$$1.5 \times \text{Load Induced (PSI)} \times \text{Flow through Flow Control (GPM) Valve} \atop \text{Pressure}$$

longer can pass over the smaller restriction in the flow control *at load* pressure, is diverted to the cylinder, causing an increase in speed. Of course, the exact opposite happens when we open the flow control and cause a lesser resistance to flow.

You can easily see that the only heat generated by this system is that which is caused by the flow across the flow control at load induced pressure. It stands to reason, that at low actuator speeds we have maximum heat generation, because of maximum flow through the flow control. The advantage is that with low loads we have low heat generation, as opposed to the maximum heat generation by series control at low speeds and low load.

SPEED VARIATION WITH BY-PASS CIRCUITS

Unfortunately, the energy conservation merits of by-pass circuits are often offset by their extremely poor ability to maintain set speed. By-pass circuits are influenced by all factors which affect speed variation in flow control circuits, namely: pump leakage, actuator leakage, and changes in pressure drop and viscosity. Component selection can reduce variations in speed due to pressure drop changes and viscosity changes, but even the finest control devices will not eliminate these effects. The following two schematics show the extremes of speed variation, even if a pressure temperature compensated flow control is used.

This is not to say that by-pass circuits are so inaccurate in speed regulation that their energy saving merit should not be considered. However, by-pass circuits almost always use

Highest Speed is at Cold Start-Up with No Load

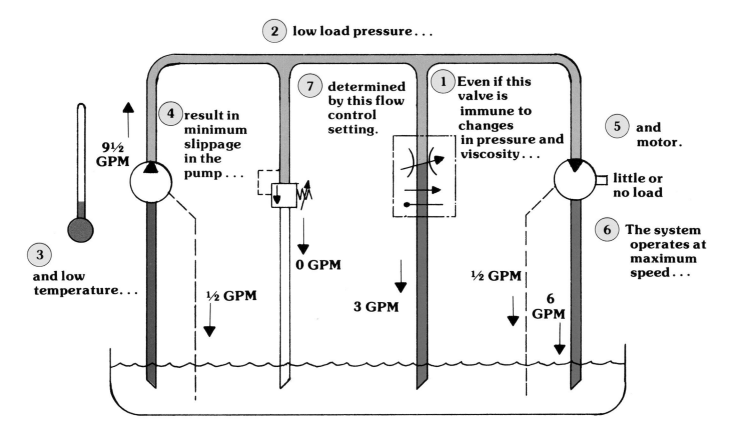

② low load pressure...

⑦ determined by this flow control setting.

① Even if this valve is immune to changes in pressure and viscosity...

④ result in minimum slippage in the pump...

⑤ and motor.

9½ GPM

little or no load

③ and low temperature...

⑥ The system operates at maximum speed...

½ GPM

0 GPM

3 GPM

½ GPM

6 GPM

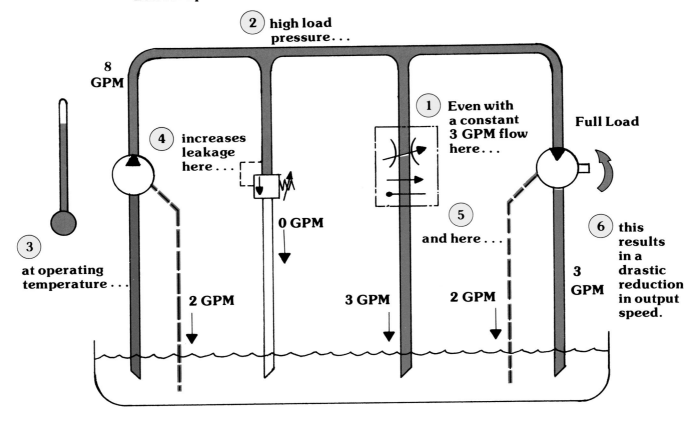

Lowest Speed Results with Full Load at Operating Temperature

2 high load pressure...

8 GPM

1 Even with a constant 3 GPM flow here...

Full Load

4 increases leakage here...

0 GPM

5 and here...

6 this results in a drastic reduction in output speed.

3 at operating temperature...

2 GPM

3 GPM

2 GPM

3 GPM

---

pressure compensated flow controls. They are generally better when used with cylinder circuits and highly volumetric efficient pumps.

APPLICATION NOTES ON BY-PASS CIRCUITS

In by-pass circuits, unlike series circuits, flow which is not needed passes to tank through the flow control. Consequently, it would not be available for operating other branch circuits, as it is with meter-in or meter-out control. This means that a separate pump must be provided for each simultaneous operation.

Likewise, by-pass circuits, like meter-in circuits, have no way of resisting over running loads. Needless to say, a by-pass circuit should never be used if there is a possibility of a negative load.

3-WAY BY-PASS STYLE PRESSURE COMPENSATED FLOW CONTROL

By adding a third port, and modifying the hydrostat of the 2-way pressure compensated valve (discussed earlier in this chapter), we can obtain a completely different flow control function. Since the method of sensing and maintaining pressure drop has already been discussed, we will now concern ourselves only with the hydrostat and its operating function.

We said that the hydrostat of the 2-way pressure compensated valve was essentially a normally open self-regulating pressure reducing valve. This valve self-adjusts to maintain the inlet pressure at the main control orifice at a constant value (45 to 170 PSI) higher than outlet pressure. Actually, the function of a 3-way hydrostat is not that different.

It stands to reason that if we can regulate the inlet pressure of the controlling orifice by reducing supply pressure, we can also regulate this pressure by *relieving* the excess flow to tank. A 3-way by-pass style flow regulator is essentially a main control orifice mounted in series with the load and downstream of a self regulating pressure relief valve hydrostat.

In the operational cross section, you can see that downstream pressure is sensed on one area of the hydrostat, while the inlet pressure opposes this force on the opposite, but

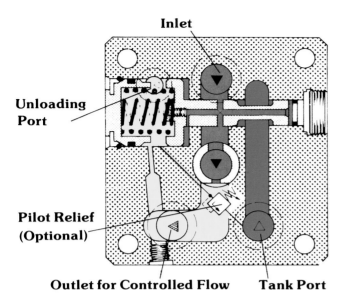

Inlet

Unloading Port

Pilot Relief (Optional)

Outlet for Controlled Flow

Tank Port

Pressure Compensated By-Pass Flow Control

equal area of the spool. The moment the inlet pressure increases to the point where it will exceed the downstream pressure plus spring pressure, the spool shifts and relieves the excess flow to tank. In comparing this hydrostat with a spool type pilot operated relief (Chapter 2), all that is needed would be to add a pilot relief and we would be able to perform both relief and flow control functions with one valve.

PILOT RELIEF OPTION FOR 3-WAY PRESSURE COMPENSATED FLOW CONTROLS

Since a 3-way flow control by-passes pump flow to tank at a pressure of approximately 75 PSI higher than load induced pressure, the hydraulic circuit can only be designed to perform one function per pump. Since the hydrostat in a 3-way by-pass style pressure compensated flow control performs a basic relief valve function, it seems to be repetitious to add a separate system relief. For this reason, optional pilot reliefs are often included in the 3-way control package.

CAUTION: NEVER USE A 3-WAY BY-PASS FLOW REGULATOR WITHOUT A MAIN SYSTEM RELIEF UNLESS THE PILOT RELIEF OPTION IS INCLUDED!

As shown in the operational illustration, the cartridge type direct operated relief has its pressure port connected to the spring chamber side of the hydrostat. By limiting the pressure in this chamber, we limit the maximum force holding the hydrostat in the closed position. The moment the inlet pressure increases to the point where it will exceed this limited pressure on the downstream side, the hydrostat shifts, relieving pump flow to tank. Because of the spring on the downstream side of the hydrostat, the pump relieves at a

pressure of 45 to 170 PSI higher than that set on the piloting relief.

PUMP UNLOADING WITH 3-WAY BY-PASS FLOW CONTROLS

Basically, there are two means of unloading the pump flow to tank at a low pressure during idle periods of the cycle.

One way is accomplished simply by fully closing the throttle. In some circuits, if we shut off the supply of oil to the actuator, the pressure downstream of the flow control will drop to zero. When this happens, there is no pressure on the downstream side of the hydrostat. Thus, inlet pressure opens to tank at the pressure determined by the spring force unbalancing the hydrostat. The only precaution which must be observed is that load induced pressure cannot be trapped between the actuator and the closed orifice in the flow control. This method works equally well with either a 3-way by-pass flow regulator with the built-in piloting relief, or with the standard valve with a separate system relief.

The second way in which pump unloading can be accomplished at any flow setting is through the use of the "X" port connection. Most 3-way flow controls are equipped with a separate port, which is connected to the spring chamber side of the hydrostat. Although under normal valve operation this port is plugged, solenoid venting can be accomplished by piping in a separate directional control.

As shown in the following illustration, the "X" port can be used exactly like the "X" port of a pilot operated relief. When the solenoid is de-energized, the spring chamber side of the hydrostat is connected to tank, and the pump unloads at minimum pressure. Upon enerigization, we block the free flow to tank, which loads the pump and causes the normal

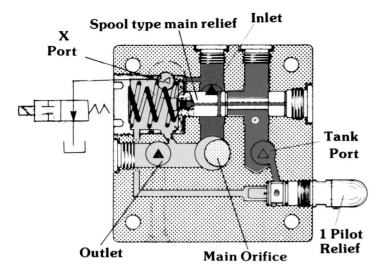

Venting a By-Pass Flow Control

3-way function to occur. As in a pilot operated relief, the "X" port could also be used for remote pressure adjustment or multiple pressure selection (see Chapter 2).

MERITS OF BY-PASS STYLE FLOW REGULATION

The by-pass style flow regulator combines the energy saving advantages of a by-pass use of a 2-way flow regulator, with the accuracy of a meter-in circuit. Its only disadvantage is that it cannot be used with multiple branch circuits and, like meter-in circuits, provides no protection against over running loads. The accuracy of speed control is no less than that of a pressure compensated meter-in circuit, since pump leakage with increased pressure is isolated from the actuator.

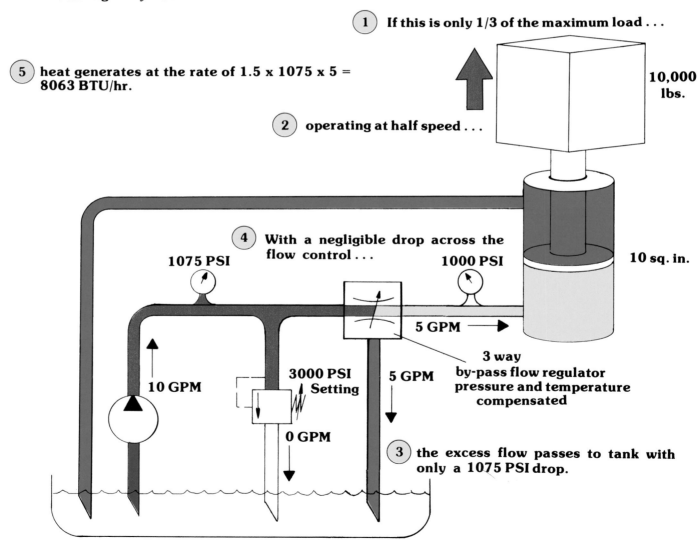

By-Pass Flow Control Saves Energy

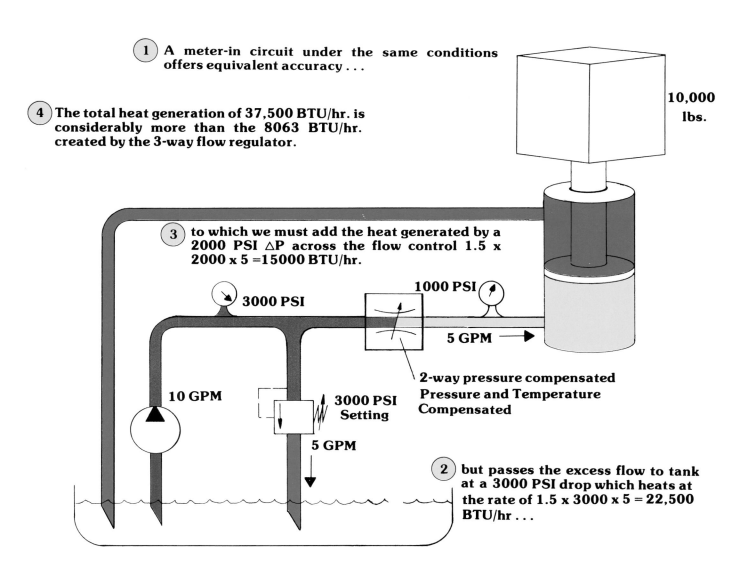

1 A meter-in circuit under the same conditions offers equivalent accuracy...

4 The total heat generation of 37,500 BTU/hr. is considerably more than the 8063 BTU/hr. created by the 3-way flow regulator.

10,000 lbs.

3 to which we must add the heat generated by a 2000 PSI △P across the flow control 1.5 x 2000 x 5 = 15000 BTU/hr.

3000 PSI

1000 PSI

5 GPM →

2-way pressure compensated Pressure and Temperature Compensated

10 GPM

3000 PSI Setting

5 GPM

2 but passes the excess flow to tank at a 3000 PSI drop which heats at the rate of 1.5 x 3000 x 5 = 22,500 BTU/hr...

2-Way Pressure Compensated Flow Controls Create More Heat.

PREVENTING "CREEP" IN BY-PASS CIRCUITS

A 2-way pressure compensated flow control, used in a by-pass circuit, or a 3-way flow regulator unloaded through its vent connection, cannot pass flow to tank at zero pressure. In some circuits, the residual pressure (45 to 170 PSI) could cause an actuator with little or no resistance on its output to drift, or "creep". If it is possible that the mechanical load cannot resist the residual pressure on the actuator, special precautions must be taken.

It is important to size the flow control large enough so that the pressure drop due to flow is at the absolute minimum when the 2-way valve is wide open, or the 3-way valve is unloaded. This will give us the minimum pressure determined by the spring on the hydrostat of 45 to 170 PSI, depending on the valve design and its size.

Assuming that our residual pressure is at a minimum, it sometimes can be isolated from the actuator by a standard check valve with a high cracking pressure. The check valve is simply mounted in the supply line to the actuator, and introduces a 65 to 75 PSI pressure drop requirement before oil can flow towards the actuator.

A better but slightly more expensive way to prevent "creep" is to use an adjustable sequence valve in place of the check valve. The adjustment capability allows the "creep" possibility to be adjusted out of the system, no matter what residual pressure may exist. Another advantage of using the sequence is that the valve will be wide open once set pressure is reached, because its spring chamber is externally drained. This means that less heat would be generated under high flow operation than would be when the check valve is used.

HIGHER EFFICIENCY THROUGH HIGHER PRESSURE

In designing a system to create a certain output power, there are two ways we can get adequate force and speed. Remembering that horsepower is flow times pressure (divided by 1714), we can design our system to operate at low pressure, if we are willing to choose a large enough actuator. Of course, the large actuator requires a higher flow. On the other hand, we can get high speed with less flow when we use a smaller actuator. All that is needed is a higher pressure to get the necessary force. As can be seen in the following examples, the latter is the more efficient choice.

A comparison of the following illustrations shows an energy savings of 4894 BTU/hr., nearly 2 HP, simply because we chose high pressure instead of high flow. Actually, with all things considered, the true energy savings would be con-

siderably more. That is, in low pressure circuits, each time we have a pressure drop across a valve, fitting, or length of pipe, the pressure drop occurs at a higher flow rate (higher horsepower loss) than it does in a high pressure circuit. The saving goes even further.

Although cubic inch for cubic inch, high pressure components are sometimes more expensive than are low pressure components, we must remember that high pressure components, job for job, can often be several frame sizes smaller. Likewise, smaller high pressure components have less area for internal leakage, which considerably increases overall efficiency. If, in our example, we chose a 43 GPM vane or gear pump, we would find that it has an overall efficiency of between 80 to 85 percent. The 5000 PSI piston pump required by the high pressure system would be over 90% in overall efficiency. Since both our circuits are doing work at the rate of 12½ HP, pump selection alone can mean a 2 to 3 horsepower savings.

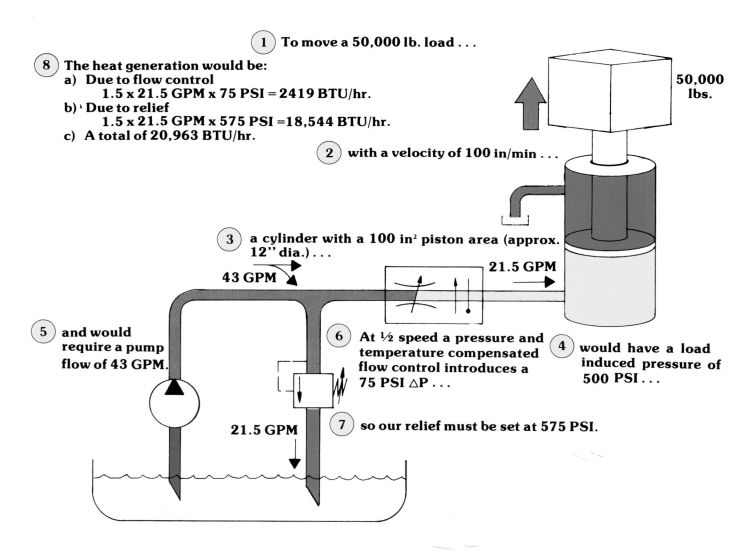

① **To move a 50,000 lb. load . . .**

⑧ **The heat generation would be:**
  a) **Due to flow control**
     1.5 x 21.5 GPM x 75 PSI = 2419 BTU/hr.
  b) **Due to relief**
     1.5 x 21.5 GPM x 575 PSI = 18,544 BTU/hr.
  c) **A total of 20,963 BTU/hr.**

50,000 lbs.

② **with a velocity of 100 in/min . . .**

③ **a cylinder with a 100 in² piston area (approx. 12" dia.) . . .**

43 GPM

21.5 GPM

⑤ **and would require a pump flow of 43 GPM.**

⑥ **At ½ speed a pressure and temperature compensated flow control introduces a 75 PSI △P . . .**

④ **would have a load induced pressure of 500 PSI . . .**

21.5 GPM

⑦ **so our relief must be set at 575 PSI.**

High Flow-Low Pressure Circuit

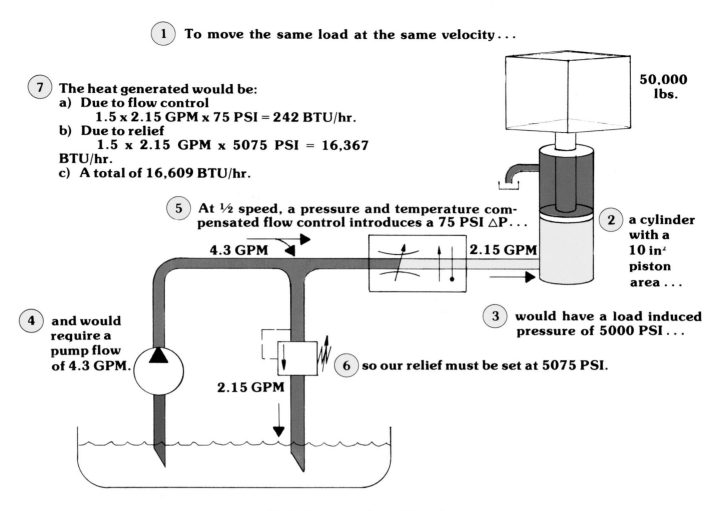

① To move the same load at the same velocity...

50,000 lbs.

⑦ The heat generated would be:
  a) Due to flow control
     1.5 x 2.15 GPM x 75 PSI = 242 BTU/hr.
  b) Due to relief
     1.5 x 2.15 GPM x 5075 PSI = 16,367 BTU/hr.
  c) A total of 16,609 BTU/hr.

⑤ At ½ speed, a pressure and temperature compensated flow control introduces a 75 PSI △P...

4.3 GPM   2.15 GPM

② a cylinder with a 10 in² piston area...

④ and would require a pump flow of 4.3 GPM.

2.15 GPM

③ would have a load induced pressure of 5000 PSI...

⑥ so our relief must be set at 5075 PSI.

High Pressure Low-Flow Circuit

FLOW CONTROLS WHICH CONTROL ACCELERATION AND DECELERATION

In many applications we must avoid abrupt starting and stopping of the mechanical motion we wish to perform. To achieve this type of control, we can make use of a specialized flow control which is called a deceleration valve.

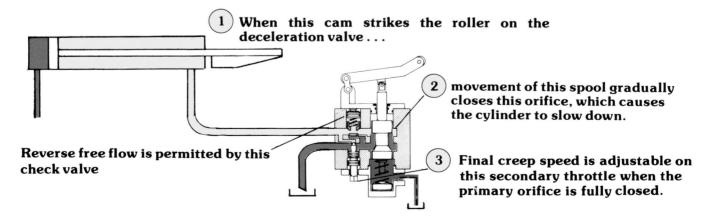

① When this cam strikes the roller on the deceleration valve...

② movement of this spool gradually closes this orifice, which causes the cylinder to slow down.

Reverse free flow is permitted by this check valve

③ Final creep speed is adjustable on this secondary throttle when the primary orifice is fully closed.

Meter-Out Deceleration Valve Application

Deceleration valves are really nothing more than cam operated orifices. The valve is physically mounted close to the work being done, and can be piped into the hydraulic system in either meter-in, meter-out, or a by-pass flow control arrangement. It should be noted, however, that because of the load's inertia, meter-in circuitry with a counterbalance (or brake) valve (Chapter 2) is more often desired, in order to prevent excessive cylinder pressures.

In cylinder circuits, for instance, as the load reaches the end of its travel, a mechanical cam positions the orifice in the deceleration valve to a more restrictive position. The time for the deceleration period is determined by the cam design, the velocity of the cam, and the stroke length as related to metering characteristics of the valve.

As shown in the previous illustration, deceleration valves are usually tapered spools which slide in close fitting bores. Depending on the spool design, a *normally open valve* meters flow as the plunger is depressed, while *normally closed valves* increase their orifice size as the cam depresses the plunger. The choice of normally open or normally closed depends upon the cam design selected.

It is easy to see that proper operation depends on how accurately the cam arrangement positions the orifice. As shown in the illustration, the height of the cam is directly related to actuator speed. Likewise, the time period for deceleration is dependent on three variables, namely: cam velocity, cam angle α, and stroke distance. Needless to say, considerable time and money can be spent in designing the mechanical linkage and proper cam for a specific installation. It becomes even more complicated if adjustable acceleration or deceleration rates are required. Fortunately, deceleration valves can be ordered with adjustment options which can facilitate cam design.

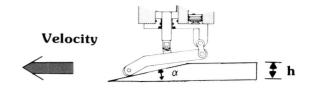

Velocity

This lever multiplies stroking distance by the ratio of 1:3

Variables to be considered in cam design

ADJUSTMENT OPTIONS FOR DECELERATION VALVES

The first option which is extremely important for precise control is the *primary flow adjustment*. A problem arises in selecting a valve size for a particular operation. It can occur that a valve sized large enough for the flow to be handled, is actually large enough to pass considerably more flow in its wide open condition. As the cam strikes the roller, the spool begins closing the orifice. However, because of the relatively low flow through the valve, the initial closing adds little or no resistance to flow. This results in a dead band region, where the cam is depressing the deceleration valve plunger, but nothing happens. The primary flow adjustment allows adjustment of an initial pressure drop without shortening the stroke length of the spool.

As shown in the cross sectional illustration, this design incorporates a hollow spool with rectangular radial opening.

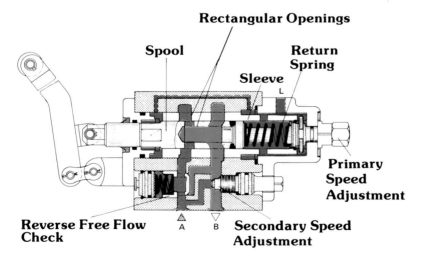

Rectangular Openings

Spool

Return Spring

Sleeve

Primary Speed Adjustment

Reverse Free Flow Check

Secondary Speed Adjustment

Cam Operated Deceleration Valve

The spool slides inside a sleeve, which also has a rectangular opening. In the wide open position of the valve, the rectangular openings are lined up with those in the spool.

Primary flow adjustment is made by rotating the outside sleeves position with respect to the spool.

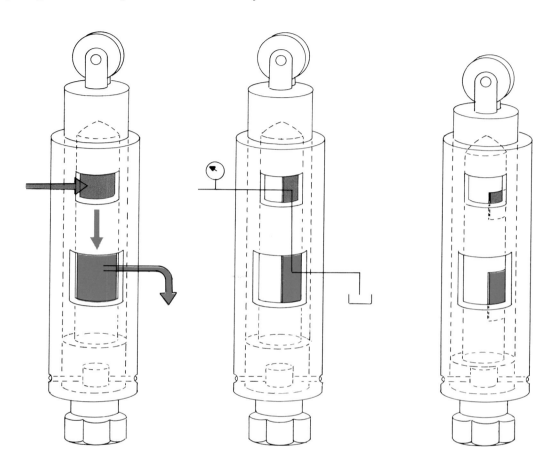

Primary Flow Adjustment

Because we can preset an initial pressure drop, we can cause deceleration to begin with the first movement of the spool. Since the full stroke of the spool causes deceleration to occur, the ramp of the cam is less critical.

We said before that the height of the cam is directly related to actuator speed. Consequently, if you want the actuator to decelerate to some minimum speed rather than to a stop, the height of the cam becomes extremely critical. Likewise, to adjust minimum speed, we would have to be able to adjust the maximum cam height. Fortunately, we can simplify this mechanical arrangement by selecting a deceleration valve with secondary speed adjustment.

The *secondary speed adjustment* is nothing more than a small needle valve mounted in parallel with the deceleration orifice. By incorporating this by-pass needle valve, the cam can always move the deceleration plunger to the fully closed position. The *creep speed* is then set by the by-pass opening allowed by the position of the small needle valve.

HYDRAULIC OPERATED FLOW CONTROLS

The hydraulically operated flow control is unique in its ability to accomplish electrically remote controlled flow, which is immune to pressure and temperature. The valve consists of a standard pressure and temperature compensated flow control, which is modified to accept a hydraulically operated rack and pinion actuator. The control operation is usually via push buttons, by which the operator can increase or decrease speed proportional to the time the button is depressed. The valve can be tuned to meet application requirements by the adjustment of needle valves in the actuator's pilot circuit. Opening and closing times for the main orifice are independently adjustable, from almost instantaneous (.135 seconds), to over one minute. Adjustable stroke limiters are also provided for setting maximum and minimum speed values.

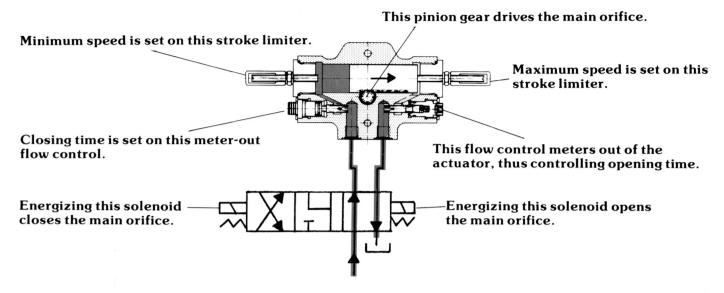

This pinion gear drives the main orifice.

Minimum speed is set on this stroke limiter.

Maximum speed is set on this stroke limiter.

Closing time is set on this meter-out flow control.

This flow control meters out of the actuator, thus controlling opening time.

Energizing this solenoid closes the main orifice.

Energizing this solenoid opens the main orifice.

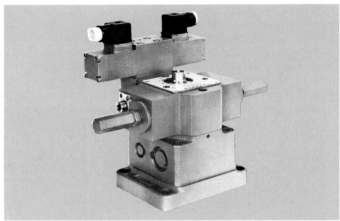

ACCELERATION AND DECELERATION CONTROL WITH THE HYDRAULICALLY OPERATED FLOW CONTROL

The second even more unique application of the hydraulically operated flow control is its ability to achieve all in one compact package, the following; independent acceleration, deceleration, uniform intermediate speed which is pressure and temperature immunized to within ±2% of maximum speed, maximum speed limiter, minimum speed adjustment, or shut-off. To further explain this application, let us consider the following hypothetical situation.

A transfer line is to accelerate its load to uniform speed and then decelerate at the end of the stroke, so that it kisses a mechanical stop. Acceleration and deceleration must be adjustable so that maximum production can be achieved without damaging the load or mechanism.

The optimum cycle is represented in the following illustration:

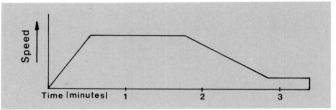

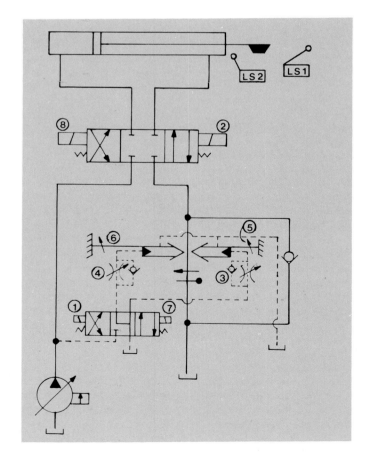

Initially, the flow control is at minimum, and the directional valve is centered. Solenoid 7, which increases speed on the flow control, is energized at the same time that the "advance" solenoid 2 is actuated on the directional valve. The cylinder will accelerate at the rate set on pilot flow control 3. Limit switch #1 is tripped towards the end of the stroke, dropping out solenoid 7 and energizing solenoid 1. This initiates deceleration at the rate set on flow control 4. Maximum speed can be adjusted on stroke limiter 5, while kissing speed is set on stroke limiter 6. The cycle is duplicated in the reverse direction by energizing solenoid 7 with solenoid 8.

Deceleration begins with limit switch #2 in the reverse direction.

The particular advantage that this type of valve offers over cam operated deceleration valves is that mechanical linkage and complicated cam design is replaced simply and compactly by limit switches. Likewise, adjustable acceleration and deceleration rates, which would necessitate a different cam angle in the mechanical system, are easily set on their respective flow controls in the pilot circle.

SYMBOLS

SYMBOL	EXPLANATION
	Non-adjustable orifice, which is not pressure or temperature compensated
	Adjustable, but not pressure or temperature compensated.
	Adjustable orifice with reverse free flow check; not pressure or temperature compensated.
	Dual sandwich flow control, with reverse free flow checks; not pressure or temperature compensated.

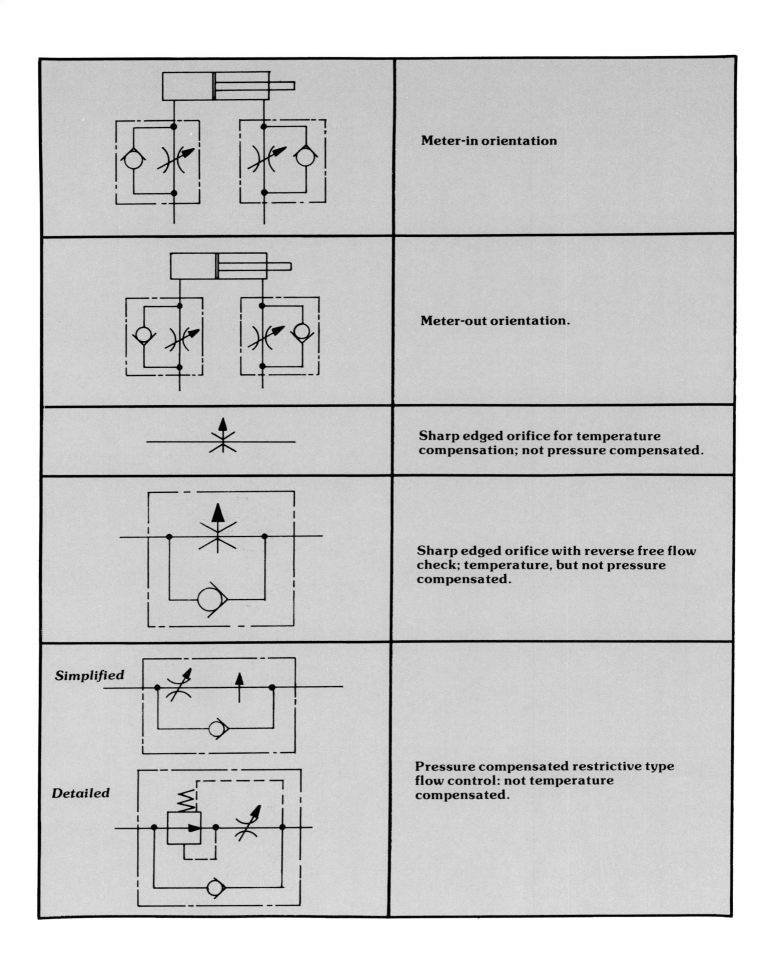

Meter-in orientation

Meter-out orientation.

Sharp edged orifice for temperature compensation; not pressure compensated.

Sharp edged orifice with reverse free flow check; temperature, but not pressure compensated.

Simplified

Detailed

Pressure compensated restrictive type flow control: not temperature compensated.

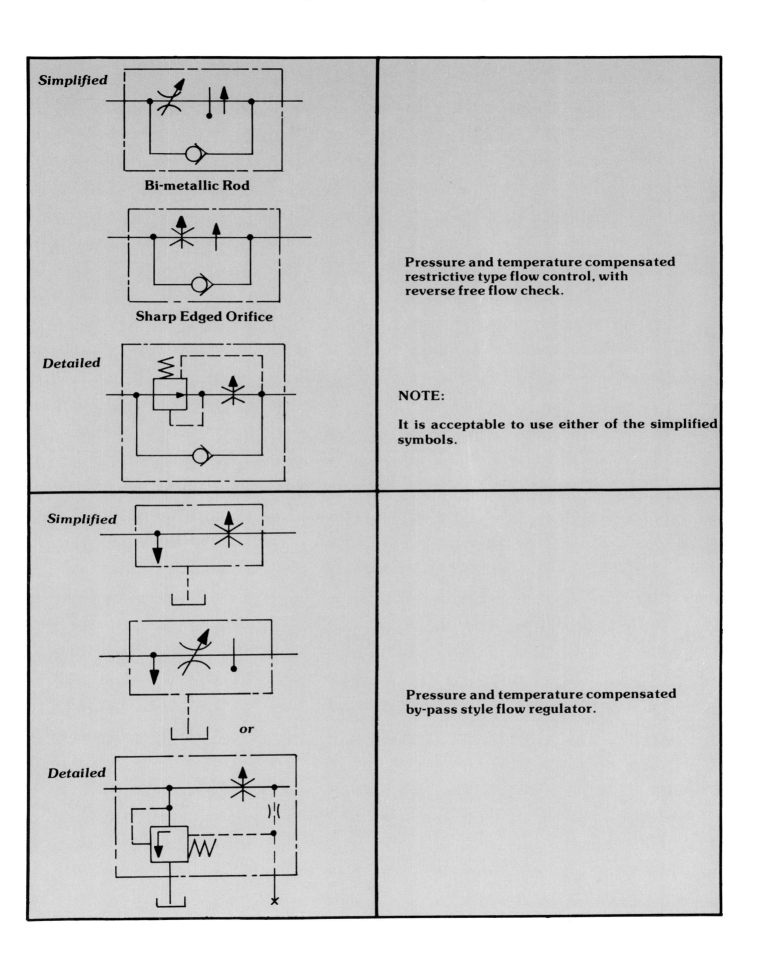

Simplified

Bi-metallic Rod

Sharp Edged Orifice

Detailed

Pressure and temperature compensated restrictive type flow control, with reverse free flow check.

NOTE:

It is acceptable to use either of the simplified symbols.

Simplified

or

Detailed

Pressure and temperature compensated by-pass style flow regulator.

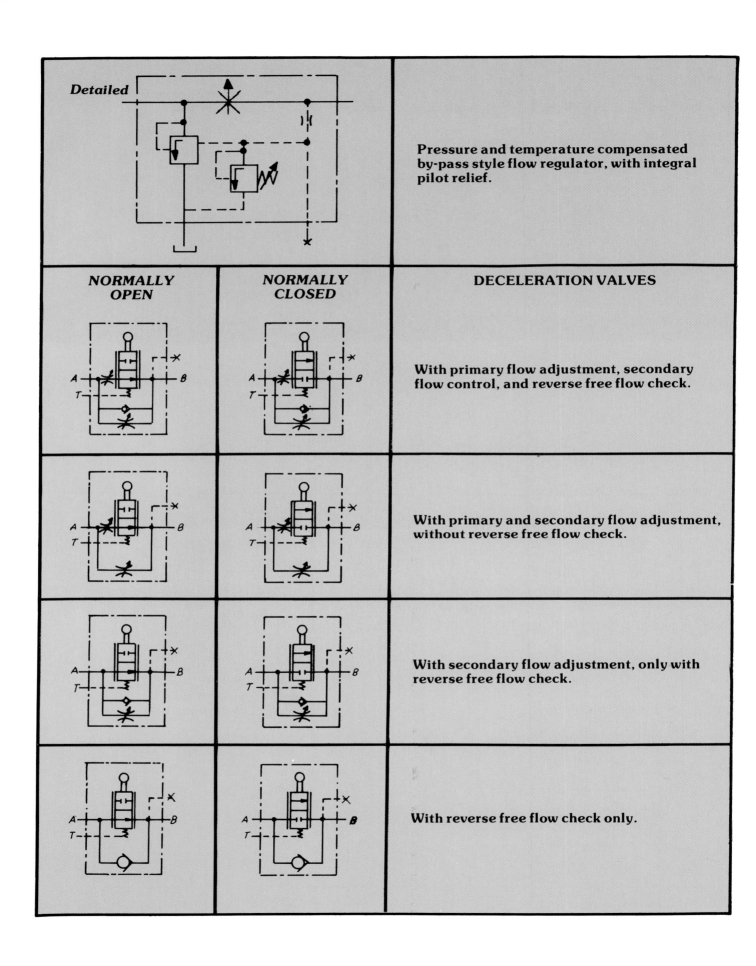

Detailed

Pressure and temperature compensated by-pass style flow regulator, with integral pilot relief.

NORMALLY OPEN	NORMALLY CLOSED	DECELERATION VALVES
		With primary flow adjustment, secondary flow control, and reverse free flow check.
		With primary and secondary flow adjustment, without reverse free flow check.
		With secondary flow adjustment, only with reverse free flow check.
		With reverse free flow check only.

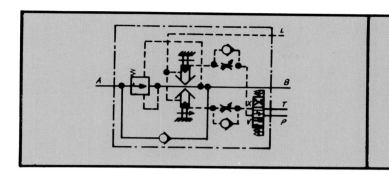

Hydraulically actuated pressure and temperature compensated, restrictive type flow regulator, with reverse free flow check, opening and closing time adjustments, directional control, and maximum and minimum flow limiters.

CONCLUSION

In this chapter, we have covered the construction and operation of various flow control components, along with their applications in various types of installations. A good general knowledge of flow controls and their applications would include an understanding of the following points:

Pressure as resistance to flow.
Non-compensated valves.
Pressure drop across an orifice.
Needle valve.
Reasons for reverse free flow checks.
Adjustment sensitivity.
Sandwich mounting flow controls.
Variables affecting accuracy of speed setting.
Restrictive type pressure compensation.
By-pass type pressure compensation.
Hydrostat.

Anti-lunge adjustment.
Methods of achieving temperature compensation.
Meter-in, and its merits.
Meter-out, and its merits.
By-pass circuits.
Heat generation.
Pressure intensification.
Higher efficiency through higher pressure.
Acceleration and deceleration control.
Symbol terminology.

CHAPTER 4
CHECK VALVES

Check valves are one of the easiest understood components in the hydraulic industry. In fact, in Chapters 2 and 3 we have already mentioned their use, without fully explaining their function. However, we must not let simplicity of a check valve detract, in our minds, from its importance to the hydraulic system. Although check valves are normally used to control the direction of fluid flow, their operation and possible applications are similar to those of a direct operated relief. This chapter will be devoted to an explanation of operation and application possibilities for both check and pilot operated check valves. We will then cover prefill valves and logic elements, which are speciality components related to the basic check valve function.

SIMPLE CHECK VALVE

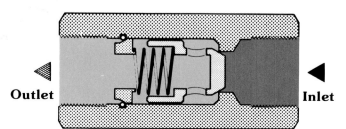

Outlet   **Inlet**

The operating principle of the simple check valve is quite similar to that of the direct operated relief, as discussed in Chapter 2. As shown in the cross-sectional illustration, the check valve consists of a stationary seat, a moveable poppet, and a spring. The valve is closed against flow until pressure at its inlet, working over the exposed area of the poppet, creates sufficient force to overcome the spring. Once the poppet is forced from its seat, the flow of hydraulic fluid is around and through the poppet to the outlet of the valve.

It is interesting to note that the valve remains closed, except when there is sufficient pressure and flow potential at its inlet. For instance, we said in Chapter 1 that the moment flow stops, pressure in all parts of the hydraulic system equalizes under the principle of Pascal's Law. As pressure equalizes, the hydraulic forces on both sides of the poppet are nearly equal. We say nearly, because the valve actually closes when pressure at its outlet, plus spring force, equals inlet pressure. In actual application in a static system, the pressure at the outlet is lower than the inlet pressure, in the amount equal to the cracking pressure of the valve.

Ideally, this means that we can capture a pressurized column of fluid between a stalled actuator and a check valve. Of course, we must assume that the cylinder is perfectly rigid when stalled. We must also assume that there is no leakage in either the actuator or the valve itself.

In addition to being similar in operation to a relief valve, a check valve can also be used to control the direction of flow. You can see that the example (page 4-2) would have little practical use, because the check valve would never allow the return of the cylinder's piston. Actually, the more we tried to force oil backward through the check valve, the harder we would press the poppet into its seat. In the hydraulic industry, when we refer to this non-return feature, we call it *checking* reverse flow.

SEALING ABILITY FOR A CHECK VALVE

The advantage of a check or pilot operated check valve is its poppet and seat design, which offers the only sure way to prevent crossport valve leakage in the hydraulic system. Most hydraulic check valves are designed with a metal to metal contact between the poppet and its seat. Likewise, the

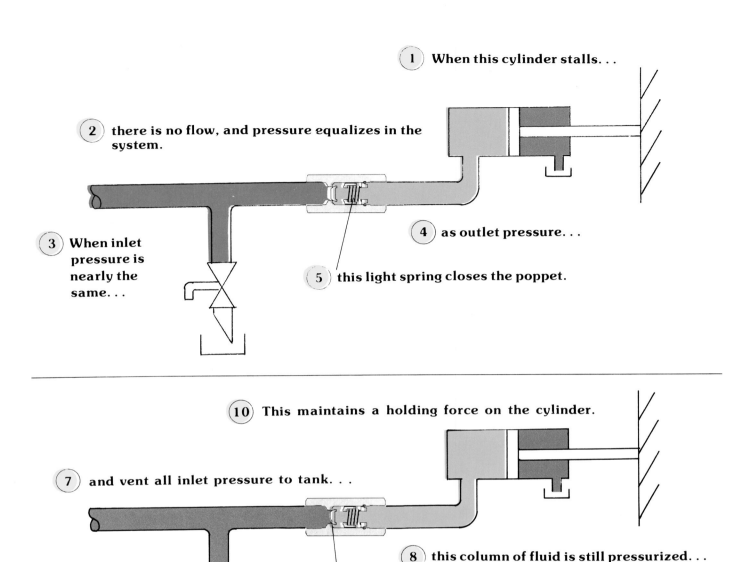

① When this cylinder stalls . . .

② there is no flow, and pressure equalizes in the system.

③ When inlet pressure is nearly the same . . .

④ as outlet pressure . . .

⑤ this light spring closes the poppet.

⑩ This maintains a holding force on the cylinder.

⑦ and vent all inlet pressure to tank . . .

⑧ this column of fluid is still pressurized . . .

⑥ Then, if we open this valve . . .

⑨ while this poppet remains closed.

poppet is usually considerably harder than its respective seat. In the closed position, hydraulic pressure forces the poppet into the seat, thus forcing the seat to assume the exact contour of the poppet nose. This guarantees a metal to metal contact around the full circumferential contact area, virtually eliminating the possibility of leakage.

DESIGN VARIATIONS

The basic check valve, like the direct operated relief, is available in ball, poppet, or guided poppet designs. However, since check valves incorporate a relatively weak spring, they cannot produce the same high performance characteristics as a relief nor are they intended to do so. For this reason, we normally are not too concerned with the stability or pressure override characteristics of a check valve. Nevertheless, there are two reasons why a guided poppet check valve is usually preferred.

The first reason is that guided poppet designs have a considerably longer life expectancy. This is true because the poppet always contacts the seat squarely, and in the same position. By protecting the contact area in this manner, the leak-free life of the valve is greatly extended. Likewise, most guided poppet designs limit the stroke of the poppet. This, of course, prevents over-stressing and breaking the spring.

The second reason for choosing a guided poppet check becomes apparent when the valve is subjected to high flow rates. In the unguided models, the high flow rate causes the ball or poppet to chatter in the flow stream, creating a source of noise in the hydraulic system. This does not occur in the guided poppet design.

CRACKING PRESSURES

We said earlier that the basic difference between a check valve and a direct operated relief is the strength of the spring. Another difference is that the spring force in a simple check valve is not adjustable. Nevertheless, the application possibilities of check valves can be greatly extended through the selection of any of three basic spring options. The first option is the standard spring; the second is the choice of a check valve from a group which has any number of higher cracking pressures; the third option is to have no spring at all. Let us now look at the application possibilities of each type.

STANDARD CRACKING PRESSURE

Standard check valves are supplied with a spring which allows the valve to crack in the 5 to 10 PSI range. Actually, the only purpose of the spring is to assure positive closing, while allowing the valve to be mounted in any position. Valves with light springs are used in hydraulic systems to rectify flow. For instance, as mentioned in previous chapters, they can be used as reverse free flow checks when they are piped in parallel to a flow or a pressure control.

HIGHER CRACKING PRESSURES

Most check valves can be obtained with stronger springs for higher cracking pressures. This offers an inexpensive way to accomplish some pressure control functions. Normally, three or four spring options are offered, with the highest cracking pressure being in the neighborhood of 75 PSI. Of course, check valves with high cracking pressures can simulate some sequences or relief valve functions. Typical applications of the check valve include its use in maintaining pilot pressure for pilot operated directional controls (See Chapter 5), and its use as a safety bypass for return line heat exchangers or filters.

When the check valve is used as a relief type bypass,

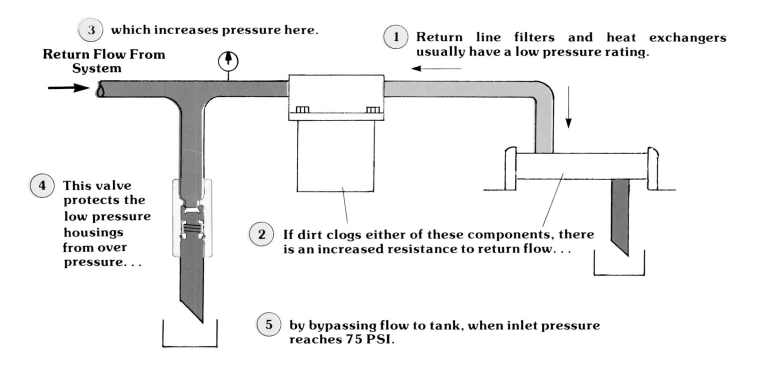

3) which increases pressure here.

Return Flow From System

1) Return line filters and heat exchangers usually have a low pressure rating.

4) This valve protects the low pressure housings from over pressure...

2) If dirt clogs either of these components, there is an increased resistance to return flow...

5) by bypassing flow to tank, when inlet pressure reaches 75 PSI.

precaution must be taken in checking the valves pressure versus flow characteristics, and sizing the component accordingly. For instance, a check valve which cracks at 75 PSI may provide a 150 PSI resistance to flow when passing 10 GPM. This, of course, could damage a heat exchanger, if it had a shell pressure rating of 100 PSI.

NO SPRING VERSIONS

The third option is to obtain a check valve with no spring at all. The use of these valves, however, should be limited to applications where the check valve function is required, with an absolute minimum resistance to flow in the free flow direction. A foot valve for facilitating pump priming, although not required for most hydraulic pumps, is a typical application.

(2) **The pump can be initially primed by filling the inlet with oil. . .**

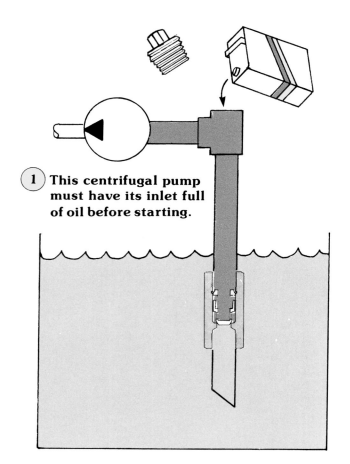

(1) **This centrifugal pump must have its inlet full of oil before starting.**

(3) **since this foot valve prevents the column of oil from falling.**

If your system requires the use of a check valve without a spring, the valve should be mounted with its outlet vertical and upward. When it is mounted this way, gravity will assist in closing the poppet. Needless to say, if it is mounted in any other position, the only available closing force would be that of the dynamic flow of fluid. It is possible that the valve would remain open if it were subjected to relatively low reverse flow rates, especially if the inlet were to be mounted vertically and upward.

MOUNTED CONFIGURATIONS

Line Mounted

Check valves and pilot operated checks are available with in-line threaded connections up to 1½" line sizes. Above 1½", they are supplied with flanged connections for pipe sizes up to 6". Usually, line mounted valves are stamped with an arrow on their housing which indicates the direction of *free flow*.

Subplate Mounted

For service convenience, or for custom manifolding, the

check valve unit can also be supplied in a housing for use in subplate mounting. Subplate mounted valves up to 1½" are available with mounting configurations which conform to ANSI/NFPA and International Standard interfaces. Above 1½" the valves are designed specifically for custom manifolding since there are no standard interfaces for the larger valve sizes. Also, for simplified installation, check valves are available in sandwich housings for mounting between the directional control valve and its subplate. These sandwich units can be supplied with check functions in one or more of the port connections to the directional control valve, with either direction of free flow.

CARTRIDGE UNITS

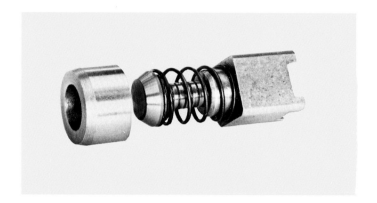

Right Angle Cartridge

Inline Cartridge

In addition to inline, subplate, and sandwich mounted valves, cartridge units are available for installation internally in custom manifold blocks. The cartridges are supplied with seat, poppet, and spring in two configurations. These two different cartridges are available for design convenience, with one style for use in an inline passage, and the second style for use in passages which meet at right angles.

PILOT OPERATED CHECK VALVES

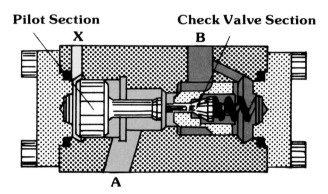

Pilot Section   **Check Valve Section**

X   B

A

The pilot operated check performs the same function as the simple check valve in that it allows free flow in one direction and *checks* reverse flow. Like the simple check, it can also be supplied with different springs for various cracking pressures. In contrast to the simple check, however, a pilot operated check can be piloted open when a reverse flow is required.

As shown in the illustration, the valve has two distinct sections: the check valve section and the pilot section. The check valve allows free flow from port A to port B, while checking flow from B to A, sealing without leakage. When it is necessary to allow a flow from port B to port A, the valve can be piloted open by supplying a pilot pressure signal at port "X". Pilot pressure works over the area of the pilot piston, and forces the piston rod against the check valve poppet. This unseats the poppet, allowing free flow from port B to port A.

PILOT RATIO

In working with pilot operated check valves, you will have to consider the pilot ratio of the valve. The pilot ratio is

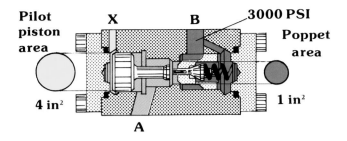

Pilot piston area **4 in²** X B **3000 PSI** Poppet area **1 in²** A

basically a comparison of the effective area of the pilot piston with the effective area of the check valve poppet, which is being pressurized by the system. When you are estimating the pilot pressure needed to open the valve, remember that the pressure at port X is simply the pressure at port B divided by the pilot ratio. In our example, the pilot pressure requirements would be:

$$P_p = \frac{3000 \text{ PSI}}{4} = 750 \text{ PSI}$$

It must be mentioned that the above formula can only be used to estimate pilot pressure conditions. As will be shown later, the pilot pressure requirements are closely related to the actual application in which the valve is used. It is important that pilot pressure not only be sufficient to open the valve fully, but also to keep it open during the required portion of the cycle. However, we will postpone further discussion of pilot pressure requirements in the system until we introduce two other important construction details.

DECOMPRESSION FEATURE

In order to determine the pilot pressure requirements of the valve more accurately, we can first total up all the forces which tend to close the poppet. In the same manner, we can also add up any constant forces which aid in opening the poppet. Then, by assuming that the closing forces are greater than the opening forces, we can subtract the one from the other, and determine the additional opening force required by the pilot piston. By distributing this force over the area of the pilot piston, we then determine the pilot pressure requirements.

Although there are other forces which tend to close the main poppet, the major closing force is caused by pressure at port B, exposed over the effective area of the main poppet. In some applications, such as in press circuits, the pilot pressure requirements can be reduced by bleeding off pressure behind the main poppet before opening the main flow path. This loss of pressure before opening is referred to as *decompression* and can easily be accomplished by using a valve with a two stage poppet.

A two stage poppet is nothing more than a smaller *decompression poppet* built into the main poppet. It takes considerably less force to open this decompression poppet, since it has less effective area exposed to the pressure at port B. As will be shown in our discussion of pilot operated check valve applications, the decompression feature is quite important when it is necessary to release the stored potential energy in a pressurized volume of fluid.

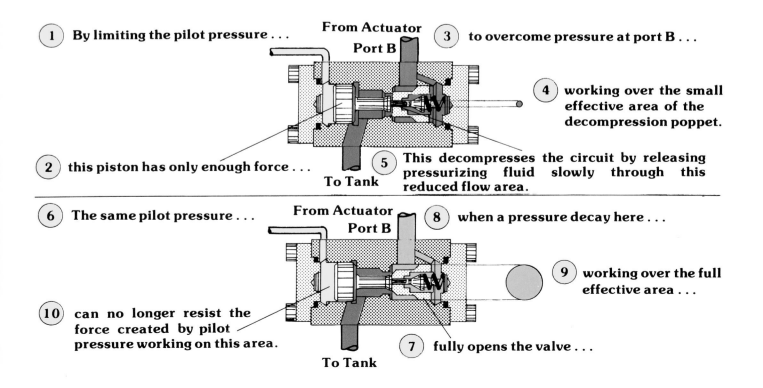

1 By limiting the pilot pressure . . .

From Actuator Port B

3 to overcome pressure at port B . . .

4 working over the small effective area of the decompression poppet.

2 this piston has only enough force . . .

5 This decompresses the circuit by releasing pressurizing fluid slowly through this reduced flow area.

To Tank

6 The same pilot pressure . . .

From Actuator Port B

8 when a pressure decay here . . .

9 working over the full effective area . . .

10 can no longer resist the force created by pilot pressure working on this area.

7 fully opens the valve . . .

To Tank

PILOT OPERATED CHECKS WITH INTERNAL DRAINS

Up to this point, we have discussed pilot operated checks which have the rod end of their pilot piston connected internally to the A port of the main valve. Since the rod end side of the pilot piston is exposed to the A port, pressure in this passage influences the pilot pressure requirements of the valve. Actually, this pressure works on an effective area which can be calculated as if the pilot piston had a rod equivalent in diameter to that of the main poppet, as long as the main poppet is seated. You can see that pressure in the A port not only works against the ring area of the pilot piston, but also on the end of the piston rod. This force to the left is partially offset, however, because of an equal pressure working on the nose area of the main poppet to the right. Consequently, the net effective area which opposes valve opening is the ring area, which has an inside diameter the same as the main poppet diameter, and the outside diameter of the pilot piston.

When we study the illustration, we will have enough information to determine more accurately the pilot pressure requirements for internally drained valves. We can do this simply by comparing opening forces to closing forces, with the following formula:

Opening forces must equal closing forces
$$\textbf{or } P_p (A_3) = P_B (A_1) + P_A (A_3 - A_1) + C_1$$

The C_1 in the formula takes into account the closing force due to the spring, plus any frictional forces which must be overcome in opening the valve. Mathematically, this formula reduces to:

$$P_p = \frac{P_B - P_A}{\textbf{Area Ratio}} + P_A + C$$

Since C differs for different valves, this constant factor is usually given by the valve manufacturer. If no value is available, it is usually safe to assume that C is equal to or less than 75 PSI.

We said earlier that the area ratio of the pilot operated check valve is the comparison of the area of the pilot piston to the area of the check valve main poppet. For valves with two stage decompression poppets, the increased ratio of the pilot piston to decompression poppet can be used only if the circuit allows a decay in B port pressure once the decompression poppet opens.

In actual application, internally drained pilot operated check valves must have the A port connected directly to tank when

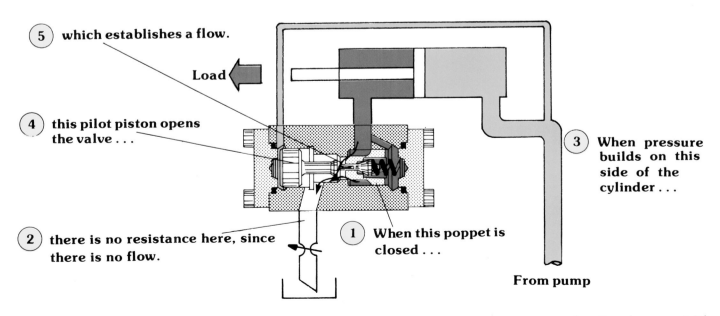

③ and increases the pilot pressure requirement of the valve.

P_p P_b

② works against this effective area . . .

P_a A_3

A Port A_1

① Back pressure in this port . . .

⑤ which establishes a flow.

Load

④ this pilot piston opens the valve . . .

② there is no resistance here, since there is no flow.

① When this poppet is closed . . .

③ When pressure builds on this side of the cylinder . . .

From pump

(continued on page 4-8)

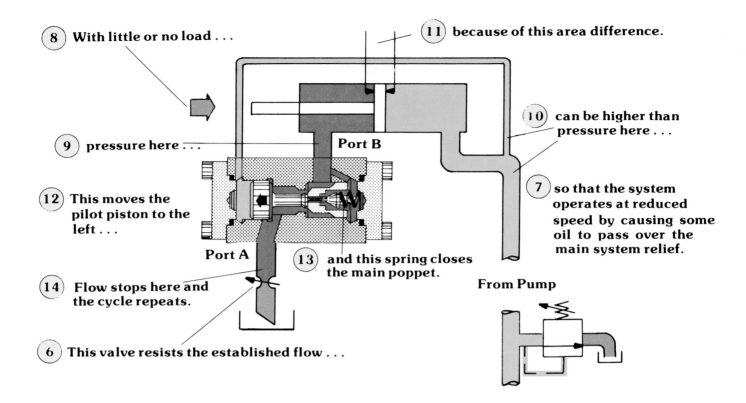

(8) **With little or no load . . .**

(11) **because of this area difference.**

(9) **pressure here . . .**

Port B

(10) **can be higher than pressure here . . .**

(12) **This moves the pilot piston to the left . . .**

(7) **so that the system operates at reduced speed by causing some oil to pass over the main system relief.**

Port A

(13) **and this spring closes the main poppet.**

(14) **Flow stops here and the cycle repeats.**

From Pump

(6) **This valve resists the established flow . . .**

---

operating in the piloted open condition. If, for instance, we back pressured the A port with a meter-out flow control, the check valve could open and close erratically as the cylinder was extended. This, of course, would cause the actuator to stop and start with an undesirable jerky motion.

You can see from the two examples that the circuit will oscillate automatically between the open and closed positions of the pilot operated check. To avoid this complication, we must place the flow control on the B side of the valve, or use an externally drained pilot operated check.

PILOT OPERATED CHECKS WITH EXTERNAL DRAINS

The external pilot drain is a simple conversion, or in some cases, a modification to the standard pilot operated check. As shown in the operational cross section, the rod end of the pilot piston is isolated from the A port, and given its own separate connection. Because of this, the operation of the pilot piston is identical to that of a double acting hydraulic cylinder.

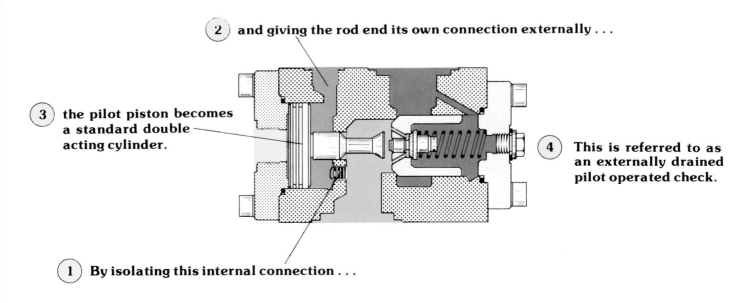

(2) **and giving the rod end its own connection externally . . .**

(3) **the pilot piston becomes a standard double acting cylinder.**

(4) **This is referred to as an externally drained pilot operated check.**

(1) **By isolating this internal connection . . .**

In many applications, proper operation is obtained simply by draining the rod end of the pilot cylinder to the tank separately. Being isolated from the pilot piston, the A port can now be pressurized by using a flow control or counterbalance valve. The pilot piston is spring returned to the closed position when pilot pressure is released, and the spring closes the check valve poppet.

In some applications, however, accelerated closing can be achieved by connecting a 4-way directional control to the X and L ports of the pilot section. In powering the pilot cylinder to its retracted position, more force is available to displace the oil which must be moved out of the pilot cylinder's blind end. However, this method of pilot operation can only be used with valves which can accept an operating pressure on their drain port.

The operational illustration shows that the pilot piston is hydraulically moved out of the path of the main poppet, so that full spring force is available for closing the valve. This should not be confused with a pilot to close check valves.

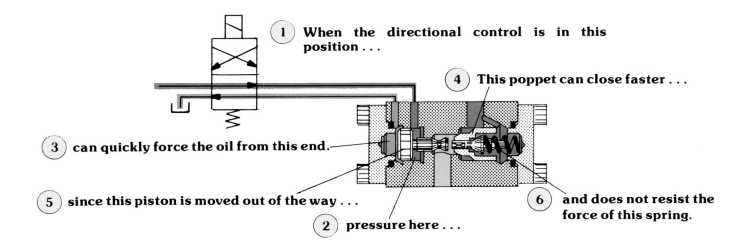

1. When the directional control is in this position . . .

4. This poppet can close faster . . .

3. can quickly force the oil from this end.

5. since this piston is moved out of the way . . .

2. pressure here . . .

6. and does not resist the force of this spring.

CALCULATING PILOT PRESSURE FOR EXTERNALLY DRAINED VALVES

In determining the pilot pressure requirements for an externally drained valve, we find that residual pressure in the A port actually helps open the valve. Assuming a negligible pressure in the L port during valve opening, the pilot pressure formula for externally drained valves becomes:

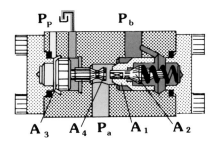

P_p P_b

A_3 A_4 P_a A_1 A_2

Opening Forces   **Must Equal Closing Forces**

$$P_p (A_3) + P_a (A_1) = P_b (A_1) + P_a (A_4) + C_1$$

Mathematically, this reduces to:

$$P_p = \frac{P_b (A_1) + P_a (A_4 - A_1)}{A_3} + C$$

or

$$P_p = \frac{P_b - P_a}{\text{Area Ratio}} + P_a \frac{A_4}{A_3} + C$$

As in the internally drained model, C is a constant factor which usually can be assumed to be 75 PSI. Also, the area of the decompression poppet can be used in determining the pilot ratio, only if a decay in pressure occurs at port B after opening the decompression poppet.

APPLICATIONS OF PILOT OPERATED CHECK VALVES

Basically, the pilot operated check valve is used in a hydraulic circuit to perform one of two basic functions. In

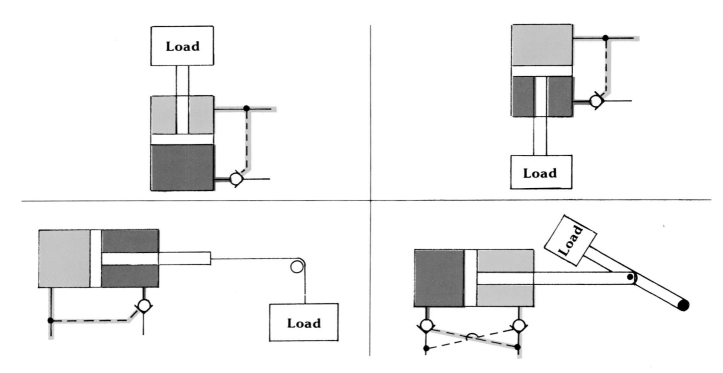

Possible Load Conditions Which Require a Pilot Operated Check for Positive Holding

either case, the intended operation depends on its use with a high quality hydraulic cylinder with leak free piston sealing. Let us now consider the pilot operated check valve in each of its two basic applications: in load holding, and in decompression type hydraulic press circuits.

LOAD HOLDING APPLICATIONS

The pilot operated check valve is the only sure way to hydraulically lock a suspended load in position. Although this load condition can occur in a multitude of applications, in our discussion we will use a vertical down acting cylinder. We have chosen this application because of a dangerous possibility peculiar to it.

The following example is a typical down acting vertical cylinder application of load holding, with a pilot operated check valve. With this particular orientation, it is somewhat difficult to determine the pilot pressure required to open the pilot operated check. Let us now take a closer look.

In this example, as long as there is no pressure on top of the piston, the load induced pressure on the B port is 3000 PSI. The A port is at atmospheric pressure, since it is connected directly to tank. When we use our pilot pressure formula for internally drained valves, we will find that we must use the area ratio, which is determined by comparing the area of the pilot piston to the full areas of the main poppet. To assure full opening of the valve, we cannot use the area of the

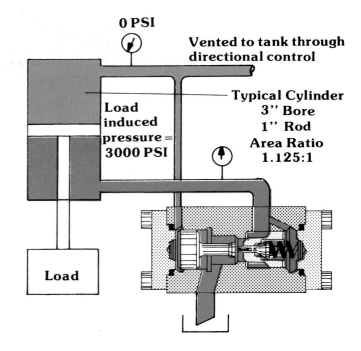

0 PSI

Vented to tank through directional control

Load induced pressure = 3000 PSI

Typical Cylinder
3" Bore
1" Rod
Area Ratio
1.125:1

Load

decompression poppet, since load induced pressure would not decay once the first stage poppet opened. That is, if we only supplied enough pilot pressure to open the decompression poppet, the load would move downward only at the rate oil could flow through the small decompression flow area, at a pressure drop of 3000 PSI. Throughout the stroke of the cylinder, 3000 PSI load induced pressure would be

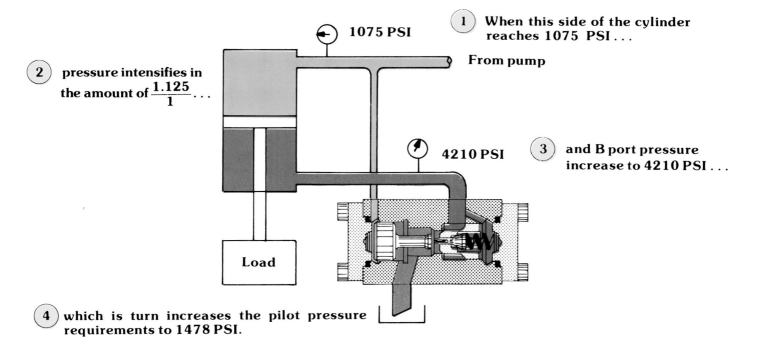

1 When this side of the cylinder reaches 1075 PSI . . .

1075 PSI

From pump

2 pressure intensifies in the amount of $\frac{1.125}{1}$ . . .

4210 PSI

3 and B port pressure increase to 4210 PSI . . .

Load

4 which is turn increases the pilot pressure requirements to 1478 PSI.

maintained behind the main poppet. Consequently, to assure full opening, we must use the full area of the main poppet. In our example, let us assume the pilot ratio is 3:1, so that our pilot pressure calculation will be as follows:

$$P_p = \frac{3000\,PSI - 0\,PSI}{3} + 0\,PSI + 75\,PSI = 1075\,PSI$$

Our typical circuit is designed so that when we want to move the load downward, pump flow will be directed to the top of the cylinder, and to the X port of the pilot operated check. Initially, the load will not move, since pressure on top of the cylinder piston will not be high enough to pilot open the check valve. However, since the supply oil has nowhere to go, pressure will build rapidly both on the blind end of the cylinder and the X port of the valve. We will find, however, that the load still will not move when pressure on top of the cylinder reaches 1075 PSI, or the pressure level at which the check valve was supposed to open.

On closer examination, we will see that as pressure is being developed on the pilot port of the check valve, it is also increasing on the B port of the valve. If we looked at the pressures in the system, just before the 1075 PSI pilot pressure was reached, we would find that, due to intensification of pressure across the main cylinder, B port pressure has increased to:

$$3000\,PSI + 1075\,PSI\,(\frac{1.125}{1}) = 4209\,PSI$$

If we then recalculate the pilot pressure requirements, we find:

$$P_p = \frac{4209\,PSI}{3} + 75\,PSI = 1478\,PSI$$

By the time we reach a pilot pressure of 1478 PSI, the B port pressure would increase the pilot pressure requirements even further.

At first glance, it appears as if we have a condition in which the pilot operated check valve will never open. Nevertheless, if we successively calculate pilot pressure, and its effect on pressure at the B port, we will find that we eventually reach a point of equilibrium. What happens is that for each increase in pressure the force caused by the pilot section of the check increases more than the force caused by the pressure intensification of the cylinder. This is true because the pilot section has the larger area ratio. To avoid lengthy calculations, we can determine the point at which the valve will open by using the following formula:

With No Pressure at Valve A Port

$$P_p = \frac{\frac{LP}{AR_v} + C}{(1 - \frac{AR_c}{AR_v})} = \frac{\frac{3000}{3} + 75}{(1 - \frac{1.125}{3})} = 1720\,PSI$$

With a Residual Pressure at the A Port of the Valve

$$P_p = \dfrac{\dfrac{LP - P_a}{AR_v} + P_a + C}{\left(1 - \dfrac{AR_c}{AR_v}\right)}$$

Where:

P_p = Pilot pressure required (PSI)
LP = Load-induced pressure (PSI)
AR_v = Pilot piston to main poppet area ratio of the pilot operated check.
AR_c = Blind end to rod end area ratio of the cylinder.
C = Constant factor of pilot operated check (PSI)
P_a = Residual pressure at A port of the valve (PSI)

Once the pilot pressure point at which the valve opens has been determined, it will be necessary to check the pressure at the B port just before the valve opens. In many cases, you may find that it considerably exceeds the pressure rating of the components you initially intended to use. For example:

$$P_b = L.P. + P_p (AR_c)$$

$$P_b = 3000\ PSI + 1720\ PSI \left(\dfrac{1.125}{1}\right)$$

$$P_b = 4935\ PSI$$

Where

P_p = Calculated pilot pressure (PSI)
P_b = B Port pressure (PSI)
LP = Load induced pressure (PSI)
AR_c = Blind end to rod end area ratio of cylinder.

In our example, it looked, at first, as if 3000 PSI components would adequately handle the job. Nevertheless, our pressure calculation indicated that 5000 PSI components were required. If, however, pressures are calculated to be in excess of readily available components, several options are left open. First, we can choose a pilot operated check valve with a larger pilot piston to maintain poppet ratio. Or, second, we can select a cylinder with a smaller area ratio. Also, by selecting a large cylinder bore, we can reduce the required

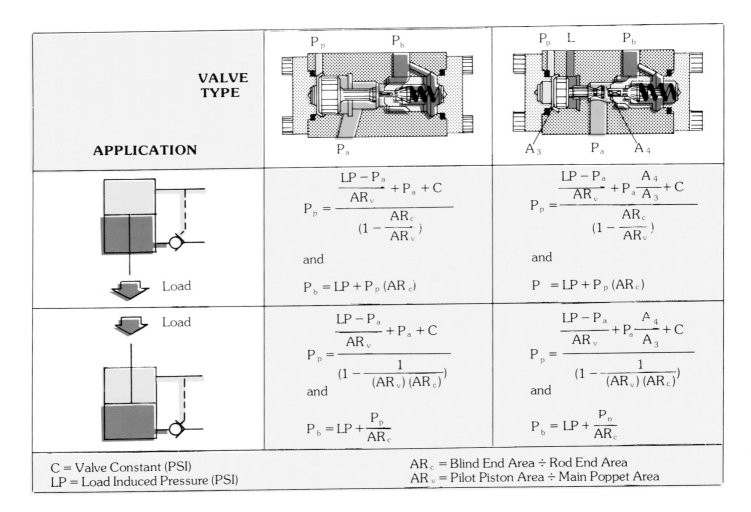

VALVE TYPE APPLICATION		
 (Load, down) ↓ Load	$P_p = \dfrac{\dfrac{LP - P_a}{AR_v} + P_a + C}{\left(1 - \dfrac{AR_c}{AR_v}\right)}$ and $P_b = LP + P_p (AR_c)$	$P_p = \dfrac{\dfrac{LP - P_a}{AR_v} + P_a \dfrac{A_4}{A_3} + C}{\left(1 - \dfrac{AR_c}{AR_v}\right)}$ and $P = LP + P_p (AR_c)$
↓ Load	$P_p = \dfrac{\dfrac{LP - P_a}{AR_v} + P_a + C}{\left(1 - \dfrac{1}{(AR_v)(AR_c)}\right)}$ and $P_b = LP + \dfrac{P_p}{AR_c}$	$P_p = \dfrac{\dfrac{LP - P_a}{AR_v} + P_a \dfrac{A_4}{A_3} + C}{\left(1 - \dfrac{1}{(AR_v)(AR_c)}\right)}$ and $P_b = LP + \dfrac{P_p}{AR_c}$

C = Valve Constant (PSI)
LP = Load Induced Pressure (PSI)

AR_c = Blind End Area ÷ Rod End Area
AR_v = Pilot Piston Area ÷ Main Poppet Area

load induced pressure.

The condition described also occurs when we use a pilot operated check valve on the blind end of a hydraulic cylinder. However, under these conditions, the area ratio of the cylinder works with, rather than against, the valve opening. At this point, we will avoid lengthy discussions of internally drained valves used on the blind end, or of externally drained valves used on the rod end or the blind end of a cylinder. We will simply list the formulas for each, and let the reader come to his own decisions by working through each application according to the previously described process.

PREVENTING CYLINDER CHATTER

In load holding applications, the fact that we need a pilot operated check also indicates that we must prevent the load from overrunning. Unfortunately, a pilot operated check valve opens at the required pressure and closes the moment pilot pressure is lost. The valve has no means of modulating a flow orifice to prevent the load from free falling. If some method of preventing the load from running ahead of the pump supply is not provided, the valve will open and close erratically as the load is lowered.

In order to overcome this problem, load holding pilot operated check applications should always incorporate either a counterbalance valve (Chapter 2), or a meter-out flow control (Chapter 3). Remember, with an internally drained pilot operated check valve, the resistance to flow must be added upstream of the valve's B port. Likewise, with a remotely piloted or externally drained counterbalance valve, the valve must be used downstream of an externally drained pilot operated check. If it is used between the ac-

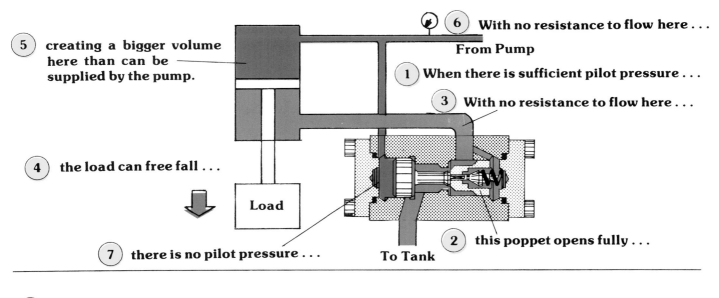

⑤ creating a bigger volume here than can be supplied by the pump.

⑥ With no resistance to flow here . . .

From Pump

① When there is sufficient pilot pressure . . .

③ With no resistance to flow here . . .

④ the load can free fall . . .

Load

② this poppet opens fully . . .

⑦ there is no pilot pressure . . .

To Tank

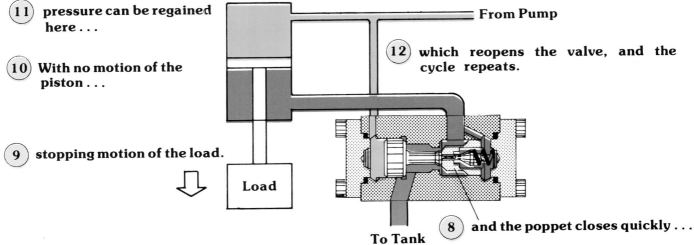

⑪ pressure can be regained here . . .

From Pump

⑩ With no motion of the piston . . .

⑫ which reopens the valve, and the cycle repeats.

⑨ stopping motion of the load.

Load

⑧ and the poppet closes quickly . . .

To Tank

tuator and a pilot operated check, there would be a leakage path to tank (Y port) or to the opposite side of the actuator (X port), which would allow the load to drift.

VENTING THE X PORT

Although the directional control will be discussed in detail in Chapter 5, we must mention it at this point, since it plays a very important part in the proper operation of any pilot operated check valve. More often than not, pilot operated checks are used with three position directional controls. For the purposes of this chapter, it is sufficient to say that a three position valve can select from three different combinations of flow paths. In one position, pump flow is directed to the blind end of the cylinder while, at the same time, the rod end is connected to tank through the directional control. This, of course, causes the cylinder to extend. In another position, the cylinder retracts, when pump flow is directed to the rod end, while the blind end of the cylinder is connected to tank. The third position positively locks the load in a given position when a pilot operated check is used between the directional control and the cylinder.

This third position is normally referred to as the *center position*. When you are selecting a directional control, there will be a multitude of center position flow paths from which

you can choose. However, only a few of them are suitable for use with pilot operated checks. The reason is that the directional control must, at the very least, vent the X port to tank in its center position. This will allow pilot oil to escape from the blind end of the pilot piston, so that the piston can return from its previously open position. The main poppet can then close, preventing drifting of the load due to gravity.

When a pilot operated check is used with the wrong directional control, the load may sometimes drift upward against gravity. This happens when a leakage path is established from the high pressure pump circuit, across the directional valve, through the free flow direction of the pilot operated check valve, to the actuator. To prevent this possibility, we suggest that you select a directional control which also vents the A port of the pilot operated check in the load holding position. With both the X and the A port vented, load holding is assured by the free movement of the main poppet.

THERMAL EXPANSION AND PILOT OPERATED CHECKS

You must be cautious when you use the pilot operated check valve in applications where the actuator is exposed to changes in temperature. Such exposure can take place, for

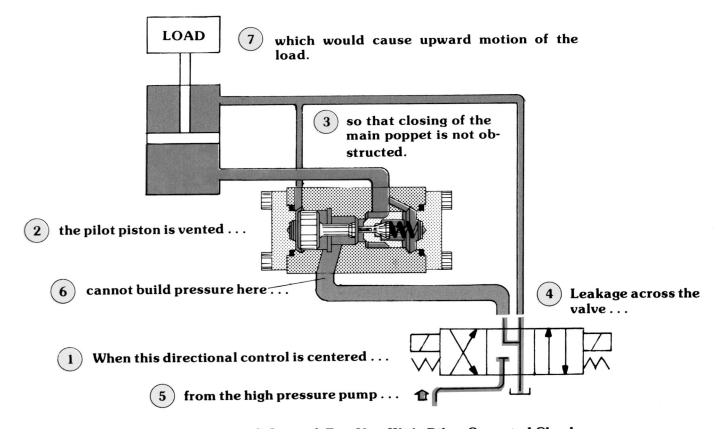

Correct Directional Control For Use With Pilot Operated Checks

example, in mobile equipment sitting idle on a hot summer day, or in industrial cylinders on furnace doors. In these kinds of applications, the increase in ambient temperature causes the hydraulic fluid to warm up. Of course, as the oil is heated, it has a tendency to expand.

The problem is that a pilot operated check seals leak free, leaving no room for expansion in the captive column of fluid. This, in turn, increases the pressure in the fluid to the point where it will move the load in order to provide more room in the actuator for the expanded fluid. Needless to say, if the motion of the load is obstructed, the fluid pressure will simply increase until something breaks.

To avoid damage to either the load or the hydraulic system, because of possible changes in ambient temperatures, it is good practice to install a port relief between the pilot operated check and its actuator. To prevent the load from drifting under normal operating conditions, the relief should be set somewhat higher than maximum load induced pressure, and it should be a leak free direct acting poppet design. Since expansion rates are usually relatively low, a thermal relief normally does not have to relieve high flow rates. Consequently, a ¼" or ½" relief is normally adequate.

SANDWICH MOUNTED DOUBLE PILOT OPERATED CHECK VALVES

Directional Valve

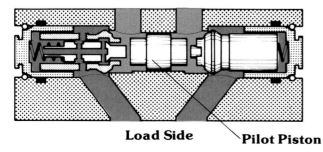

Load Side **Pilot Piston**

As a convenience item, particularly for load holding applications, a dual pilot operated check valve sandwich is available for mounting between the directional control valve and its subplate. As shown in the operational cross section, the valve housing incorporates two check valve assemblies with a single pilot piston common to both.

In the center position of the directional control, both sides of the pilot piston, and the nose area of both check valve poppets, are vented to the tank. The cylinder is positively locked against motion in either direction, since the check valve poppets are close and capture a column of fluid on both ends of the actuator.

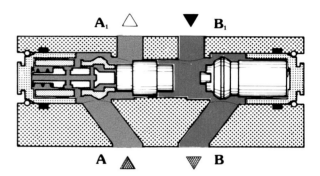

When the directional control valve is shifted into a position, which causes the cylinder to advance or retract, pump flow is directed to either the A_1 or B_1 port of the valve. At the same time, it connects the opposite side of the pilot piston to tank. As shown, pump flow over one of the check valve poppets establishes a flow path to the actuator, while, at the same time, it exposes pressure to the full area of the pilot piston. When sufficient pilot pressure is achieved, the other poppet is piloted open, and the actuator motion begins.

It is important to note that sandwich mounted dual pilot operated check valves are influenced by the same factors that determine pilot pressure requirements and the proper operation of *internally drained* pilot operated check valves. Consequently, the built-in two-stage poppet does not reduce the pilot pressure requirements in load holding applications, but it serves to allow for smoother acceleration of the actuator during opening of the check valve poppet.

USING THE PILOT OPERATED CHECK VALVE FOR DECOMPRESSION

The pilot operated check valve is used quite frequently in press applications as a means of releasing stored energy at the end of a press stroke. Its second purpose is to hold pressure during short cure periods, as already discussed in relation to the simple check valve.

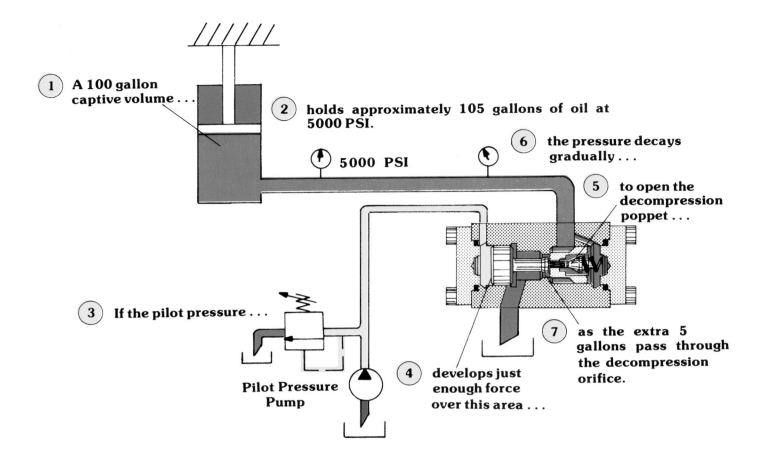

In press applications, a major problem arises from the fact that oil is not perfectly rigid. Actually, for each 1000 PSI increase in pressure, mineral oil reduces its original volume by approximately ½ percent. It takes energy to *move* this oil into a smaller space. Although part of this energy is wasted in the form of heat given off during compression, most of it is stored in the pressurized fluid. This storage of energy is identical in principle to the manner in which potential mechanical energy is stored in a compressed spring.

In actual application, the energy stored is directly proportional to the initial volume of oil and pressure in the system. It is relatively easy to calculate the volume of fluid being held under pressure in the ram. Likewise, we can estimate with reasonable accuracy the volume of fluid in the pipe between the main ram and the pilot operated check. By adding the two volumes, we obtain the final volume of pressurized fluid. Assuming that we know the pressure at which the system will operate, we can now calculate the increase in oil volume obtained as we lower the pressure to atmospheric conditions.

Although mineral oil actually compresses only ½ percent by volume per 1000 PSI, it is safer to estimate this compression at 1% per 1000 PSI. This margin of safety compensates for mechanical stretching of the press frame and aeration of the hydraulic fluid. Needless to say, the more air entrained in the fluid, the more compressible it becomes.

Let us assume that we have calculated the captive volume of fluid in our system, and found that between the piston of the ram and the poppet of the pilot operated check we have a 100 gallon volume of pressurized fluid. Using the 1% figure, there would be an additional 5 gallons of compressed oil in our system at 5000 PSI. Of course, these 5 gallons of pressurized fluid represent stored potential energy. Let us now consider what happens as this energy is released.

In the above example, the stored potential energy in the compressed fluid is released gradually as the 5 gallons are bled through the decompression orifice. If you were to watch a pressure gauge as the decompression poppet was opened, you would see a gradual decay in pressure from 5000 PSI to zero. What is actually happening is that pressure is forcing the compressed fluid to flow across the area of the decompression poppet. The pressure reaches zero the moment the last of the compressed fluid is forced through the orifice. At this point, we could then open the large poppet area and let the rest of the 100 gallons of pressureless fluid return to the tank during retraction of the cylinder.

Needless to say, in this example, the stored potential energy is converted into heat as the 5 gallons flow across the decompression orifice. The amount of heat generated is equivalent to the initial potential energy of the system.

Since the pressure decays while the compressed fluid is

released, the average pressure can be assumed to be 2500 PSI. This means that the initial potential energy was approximately:

$$5 \text{ Gallons} \times \frac{231 \text{ in.}^3}{\text{Gallon}} \times 2500 \frac{\text{lbs.}}{\text{in.}^2} \times \frac{1 \text{ ft.}}{12 \text{ in.}}$$
$$= 240,625 \text{ Ft.-Lbs.}$$

Consequently, the heat generated during decompression is:

$$240,625 \text{ Ft.-Lbs.} \times \frac{1 \text{ BTU}}{778 \text{ Ft.-Lbs.}} = 309 \text{ BTU}$$

You can easily see that some heat is developed as the press circuit decompresses. The fact is that the smaller the decompression orifice, the longer it takes to transform the potential energy. On the other hand, the larger we make the decompression orifice, the faster the potential energy is transformed. The approximate time required for decompression over a prefill valve can be calculated from the following formula:

$$T = \frac{V \sqrt{P}}{A \, (6.3 \times 10^6)}$$

Where:
T = Time (seconds)
V = Total volume of compressed fluid (in^3)
A = Total area of decompression orifice (in^2)
(6.3×10^6) = Conversion constant
P = Initial system pressure (PSI)
(Note: This formula assumes a fluid having a specific gravity of .895 and a bulk modulus of 2.0×10^5 lbs./in.^{2})

Unfortunately, as we make the decompression orifice larger and larger, our system becomes less efficient in its ability to convert potential energy into heat. In our previous example, it would be possible to open the full poppet area of the pilot operated check, assuming we had enough pilot pressure. However, if we were to open this large flow area, there would be little or no resistance to the flow of compressed fluid. Since there would be no orifice, heat could not be generated due to pressure drop. We would then have to ask ourselves, "What happened to the potential energy?"

Under these conditions, the potential energy has the ability to do work. With little resistance, the compressed fluid expands almost instantaneously in the form of an explosion. Since heat is not generated, the full energy level rapidly does work on anything that is in its way downstream of the main poppet in the pilot operated check. Actually, the energy is dissipated in accelerating the oil contained in the pipe, stressing pipes, joints, and hoses, and in noise. At this point, the energy works on the "weakest link in the chain." Since the energy level can be quite high, it is not uncommon to see poorly designed press circuits break pipe joints or hoses downstream of the pilot operated check.

In order to avoid the detrimental effects of decompression, we must allow time for the potential energy to be converted into heat. In addition, we can use a short pipe between the pilot operated check and the tank, so that there is no large oil mass to accelerate. In this way, the oil column becomes the weakest link, and prevents overstressing of the piping.

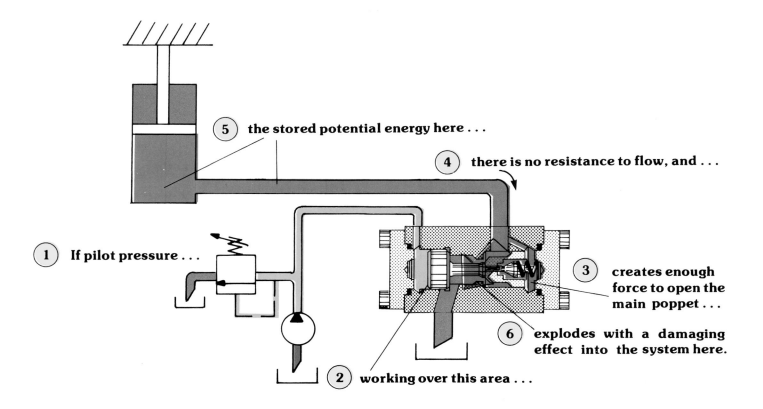

5 the stored potential energy here . . .

4 there is no resistance to flow, and . . .

1 If pilot pressure . . .

3 creates enough force to open the main poppet . . .

6 explodes with a damaging effect into the system here.

2 working over this area . . .

PILOT CIRCUITS FOR DECOMPRESSION

We have shown how a pilot operated check valve with a decompression poppet can be used to prevent the detrimental effects of decompression. However, it is your responsibility to design the pilot circuit so as to prevent full poppet opening under pressure. In most applications, however, we are not at liberty to allow as much time as is needed to fully decompress the system. This, of course, would cause an objectionable delay in production. For this reason, your design must include some method of minimizing decompression shock, while, at the same time, providing for optimum cycle time.

ADJUSTABLE DECOMPRESSION BY LIMITING PILOT PRESSURE

We have already shown how we can limit the pilot pressure so that the pilot piston has only enough force to open the decompression poppet. This means that we can adjust the output force of the pilot piston simply by using a pressure reducing valve in series with the pilot operated check valve's X port.

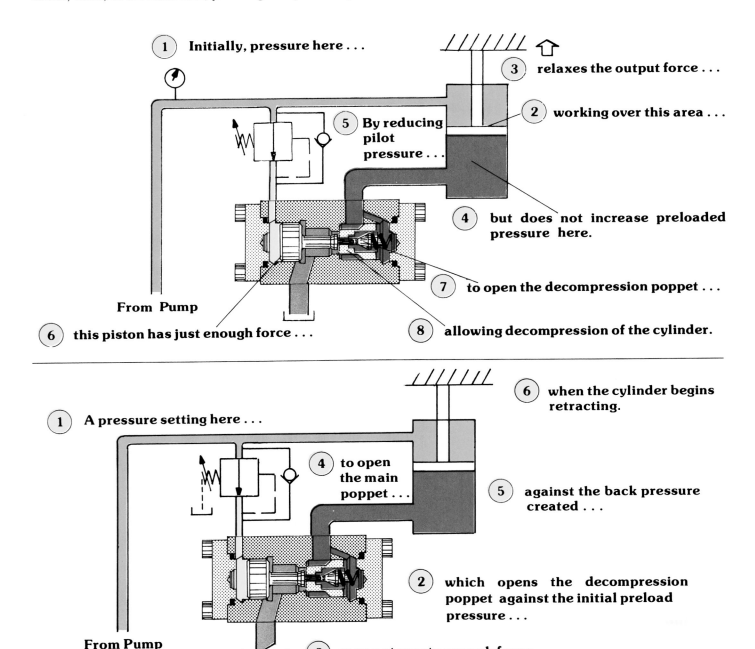

1   **Initially, pressure here . . .**

3   **relaxes the output force . . .**

2   **working over this area . . .**

5   **By reducing pilot pressure . . .**

4   **but does not increase preloaded pressure here.**

From Pump

7   **to open the decompression poppet . . .**

6   **this piston has just enough force . . .**

8   **allowing decompression of the cylinder.**

1   **A pressure setting here . . .**

6   **when the cylinder begins retracting.**

4   **to open the main poppet . . .**

5   **against the back pressure created . . .**

2   **which opens the decompression poppet against the initial preload pressure . . .**

From Pump

3   **may not create enough force . . .**

In the illustrated circuit, preloaded pressure is bled from the blind end of the cylinder once the decompression orifice opens. When preload pressure drops to the point where it can no longer balance main system pressure working on the rod end area of the cylinder, the cylinder begins to retract. Its speed is limited by the amount of flow which is allowed to pass over the decompression orifice. In functioning like a meter out flow control (see Chapter 3), the back pressure in the blind end is at the level necessary to resist the flow entering the rod end of the cylinder, up to the point at which the main system relief is opened. Assuming no load on the cylinder, this back pressure can be determined simply by using the area ratio of the cylinder. We are now faced with the fact that our pilot pressure must also be high enough to open the main poppet against this residual back pressure.

By now, it should be apparent that the design engineer must be aware of what is happening at the B port of the valve whenever a pilot operated check is being piloted from the line supplying the opposite end of a cylinder actuator. It is important to realize that decompression circuits, although different from load holding circuits, can be influenced by pressure conditions on the opposite end of the actuator. In reference to our previous circuit, let us assign some arbitrary values and then calculate our pilot pressure requirements.

Parameters:

    Cylinder: 4" ∅ bore x 1½" ∅ rod
    Cylinder: area ratio: 1.165 : 1
    Pilot piston to decompression poppet area
       ratio: 12 : 1
    Pilot piston to main poppet area ratio: 3 : 1
    Main system pressure: 3000 PSI
    Preload pressure: 3000 PSI
    P_a **= 0 PSI**
    L_p **= Load induced pressure = 0**
    P = Pump pressure (PSI)

Initially, the pilot pressure must be high enough to open the decompression poppet against the preloaded pressure, or:

$$P_p = \frac{P_b - P_a}{AR_v} + P_a + C = \frac{3000 \text{ PSI} - 0 \text{ PSI}}{12} +$$

$$0 \text{ PSI} + 75 \text{ PSI} = 256 \text{ PSI}$$

Where:
$AR_v = 12 : 1$

However, when the cylinder begins moving, and we want to open the main poppet, our pilot pressure requirements become:

$$P_p = L_p + P \left(\frac{1}{AR_c} \right)$$

$$P_b = 0 + 3000 \text{ PSI} \times \frac{1}{1.165} = 2575 \text{ PSI}$$

Consequently:

$$P_p = \frac{P_b - P_a}{AR_v} + P_a + C = \frac{2575}{3} + 75 = 933 \text{ PSI}$$

Where AR_v becomes 3 : 1

This means that for satisfactory operation of our previous circuit, the optimum setting of our pressure reducing valve would be the higher of the two figures, or 933 PSI. At this pressure, the pilot piston would fully open the decompression poppet, but would stall against the main poppet until B port pressure decayed to the 2575 PSI level. If the pressure reducing valve were set any lower than 933 PSI, only the decompression poppet would open, never allowing the cylinder to retract at full speed. Likewise, if the pressure were set higher than 933 PSI, the main poppet would open sooner, which would increase the decompression shock. You can easily see that by adding a load induced pressure during retraction of the cylinder, you would also cause a change in your optimum pilot pressure. This, of course, makes pilot pressure adjustment a somewhat sensitive operation.

In most press applications, the pilot oil for the pilot operated check valve is taken from a separate pilot source, or from the *rod end* of a cylinder with a large area ratio. In fact, most press circuits use separate "kicker" cylinders to push back a single acting ram. In these applications, the transmittal of pressure across the actuator's piston is so insignificant that the formulas for calculating pilot pressure reduce simply to:

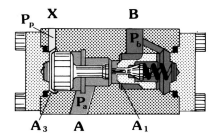

$$P_p = \frac{P_b - P_a}{AR_v} + C$$

Where:

P_p = Pilot Pressure (PSI)
P_b = Preloaded Pressure (PSI)
P_a = A Port Pressure (PSI)
AR_v = Pilot Piston area divided by decompression poppet area

or, for externally drained valves:

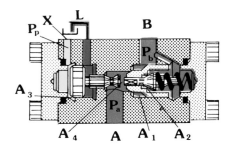

$$P_p = \frac{P_b - P_a}{AR_v} + P_a \left(\frac{A_4}{A_3}\right) + C$$

C = Valve constant which is equal to or less than 75 PSI

ADJUSTABLE DECOMPRESSION USING A FLOW CONTROL

A second, sometimes preferred method of adjusting decompression is to control the speed of opening by using a meter in flow control to the valve's X port. The advantage of this method is that the adjustment is *time* related, and is somewhat less sensitive that the force balancing method of pressure control. By simply putting a flow control in series with the valve's X port, we can severely restrict the speed at which the pilot piston first opens the decompression poppet. Then, at some later time, the piston contacts and opens the main poppet. The time period between contact with the nose of the decompression poppet and contact with the main poppet

allows for decompression of the cylinder.

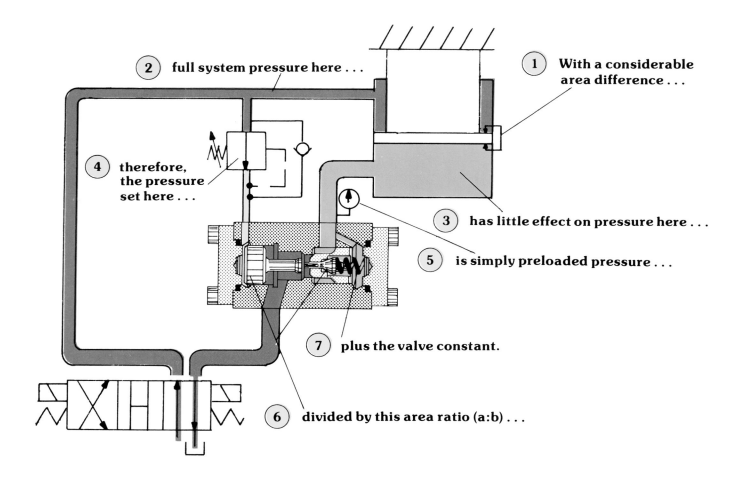

Simple Circuit For Adjustable Decompression of A Small Press

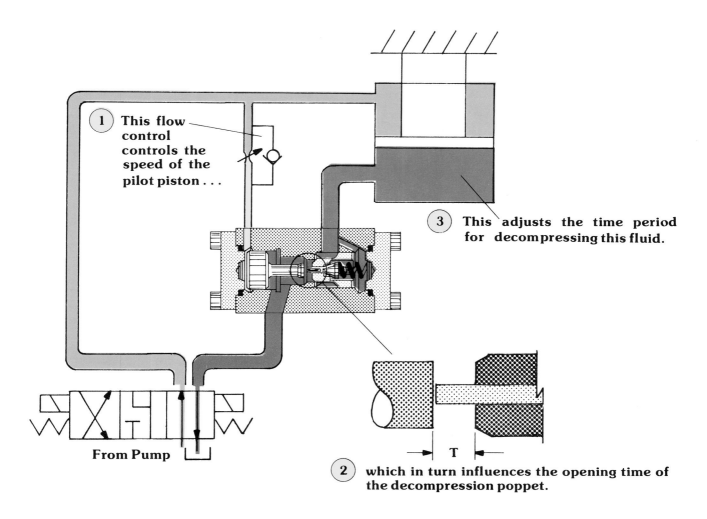

① **This flow control controls the speed of the pilot piston . . .**

③ **This adjusts the time period for decompressing this fluid.**

② **which in turn influences the opening time of the decompression poppet.**

From Pump

EXTERNALLY DRAINED PILOT OPERATED CHECKS FOR DECOMPRESSION CIRCUITS

Earlier in the chapter, we mentioned that some externally drained valves can be made to close more rapidly if the L port is use in conjunction with a 4 way directional control. This method of piloting is always preferred in the installation of a pressure regulator or flow control in the valve's X port for the purposes of adjusting decompression.

When this method is not used, the valve may not close quickly enough when the circuit is required to build tonnage. Actually, with a standard pilot operated check valve, the only force available to move the oil out of the pilot section is that of the spring behind the main poppet. This force, when distributed over the full area of the pilot piston, may not generate enough pressure to open the reverse free flow check valve of the flow or pressure regulator in the valve's X port. Needless to say, the closing time of the main poppet can be severely restricted.

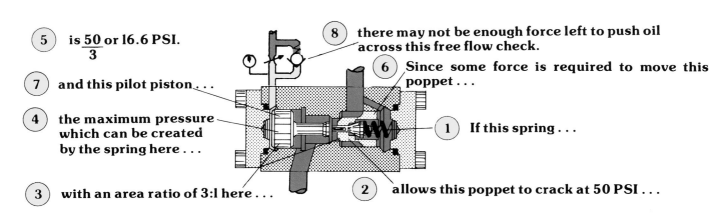

⑤ **is $\frac{50}{3}$ or l6.6 PSI.**

⑧ **there may not be enough force left to push oil across this free flow check.**

⑥ **Since some force is required to move this poppet . . .**

⑦ **and this pilot piston . . .**

④ **the maximum pressure which can be created by the spring here . . .**

① **If this spring . . .**

③ **with an area ratio of 3:l here . . .**

② **allows this poppet to crack at 50 PSI . . .**

PREFILL VALVES

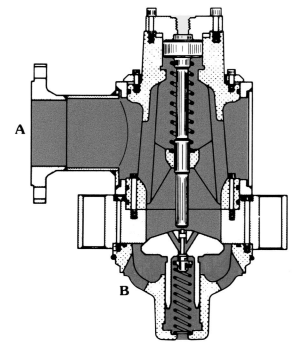

The operation of a prefill valve is identical to that of a standard pilot operated check. As shown in the cross-sectional illustration, the valve allows a free flow of oil from port A to port B. You can achieve reverse flow through the valve by supplying a pilot pressure at port X sufficient to open the main poppet.

The major difference between a prefill and a pilot operated check is that a prefill is only capable of handling high pressure on its B side. The high pressure capability on the A port is replaced with a larger low pressure housing, which offers less resistance to flow in the free flow direction. Likewise, the cracking pressure in the free flow direction is approximately 3 PSI, which is considerably less than the cracking pressure in a standard pilot operated check valve.

In addition, prefill valves include a housing design for mounting directly into the body of the cylinder with which the valve is used, and a single acting spring returned pilot piston.

APPLICATION OF PREFILL VALVES

The prefill valve has been designed specifically to eliminate the need for high volume pumps on large press circuits. In a prefill circuit, a relatively large ram, sometimes as large as 60" in diameter, is moved into and out of its working position by a number of smaller, double acting "kicker" cylinders. During extension of the ram, a huge flow rate, which would otherwise have to be supplied by a number of high volume pumps, is pulled into the ram as a vacuum is created. The moment the ram stops, the light spring forces the main poppet to close. A considerably smaller high pressure pump can then build tonnage during the working stroke.

SUCTION CONDITIONS DURING PREFILL

As the ram is being prefilled, the inlet is subject to the same conditions that exist at the inlet of a hydraulic pump (Chapter 1). This means that proper sizing of components and lines is of utmost importance for the proper operation of the system. The problem is that if the inlet is undersized, the flow rate is not high enough to fill the cylinder completely as it is extended. When the ram meets its resistance, too much time is required to finish the prefilling cycle so that tonnage can be developed. We have found the following facts helpful in achieving the proper applications.

First of all, a 14" prefill valve means that the *minimum* flow area through the valve is equivalent to an orifice with a diameter of 14". This is not always true for standard pilot operated check valves, where the actual flow area can be somewhat smaller than the nominal port size. Consequently, for prefill valves, we can calculate our oil velocity from the formula given in Chapter 1.
Namely.

$$V = \frac{GPM \times 0.3208}{A}$$

Where:
V = oil velocity in F.P.S.
A = flow area in square inches

In 99% of all press applications, the minimum height of the oil level in the reservoir is *above* the top of the ram. In these flooded suction applications, we have found that proper prefilling will normally occur as long as the oil velocity is kept below 12 F.P.S. for mineral oil or 8 F.P.S. for phosphate

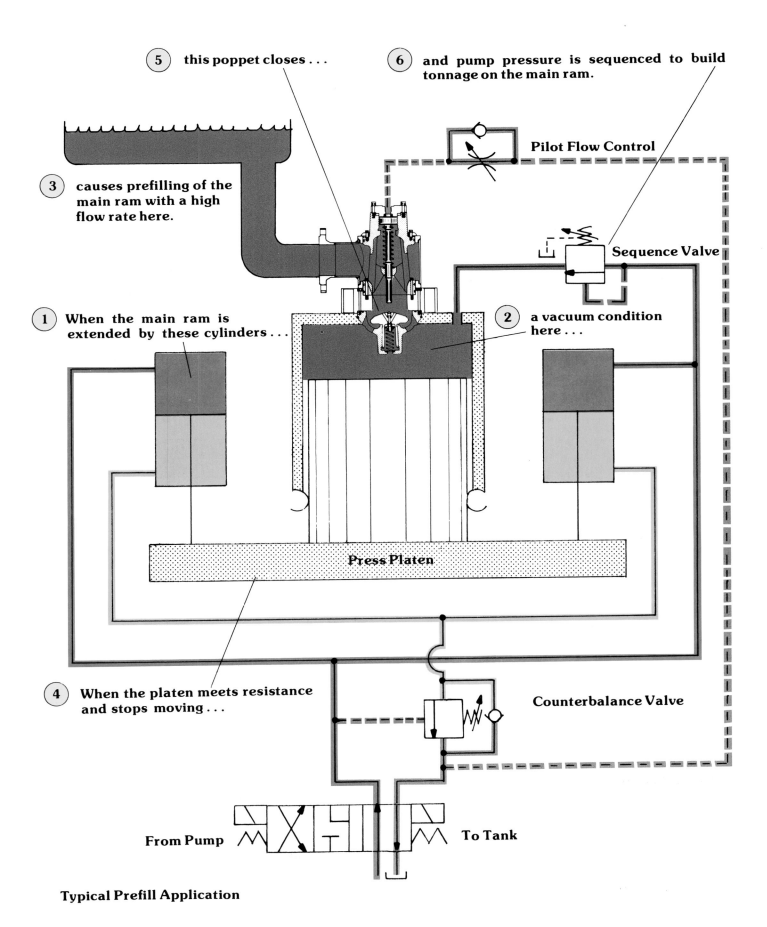

⑤ this poppet closes . . .

⑥ and pump pressure is sequenced to build tonnage on the main ram.

Pilot Flow Control

③ causes prefilling of the main ram with a high flow rate here.

Sequence Valve

① When the main ram is extended by these cylinders . . .

② a vacuum condition here . . .

Press Platen

④ When the platen meets resistance and stops moving . . .

Counterbalance Valve

From Pump

To Tank

Typical Prefill Application

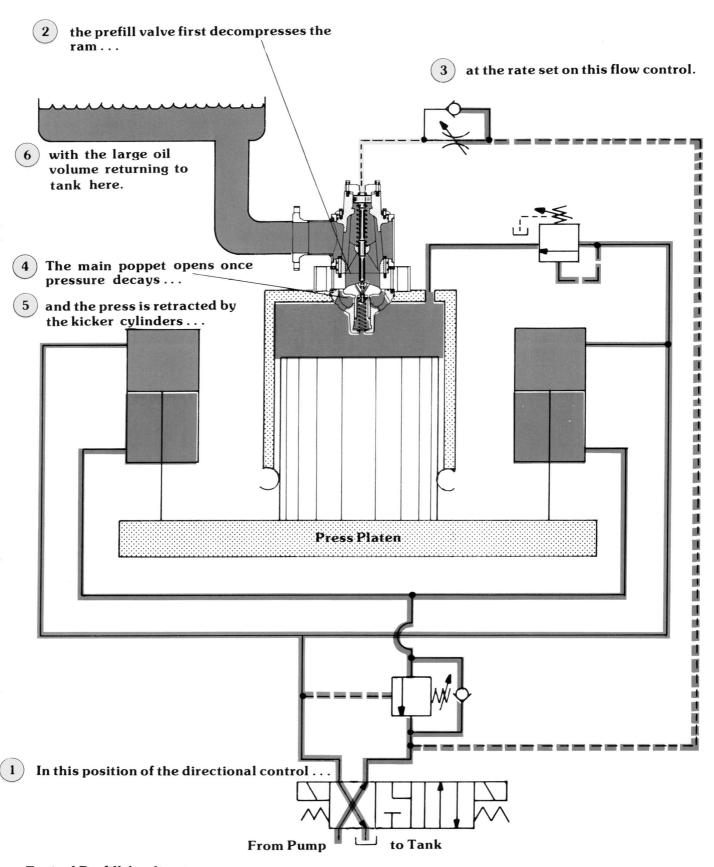

② the prefill valve first decompresses the ram . . .

③ at the rate set on this flow control.

⑥ with the large oil volume returning to tank here.

④ The main poppet opens once pressure decays . . .

⑤ and the press is retracted by the kicker cylinders . . .

Press Platen

① In this position of the directional control . . .

From Pump   **to Tank**

Typical Prefill Application

ester fluids. Remember, the only pressure we have available to cause a flow to occur is the atmospheric pressure and the static head pressure of the oil. Likewise, we must subtract from the available pressure the 3 PSI which is necessary to open the main poppet of the prefill valve.

On the other hand, it is possible to prefill with a higher flow rate for a given valve size if the reservoir is designed so that the oil can be pressurized to approximately 100 PSI. Here you can easily see that considerably more pressure is available for prefilling the main ram. For these prefill applications, oil velocities up to 20 F.P.S. provide satisfactory operation.

Assuming the kicker cylinders can supply enough force, the main ram has the capability of pulling a nearly perfect vacuum. We must consider this fact and size our prefill lines and components so that we fill the cylinder with oil rather than pulling an excessive vacuum. When you are sizing a valve of this nature, we ask that you consider the information as presented under Suction Conditions for Hydraulic Pumps in Chapter 1.

DECOMPRESSING WITH A PREFILL VALVE

Decompressing with a prefill valve is accomplished in basically the same manner as already discussed for pilot operated check valves. Because of its specialized application, the decompression features built into a prefill valve are somewhat more sophisticated.

First of all, the pilot piston of a prefill valve is designed as a single acting spring returned cylinder. Since it is assumed that some control component will always be used to provide adjustable decompression, the spring return is designed strong enough that the pilot spool will always return to its retracted position when the pilot pressure signal is removed.

Secondly, it is virtually impossible to open the main poppet of a prefill valve before decompression of the main ram occurs. The circuit is protected from damaging decompression shock because, unlike the pilot operated check valve, *the main poppet has an area advantage over the pilot piston.* Even if full system pressure is put on the pilot port, the pilot piston can only generate enough force to open the decompression poppet. This assures high pressure bleeding before the opening of the large flow area.

The area ratio of the pilot piston to the main poppet of a typical prefill valve is in the order of 0.25:1. Assuming that the pilot pressure is equal to the preloaded pressure on the main ram, even at 5000 PSI, the pilot piston will not open the main poppet until the preloaded pressure is bled to 1250 PSI. Since satisfactory decompression is assured at virtually any pilot pressure, the time related speed control method of decompression is usually preferred in prefill circuitry.

In calculating the minimum pilot pressure requirements to open the decompression poppet, we must remember that we are working against a spring returned pilot piston which requires a minimum pressure of 75 PSI. However, this shows up in our formula simply as a larger valve constant. For the area ratio of the valve, we divide the pilot piston area by the decompression poppet area. This figure is typically in the order of 10:1. Consequently, our minimum pilot pressure can be calculated simply from the following formula:

$$P_p = \frac{P}{AR_v} + C$$

Where:

P_p = Minimum pilot pressure at port X (PSI)
P = Preloaded pressure on main ram (PSI)
AR_v = Pilot piston area (in.) ÷ decompression poppet area (in)
C = Valve constant which is usually equal to 150 PSI.

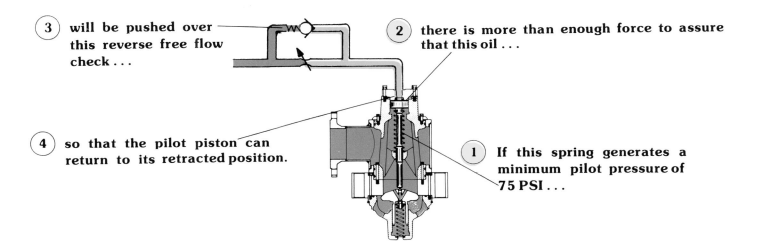

③ **will be pushed over this reverse free flow check . . .**

② **there is more than enough force to assure that this oil . . .**

④ **so that the pilot piston can return to its retracted position.**

① **If this spring generates a minimum pilot pressure of 75 PSI . . .**

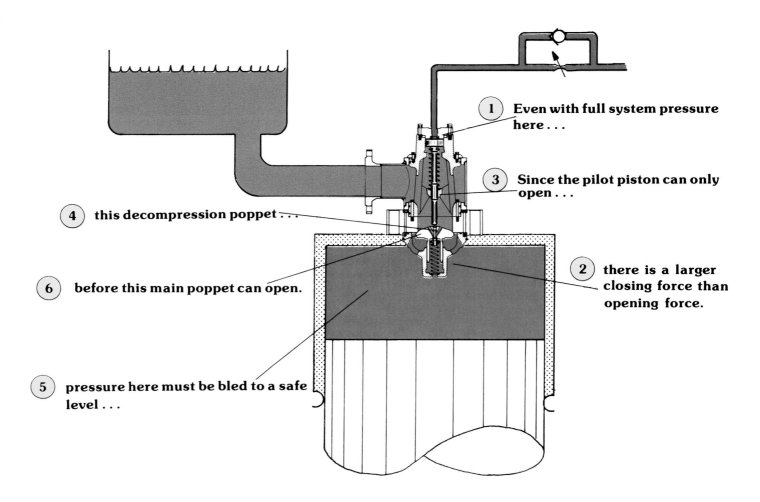

① **Even with full system pressure here...**

③ **Since the pilot piston can only open...**

④ **this decompression poppet...**

② **there is a larger closing force than opening force.**

⑥ **before this main poppet can open.**

⑤ **pressure here must be bled to a safe level...**

MOUNTING VARIATIONS FOR PREFILL VALVES

It is relatively easy to sit down and design a prefill application on paper. However, when it comes time to do the actual installation, either space limitation on smaller presses or the bulky piping on larger systems can become quite frustrating. To simplify installation, however, prefill valves are available which are designed on the modular concept. In applications with limited space requirements, the functional parts can be integrated into the cap of the cylinder. On larger installations, plumbing can be simplified because the low pressure housing module can be rotated so that the A port can be aligned with the high flow plumbing throughout 360° of housing rotation. The following are but a few examples of possible installations.

Mounting of check valve cartridge in the cylinder cap

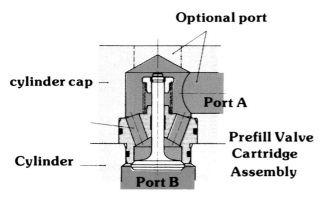

Optional port

cylinder cap

Port A

Cylinder

Port B

Prefill Valve Cartridge Assembly

Application of cartridge as an anti-cavitation check valve

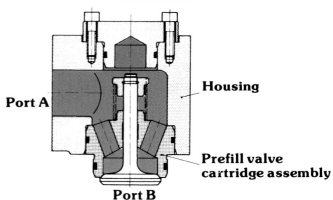

Housing

Port A

Prefill valve cartridge assembly

Port B

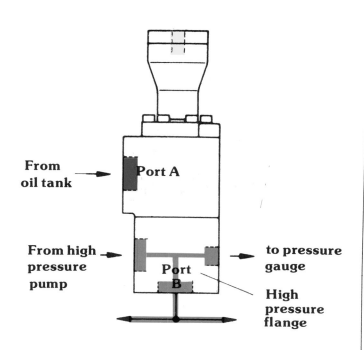

Prefill valve with high pressure flange to supply several cylinders

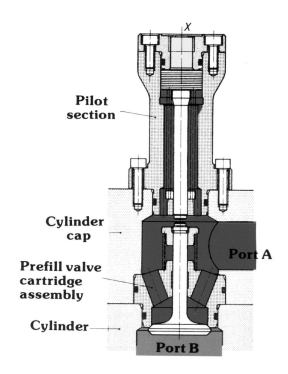

Valve cartridge assembly and pilot section mounted into the cylinder cap

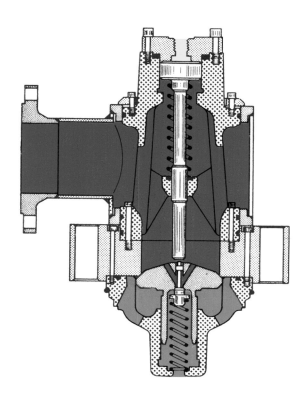

Cross section of a prefill valve with low pressure housing which can be rotated through 360°

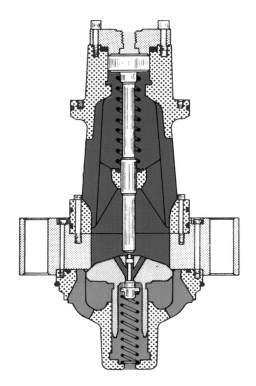

Cross section of a prefill valve for mounting directly in a tank which is located on top of the cylinder

4-27

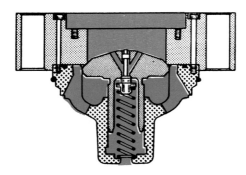

Cross section of a prefill valve main poppet without control cylinder, for use as an anti-cavitation check valve.

LOGIC ELEMENTS

The logic element revitalizes some of the early concepts which led to development of the hydraulic industry as we know it today. In the infancy of hydraulics, water was the medium used to transfer energy. Spool type directional controls, which will be discussed in Chapter 5, found universal application only after the introduction of oil hydraulics many years later. Since economic conditions are again causing us to consider water as our hydraulic medium, many manufacturers are reconsidering the poppet valve as the controlling element. In combining the older poppet theory with modern technology, we find that the logic element provides economical solutions to hydraulic systems incorporating either water or oil.

The modern day logic element is a cartridge poppet which must be mounted in a manifold block. Although its operation is dependent on a custom designed manifold, its simplicity provides technical and economical solutions to many hydraulic problems. It is especially desirable on high speed equipment with high flow hydraulic circuits. Let us now take a closer look at how it works.

LOGIC ELEMENT OPERATION

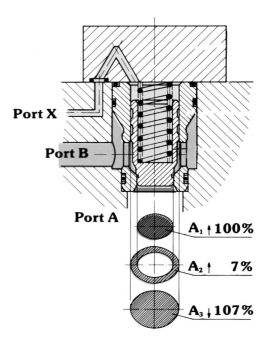

As shown in the operational cross section, the basic logic element is a three-piece assembly consisting of a poppet, bushing, and a spring. The standard poppet is machined in graduated steps, so that when positioned inside its bushing, there are three separate areas for pressure to act upon. Depending on the prevailing pressure conditions at port X, A, and B, the poppet is either open, closed, or in some modulating position between fully open and fully closed.

In defining the surface areas, the nose of the poppet is area A_1, which we will assume is 100%. The ring area, A_2, is then defined as the area which has the ID of the seat diameter and the OD of the poppet guide. Depending on the model selected, this area can be either 7% or 50% of the nose area, A_1. Obviously, the third effective area, A_3, is that of the full diameter of the poppet. Likewise, this area is dependent on poppet design, and is either 107% or 150% of the nose area, A_1. For any given element size, area A_3 has the same diameter. Consequently, the area ratios of A_1 and A_2 are changed by modifying the maximum diameter of the poppet nose. As shown, a logic element which has an A_2 area which is 50% of area A_1 has considerably less flow area when open than an element with a 7% A_2 area.

Needless to say, pressure working over area A_3 creates a force which tends to seat the poppet and block the flow path from A to B. Opening forces, on the other hand, are established by pressure working over areas A_1 or A_2. Of course, if pressure exists in the A and B ports simultaneously, the force trying to open the valve poppet is the sum total of both of these pressures.

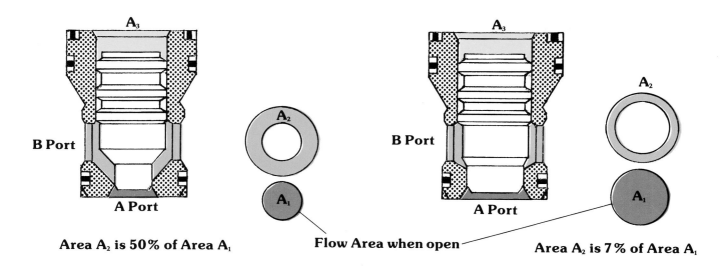

Area A₂ is 50% of Area A₁

Flow Area when open

Area A₂ is 7% of Area A₁

As will be shown, depending on the method of piloting, the elements can be used to perform check, directional, or flow control functions. In addition, some forms of pressure control can be obtained. However, when strict pressure control functions are required, two variations of the basic logic element give more precise control.

LOGIC ELEMENT CARTRIDGES FOR PRESSURE CONTROL FUNCTIONS

If we think back for a moment to the pilot operated pressure controls discussed in Chapter 2, there were only two basic main poppet configurations. The first, in reducing valves, used a normally open cartridge, while the second, in relief and multifunction valves, used a normally closed poppet. Elements with identical functions are also available for mounting in a standard logic element cavity.

Pressure control with logic elements can accomplish relief, sequence, unloading, and counterbalance functions simply by modifying the method by which we modulate the pressure on area A_3. However, for precise pressure control, we want the pressure in chamber A_3 to be identical to the pressure working on area A_1 just before valve opening. In this manner, the moment pressure is limited in the pilot chamber, the slightest pressure differential will overcome the light spring force which causes the poppet to open. Likewise, the moment the pilot closes, and chamber A_3 becomes static, hydraulic forces must balance so that the spring force can close the poppet quickly. Remember that between these two points, there is a dynamic range of operation where the main poppet must have stable modulation so that just enough fluid is passed to maintain the desired pressure control function.

If a standard stepped logic element were used to perform a relief function, for instance, the moment the cartridge opened to flow, area A_2 would become effective and add to the available force for opening. This means that it would take

more force to close the poppet than was initially required to hold it closed. In the dynamic position, the pilot section can only determine one closing pressure force working over area A_3. Consequently, once opened, the standard logic cartridge would inherently become unstable, since the exact balance of forces necessary for stable operation would be lost.

For this reason, a logic element is available which has an area A_1 which is equal to the area A_3. For pressure control functions this design is inherently stable, since hydraulic forces tending to open or close the poppet are always in balance.

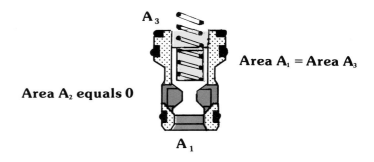

Area A₂ equals 0   **Area A₁ = Area A₃**

Logic Cartridge For Normally Closed Pressure Control Functions

NORMALLY OPEN LOGIC ELEMENT CARTRIDGES

In performing reducing valve functions, the cartridge must be normally open, allowing flow from inlet to outlet. When pressure in Chamber A_3 reaches a predetermined limit, as established by the pilot network, the cartridge spool must modulate toward a closed position. This causes a pressure drop across the orifices established by the cross drillings, so that downstream pressure remains at the required setting. To provide stable operation, area A_1 is equal to area A_3.

With the A port being the reduced pressure port, hydraulic forces above and below the cartridge spool are always stably in balance during dynamic operation.

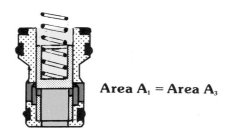

Area A_1 = Area A_3

A = Reduced Pressure Port

Normal Open Logic Element Cartridge

CONTROLLING THE LOGIC ELEMENT

Up to this point, we have only discussed the operation of the actual logic element cartridges. The flexibility of this element, however, does not really become apparent until the design engineer considers the various functions which can be designed around a few basic logic elements, simply by doing tricks with the pilot circuitry. The simplicity of the cartridge itself, allows us to build a valve to meet the requirements at hand. The poppet opens, closes, or modulates as dictated by the prevailing pressure conditions on two or three of its surface areas. Pilot control circuitry performs the required function by manipulating the interaction of pressure forces, while at the same time, the logic element interfaces this control with high flow in the system.

MOUNTING CAVITY & PILOTING

As already mentioned, the logic element fits in a standardized bore in a custom manifold block. Although main flow ports and the bore itself are designed to a particular standard, the designer is at liberty to pilot area A_3 from virtually any required source. As shown in the cavity drawing for a typical cartridge, the element is held in its respective bore by a cover.

The cover is fed by two pilot passages, ports X & Y. Depending on the function desired, either of the pilot passages can be drilled to connect with either of the main flow passages. Likewise, it is just as easy to connect the X & Y ports to some other pilot source within the manifold, or to externally pilot the A_3 area through port connections in the cover. Since pressure on area A_3 must be ported through the cover, considerable design flexibility is possible because of the availability of a large selection of standardized covers.

PLAIN BLOCK COVER

This basic cover connects area A_3 to pilot passage X. Although the X port can be internally connected to virtually any source, as shown here, the simple check valve function is accomplished by piloting from the B passage to the element area A_3. In this example, the logic element allows free flow from port A to port B. In the reverse direction, flow is checked without leakage. Since area A_3 is larger, simultaneous pressure on A_2 and A_3 keeps the poppet seated.

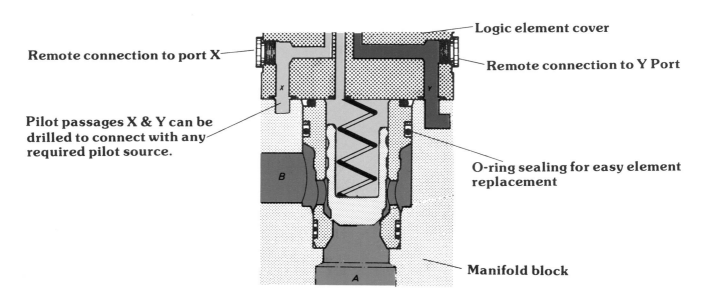

Remote connection to port X

Pilot passages X & Y can be drilled to connect with any required pilot source.

Logic element cover

Remote connection to Y Port

O-ring sealing for easy element replacement

Manifold block

Typical Logic Element Cavity

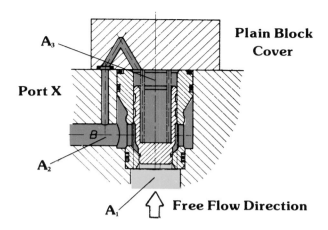

Plain Block Cover

A₃

Port X

B

A₂

A₁ ⬆ **Free Flow Direction**

DIRECTIONAL CONTROL COVERS

The use of logic elements for directional control will be covered in more detail in Chapter 5. At this point, however, it is sufficient to say that the directional control simply selects whether area A_3 will be pressurized or vented to tank. Normally, port X is used to supply the pressure port of the directional control, while port Y is used as the tank connection. Design flexibility can be extended by using sandwich mounted flow or pressure regulating valves between the directional control and the cover. That is, by metering the flow to or from area A_3, the opening and closing of the logic

element poppet can be cushioned. In addition, when a sandwich mounted pressure control is used, directional and pressure control functions can be combined into one element.

SHUTTLE VALVE COVER

In many applications, it is necessary to pilot area A_3 from the highest of two possible pressure sources. For instance, with an over center counterbalance function, it can be desirable to pilot area A_3 from the working pressure side of a cylinder's piston until load conditions change. Then, when the over running load induces pressure on the opposite side of the cylinder's piston, we will want this pressure to affect the pilot circuitry.

This type of piloting is easily accomplished by piloting area A_3 with a shuttle valve cover. As shown, the simple shuttle valve cover pilots area A_3, with the highest of the two separate pilot pressures occuring in either the X or Y pilot passages. Remember, X and Y ports can be drilled to connect with any required pressure sources as determined by the function being accomplished.

When a shuttle valve is combined with a directional control cover, area A_3 can be piloted from the highest pressure in either the A or B main flow passages to the logic element.

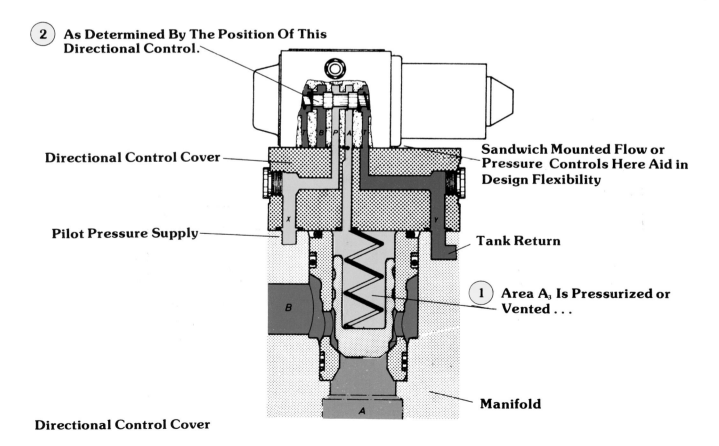

② **As Determined By The Position Of This Directional Control.**

Directional Control Cover

Pilot Pressure Supply

B

Sandwich Mounted Flow or Pressure Controls Here Aid in Design Flexibility

Tank Return

① **Area A₃ Is Pressurized or Vented . . .**

Manifold

A

Directional Control Cover

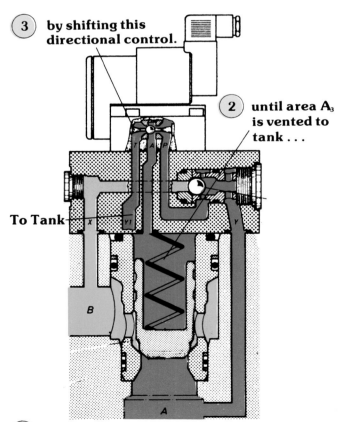

Shuttle Valve

Option Orifice

Optional Orifice

To Area A₃ Piloting Circuit

B

To X Pilot Source

To Y Pilot Source

This assures that the poppet will always be closed until area A₃ is vented to tank by the directional control. In our example, if area A₃ were only piloted from the B passage, high pressure at port A could open the poppet and allow a flow from A to B.

③ **by shifting this directional control.**

② **until area A₃ is vented to tank . . .**

To Tank

B

A

① **High pressure at either port will keep the poppet closed . . .**

STROKE LIMITER COVER

When the flow control function is used with logic elements, a cover is available which will adjust the maximum opening stroke of the poppet. We must be aware, however, that the flow control function may not be as precise as it is when we use a valve designed specifically for performing flow control. That is, even if a very fine thread were used on the stroke limiter, the logic poppet, because of its design, would open a large flow area in a very short stroke. This would definitely limit the accuracy of adjustment, as discussed in Chapter 3. Nevertheless, a logic element used with a stroke limiter cover is a good example to bring home the fact that logic elements can be an economical solution to some problems in high flow hydraulic circuits. The following circuit not only replaces the large spool type directional control and two meter out flow controls economically, but it also provides a leak free hydraulic locking of the cylinder. In addition, because the logic elements are held closed by a *limited* system pressure, the cylinder is automatically protected from being overloaded.

③ **Also, if held under load, this cylinder can creep . . .**

② **these three valves must be quite larger. (2 ½'')**

④ **because of leakage across this spool.**

① **With high flow here . . .**

200 GPM

Conventional Circuit

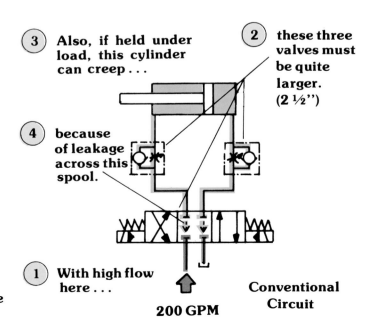

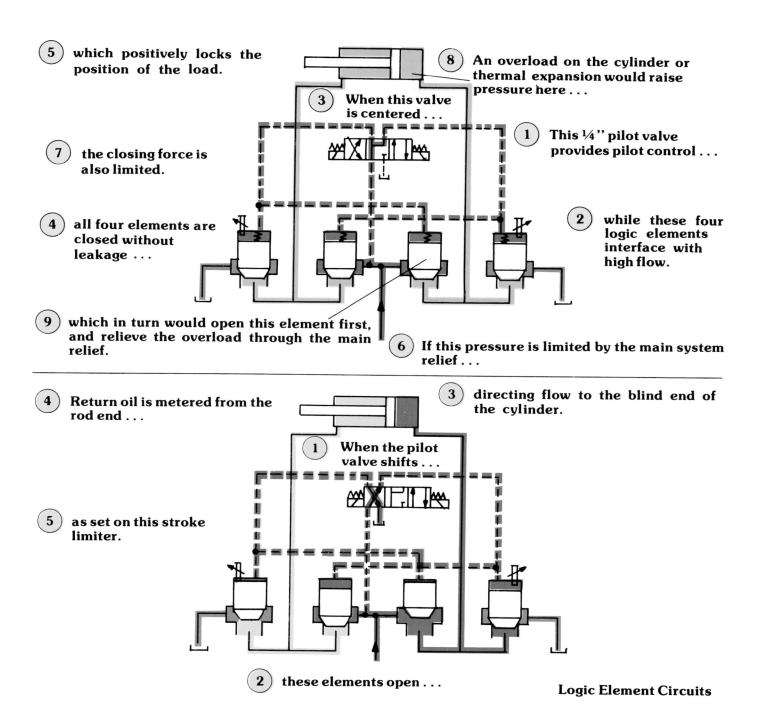

(5) which positively locks the position of the load.

(3) When this valve is centered . . .

(8) An overload on the cylinder or thermal expansion would raise pressure here . . .

(1) This ¼" pilot valve provides pilot control . . .

(7) the closing force is also limited.

(4) all four elements are closed without leakage . . .

(2) while these four logic elements interface with high flow.

(9) which in turn would open this element first, and relieve the overload through the main relief.

(6) If this pressure is limited by the main system relief . . .

(4) Return oil is metered from the rod end . . .

(3) directing flow to the blind end of the cylinder.

(1) When the pilot valve shifts . . .

(5) as set on this stroke limiter.

(2) these elements open . . .

Logic Element Circuits

PRESSURE CONTROL COVER

Since we have already discussed the operation of various pressure controls in Chapter 2, it would be repetitious at this point to open the discussion again. It is more important to mention the fact that various pressure control covers are available for performing relief, sequence, reducing, counterbalance, and unloading functions. The cover itself includes the necessary pilot orificing for stable operation, and it has a mounting surface for accepting a miniature pilot pressure control. Virtually any pressure control function can

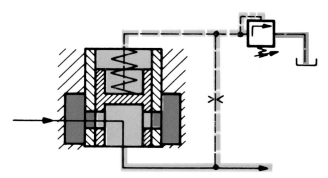

be achieved by using a relief, sequence, or reducing pilot valve in conjunction with either the normally closed or normally open pressure control logic element.

DESIGNING WITH LOGIC ELEMENTS

When you combine a knowledge of logic element hardware with the application knowledge of pressure, flow, and direction control, as presented in other chapters in this book, you will be well on the road to designing with logic elements. However, we must warn you that circuits involving logic elements are relatively new to modern hydraulics. For this reason logic element design is more of a theory than an application fact.

The logic element is quite simple in design, and, therefore, very versatile. However, because it depends solely on pressure, you will have to follow a logical but complicated process early in the design stage, and think through the interactions of pressure during each step of the machine cycle. Unfortunately, it is quite difficult to symbolize pressure in design drawings. This complicates both the design and the trouble shooting of prototype manifolds. Nevertheless, your

work will be worth the effort, because it will put you well on your way to working with the most modern hydraulic system in our industry.

SYMBOLS

Symbols for check valves clearly represent the intended function. As shown in the chart, the seat is represented by a symbol similar to an arrowhead, while the poppet is represented by a circle. To avoid confusion, be aware that the arrowhead is not to be interpreted as an arrow indicating the direction of free flow. Free flow is that which pushes the poppet (circle) away from the seat (arrowhead).

When you are trying to interpret a circuit function, you can also avoid confusion by paying attention to the symbol representing the spring. In actual practice, though, the cracking pressure springs are seldom used in design drawings. For this reason, we recommend that when cracking pressure is important to the circuit function, the cracking pressure in PSI should be listed next to the valve symbol.

SYMBOL	DESCRIPTION
Alternate	**Simple check valve (free flow from left to right)**
75 PSI	**Simple check valve with high cracking pressure.**
B A X	**Pilot operated check valve internally drained.**
B Y A X	**Pilot operated check valve externally drained.**

SYMBOL	DESCRIPTION
Detailed: A_1 B_1 A B Simplified: A_1 B_1 A B	Sandwich mounted dual pilot operated check.
X --- A $\otimes$ B	Prefill valve
X B A	Logic element with three effective pressure areas.
X B A	Logic element without area A_2. Normally closed pressure control.

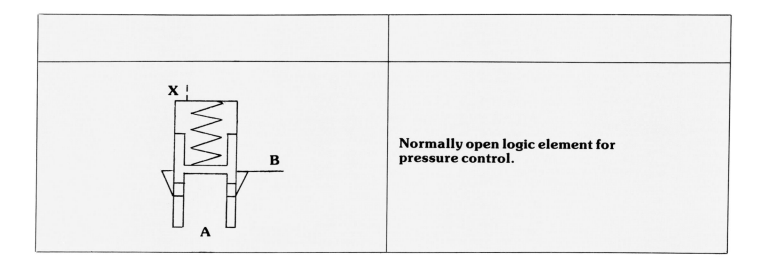

Normally open logic element for pressure control.

CONCLUSION

This chapter has compared the operation of a simple check valve to that of a low pressure direct operated relief. Although the main purpose of a check valve is to provide leak free directional control, we have shown how some pressure control functions can also be achieved.

In addition to the discussion of a simple check valve, the operation and application of pilot operated valves have been discussed. When working with pilot operated check valves, we must understand how pilot ratios, decompression poppets, and external drains affect the operation of the valve. In actual application, we must also consider the pilot pressure requirements needed to open the main poppet. We should be aware of the pilot pressure considerations for both load holding and decompression applications. Circuit examples for venting the X port and pressure or flow control ad-justment of decompression have been explained.

Prefill valves are quite similar to pilot operated check valves, but are designed specifically for use in press applications. The basic design variations allow considerably high flow rates with minimum pressure drop in the free flow direction. Because of its specialized application, the decompression features of a prefill valve are somewhat sophisticated.

In this chapter we have also introduced the logic element as a viable means of controlling hydraulic circuits. The simplicity of the logic element poppet often allows us to combine directional, flow and pressure control in one unit. However, since the open or close position of the poppet is determined strictly by the prevailing pressure conditions, pilot circuit design in this case, is somewhat complicated. Nevertheless, the advantage the logic element offers in interfacing small control circuits with high flow systems makes it an interesting technology in modern hydraulic control.

CHAPTER 5
DIRECTIONAL CONTROL

One of the most versatile aspects of hydraulics is the ease with which the direction of energy transfer can be manipulated. No other method of power transmission provides as many control options for reciprocating linear motion or reversing a rotary drive. Virtually hundreds of horsepower can be made to change direction almost instantaneously at the flick of a wrist. On the other hand, the machine function can also be totally automated by interfacing the directional control components with hydraulic, pneumatic, electrical or electronic control circuits.

The check valve, as outlined in Chapter 4, is but one of a multitude of components available for controlling the direction of flow in hydraulics. In this chapter, the components and methods used to control the direction of work output will be studied. The chapter is divided into two parts in order to study both sliding spool type and poppet style directional controls. The discussion has been limited to valve control, leaving the discussion of the possibility of pump control of direction for Chapter 6.

SLIDING SPOOL TYPE DIRECTIONAL CONTROLS

Once the conditions of the load have been defined, there is a logical hydraulic design sequence in which a suitable actuator is selected which will give the desired linear or rotary motion. Of course, in the selection of the actuator, the pressure and flow requirements must be considered so that sufficient force and speed can be obtained from the system. When we are satisfied with the selection of pressure and flow controls, we are convinced that we can adjust system speed and maximum output force, while always keeping the motion of the load under the control of our hydraulic system. In the back of our mind, we also know that eventually we can select a suitable pump to supply a flow of fluid to our system from some storage reservoir. But, at this point, we must concern ourselves with tying it all together into a meaningful system.

We are, therefore, faced with the fact that we have a rotary

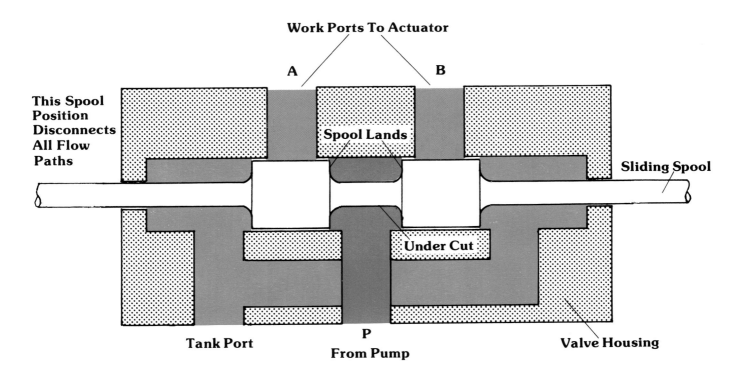

Work Ports To Actuator

A   B

This Spool Position Disconnects All Flow Paths

Spool Lands

Sliding Spool

Under Cut

Tank Port

P
From Pump

Valve Housing

BASIC SPOOL VALVE OPERATION (ALL PORTS BLOCKED)

or linear actuator which normally has two port connections. Likewise, we know that if oil is pumped into one of the ports while the other port is connected to tank, the actuator will move in one direction. To reverse its direction of motion, the pump and tank connections at the actuator must be reversed. Over the years, sliding spool type directional controls have been found to be the most acceptable way to accomplish this change in plumbing compactly and quickly.

BASIC OPERATION

The sliding spool directional control has a cylindrical piece called a spool which slides in a machined bore in the valve housing. The housing has a number of ports to which the pump, tank and working lines for the actuator are connected. Internally, the ports are connected to cast or machined

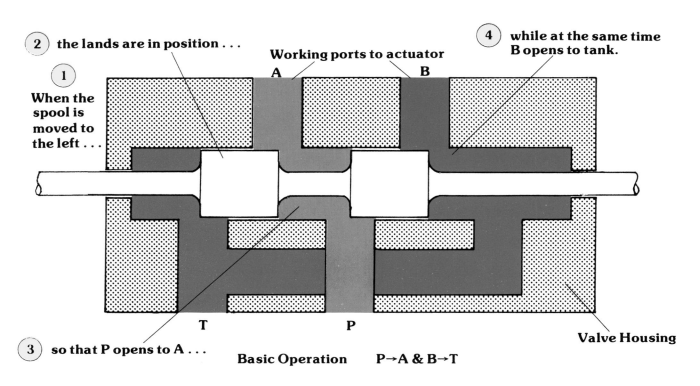

(1) When the spool is moved to the left . . .

(2) the lands are in position . . .

Working ports to actuator
A   B

(4) while at the same time B opens to tank.

Valve Housing

(3) so that P opens to A . . .

T   P

Basic Operation   P→A & B→T

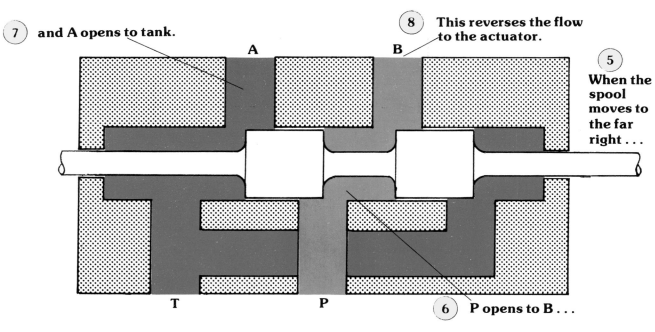

(7) and A opens to tank.

A   B

(8) This reverses the flow to the actuator.

(5) When the spool moves to the far right . . .

T   P

(6) P opens to B . . .

Basic Operation   P→B & A→T

passages in the valve housing which terminate at the machined bore where the spool is located. The number of ports designates the valve type. For instance, a 4 ported valve is referred to as a 4-way valve, while a valve with 3 working port connections would be called a 3-way.

The sliding spool is closely fitted into the machined bore so that when its maximum diameter is in line with a port channel, flow to or from that channel is blocked by the spool. As the spool is repositioned, the previously blocked port can be interconnected with another port in the valve housing through machined undercuts in the spool. As shown in the basic directional valve cross section, the larger diameters of the spool are referred to as *lands*.

THREE POSITION SPOOL TYPES

For any given directional control, the housing is always the same. Flexibility in hydraulic system design comes from the ability to select from a number of different spool types. For instance, the previous example shows a valve which can be shifted to any one of three positions. In one position, it directs pump flow to A, and return flow from the actuator through the B port to tank. Likewise, in another position, the flow paths reverse, connecting P to B and A to T. The third position occurs when the spool is physically centered in the

housing. This disconnects all ports since the lands block all possible flow paths.

It stands to reason that if we machine spools with lands and undercuts of different dimensions, we can achieve any number of different flow paths. For instance, if we wanted our actuator to *float* in the center position of the directional control, all we need do is machine the spool with shorter lands. As you can see, this would connect both actuator ports to tank in the center position, so that oil could enter or leave the actuator as required during motion of the cylinder's piston. The basic 4-way function would be maintained if the spool were repositioned to the left or the right.

GRAPHIC SYMBOLS FOR THREE POSITION SPOOLS

Unfortunately, it would be impractical at this point to demonstrate each and every combination of flow paths offered by differently dimensioned spools. It is, however, important to understand how the different flow paths are achieved, and to realize which ones are standardly available. Throughout this chapter, spool types will be designated in symbol form. Consequently, it is important that the graphic representations be understood.

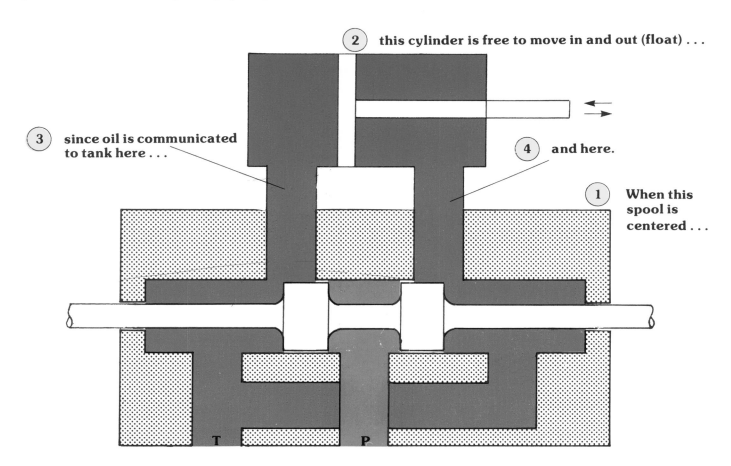

2 this cylinder is free to move in and out (float) . . .

3 since oil is communicated to tank here . . .

4 and here.

1 When this spool is centered . . .

Typical Directional Valve Spools

Although we have not yet described the methods available to shift the spool to its various positions, we can mention the fact that most three position valves are held in the center or neutral position by a set of centering springs. The valve is then shifted to one of its end positions by some external actuator force. In symbol terminology, the port connections to the valve are normally connected to the square which represents the valve's center or deactivated position. As shown in our symbol for a three position closed center directional valve, arrows are used to indicate flow paths in the shifted position. The springs indicate that the valve self centers when the shifting force is removed. Our symbol at this point indicates the flow positions only, since actuator symbolism will be discussed later in this chapter.

In graphically representing a directional valve's spool, each of its possible flow positions within the valve housing is represented by a square. This means that a three position valve symbol would consist of a row of three squares.

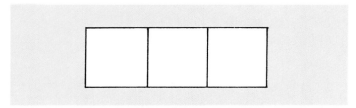

Basic Symbol Representation Of Three Valve Positions.

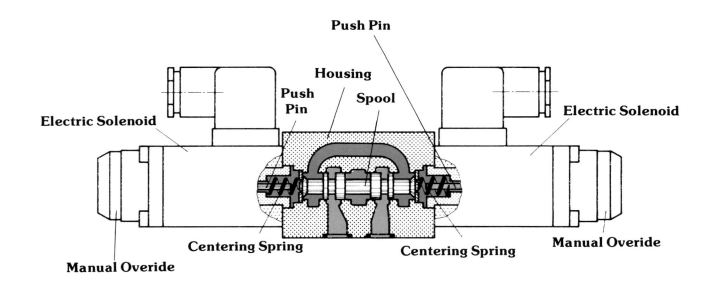

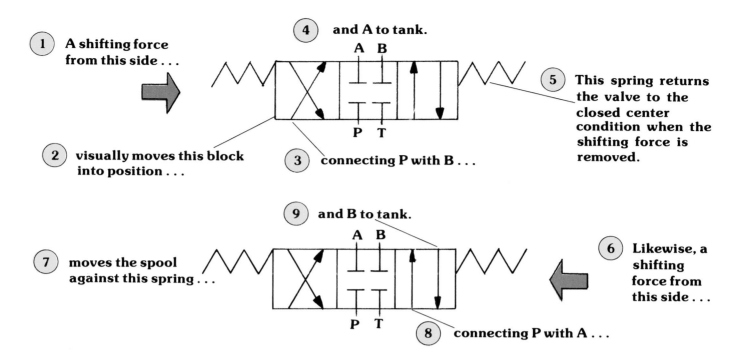

① A shifting force from this side . . .

④ and A to tank.

② visually moves this block into position . . .

③ connecting P with B . . .

⑤ This spring returns the valve to the closed center condition when the shifting force is removed.

⑨ and B to tank.

⑦ moves the spool against this spring . . .

⑥ Likewise, a shifting force from this side . . .

⑧ connecting P with A . . .

Symbols For A Spring-Centered 3 Position Closed Center Valve.

TYPICAL FLOW PATHS AVAILABLE WITH 3 POSITION VALVE SPOOLS			
	Closed Center		Restricted Open Center
	Open Center		Regenerative End Closed Center
	Tandem Center		B Blocked P & A→T
	Float Center		P & B→T A Blocked
	Regenerative Center		P & B Blocked A→T
	Restricted Float Center		P & A Blocked B→T

The spool chart shows that most three position valves cause forward and reverse operation of the actuator in their two end positions. The flow paths indicated in the center positions actually designate the *spool type*. Discussion of the possible applications of various spool types will be postponed until other important operating details have been covered.

TWO POSITION DIRECTIONAL CONTROLS

The three position valve is quite popular in industrial hydraulic systems. The flexibility of the three position valves lies in the fact that it not only provides forward and reverse motion of the actuator, but it also allows a neutral position, where any number of possibilities of holding or unloading the actuator and/or pump are possible. However, there are a multitude of applications in which a neutral position is not required. Two examples are cylinders which only have to extend and retract to their fullest positions, and hydraulic motors which only run in forward or reverse direction. For these applications, all that is needed is a two position directional control.

Actually, two position valves are quite similar in design to three position valves. The only real difference is that the two position valve has no way to stop or to hold the valve in its center position. In these valves, as the spool shifts from one extreme to the other, the center position is simply *crossed over*.

TWO POSITION SPRING OFFSET

As shown in symbol form, one of several methods to achieve the two position function is to hold the spool in one end position by a light spring force. Then, by actuating the valve with a force opposite the spring, the spool is moved into its second position.

TWO POSITION NO SPRING VERSION

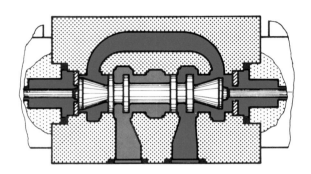

Depending on the type of actuator and the required control, it is sometimes advantageous to have a two position valve which has its spool position determined only by the valve actuator. This method of operation is most popular with directional controls which have two electric solenoid actuators. Since spool position is determined only by the external actuator force, Bernoulli flow forces could cause the spool to self-shift if both actuator forces were simultaneously relaxed. For this reason two position no spring versions are normally used on high cycling applications, and the valve should always be mounted with its spool in a horizontal position. As

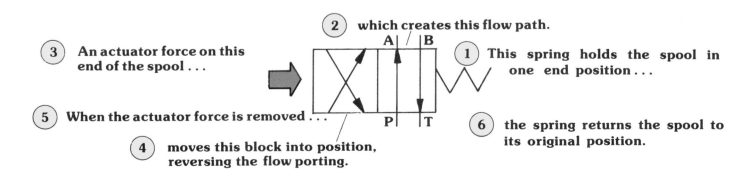

③ An actuator force on this end of the spool . . .

② which creates this flow path.

① This spring holds the spool in one end position . . .

⑤ When the actuator force is removed . . .

④ moves this block into position, reversing the flow porting.

⑥ the spring returns the spool to its original position.

Symbol For A Two Position Spring Offset Directional Valve

shown in the valve symbol for a double solenoid operated two position valve, the spring return is simply replaced by a second actuator.

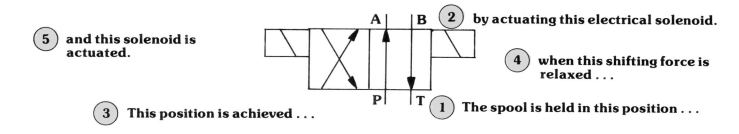

⑤ **and this solenoid is actuated.**

② **by actuating this electrical solenoid.**

④ **when this shifting force is relaxed . . .**

③ **This position is achieved . . .**

① **The spool is held in this position . . .**

Double Solenoid Two Position Valve Symbol Without Springs

TWO POSITION DETENTED

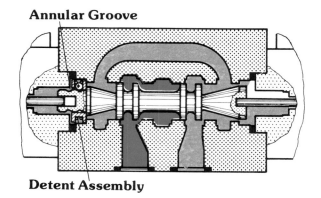

Annular Groove

Detent Assembly

The *detented spool* is an option commonly used with two position valves with dual actuators. Mechanically, the detent is nothing more than a set of spring loaded balls which ride on the spool shaft. For each of the two spool positions, an annular groove is machined on the spool shaft. These grooves are lined up with the ball detent assembly when the spool is shifted to one of its two flow positions. That is, when the actuator shifts the spool into one of the flow positions, the detent ball clicks into its groove, providing a

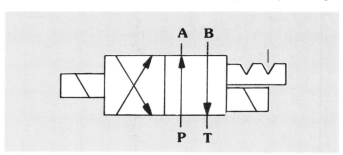

Symbol For A Two Position Double Solenoid Valve With Detents

holding force on the spool. The actuator force can then be relaxed, since the spool is held in position by the detent. The valve will remain in this position until the opposite actuator "clicks" the spool out of its original position into the second detented flow position.

CROSSOVER CONDITIONS FOR SLIDING SPOOL VALVES

With spool type directional valves, it is physically impossible to instantaneously change the position of the spool with respect to the porting in the valve housing. Even though the spool stroke is quite small (approximately 7/32" - ¼" overall stroke for a 12 GPM directional control), it requires a specific time period to move fully into any one of the flow positions. In actual valve design, there are several options which affect the pressure and flow conditions during this crossover period. Consequently, in selecting a directional control for a particular function, the design engineer should consider the manner in which the spool overlaps the ports in the valve housing. In application, smooth valve shift and proper system operation are affected by metering notches machined on the spool lands and two major types of spool overlapping, all of which affect crossover.

METERING NOTCHES

If we go back for a moment to our basic representation of directional valve operation, we find that, as the spool is shifted from its closed center position, there is a dead band region where spool movement provides no valve opening. Then, when the edge of the spool land meets the leading edge of the port opening in the valve housing, an annular flow area opens quite rapidly. The fact is that there are actually two flow areas opening simultaneously: one from the pump to the actuator and one from the actuator to tank.

A problem arises when the ports which are being connected are at considerably different pressure levels. Because energy is stored in pressurized fluid by compression, an explosion of fluid will occur as the high pressure port opens to a port at lower pressure. Of course, the faster the opening occurs, the quicker the energy will exchange. This will cause a *water hammer*, which will stress pipe joints, fittings, and hoses, and which can eventually cause them to either leak or break.

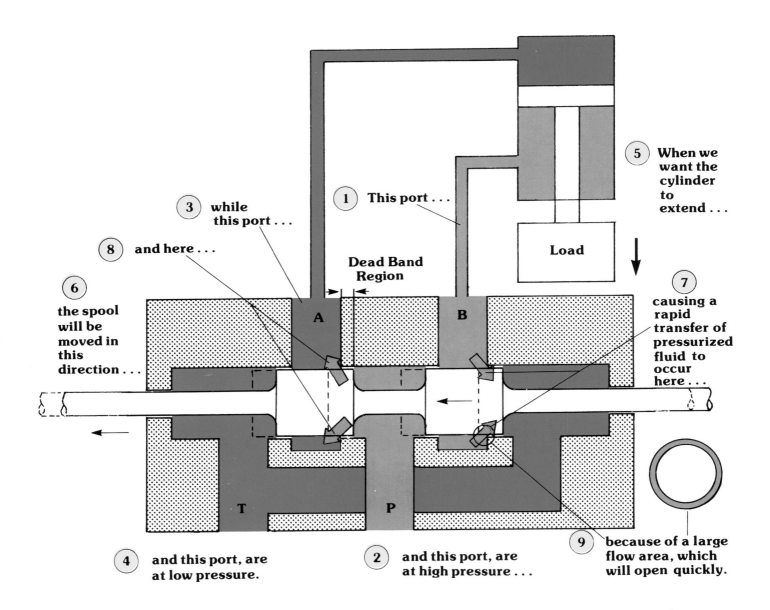

In order to obtain a smoother valve shift, metering notches can be machined onto the edge of the spool lands. During the time when the spool land and the housing are still overlapped, a number of equally spaced notches will provide small flow passage connections between the two ports.

Pressure differences between the two ports will gradually equalize, prior to the opening of the full flow area. In valves which incorporate metering notches on the spool, a more gradual transfer of energy will occur as the spool is shifted from one position to another.

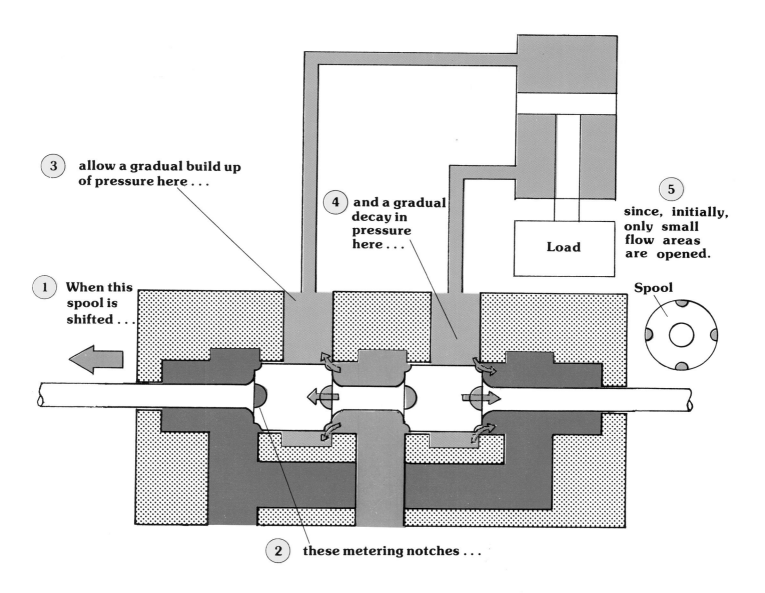

③ **allow a gradual build up of pressure here . . .**

④ **and a gradual decay in pressure here . . .**

⑤ **since, initially, only small flow areas are opened.**

① **When this spool is shifted . . .**

Load

Spool

② **these metering notches . . .**

POSITIVE SPOOL OVERLAP

Whenever three or more ports are influenced by the movement of the spool, land dimensions will determine how the ports interconnect and disconnect. Since the operation of the actuator is affected by spool overlap, the crossover condition for the control function at hand must be considered. One type of spool overlapping is referred to as *positive overlap.*

We will consider how the pressure port P will be disconnected from the A port and connected to the B port as the spool moves to the right. As illustrated, pressure will be

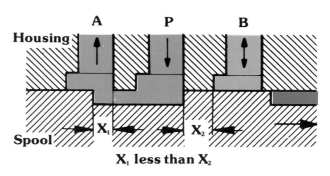

Diagram Showing the Principle of Positive Overlapping

blocked from the A port when the spool moves to the right through dimension X_1. It must, however, move through dimension X_2 to allow pressure to connect with port B. In matching the spool so that dimension X_1 will be less than dimension X_2, A will be disconnected from P before P opens to B. This means that during the crossover condition, all ports will be momentarily isolated from each other. With this type of overlapping, there will be no loss in pressure since the ports are never interconnected. In applications with overhung loads, the actuator cannot drift during crossover.

The disadvantage with positive overlapping, however, is that during the short time period of crossover, pump flow has nowhere to go. Besides, the duration of crossover is usually less than the response time required for opening the relief valve. An unavoidable pressure surge is created, which appears in the system as an audible pressure knock. Nevertheless, the damaging affects of this pressure surge can be reduced by metering notches on the spool lands and capacitances in the system. Hoses for instance, dampen the knock, since they can stretch slightly during the pressure surge.

NEGATIVE SPOOL OVERLAP

The counterpart of positive overlapping is simply referred to as *negative overlap*. Negative overlapping is achieved by changing the proportions between dimensions X_1 and X_2 as shown in our previous illustrations. In reconsidering the interconnection of the three ports P, A and B, you an see that a differently machined spool will obtain the same end results, but with a different crossover configuration.

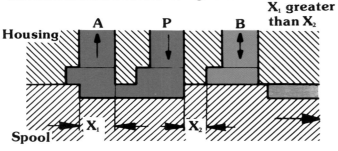

Diagram Showing the Principle of Negative Overlapping

In this illustration, pressure is opened to port B before it is disconnected from port A. Since the X_2 dimension is less than dimension X_1, all ports momentarily interconnect as the spool moves to the right. During the crossover period, pump flow can take the path of least resistance to either the A or B port of the actuator. Since pump flow is never blocked, pressure surges, as found in positively overlapped valves, are avoided. Consequently, negative overlapped valves can be incorporated to obtain smoother and quieter shifting, while at the same time protecting the system and components from high pressure surges.

Unfortunately, the advantages of negative overlapping are of-

ten offset by one serious disadvantage. In the example, during the crossover period, both ports of the actuator are interconnected. If the actuator is exposed to an overhung load, the directional control, in itself, cannot prevent drift during crossover. Since holding pressure can be lost, negatively overlapped valves are often used with some type of counterbalance or with a pilot operated check valve.

ZERO SPOOL OVERLAP

The compromise between positive and negative overlap is referred to as *zero overlap*. With this type of spool, the X_1 dimension is exactly equal to the X_2 dimension. During crossover, pump flow opens to port B at the same time that it is disconnected from port A.

Needless to say, this type of overlapping requires a high degree of accuracy in the machining of both the spool and the housing. Since it is difficult to manufacture correctly, the cost generally limits its use to electronic servo type directional controls.

SYMBOL REPRESENTATION OF CROSSOVER CONDITIONS

The flow path during spool shift can be represented in symbol form, which will be an aid to you in valve selection. We already know that a positively overlapped spool disconnects one passage before opening to another. Therefore, the symbol for a *two position* 4-way valve can be expanded to incorporate this crossover condition.

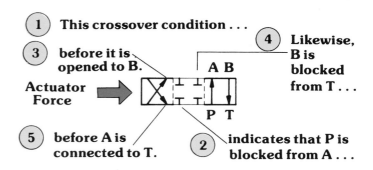

Symbol For A Positively Overlapped 2 Position Valve

Notice that the crossover condition is separated from the symbols for the actual flow position by dash lines. This is done in order to avoid confusing the symbol with that of a 3 position closed center spool. The crossover condition for two and three position valves with a positive and negative

overlap are summarized in the chart.

SYMBOL	DESCRIPTION
	Two Position Valve With Positive Overlap
	Two Position Valve With Negative Overlap
	Three Position Closed Center Valve With Positive Overlap
	Three Position Tandem Center Valve With Negative Overlap

SEALING ABILITY OF SLIDING SPOOL DIRECTIONAL CONTROLS

Since the spool must slide in the valve housing, there must be a clearance fit. To provide this sliding fit, the spool diameter must be slightly smaller than the diameter of the bore in the valve housing. Because this clearance also provides a leakage path, the sliding spool directional control never completely seals one port from another. Nevertheless, leakage is minimized by holding exact tolerances in three different areas. Modern machine tools allow valve manufacturers to machine to extremely accurate tolerances on clearance, concentricity and spool overlap, all of which influence the leakage rate of the valve.

WHAT IS A MICRON

To understand the sealing ability of a sliding spool directional control, you must first realize the order of magnitude with which the spool and bore are dimensioned. In measuring diameter and concentricity, the units of *microns* are often used. The micron, a familiar term in connection with filtration, is equivalent to a millionth of a meter, or

.000039 inches (39 millionths of an inch. The exact conversion is: 1 micron equals 39.37008 micro–inches).

Since the lower limit of visibility with the unaided eye is approximately 40 microns, it is difficult to visualize a dimension of 1 micron. Some familiar items can, however, be described in micron dimensions. For instance, this page is printed on paper which is approximately 120 microns thick. Also, if you are a normal human being, the hair on your head ranges somewhere between 65 and 75 microns in diameter; your white blood cells have a diameter of approximately 25 microns; your red blood cells measure in at about 8 microns. We will now consider the dimensional criteria for a standard hydraulic directional control valve.

DIMENSIONS WHICH AFFECT LEAKAGE

For a standard 12 GPM directional control, the nominal clearance held in production ranges from 8 to 10 microns. When the spool is concentric with the bore, there is a radial clearance of 4 to 5 microns between the circumference of the spool and the inside bore diameter. Although this clearance allows some oil leakage (in an overlapped position), the spool land would prohibit even something as small as a human red blood cell from passing from one port to another.

Actually, the clearance fit of a directional control is nothing more than a flow orifice, and, for any particular valve and fluid, the leakage rate is influenced by the orifice size as well as by the pressure differential. Since we cannot change the prevailing pressure conditions, the orifice size and shape will determine the leakage characteristics of the valve.

Although the clearance fit of the spool drastically influences the leakage characteristics of the valve, it is not the only determining factor. For instance, if the two similar valves are compared, we find that the clearance between the spool and valve housing is 8 microns nominal for both valves. Nevertheless, when tested for leakage, it has been found that valve A leaks considerably more than valve B.

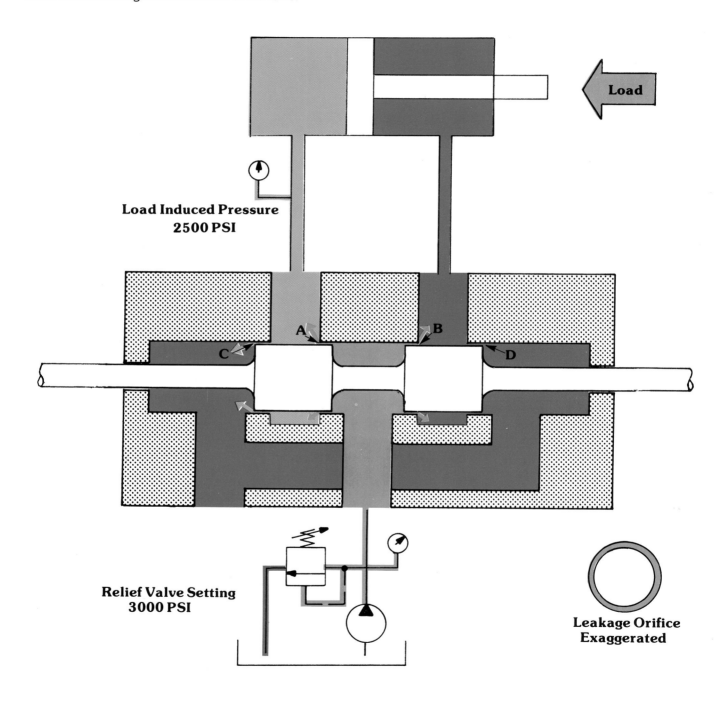

Typical Leakage Path Of A 4-Way Closed Center Directional Control

Viscosity 120 SUS @ 100° F.	Valve A Leakage in.³/min.			Valve B Leakage in.³/min.		
Pressure At Port(s)	P	P-A	P-B	P	P-A	P-B
Leakage Measured At Ports	A,B,T	B,T	A,T	A,B,T	B,T	A,T
750 PSI	1.04	1.16	9.76	.49	.43	.30
1500 PSI	2.75	2.75	2.32	1.03	.92	.55
3000 PSI	8.54	8.54	7.02	3.36	1.89	1.71
4500 PSI	17.08	17.70	15.56	9.15	4.88	4.27

Actually, two additional dimensional considerations have an important influence on a valve's leakage characteristics. If, for instance, the *shape* of the leakage orifice is considered, it is easy to see how both concentricity and length of overlap will affect leakage rates.

In production, it is important to maintain a *concentricity* tolerance of about 2 microns. Of course, this tolerance must be maintained on both the bore and spool diameters. As shown, if the concentricity varies too greatly, the resulting flow area can be considerably enlarged. It is important to note that both valves can display similar nominal clearances.

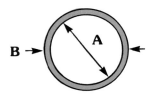

Ideal Concentricity

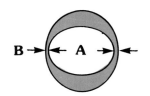

Increased Orifice Area Due To Elliptical Bore And Spool

Concentricity Affects Leakage

Likewise, the fact must also be considered that the *length* of the leakage orifice affects the overall leakage performance of the valve. It has been shown in Chapter 3 (in the discussion of temperature compensation) how the length of an orifice affects the flow rate at a particular pressure drop. In directional controls, the flow through the leakage orifice must be minimized. Consequently, the more the spool land overlaps the bore in the valve housing, the longer is the length of the resulting leakage orifice. This increases the resistance to leakage because of increased friction in the flow path.

FIELD SERVICING OF SPOOL TYPE DIRECTIONAL CONTROLS

It is important for those who work with hydraulic systems to be concerned with directional valve leakage both in valve selection and in field service. Leakage can affect both the accuracy of speed control (Chapter 3) and heat generation. For this reason, proper care must be taken in field servicing of spool type directional controls.

The common cause of directional valve malfunction, which inevitably renders the system inoperative, is *stuck spools*. Even though spools are hardened (68 Rockwell C), they are susceptible to damage by contamination in the hydraulic fluid. New spools are ground to a mirror finish so that proper leakage characteristics can be obtained. Needless to say, visible scratches on the spool lands drastically change the original dimensional criteria established for the valve.

Typical Spool Damaged By Contamination

Although it is practically impossible to field repair a valve to achieve new valve performance, freeing the stuck spool can get the system back into operation. However, excessive material should not be removed from either the bore or the spool in the repair process. This means that nothing more should be done than to *polish* the sliding surfaces. This can be accomplished by buffing the surface with a very fine automotive type polishing compound or a (1A to 6A) lapping compound. Of course, proper cleaning after polishing is of utmost importance. Emery cloth or similar abrasives should not be used.

BALANCING GROOVES

You may notice that, on most spool lands, there are a number of grooves cut around the circumference of the land. These grooves serve to center the spool in its bore, while simultaneously providing better lubrication between the sliding surfaces.

In a spool type directional control, pressure conditions tend to unbalance the spool. The net result is that the spool is forced against the side wall of the bore. Inevitably, this can cause wear and subsequent seizure. The balancing grooves provide a path whereby high pressure fluid can equalize around the diameter of the spool. This balances the forces on the spool so that it remains concentric with the bore.

Although adequate lubrication can occur under pressure with oil films as thin as ½ of a micron, the balancing grooves also aid in lubricating the closed tolerance fit. Under low pressure operating conditions, the oil which is stored in the groove is distributed over the sliding surfaces as the valve is operated.

MAXIMUM FLOW RATE FOR DIRECTIONAL CONTROLS

In comparing modern directional controls with those of 20 years ago, it is evident that, today, considerably smaller valves are able to handle higher flow rates. For instance, in the late 1950's, a typical 80 GPM directional control was 26" long, 6.3" wide, 9" high, and weighed 245 pounds. Today a directional control for 80 GPM can be as small as 10" × 4.5" × 7.3", with a weight of only 40 pounds.

Basically, the flow capability of a directional valve is determined by the cross-sectional flow area of the ports in the valve housing. Modern casing materials and innovative coring techniques have allowed valve manufacturers to cast housing with thinner walls, which allows for larger internal porting without compromising the pressure rating of the valve. Likewise, today's valves incorporate large *cast* passages, which had to be drilled with older manufacturing techniques.

In addition to the size of the passageway in the valve

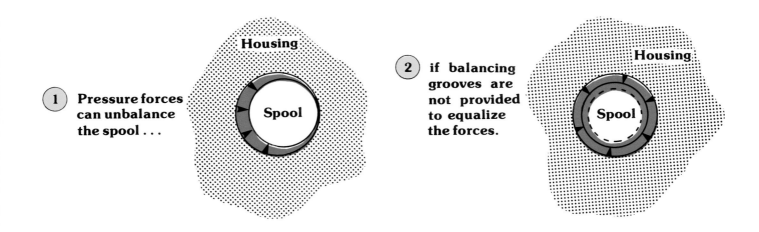

Balancing Grooves Center The Spool

Modern Cast Iron And Innovative Coring Techniques Allow For Larger Internal Flow Passages.

housing, spool diameter and spool stroke also influence the maximum flow capability of the valve. It is easy to see that when a spool is shifted to interconnect two ports, the size of the flow area which is opened is determined by the diameter of the bore in the valve housing. Of course, the larger the diameter of the bore, the larger the final flow area. As shown in the illustration, stroke length of the spool also influences the final flow area.

MAXIMUM FLOW BEFORE VALVE MALFUNCTION

With any spool type directional control, a point is reached where the spool can no longer be shifted by the actuator against the flow rate to which the valve is exposed. Also, with some spool configurations, an excessive flow rate can cause the spool to self-shift. This phenomenon is caused by a flow related pressure imbalance.

Virtually every spool type directional control is designed with equal opposing areas for pressure to work against. This means that in a *static condition*, the pressure force on the spool to the left is balanced by equivalent forces to the right. It is important to realize that this balanced condition only exists when there is *no flow* through the directional control. The moment fluid starts flowing, a reduced pressure area is created where the flow area is the smallest, and the fluid velocity is the greatest.

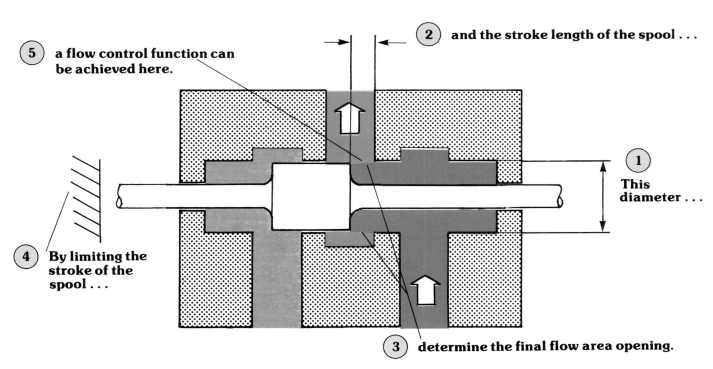

Mechanical Factors Which Affect Flow Rate

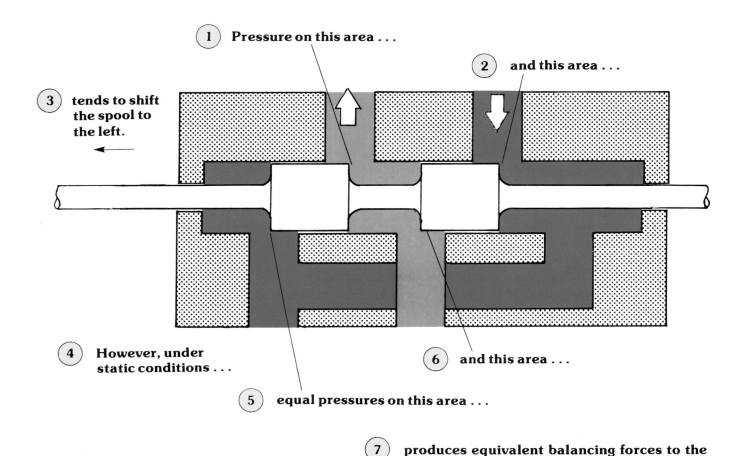

① **Pressure on this area . . .**

② **and this area . . .**

③ **tends to shift the spool to the left.**

←

④ **However, under static conditions . . .**

⑥ **and this area . . .**

⑤ **equal pressures on this area . . .**

⑦ **produces equivalent balancing forces to the right.**

BERNOULLI'S THEOREM

In the 18th century, a Swiss scientist named Daniel Bernoulli, developed a theory for the relationship between fluid velocity, pressure and elevation. Although it is beyond the scope of this text to fully explain this theory, we will attempt to explain how this principle affects the maximum flow capacity of a spool type directional control.

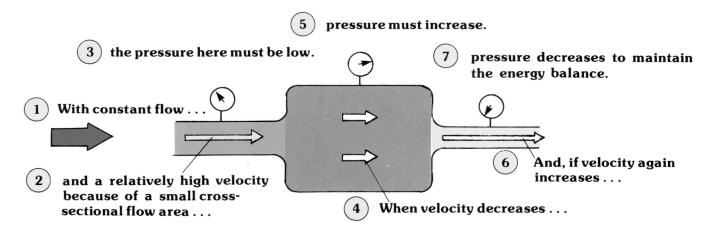

⑤ **pressure must increase.**

③ **the pressure here must be low.**

⑦ **pressure decreases to maintain the energy balance.**

① **With constant flow . . .**

② **and a relatively high velocity because of a small cross-sectional flow area . . .**

④ **When velocity decreases . . .**

⑥ **And, if velocity again increases . . .**

Bernoulli's Theorem

Based on the fact that *energy cannot be created or destroyed* (chapter 1), Bernoulli implied that the energy level in a hydraulic system is always constant. However, since oil moves through the hydraulic system, this energy exists in two forms: *Kinetic energy* and *potential energy*. Potential energy has the *potential* for doing work and is stored in the hydraulic system in the form of *pressure*. Kinetic energy, on the other hand, is energy in *motion* and is related to the mass and velocity of the fluid.

In a hydraulic system with a constant flow rate, this means that for each decrease in pressure (potential energy), there must be an increase in fluid velocity (kinetic energy). Likewise, when fluid velocity increases, pressure must decrease to maintain the constant balance between kinetic and potential energy. This, of course, is based on the assumption that the system is 100% efficient, and does not convert any energy into heat because of friction.

In actual application, each time the cross-sectional area of the fluid conductor changes, there is a change in the velocity of the fluid. In turn, changes in the pressure levels occur, however, they are not easily detectable. The problem is that friction will convert more and more of the potential energy (pressure) into heat as the fluid passes through the system. This conversion of energy has the tendency to camouflage the effects of the Bernoulli principle.

Nevertheless, velocity changes are prevalent as oil passes through spool type directional controls. These velocity changes, in turn, unbalance the pressure forces in the valve. Consequently, at some maximum flow, the change in fluid velocities upsets the pressure balance so drastically that the axial forces on the spool, due to flow, are greater than the shifting force of the actuator. This ultimately results in malfunction of the valve.

PERFORMANCE DATA FOR DIRECTIONAL CONTROLS

In sizing a directional control for a hydraulic system, one of your main concerns should be the pressure and flow information which is published in the manufacturer's technical data sheet. This information tells you the amount of pressure necessary to push the required flow through the directional control, and the maximum flow before valve malfunction at the pressure at which the system will be operating.

As mentioned in Chapter 1, the pressure required to cause a flow of fluid through a directional valve creates no useful work. For this reason, the loss in pressure shows up as heat in the hydraulic system.

In this typical pressure versus flow graph, pressure drops are given for various directions of flow through the valve. It is important to understand that when the 4-way valves are used in normal installations, there are simultaneous flows through

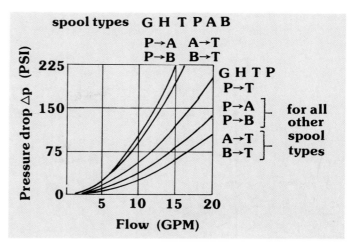

Typical Pressure Versus Flow Characteristics

two different passages in the valve. The term "loop-drop" expresses the total pressure loss for these simultaneous flows. For instance, in one position of the valve, there is a simultaneous flow from P to A and B to T. If the directional control is used with a cylinder having a 2 to 1 ratio, the pressure drop can become considerable.

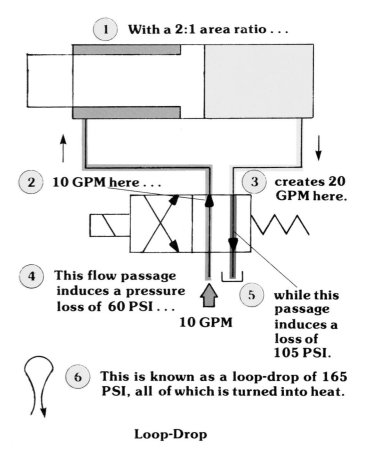

Loop-Drop

A second area of concern is establishing the maximum flow at which the selected valve will malfunction. Unfortunately, this value cannot be simply stated as some maximum flow in GPM. The maximum flow value is dependent on both the pressure at which the valve will operate and the application in which the valve is used. As shown in the chart labeled "Maximum Performance Data," the maximum flow value decreases as operating pressure increases. Likewise, the figures are based on using the directional control in a pure 4-way function with equivalent simultaneous flows. If the valve is used with large rod cylinders or as a 3-way valve (one cylinder port plugged), the maximum flow value could be considerably lower. If the valve under consideration appears marginal for the application, a larger valve should be selected.

Maximum Performance Data					
Flow (GPM) for spool types	at pressure (PSI) of				
	750	1500	3000	3750	4500
E, C/O, D/O	21	21	19.8	15.8	15.8
J,H,M,C,L,Q,W,U,V	21	21	19.8	13.2	11.9
G,D,R,F,P,T	19.8	18.5	15.8	13.2	11.9
A,B	13.2	11.9	9.3	7.9	6.6

Typical Maximum Performance Data

DIRECT OPERATED VALVES

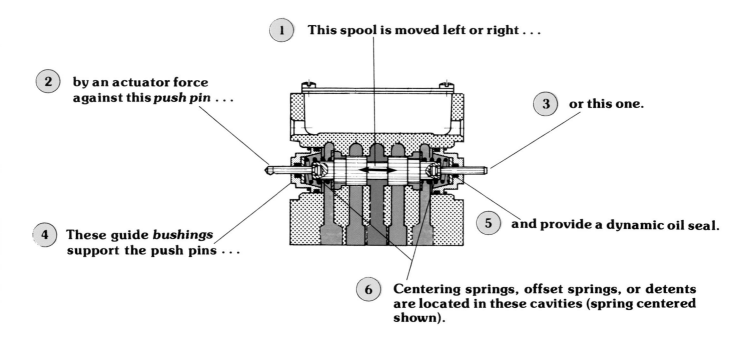

1 This spool is moved left or right . . .

2 by an actuator force against this *push pin* . . .

3 or this one.

4 These guide *bushings* support the push pins · · ·

5 and provide a dynamic oil seal.

6 Centering springs, offset springs, or detents are located in these cavities (spring centered shown).

Cross Section Of A Direct Acting Valve Housing Without Actuators

Double Solenoid

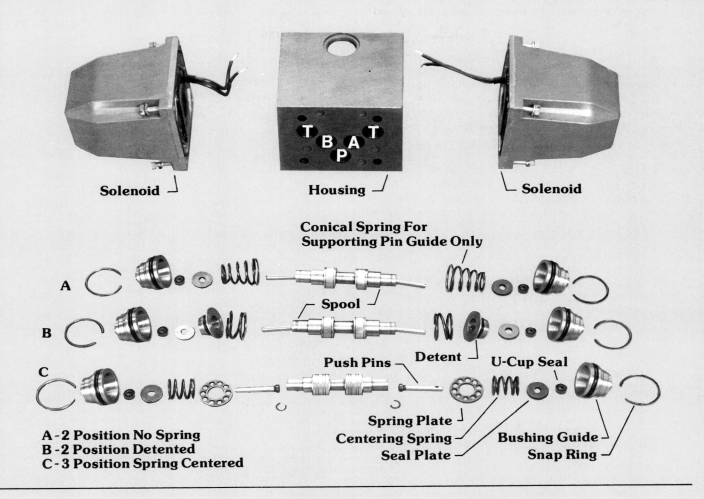

Solenoid

Housing

Solenoid

T B A T
B A
P

Conical Spring For Supporting Pin Guide Only

A

B

C

Spool

Push Pins

Detent

U-Cup Seal

Spring Plate

Centering Spring

Seal Plate

Bushing Guide

Snap Ring

A - 2 Position No Spring
B - 2 Position Detented
C - 3 Position Spring Centered

Single Solenoid

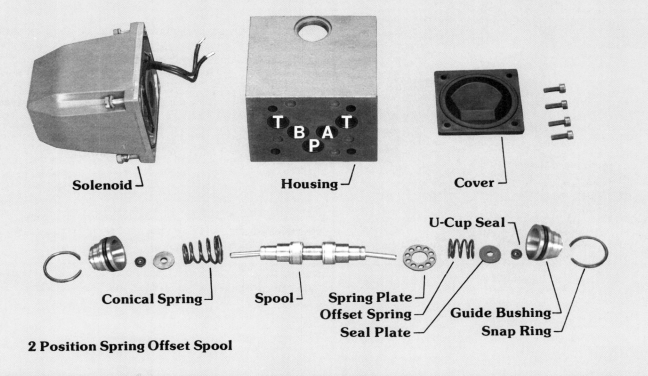

Solenoid

Housing

Cover

T B A T
B A
P

U-Cup Seal

Conical Spring

Spool

Spring Plate

Offset Spring

Seal Plate

Guide Bushing

Snap Ring

2 Position Spring Offset Spool

Direct acting valves are those in which the shifting force of the actuator works directly on the valve spool. Up to this point, the directional spool valve function has been described in terms of some external force being available for positioning the spool in the valve housing. Although the methods of positioning have been discussed (spring centered, spring offset, no spring, and detented), the different types of actuators have not yet been covered. A great deal of circuit design flexibility is offered by different types of actuators. In addition, operator convenience and safety depend on the selection of the proper actuator for the intended application. We will now discuss a representative cross section of the various actuators available.

In general, direct operated valve actuators can be classified as mechanical, pilot operated or electrical solenoid. In turn, each classification can be subdivided into distinctly different types of actuators. For instance, if only mechanical actuators were considered, a selection could be made from three basic types: hand lever, rotary hand knob, and roller cam operators. Unfortunately, it would be impractical to discuss the intricacies of each type of actuator. For this reason, we have selected representatives from each group for discussion of operation and application. The subject matter will be devoted directly to the actuator itself with the assumption that its purpose is to position the spool in the valve housing.

MECHANICAL ACTUATORS

Mechanical actuators are used to interface shifting force working on the spool with a mechanical command from the machine, or a manual command from the machine operator. Manual actuators are intended for mounting at the operator's control station, and, they take the form of a hand lever, rotary knob or palm button. On the other hand, mechanical operators are intended to operate automatically during the machine's cycle, and they usually take the form of a roller cam operator, mounted on the machinery.

The hand lever actuator is by far the most popular manual control. It is one of the few valve actuators which pushes and pulls on the spool to achieve the desired spool position. In fact, most actuators, other than manual, are only capable of pushing on the spool.

The operational cross section shows a three position, spring centered, hand lever actuator. When no force is applied by the operator, the spool is centered by the two centering springs which position the hand lever in the vertical position. As shown in the illustration, when the operator pushes on the hand lever, the force passes through the ball pivot joint and moves the slide so that the spool is pulled to the left, compressing the left hand centering spring. Then, when the hand lever is pulled, the slide will push the spool to the right.

In addition to the spring centered version, the same actuator can be used with a two position spring offset spool. In this application, a different set of springs would push the spool to the far left position, which in turn would position the hand lever in the right most position. When the operator pulls on the hand lever, the spool will move to the right, compressing the offsetting spring.

A third type of operation, which can only be achieved with a push-pull type manual operator, is a three position detent. This detent assembly is located in the actuator itself rather than on the spool, as has already been discussed for detented valves with double actuators. Unlike push type actuators, the hand lever allows the *operator* to position the spool in any one of the three flow positions. This position is then maintained by the detent.

Mechanically, the detent is achieved by having a spring loaded ball position itself in grooves machined on the slide in

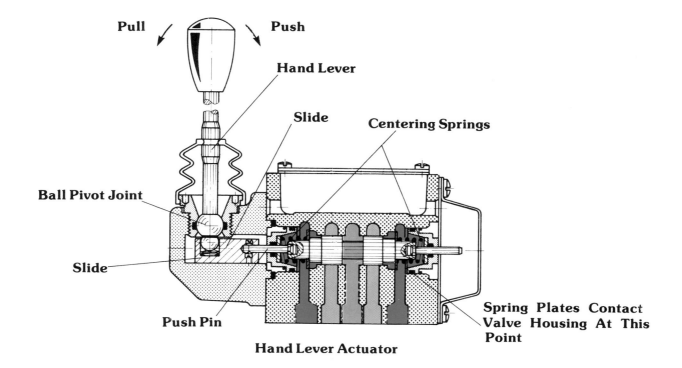

Hand Lever Actuator

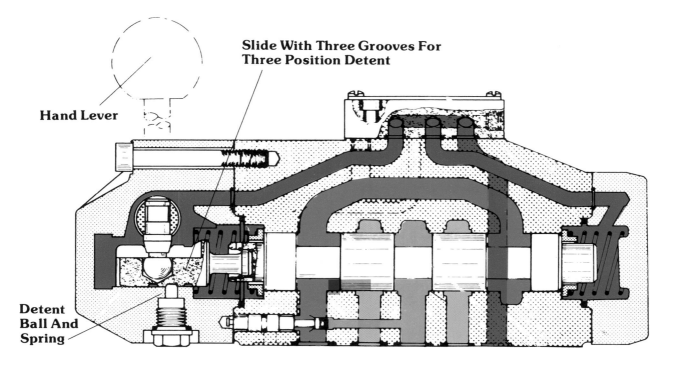

the actuator. Needless to say, the slide for a three position function would have three grooves, while a two position detent would have a slide with only two grooves.

Instead of using manual operation, it is sometimes necessary to automate the directional function by allowing the machine to determine the position of the directional control spool. Mechanically, this is normally accomplished by positioning the spool by means of a cam. Sequential applications can be

achieved by operating the valve with a cam which follows the stroke of a cylinder. Time sequenced operation can also be achieved by operating one or more directional valves with a motor driven cam.

An important fact to consider when you deal with cam operated directional controls is that it is relatively difficult to achieve a pulling force for positioning the spool. For this reason, cam operated valves are usually spring offset to one end position, even if the valve being used is a three position valve. In this way, the cam pushes the spool approximately half stroke to achieve the center flow conditions, while reverse flow in the third position is achieved when the cam pushes the spool full stroke against the spring.

As shown in the cross-sectional illustration of a three position, cam operated directional control, the spool is shifted from one position to another in a total stroke of approximately 1/8 of an inch. Since all three positions must be achieved in 1/4" of travel, the cam must be designed and manufactured quite accurately. Likewise, since there is no allowance for over travel, precautions must be taken, especially during set-ups, so that the cam cannot force the spool past its fully depressed position. Also, as shown in the example, the approach angle of the cam must be limited to 30° in order to minimize the radial forces on the plunger.

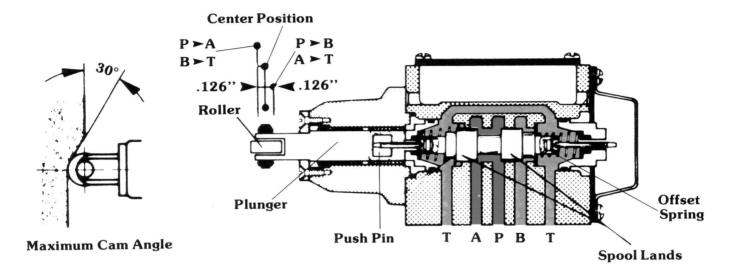

Maximum Cam Angle

Typical Three Position Cam Operator

PILOT ACTUATORS FOR DIRECT OPERATED VALVES

In many hydraulic circuits, it is desirable to interface the shifting of a directional control spool with either a pneumatic or hydraulic pressure signal. One application which often uses this type of actuator is a hydraulic system which must be operated in an explosive atmosphere. In this type of application, it is usually more economical to use a pneumatic or hydraulic control circuit, than an explosion proof electrical solenoid control.

The cross-sectional illustration shows a typical two position

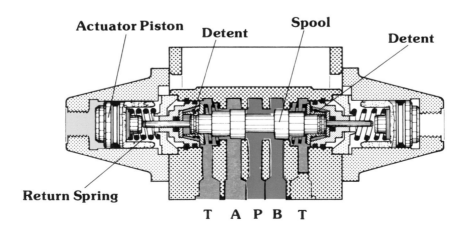

detented valve with two opposing pilot actuators. The actuator is a push type design, consisting of a housing sealed piston and return spring. As shown, pilot pressure on the left-hand actuator pushes the spool to the right, connecting P with B and A with tank. Notice that when the spool is moved into position, it is held by the ball detent assembly on the left-hand side of the valve. Even if pilot pressure is lost in the left actuator, the spool will remain in this position until a pressure signal activates the opposite actuator. When pilot pressure is applied to the right-hand actuator, the spool is pushed into its second detented position. The spring return in the actuator overcomes the static friction of the piston seal, and causes the piston to retract when the pressure signal is removed.

Normally, pilot actuators are not capable of withstanding full system pressure. Consequently, the pressure in the control circuit must be limited to the pressure rating of the pneumatic or hydraulic actuator. The hydraulic actuator, for instance, will operate satisfactorily within a range of 60 to 900 PSI. A similar pneumatic actuator will work in a range of 60 to 180 PSI.

The pilot actuators, as shown, require a minimum of 60 PSI to assure that there will be sufficient force available for shifting the spool. The upper pressure limit (180 PSI pneumatic, or 900 PSI hydraulic) is simply the maximum pressure rating of the piston seal and/or housing. With pneumatics, it is sometimes advantageous to operate the directional valve within a considerably lower pressure range. This is accomplished by using an actuator with a larger piston area. The large piston provides adequate shifting force with a supply pressure somewhere between 22 and 90 PSI.

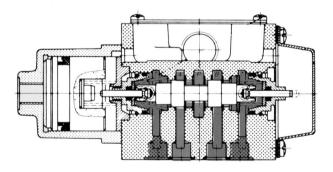

Low Pressure Pneumatic Actuator

ELECTRICAL ACTUATORS

Electric *solenoid* actuators are by far the most popular of all possible actuators for direct operated directional controls. Automation has caused a trend toward electrical and away from manual or mechanical controls. Automatic or semi-automatic control is far more versatile and more easily accomplished with electrical control circuitry. Push buttons,

relays, limit switches and programmable timers are relatively inexpensive electrical components which simplify control circuit design. Likewise, compactness, aesthetics, remote control, and the ability to intermix manual and automated control are all facts in favor of solenoid actuators.

The solenoid, although simple in principle, is offered in a variety of styles. Since different solenoid designs offer different advantages, depending on the application, we will discuss the most popular models. In general, solenoids are available for a variety of voltages (and frequencies) in both AC and DC versions. Both *air gap* solenoids and *wet pin* solenoids have application dependent advantages.

BASIC SOLENOID OPERATION

Whenever electric current flows through a wire, there is a magnetic field created around that wire. This magnetic field, although weak when considering a single strand of wire, can be concentrated in two ways. Since the shifting force from a solenoid is determined by the strength of the magnetic field, it is this force which must be optimized.

First of all, if the wire is wound into a coil, the magnetic field becomes much stronger and is generated in a circular shape around the coil windings. If the electric current is constant through the coil of wire, then the magnetic field is similar to that of a bar shaped permanent magnet. Likewise, the higher the number of turns, the stronger the magnetic field becomes.

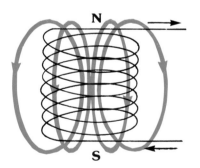

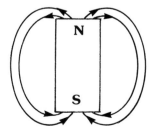

Magnetic Field Of A Permanent Magnet And An Electromagnet

Secondly, the magnetic field flows more readily through a magnetic material such as iron or steel than it does through air. Therefore, the magnetic field can be concentrated by adding a "*C-frame*" of iron around the outside of the coil. Now, if a movable iron *plunger* is placed inside the coil, the magnetic field will be more intense when the plunger is in such a position that the C-frame and plunger are totally within the magnetic field. The magnetic force of the solenoid will develop when the coil is energized. This attraction will pull the plunger to its point of equilibrium within the magnetic field.

1 **When there is no electric current through this coil of wire . . .**

3 **which allows free movement of this plunger.**

2 **there is no magnetic field in this C-frame . . .**

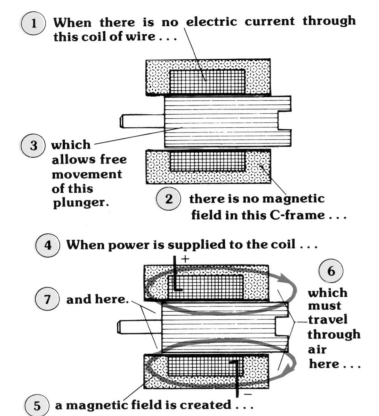

4 **When power is supplied to the coil . . .**

7 **and here.**

6 **which must travel through air here . . .**

5 **a magnetic field is created . . .**

8 **This attracts the plunger to an equilibrium position . . .**

9 **creating an output force . . .**

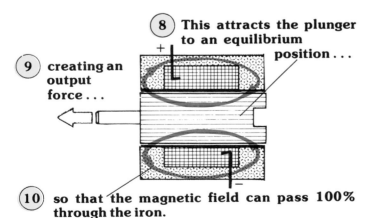

10 **so that the magnetic field can pass 100% through the iron.**

Principle Of Basic Solenoid Operation

DC SOLENOIDS

DC electricity, such as found in battery operated electrical systems, always has a constant polarity. In other words, using a flash light as our example, the electricity flows from the negative post of the battery, through the bulb, to the positive side of the battery, whenever the switch is in the on position. In a DC solenoid, this type of current develops a magnetic field which is constant in polarity, or, more specifically, has a definite north and south pole. When current is applied to a DC solenoid, the north and south poles of the C-frame simply attract the south and north poles of the plunger respectively. This moves the plunger against the push pin in the directional valve, causing the spool to shift.

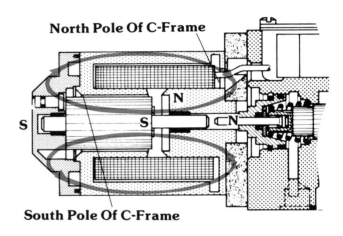

North Pole Of C-Frame

South Pole Of C-Frame

Directional Valve

When you are selecting a DC solenoid, you will discover that solenoids are available for virtually any voltage requirement. Although the solenoid will function satisfactorily over a broad range of voltage fluctuations, you must remember that if voltage increases, the current draw will also increase, since the windings for a given coil offer a fixed resistance. If the voltage is in excess of the solenoid rating, the extra current draw will produce heat which will eventually cause the solenoid to burn out. On the other hand, if supply voltage is below rating, a related loss in current may not create sufficient magnetic force to cause spool shift in the directional valve.

The DC solenoid, although slower in response when compared to an equivalent AC model (DC solenoids respond in the 50 to 60 ms range), can be cycled up to 15,000 cycles per hour without fear of overheating. The DC solenoid is also immune to burn-out problems associated with AC models. If a stuck spool prevents the solenoid from shifting, it will not burn out because of excessive current draw. This is true because DC current draw is simply related to the supply voltage and to the fixed resistance of the coil.

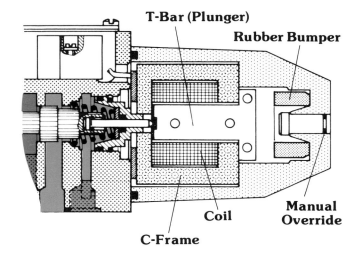

T-Bar (Plunger)

Rubber Bumper

Manual Override

Coil

C-Frame

AC SOLENOIDS

Although the AC solenoid functions in the same basic manner as the DC model, its magnetic field is influenced by the alternating current supply. In the United States, an AC solenoid operates on a voltage which alternates its polarity from positive through zero to negative at the rate of 60 cycles per second. (In most European countries, the rate is 50 cycles per second.) This has the net result of changing the polarity of the magnetic field at the same rate. Unfortunately, the magnetic force is high only when the AC current is at its positive or negative peak. As the current changes from positive to negative, or vice-versa, it must pass through a neutral point at which there is no current flow. During this short period of time, a point is reached at which there is no magnetic force. Without this magnetic attraction, the load can push the plunger slightly out of equilibrium. Then as the current builds up, the magnetism increases and pulls the plunger back into position. This movement of the solenoid in and out at a high cycle rate creates noise which is commonly referred to as "buzz."

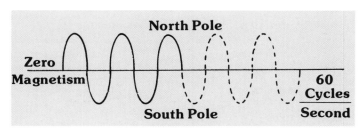

North Pole

Zero Magnetism

South Pole

60 Cycles Second

Graphic Representation Of The Magnetic Field At Either End Of An AC Coil

To eliminate "buzz" and to increase the solenoid's holding power, most AC solenoids incorporate what is known as a *shading coil.* A magnetic field passing through a coil of wire induces an electric current in the same way that electric current passing through a coil of wire creates a magnetic field. The flow of current in the shading coil in turn creates its own magnetic field. Due to a phenomenon in AC circuits which is called inductance, the current produced in the shading coil lags behind the applied current to the coil. When the applied current passes through zero in its change from one polarity to another, the current, and, thus, the magnetic field of the shading coil, is at its maximum. When the solenoid is used within its force rating, the magnetic field of the shading coil is sufficient in strength to keep the plunger in position, thus eliminating the buzz.

Shading Coils

CURRENT DRAW FOR AC SOLENOIDS

If the current draw of a DC solenoid is compared with that of an AC model, major differences can be found. In DC solenoids, the current which passes through the coil is constant at a given voltage because the resistance of the coil is also constant. With DC solenoids, wire diameter and length (number of turns) are the only variables affecting resistance. As the voltage is applied to a DC solenoid, the current draw builds from zero to the maximum value which can pass through the coil.

AC solenoids, on the other hand, display different characteristics with respect to current. Impedance is the measurement of an AC circuit's resistance to the flow of electricity. With AC solenoids, this impedance is quite low when the solenoid is open, and increases as the plunger is pulled into the closed position. Consequently, the flow of current through an AC solenoid is highest when the solenoid is open and has the least resistance to the flow of electricity.

This high flow of current, when the solenoid is open, is referred to as *inrush current.* The current draw, when the solenoid is closed, is referred to as *holding current.* Unfortunately, the high inrush current generates more heat than

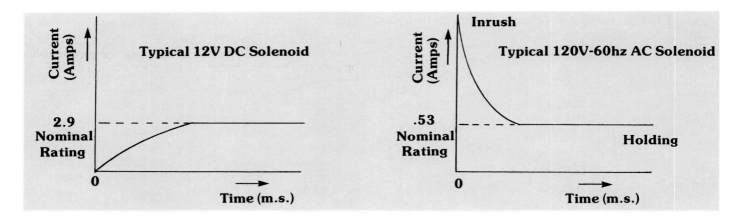

Comparison of DC And AC Solenoid Current Draw

can be continuously dissipated by the solenoid. If the plunger is not allowed to close due to a mechanical problem, the insulation will burn and the coil will short out. Since continuous duty AC solenoids can only dissipate the heat which is generated by the lower holding current, it is important that the plunger always achieves its closed position when the solenoid is energized.

Another problem created by the inrush characteristic of AC solenoids is overheating due to excessive cycling of the solenoid between the on and off positions. Each time the plunger closes, the coil winding is subjected to a high inrush current. If these inrush currents come too quickly, the heat will generate faster than it can be dissipated. Eventually, this will lead to failure of the solenoid. A typical class B AC solenoid can be cycled no more than two times per second, or 7200 cycles per hour, while class A solenoids are limited to approximately 4800 cycles per hour.

To avoid any confusion, it must be mentioned at this point that solenoids which are too hot to touch are more than likely operating at a perfectly satisfactory temperature. NEMA (National Electrical Manufacturers Association) has developed standard classifications for wire insulation. Of the four classes established by NEMA, wire used in solenoid coils is usually either class A or class B. Insulation which falls into the class A catagory must be suitable for operating continuously at temperatures up to 105° C (221° F). Class B insulation must be suitable for use up to 130° C (266° F). (The other two classes are class F - 155° C (311° F) and class H which is 180° C (356° F). The temperatures suitable for operation are far above the touchable limit of 120° F to 130° F. Normally, solenoids with class B insulation offer superior life expectancy and are recommended for all high cycling applications.

FREQUENCY AND AC SOLENOIDS

The current consumption of an AC coil is influenced by the operating frequency. Fortunately, on a worldwide basis, we normally only have to concern ourselves with two different frequencies, those being either 50 or 60 cycles. For maximum performance, coils can be wound for either a 50 or 60 cycle operation, but not for both. Now let us examine this further.

A 110V-50hz solenoid, when operating on 110V-60hz, draws too little current, and will not produce its rated force. On the other hand, a 120V-60hz coil, when subjected to 120V-50hz, will comsume too much current, causing it to overheat and burn out. If 50hz and 60hz are looked at graphically, it is easy to see that a 50 cycle current will last longer during each increment of polarity change, but will occur less frequently during a 1 second period.

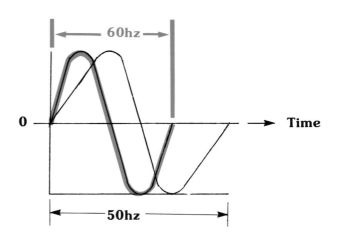

Because the current at 50hz is of longer duration, a 50 cycle coil actually will create, with fewer turns on the coil, a magnetic field identical to that of a 60hz model. Since this 50hz coil has a resistance (impedance) which is fixed by physical factors, the only thing which can be done to get the same current flow (during the shorter 60hz time period), is to increase the voltage. The amount of voltage increase is mathematically equivalent to the factor of 60/50 or 6/5. This means that in order to obtain the best performance for a 110V-50hz solenoid, it must operate at 132 volts when using 60hz;

$$110V \times \frac{6}{5} = 132V$$

A 120V-60hz solenoid, on the other hand, has more turns on its coil than does the 50hz model. The longer duration of a 50hz current saturates the magnetic field of a 60hz coil. This, in turn, lessens the impedance of the AC solenoid, which draws excessive current. Nevertheless, the thermal overload problem can be eliminated by reducing the applied voltage to 5/6 of the solenoid's rating, hence:

$$120V \times \frac{5}{6} = 100V$$

This means that the 120V-60hz solenoid will not overheat if operated on 100V-50hz.

THE SO-CALLED DUAL FREQUENCY COIL

In the United States, the power companies *nominally* rate the supply voltage at either 120 volts or 240 volts, 60hz. Ninety percent of all electrical power outside of the United States is *nominally* rated at 110 volts or 220 volts, 50hz. *Nominal* is emphasized because this is the voltage the power company strives to supply at the transformer station. When you consider that available voltage can fluctuate during a one day operating period, depending on the community's demands on the generating station, you will understand why the voltage available at the solenoid may not always be 120 volts. Likewise, long wire runs, as found in most industrial plants, also play a part in reducing the available voltage at the solenoid. Fortunately, most industrial grade solenoids will operate satisfactorily within ±10% of their rated AC voltage. Any fluctuation greater than this cause solenoid burn-out for one of two reasons. Overvoltage has the tendency to drive too much current through the solenoid, causing it to overheat, while undervoltage reduces the power of the solenoid to the point where it can no longer close. This, in turn, causes a continuously high inrush, which also burns out the coil windings. If there are solenoids which are burning out for no apparent mechanical reason, check the line voltage *at the solenoid* with a *good* volt meter, or have the local power company check the line voltage over a specific period with a chart reader.

Up to this point, we have said that coils should be wound for either 50 or 60 cycle operations. We have also indicated that voltage fluctuation in the supply from the power company is inevitable, but that it is usually kept within acceptable limits. For those of you who are familiar with the so-called dual frequency solenoid, it may seem that the previous explanation of frequency requirements was too restrictive.

Dual frequency coils (50-60hz) are actually wound for 110V-50hz and then used on valves where their reduced performance at 120V-60hz is adequate for proper valve operation. This dual frequency compromise is possible only because there is not too great of a difference in power and frequency between the 50 cycle and 60 cycle operation, and most 50 cycle voltage is 100 volts, while most 60 cycle voltage is rated at 120 volts. The previous explanation showed that if Europe operated on 110V-50hz and the U.S. operated on 132V-60hz, there would be no need for different solenoids. Unfortunately, this compromise does not leave the end user much margin of safety for fluctuations in supply voltage. In addition, if the 50hz solenoid attains sufficient shifting force when operated on 60hz, it will have too much force when operated at 50hz. This extra force can actually cause the solenoid to hammer itself to pieces.

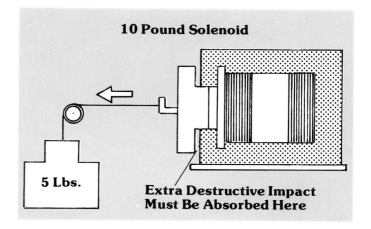

10 Pound Solenoid

5 Lbs.

Extra Destructive Impact Must Be Absorbed Here

WET PIN SOLENOIDS

Up to now, we have assumed that our solenoids are actuators which are simply bolted to the exterior valve housing. Like any of the mechanical or pilot actuators, they work against a pushpin which is dynamically sealed against leakage of oil from the tank port of the valve. These solenoids dissipate heat to the surrounding air and are commonly referred to as *air gap solenoids*. The *wet pin solenoid*

is slightly different in design since it allows tank port oil to communicate between the housing of the valve and the housing of the solenoid. This offers several major advantages.

BETTER HEAT DISSIPATION

Probably the most significant advantage of wet pin solenoids is their greater ability to dissipate heat. With AC solenoids, the high inrush current creates more and more heat the faster the solenoid cycles. However, the faster a wet pin solenoid cycles, the more cool oil from the tank port of the directional valve is circulated through its housing. The cool oil becomes a good heat sink, which absorbs the heat from the solenoid. As the oil circulates, the heat is carried into the hydraulic system where it can be easily dealt with.

DYNAMIC PUSHPIN SEAL IS ELIMINATED

The seal method incorporated with wet pin design offers several additional advantages. Because the oil flows freely in and out of the enclosed solenoid housing, the only sealing necessary is the static o-ring seal between the solenoid housing and the valve housing. By eliminating the dynamic

u-cup or o-ring seal on the pushpin, the leakage problem caused by seal wear is completely eliminated. Also, by eliminating the pressurized dynamic sealing, the overall shifting force is considerably reduced for both the solenoid and the return springs.

QUIET OPERATION

Quiet operation is another feature of wet pin solenoids. Although the clicking of a single solenoid is not all that objectionable, noise does become a problem on high cycling machines which may incorporate twenty or more directional controls. The reason for the quiet operation of wet pin solenoids is that the motion of the plunger is dampened by the hydraulic oil. As shown in the cross-sectional illustration, oil must be displaced for motion of the plunger to occur. The plungers are manufactured with axial holes or milled slots which provide a path for this oil transfer. Generally speaking, the path for oil flow through the plunger is relatively large for an AC solenoid, so as to allow the plunger to be pulled into position as quickly as possible. This, of course, lessens the heat generation by reducing the time during which the solenoid will draw a high inrush current. On the other hand, DC solenoids have a more restrictive path, which allows for extremely smooth valve shift. Typical response times are 20 to 30 m.s. for a wet pin AC solenoid, and 45 to 70 m.s. for DC versions.

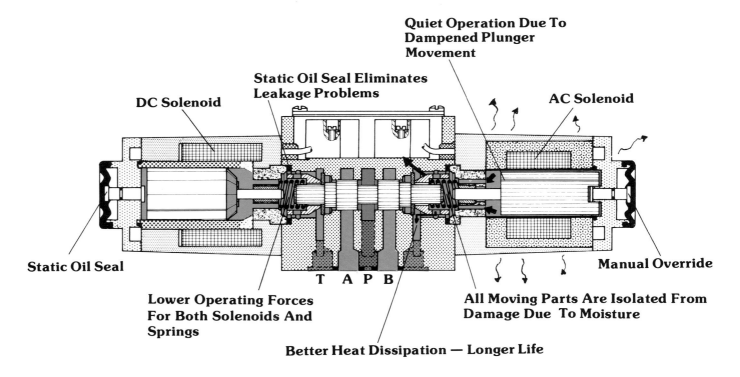

Features Of Wet Pin Solenoids

MOISTURE PROBLEMS ELIMINATED

Water is a common cause for failure of an air gap solenoid. In machine tool applications, for instance, cutting oils and water-based coolants are often splashed onto the exterior surfaces of solenoid operated directional controls and electrical conduit. Even with properly gasketed solenoids, this water will eventually work its way into the solenoid housing. Once inside, the water can cause a short circuit of the coil or, at the very least, corrosion of the pushpin which will mechanically prevent spool shift. In either, failure of the solenoid can occur. Since the wet pin solenoid is sealed to prevent oil leakage to the exterior of the valve, it also prevents water from leaking in. Consequently, problems associated with corrosion and short circuiting are eliminated.

SOLENOID LIFE EXPECTANCY

In the foregoing discussion, we have mentioned several factors which can cause premature failure of the solenoid. The major problems are summarized as follows:

—Plunger is mechanically prevented from shifting
—Excessive cycling
—Too low or too high supply voltage
—Operation on the wrong frequency
—Short circuiting due to moisture

These variables make it quite difficult to project a life expectancy for any given solenoid. For this reason, we offer the following laboratory results for comparison of the different solenoid types.

AC Air Gap Solenoids: 5 to 10 million cycles
DC Air Gap Solenoids: 30 million+ cycles
AC Wet Pin Solenoids: 15 to 25 million cycles
DC Wet Pin Solenoids: 40 million+ cycles

SOLENOID ACCESSORIES

In selecting solenoid operators, there are several options which will aid you in troubleshooting and in servicing of the valve. Manual overrides, indicator lights, and a variety of plug-in connectors are readily available and should be considered.

MANUAL OVERRIDES

Manual overrides are probably the single most important

feature available for convenience in troubleshooting a hydraulic system. In fact, most solenoids offer the manual override as a standard feature. As shown, the manual override is located in the end of the solenoid cover, and simply provides a mechanical means to apply an external shifting force to the plunger in the solenoid. This is an invaluable tool when it is necessary to *feel* if the solenoid is shifting the valve. The manual override can also be used to find out whether or not there is any type of mechanical obstruction. In some systems, emergency operation can be accomplished by using the manual override in the event of a power failure in the control circuit. Some manual overrides are push button type, while others require the use of a small screw driver, allen wrench, or welding rod for actuation.

INDICATOR LIGHTS

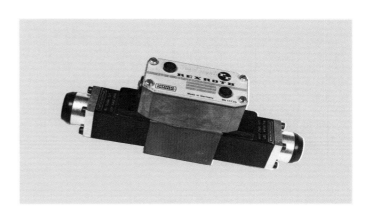

Indicator lights are either incandescent or neon bulbs which are wired *parallel* to the electrical solenoid. They are intended only to indicate when power is being supplied to the solenoid. Indicator lights are helpful in determining whether a malfunction has occured because of a valve failure or a problem in the electrical control circuit. If the valve is not shifting, but the light continues to function, a valve failure is indicated. However, if the light is not illuminated, chances are that the malfunction has occured in the control circuit. During proper operation of the equipment, indicator lights can be used to indicate what portion of the cycle the machine is in. Indicator lights are usually added to the electrical junction box and positioned adjacent to the solenoid with which they are connected.

PLUG-IN CONNECTORS

The plug-in connector is an optional feature which simplifies the replacement of a malfunctioning valve. The valve is simply unplugged, removed from its subplate and then replaced with an equivalent model. In the past, a single plug connection was made to the central electrical box on top of the valve body. This, of course, facilitates the replacement of

pressure at the valve's tank port. Needless to say, since these housings are usually constructed of molded plastic, the T port pressure must be restricted.

When the directional control is used to perform a pure 4-way function in a properly designed system, the tank port pressure should not exceed 300 to 500 PSI. Under these conditions, we would be well within the T port rating of any directional control. However, when the directional control is used in a series circuit (P port of the second valve connected to the T port of the first valve), or to perform a function other than its intended 4-way usage, the following points must be considered.

the complete valve, but requires unwiring of the solenoid during valve repair. Although this method is still quite popular (and will remain so), another type of plug-in connection is gaining in popularity.

Today, particularly with wet pin solenoids, it is not uncommon to see the coil molded into a plastic housing. With this design, it is also relatively simple to mold an inexpensive male portion of the plug in the same housing. In this way, the plug-in connection is individually made to each solenoid on a double solenoid valve. Repair can be made simply by unplugging the solenoid and removing it from the valve housing.

PRESSURE RATINGS OF PUSHPIN SEALS

In general, mechanical, air gap solenoids, or pilot operators push the spool into position by working against a *pushpin*. To prevent oil from entering the housing of the actuator, the pushpin is dynamically sealed against pressure in the T port passage in the valve housing. Either o-ring or u-cup seals, installed in the pin guide bushing, are commonly used to accomplish this seal.

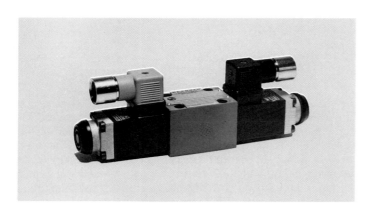

Individual Solenoid Plugs

MAXIMUM TANK PORT PRESSURE

In selecting any direct operated directional control, it is very important for you to consider the maximum tank port pressure. In general, there are two factors which can affect the maximum T port pressure rating. First, if the valve is operated by any actuator other than a wet pin solenoid, there must be a dynamic seal on the pushpin. Hence, the pressure rating of this seal becomes the limiting factor. Second, if the valve in question is a wet pin solenoid design, the pressure rating of its housing will determine the maximum permissible

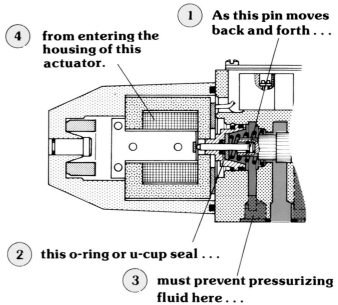

(1) **As this pin moves back and forth . . .**

(4) **from entering the housing of this actuator.**

(2) **this o-ring or u-cup seal . . .**

(3) **must prevent pressurizing fluid here . . .**

O-RING SEALS

The o-ring is the major sealing device used in all hydraulic components. The o-ring is nothing more than a molded ring of snythetic rubber which has a round cross section when in its free state. Although generally intended for high pressure

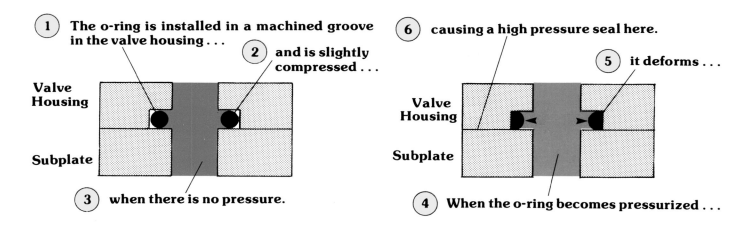

① The o-ring is installed in a machined groove in the valve housing . . .

② and is slightly compressed . . .

Valve Housing

Subplate

③ when there is no pressure.

⑥ causing a high pressure seal here.

⑤ it deforms . . .

Valve Housing

Subplate

④ When the o-ring becomes pressurized . . .

Static O-Ring Sealing (Dimensions Are Exaggerated)

static sealing, it can also provide adequate sealing for short stroke reciprocating motion at lower operating pressures.

In static applications (such as those found between the directional valve's housing and its subplate), the seal must only provide a leak free seal between the mating surfaces, which are rigidly in contact. Since there is virtually no clearance, the o-ring is fully contained in the annular groove formed by the mating surfaces. Pressure deforms the o-ring equally, causing it to fill any imperfections between the two surfaces.

DYNAMIC O-RING SEAL

The o-ring has also proven to be effective when used as a dynamic seal between close fitting parts which have relative motion. A perfect example is sealing between the pushpin and the guide bushing in the directional valves. However, o-rings in these applications are subject to failure for two reasons: pressure extrusion and friction.

As shown in the example of dynamic o-ring sealing, both friction and pressure extrusion into the clearance fit accelerates o-ring wear. The problem is compounded when relative motion must occur while the seal is pressurized. For this reason, directional valves with dynamic o-ring seals usually have two maximum T port pressure ratings. One rating is the maximum permissible pressure during valve shift, while the second rating indicates the maximum pressure while the valve is held in any one of its flow positions. These pressure limits are approximately 3000 PSI static and 1000 PSI during spool shift.

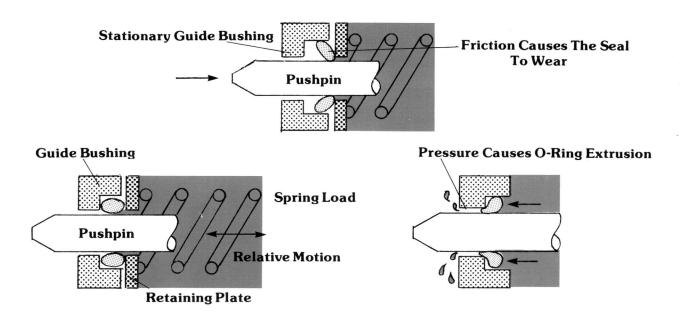

Example Of Dynamic O-Ring Sealing (Clearances Exaggerated)

Pressure Applied Here Expands The Cup, Causing A Tighter Seal

The Lip Self Compensates For Wear

Pressure Working From This Direction Cannot Be Sealed

Cross Section Of A U-Cup Seal

U-CUP PACKING

The modern u-cup packing has evolved from the compression packing, which was one of the first methods used in sealing hydraulic systems. The u-cup gets its name from the shape of its cross section, which has the shape of a U, or sometimes of a V.

U-cup packings are ideal for sealing parts which move axially with one another. Typical examples of their use are rod seals for hydraulic cylinders or in pushpin seals for direct operated directional controls. As shown in the cross-sectional illustration, the u-cup, when installed in a properly dimensioned groove, is effective for sealing against high pressure, but only in one direction. The sealing effectiveness increases with increased pressure.

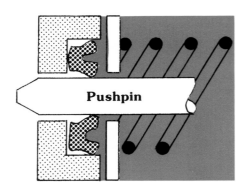

Pushpin

U-Cup Packing For Direct Operated Directional Valves

When installed in the pin guide bushing of a directional control, the flared inner lip of the u-cup contacts the pushpin at an angle with a slight preloading. The shape of the seal makes it virtually immune to pressure extrusion. Likewise, its low friction characteristics provide extremely long seal life, and allows the directional valve to be shifted with tank port pressures in the range of 2000 to 3000 PSI.

PRESSURE RATINGS OF WET PIN SOLENOID HOUSING

Generally speaking, directional valves with wet pin solenoids should not be used in series circuits, or in any circuit where T port pressure can become excessively high. Although smaller directional valves can have T port pressure ratings of up to 2300 PSI (less effective area), the larger valves are limited to a pressure rating of about 1000 PSI. Since these pressure ratings are the *static pressure* limits of the solenoid, the T port should never be used in a working line where transient pressure spikes could exceed the static pressure limit of the solenoid housing.

SYMBOLS FOR DIRECT ACTING VALVE ACTUATORS

Up to this point, we have discussed the symbol representation of spool position and of flow paths. We have also mentioned the symbolism used for spring center, three position and for spring offset or detented two position valves. However, the symbol representation of the various valve actuators has not been discussed. The chart which follows represents the symbol for the actuators only. It must be remembered that the symbols are drawn adjacent to the spool symbol, and connected to its left or right-handed side (or both sides). You must proceed logically in constructing a symbol for a particular valve function. For instance, you would not show a hand lever actuator which pushes and pulls on the spool on both sides of the spool symbol.

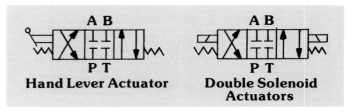

Hand Lever Actuator — A B / P T

Double Solenoid Actuators — A B / P T

Complete Valve Symbol For A Three Position Spring Centered Directional Control

SYMBOL	DESCRIPTION
	Mechanical Operation By Means Of:
	—A Spring
	—A Plunger or Tracer
	—A Roller
	Manual Operation By Means Of:
	—A Hand Lever
	—A Foot Pedal
	—A Push Button (Palm Button)
	—A Manual Actuator Without Indication of Control Type
	Pilot Operation By Means Of:
	—A Hydraulic Pilot
	—A Pneumatic Pilot
	Electrical Operation By Means Of:
	—A Push Type Solenoid
	—A Push Pull Solenoid

PILOT OPERATED DIRECTIONAL CONTROLS

NFPA DO6 Subplate Mounted Pilot Operated Directional Control

Because of their design, direct acting valves, as previously discussed, are limited in their maximum flow capability. In theory, it would be possible to make direct acting valves in larger sizes. However, in so doing, the solenoid actuator would become excessively large. For this reason, direct acting valves are usually used in systems of up to 20 to 25 GPM. For higher flow systems, pilot operated directional controls are used exclusively, because of their more compact design.

BASIC PILOT OPERATION

As shown in the operational cross section, the pilot operated directional control is simply a smaller direct operated valve mounted on top of a larger housing. This housing contains a spool of larger diameter, which is commonly referred to as a *slave spool*. The single solenoid, two position pilot valve directs pressure to the right-hand side of the slave spool, and vents the left-hand side to tank when the solenoid is de-energized. When the pilot valve shifts, pressure conditions on the ends of the slave spool reverse, which causes the spool to move to the right. This, in turn, changes the flow path through the main valve housing.

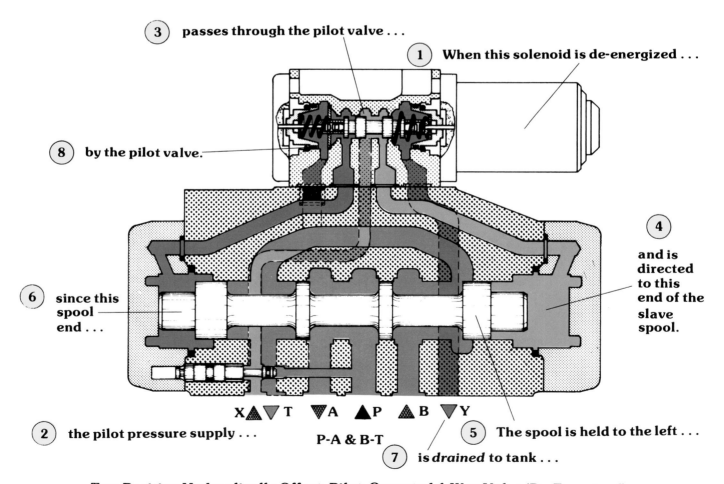

(3) **passes through the pilot valve . . .**

(1) **When this solenoid is de-energized . . .**

(8) **by the pilot valve.**

(4) **and is directed to this end of the slave spool.**

(6) **since this spool end . . .**

X △▽ T ▽ A ▲ P ▲ B ▽ Y

P-A & B-T

(2) **the pilot pressure supply . . .**

(5) **The spool is held to the left . . .**

(7) **is *drained* to tank . . .**

Two Position Hydraulically Offset, Pilot Operated 4-Way Valve (De-Energized)

It is important to realize that the main spool is hydraulically returned to its offset position when the pilot valve returns to its spring offset position. The spool is then held in position by the pilot pressure which is dead-headed against the right-hand end of the spool. If for some reason, there is a loss of pilot pressure, the slave spool could shift due to high flow forces. It is also important to mount these valves with the spool in a horizontal position. This will prevent the spool from shifting because of gravity in the event that pilot pressure is lost.

SPRING OFFSET SLAVE SPOOLS

For economical reasons, the hydraulically offset slave spool is the most common two position pilot operated valve. However, for fail-safe applications, or in circuits where pilot pressure may be lost during a portion of the cycle, a spring offset slave spool option is available. As shown in the cross-sectional illustration, this option includes an end cap with a large spring cavity. The heavy spring automatically positions the slave spool in the offset position, should pilot pressure be lost.

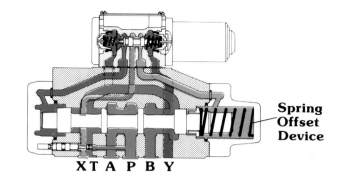

X T A P B Y

**Two Position Spring Offset, Pilot Operated
4-Way Valve (Shown De-energized)**

It must be remembered, however, that the spring must be compressed when the slave spool is shifted to the opposite flow position. This increases the minimum pilot pressure requirements two-fold. For example, the minimum pilot pressure requirement for a typical two position hydraulically offset valve is 75 PSI. However, with the spring offset slave spool option, the minimum pilot pressure requirement increases to 150 PSI.

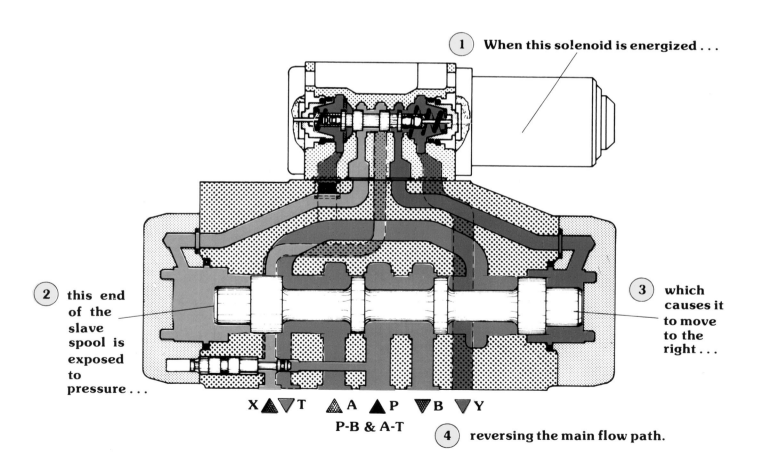

1 **When this solenoid is energized . . .**

2 **this end of the slave spool is exposed to pressure . . .**

3 **which causes it to move to the right . . .**

X A ▽ T   A A ▲ P ▽ B ▽ Y

P-B & A-T

4 **reversing the main flow path.**

Two Position Hydraulically Offset, Pilot Operated 4-Way Valve (Shown Energized)

DOUBLE SOLENOID TWO POSITION PILOT OPERATED VALVES

In the cross-sectional illustrations, the hydraulically offset or spring offset pilot operated directional controls were shown to have spring offset pilot valves. For convenience in control circuit design, two position main valves are also available with double solenoid two position pilots, with or without detents. In either of the double solenoid pilots, you must remember that the main section is still the same (either hydraulically offset or spring offset). The words "double solenoid" and "detented" only described the positioning method for the *pilot valve* spool. A complete description of these methods of positioning has been discussed previously in this chapter.

THREE POSITION SPRING CENTERED SLAVE SPOOLS

For three position pilot operated directional controls, sufficient centering force can normally be achieved by using relatively heavy *centering springs* in the end caps of the main

valve housing. With this design, a three position pilot valve is used, which vents both spring cavities to tank in its center position. As shown in the cross-sectional illustrations, the spring force pushes on the spool until the spring plate bottoms-out on the shoulder in the valve housing. Although the centering is shown from only one direction of operation, an identical spring force operates from the right-hand side when the slave spool is shifted in the opposite direction. The spring forces are high enough to center the slave spool against the Bernoulli flow forces when the valve is passing its maximum rated flow. This, in turn, determines the minimum pilot pressure required to shift the slave spool against the centering springs. The minimum pilot pressure ranges from 60 PSI for smaller pilot operated valves to approximately 200 PSI for the largest spring centered versions. It is important that the circuit be designed so that the minimum pilot pressure is always provided.

HYDRAULICALLY CENTERED THREE POSITION VALVES

For the new generation *high flow* directional controls, and for larger pilot operated directional valves (nominal port size 3"

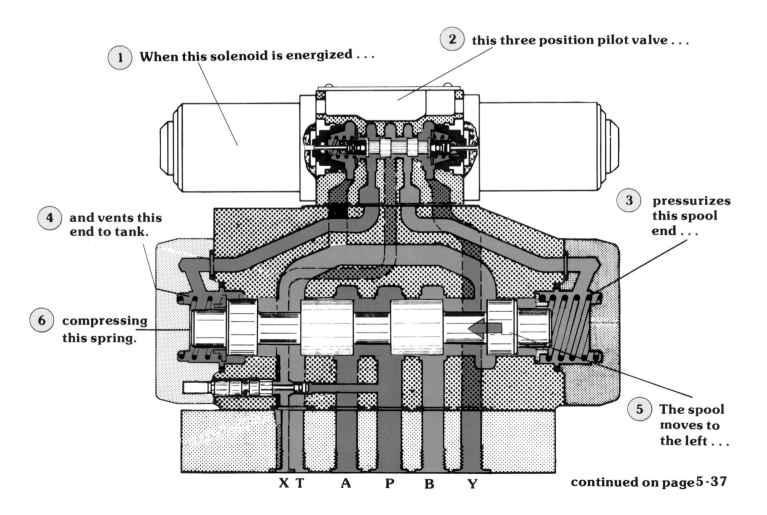

1 When this solenoid is energized . . .

2 this three position pilot valve . . .

3 pressurizes this spool end . . .

4 and vents this end to tank.

6 compressing this spring.

5 The spool moves to the left . . .

X T   A   P   B   Y

continued on page 5-37

and above), sufficient centering force cannot always be achieved through the use of centering springs. For these valves, the necessary higher forces are achieved through hydraulic centering. On large valves, the hydraulic centering is an integral part of the main valve design. However, on smaller valves, which can be ordered with either spring or hydraulic centering, the hydraulic centering device is integrated into an optional end cap. Two of the most common methods of achieving hydraulic centering will now be discussed.

INTEGRAL HYDRAULIC CENTERING

On large pilot operated directional controls, the hydraulically centered spool is an integral part of the basic valve design. To understand the operation of any three position hydraulically centered valve, it is important that one fact be kept in mind: pressure over area is equal to force. Consequently, the larger of two areas being exposed to equal pressure has the higher force. The operation of large directional controls is best described in the cross-sectional illustrations (Pages 5-38 and 5-39).

OPTIONAL HYDRAULIC CENTERING DEVICE

The new generation high flow directional controls are of a compact design, capable of handling extremely high flow rates. Because of their compact nature, the centering springs cannot be made strong enough to center the valve when it is used at its maximum flow rate. To center the valve, and to keep the minimum pilot pressure requirements within reasonable limits, a hydraulic centering device can be ordered to replace the spring centering function.

As shown in the cross-sectional (Page 5-40) the hydraulic centering device consists of a larger end cap which contains a two piece piston assembly. The inside piston has an effective area, A_1, which is less than the effective area, A_2, of the spool. On the other hand, the sum area of the inner piston and of the outside sleeve, area A_3, is greater than the effective area, A_2 of the spool. For proper operation, the centering device is used with a three position pilot valve which pressurizes both end cap chambers when it is centered.

With both ends pressurized, the small inner piston cannot shift the spool out of center position (to the right), because the right-hand area of the spool, A_2, is exposed to an equal

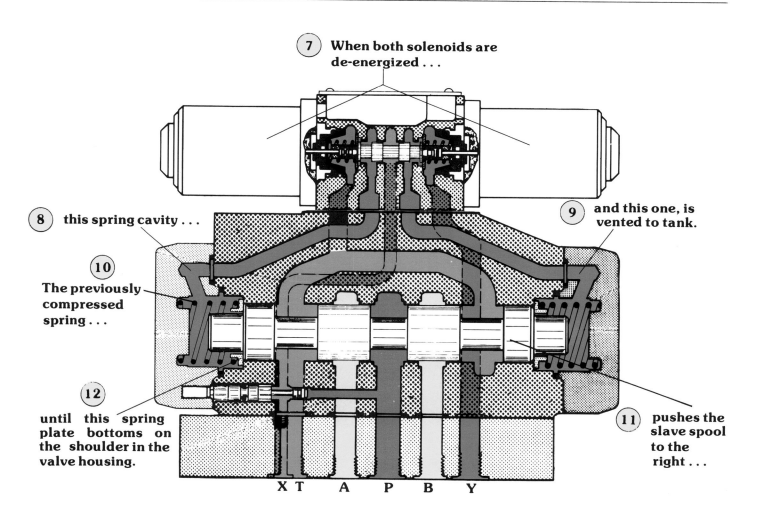

7 When both solenoids are de-energized . . .

8 this spring cavity . . .

9 and this one, is vented to tank.

10 The previously compressed spring . . .

11 pushes the slave spool to the right . . .

12 until this spring plate bottoms on the shoulder in the valve housing.

X T   A   P   B   Y

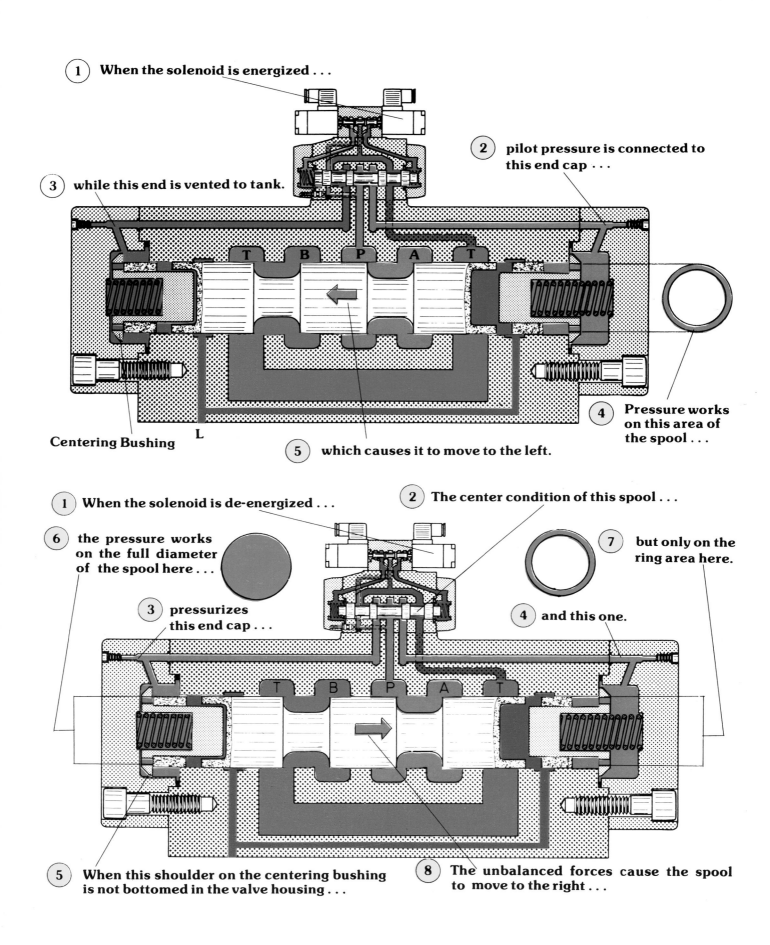

1. When the solenoid is energized . . .

2. pilot pressure is connected to this end cap . . .

3. while this end is vented to tank.

T   B   P   A   T

4. Pressure works on this area of the spool . . .

Centering Bushing   L

5. which causes it to move to the left.

1. When the solenoid is de-energized . . .

2. The center condition of this spool . . .

6. the pressure works on the full diameter of the spool here . . .

7. but only on the ring area here.

3. pressurizes this end cap . . .

4. and this one.

T   B   P   A   T

5. When this shoulder on the centering bushing is not bottomed in the valve housing . . .

8. The unbalanced forces cause the spool to move to the right . . .

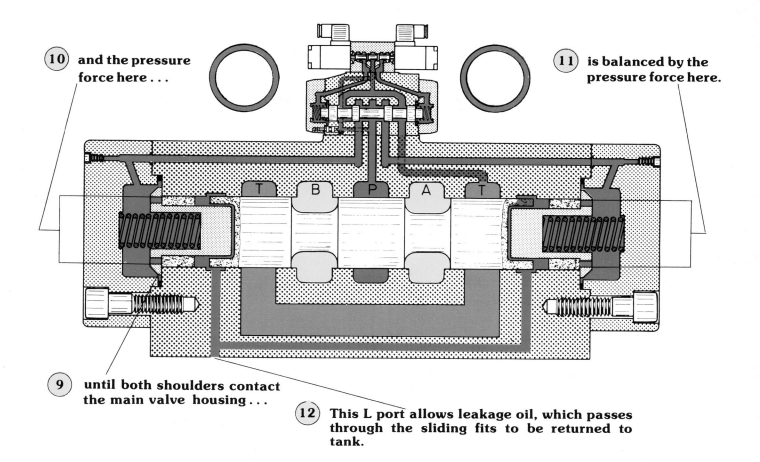

10 and the pressure force here...

11 is balanced by the pressure force here.

9 until both shoulders contact the main valve housing...

12 This L port allows leakage oil, which passes through the sliding fits to be returned to tank.

pressure. However, even though the force due to pressure on area A_2 is higher, the spool cannot be moved out of its center position to the left. This is because the outside sleeve is carried along with the spool when it moves to the left. The moment the outside sleeve loses contact with the valve housing, the force due to pressure on the full area A_3 is directed to the spool. Consequently, the spool is captured in its center position between pressure working against the two piece piston assembly on the left, and the pressure force on the spool land on the right. The center position is determined by the point at which the left-hand spool land, the valve housing shoulder, and the outside sleeve come in contact.

The springs used in conjunction with the hydraulic centering device provide additional centering forces and hold the spool in its center position when there is no pilot pressure (during start-up, for instance). However, they are not required for proper operation of the hydraulic centering device under pressurized conditions. The L drain port must also be connected directly to tank for proper operation of the valve. The operation of the valve in its shifted position is shown in the cross-sectional illustration which follows.

Turn to page 5-40

PILOT PRESSURE SUPPLY AND DRAIN

Up to this point, the cross-sectional illustrations have shown the pilot valve with separate connections for its pressure and tank ports. In fact, most pilot operated directional controls have small passages through the main valve housing so that external pressure and tank connections can be made to the pilot valve through the main valve's subplate. The pilot pressure supply port has a X designation, while the tank connection to the pilot valve is called a Y drain port.

To facilitate plumbing, it is sometimes possible to pilot and/or to drain the piloting directional valve from the same pressure and tank passages which supply the main valve. This is referred to as internally piloted and/or internally drained. Most pilot operated directional valves can be field converted from an external to an internal pilot, and from an external to an internal drain, or vice versa. Since a valve which is assembled for one type of pilot and drain will not work on a system designed for the other, it is important that we know how to make this conversion.

The two cross sections which follow show a typical valve, the first assembled with the external pilot and external drain

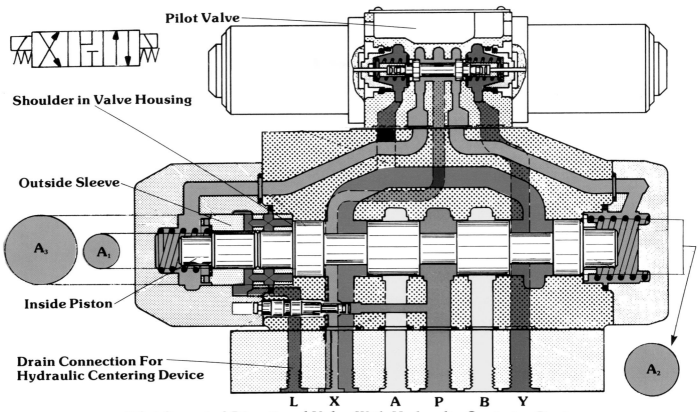

Pilot Valve

Shoulder in Valve Housing

Outside Sleeve

A_3 A_1

Inside Piston

Drain Connection For Hydraulic Centering Device

A_2

L   X   A   P   B   Y

Pilot Operated Directional Valve With Hydraulic Centering Device

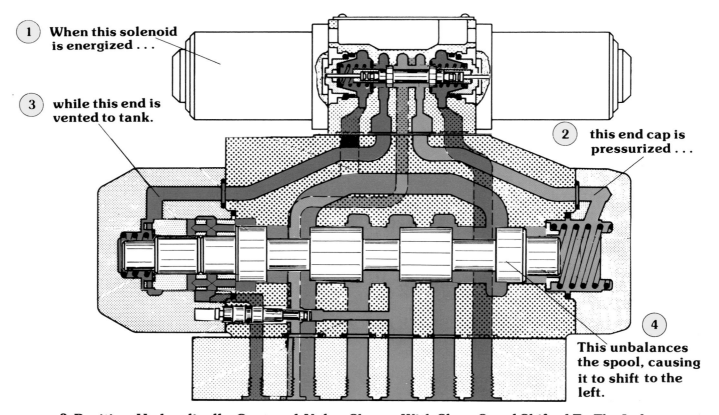

1 **When this solenoid is energized . . .**

3 **while this end is vented to tank.**

2 **this end cap is pressurized . . .**

4 **This unbalances the spool, causing it to shift to the left.**

3 Position Hydraulically Centered Valve Shown With Slave Spool Shifted To The Left

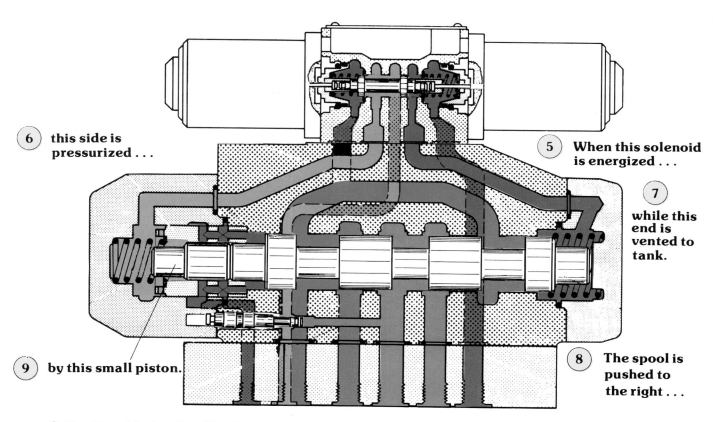

(6) this side is pressurized . . .

(5) When this solenoid is energized . . .

(7) while this end is vented to tank.

(9) by this small piston.

(8) The spool is pushed to the right . . .

3 Position Hydraulically Centered Valve Shown With Slave Spool Shifted To The Right

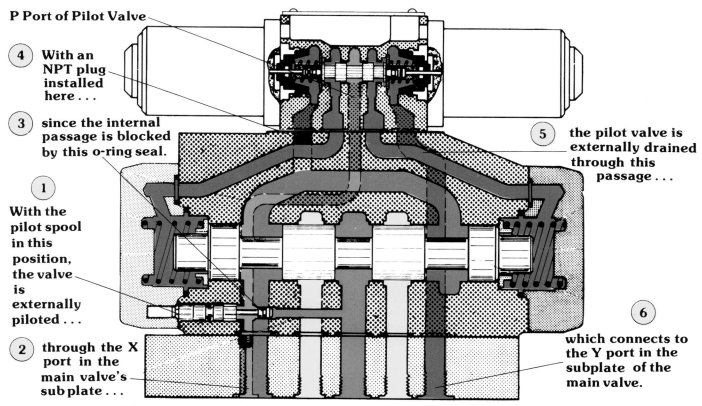

P Port of Pilot Valve

(4) With an NPT plug installed here . . .

(3) since the internal passage is blocked by this o-ring seal.

(5) the pilot valve is externally drained through this passage . . .

(1) With the pilot spool in this position, the valve is externally piloted . . .

(2) through the X port in the main valve's subplate . . .

(6) which connects to the Y port in the subplate of the main valve.

Pilot Operated Valve With External Pilot And External Pilot Drain

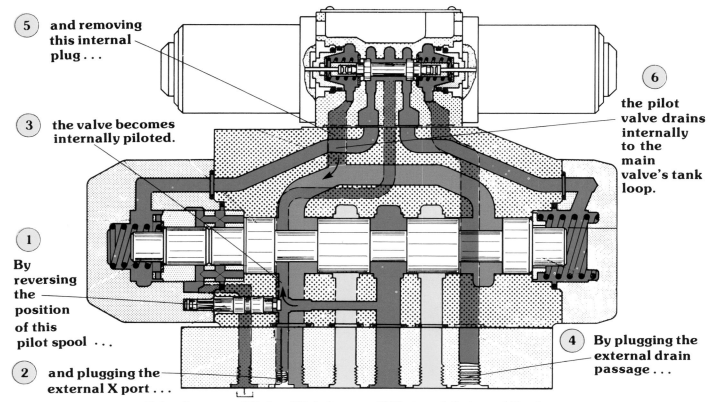

⑤ and removing this internal plug . . .

③ the valve becomes internally piloted.

① By reversing the position of this pilot spool . . .

② and plugging the external X port . . .

⑥ the pilot valve drains internally to the main valve's tank loop.

④ By plugging the external drain passage . . .

Pilot Operated Valve With Internal Pilot and Internal Drain

configuration. The second view shows the internal pilot and internal drain variation. Of course, the other two possibilities are internal pilot, external drain (which is quite popular), and external pilot, internal drain.

The method of conversion shown in the cross-sectional illustrations is a relatively modern technique. Access to the pilot spool is simply achieved by removal of the end cap on the X port side of the valve. Also, to gain access to the internal plug for internal/external drain conversion, the pilot valve is simply removed.

Another method of converting from one type of piloting (or draining) to the other is by installing pipe plugs internally in the main valve housing. A larger external pipe plug is used to allow access to these internal plugs.

The two plug method of conversion has always been an acceptable method for making the internal/external drain conversion. Many times, however, it has proven to be unsatisfactory for making the X port conversion. The problem is that the internal plug is exposed to pressure on both sides when the valve is in operation. When the pipe plug is pressurized from its top side, the tapered threads are forced together as the plug is pushed into the taper. Eventually, this makes removal of the internal plug difficult, if not impossible. This is generally not a problem in the Y drain conversion since pressures are relatively low.

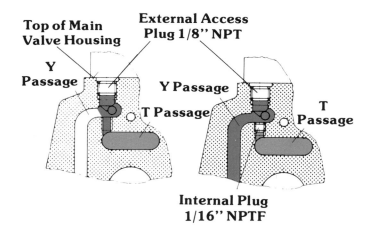

Top of Main Valve Housing

External Access Plug 1/8" NPT

Y Passage

Y Passage

T Passage

T Passage

Internal Plug 1/16" NPTF

For Internal Pilot Drain, Plug 1/16" NPTF To Be Removed And Port Y In The Subplate Plugged

Two Plug Method of Converting Internal Pilot Drain Conversion

(Note: Cross Section Is An End View Of The Main Valve Housing)

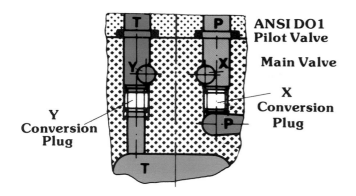

ANSI DO1
Pilot Valve

Main Valve

Y Conversion Plug

X Conversion Plug

Typical Location of Access Plugs Under Pilot Valve

One last precaution when you are installing internal plugs, is to select and use thread sealant with caution, or better still, avoid it entirely. First, any sealant which is not confined by the thread will be washed away and will contaminate the system. Second, some sealants form a bond which will aggravate the problem of future plug removal.

ASSURING MINIMUM PILOT PRESSURE

In designing a system, sufficient pilot pressure must exist during the portion of the cycle when the pilot operated directional valve is required to shift *and to remain shifted*. This means that sufficient pilot pressure must be supplied to the X port for an externally piloted valve, or at the main P port for internally piloted valves. Unfortunately, this is often overlooked in the initial system design stage. This is particularly true of designs with internal piloting and an open or tandem center slave spool.

In a internal pilot design, there must always be a resistance to flow entering the P port of the valve. If there is no resistance to flow, there is no pilot pressure, and the valve will not shift. The examples which follow show a three position valve with a fully open center spool, and a two position valve with an open center cross-over. In the first example, it is easy to see that the pump freely circulates flow to tank in the center position. This means that the valve, as shown, cannot be shifted out of its center position. However, the same slave spool assembled without springs, with a two position spring

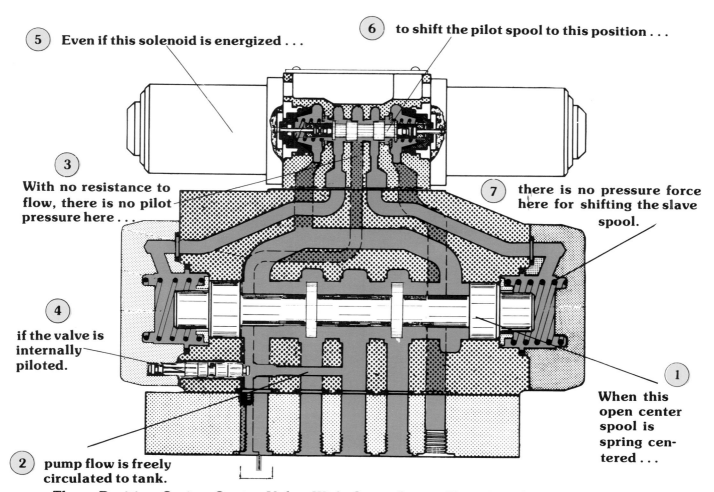

5. **Even if this solenoid is energized . . .**

6. **to shift the pilot spool to this position . . .**

3. **With no resistance to flow, there is no pilot pressure here . . .**

7. **there is no pressure force here for shifting the slave spool.**

4. **if the valve is internally piloted.**

1. **When this open center spool is spring centered . . .**

2. **pump flow is freely circulated to tank.**

Three Position Spring Center Valve With Open Center Slave Spool And Internal Pilot

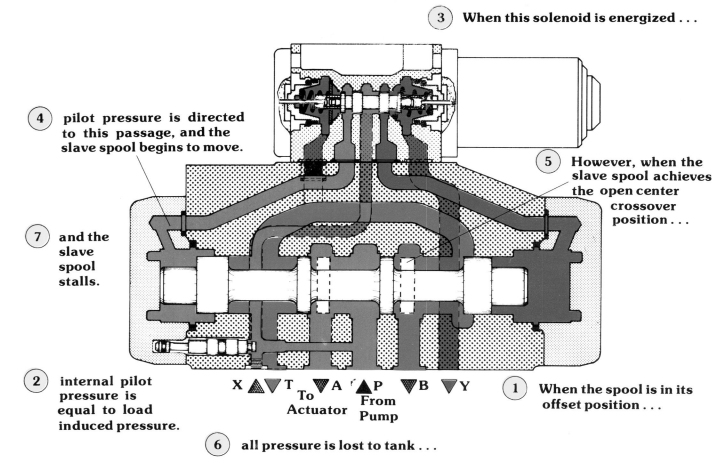

③ When this solenoid is energized . . .

④ pilot pressure is directed to this passage, and the slave spool begins to move.

⑤ However, when the slave spool achieves the open center crossover position . . .

⑦ and the slave spool stalls.

② internal pilot pressure is equal to load induced pressure.

X ▲▼ T To Actuator ▼A ▲P From Pump ▼B ▼Y

① When the spool is in its offset position . . .

⑥ all pressure is lost to tank . . .

2 Position Valve With Internal Pilot And Open Center Crossover

offset pilot valve, is a less obvious example. In the hydraulic offset position of the slave spool, it is evident that the pressure to which the pilot valve is exposed will be equivalent to that induced by the load. If the load pressure exceeds the minimum pilot pressure of the valve when the pilot valve shifts, the slave spool will begin to move. However, the moment it is moved into the crossover position, all ports will be communicated to tank, and pilot pressure will be lost. The net result will be that the slave spool will stall when it reaches its open center crossover position, and it never will reach its shifted position. Consequently, if resistance to flow at the valve's inlet can be lost, some means of assuring a positive pilot pressure must be provided. This is normally accomplished in one of two ways for internally piloted directional controls.

BACK PRESSURE T PORT CHECK VALVES

Over the years, the common method of assuring minimum pilot pressure with open center spools has been the installation of a *back pressure check valve* cartridge in the *tank* port of the main directional valve housing. This check valve

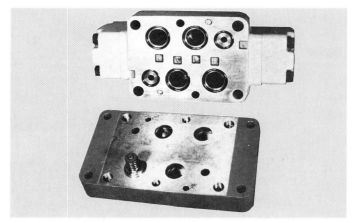

cartridge is supplied with a cracking pressure equivalent to the minimum pilot pressure requirements of the directional valve (see Chapter 4 for a complete description of cracking pressure). With the back pressure check valve installed in the tank port cavity, pump flow is circulated to tank at the pressure required to open the check valve poppet. The P port of the pilot valve is exposed to this back pressure, and it is sufficient to pilot the slave spool into its shifted position (s).

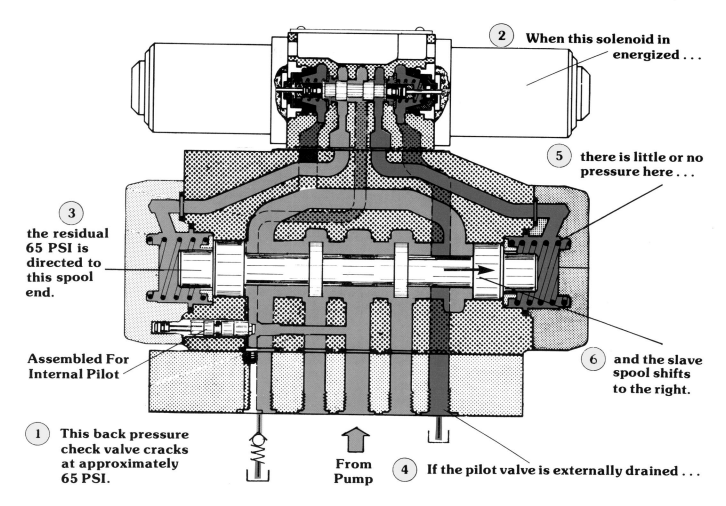

2 **When this solenoid in energized . . .**

5 **there is little or no pressure here . . .**

3 **the residual 65 PSI is directed to this spool end.**

Assembled For Internal Pilot

6 **and the slave spool shifts to the right.**

1 **This back pressure check valve cracks at approximately 65 PSI.**

From Pump

4 **If the pilot valve is externally drained . . .**

Pilot Operated Valve With Back Pressure T Port Check Valve Must Be Externally Drained

When you use a back pressure check, be sure the pilot operated directional valve is externally drained. If the valve were to be internally drained, the pressure at the T port of the pilot valve would be equal to the pressure at the P port. When the pilot valve shifted in an attempt to move the slave spool, both ends of the spool would be equally exposed to the back pressure. Since the shifting force would be balanced, the slave spool would not move.

P PORT SEQUENCE VALVES

Modern coring techniques have recently allowed valve manufacturers to cast valve housings with intricate internal passages. For this reason, it is now possible to supply directional controls with P port sequence valves for maintaining minimum pilot pressure requirements. The advantage of maintaining pilot pressure with a P port sequence cartridge is that a directional valve with internal pilot and open or tandem center spools can also be internally drained. In many applications, this eliminates the need for piping a separate drain line. The cross-sectional illustration shows the installation of this cartridge P port sequence (page 5-46).

SERIES CIRCUITS AND INTERNAL PILOTING

When only one valve is to be operated at a time, two or more valves can be supplied from a single pump, if they are piped in a *series circuit*. A series circuit is piped so that the pressure port of the second valve is piped to the tank port of the first. The third valve's P port is connected to the T port of the second valve, and so on. This method of piping should continue until the last valve in the series is reached. The last valve will then have its tank port connected to the reservoir. All valves in the series circuit use a tandem center spool, so that when they are centered, the pump will circulate its output to tank by freely flowing through the center of each directional valve. A two valve series circuit would be drawn as follows shown on page 5-47.

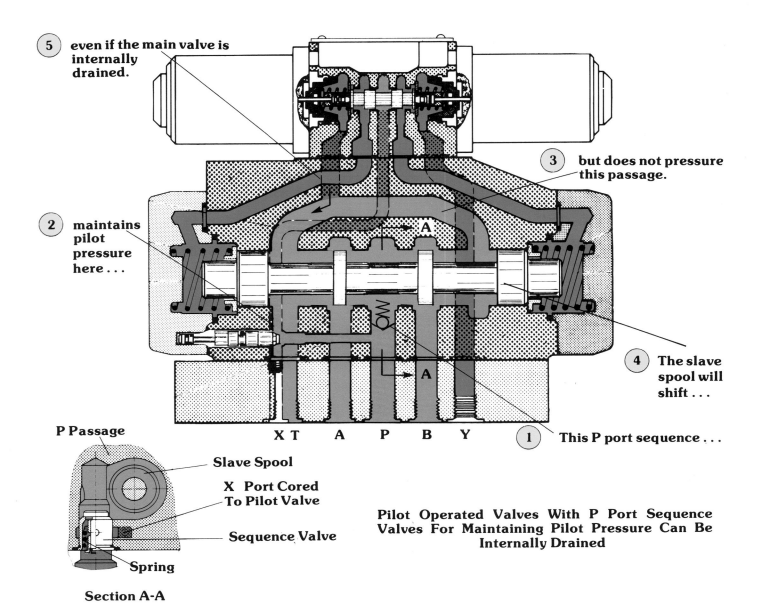

⑤ **even if the main valve is internally drained.**

③ **but does not pressure this passage.**

② **maintains pilot pressure here . . .**

④ **The slave spool will shift . . .**

① **This P port sequence . . .**

X T A P B Y

P Passage

Slave Spool

X Port Cored To Pilot Valve

Sequence Valve

Spring

Section A-A

Pilot Operated Valves With P Port Sequence Valves For Maintaining Pilot Pressure Can Be Internally Drained

A major concern in selecting directional valves for a series circuit is that they must be large enough to pass the required flow with little pressure loss. Since resistances in series are additive, the sum of the individual pressure drops dictates the pressure at the outlet of the pump when the circuit is circulating flow to tank. Remember, this pressure at the rated flow converts into heat. For this reason, it is not desirable (nor is it necessary) to use a pilot pressure insert in each of the valves. If, for instance, we had ten valves in series, each with its own 65 PSI pressure insert, the circulating pressure at the pump would be a minimum of 650 PSI. This is, of course, unnecessarily high.

All that need be done to maintain pilot pressure for all valves in the series circuit is to place a pressure insert in the *last* valve in the series (this valve can be either a P port sequence or a T port back pressure check). As shown in the circuit illustration, the back pressure which is generated is main-tained throughout the system (upstream of the back pressure valve) at a pressure equivalent to the cracking pressure of the cartridge insert. Since the pressure at both the P port and T port is equal for all valves in the series circuit, they must be externally drained.

MAXIMUM PILOT PRESSURE LIMITS

In using a pilot operated directional valve in a high pressure circuit, the maximum pilot pressure must sometimes be limited. In general, the end caps of the main valve housing have a relatively large area exposed to pilot pressure. Likewise, these end caps are usually attached to the valve body with only 4 mounting bolts. Since the large area represents a high force at high pressure, this pilot pressure

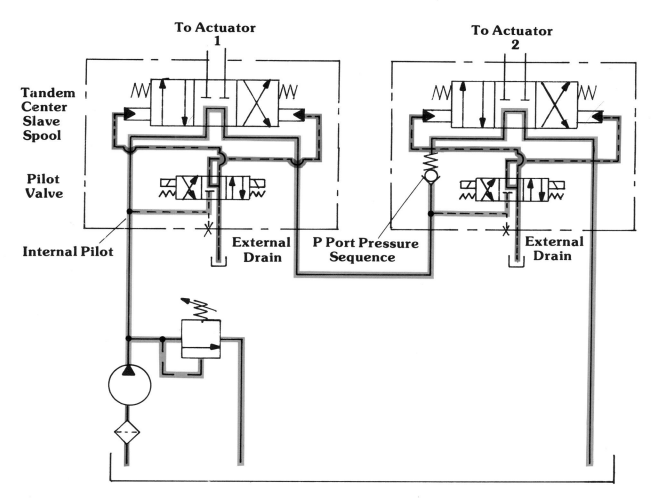

Two Valve Series Circuit With Internally Piloted Directional Valves

must be limited to prevent over stressing the mounting bolts. Although the maximum pilot pressure must be checked for the actual design selected, a typical example would be a 5000 PSI valve with a maximum pilot pressure rating of 3500 PSI.

To avoid over pressurizing the pilot circuit, a pressure reducing valve sandwich can be used between the pilot valve and the main valve housing. The reducing valve is a P port reducing valve which takes the high internal pilot pressure supply and reduces it to a level which is acceptable for the pilot circuit (see Chapter 2 for a complete explanation of sandwich type pressure reducing valves). For some pilot operated directional valves, a non-adjustable, fixed ratio reducing valve sandwich is available as an optional feature for the valve.

MAXIMUM T PORT PRESSURE

Since pressure in the main valve's tank port can also

pressure the end caps (by leakage across the end spool lands), maximum T port pressure must also be limited. For externally drained valves, this pressure limit is generally the same as the maximum pilot pressure limit. On the other hand, if the valve is internally drained, the pressure limit is determined by the maximum T port rating of the pilot valve. This should always be taken into account, especially if the directional valves are to be used in a series circuit.

RESPONSE TIME FOR PILOT OPERATED DIRECTIONAL CONTROLS

The overall response time for a pilot operated directional valve is the time period between the energizing of the solenoid, and the attainment of the fully shifted position by the slave spool. In general, the total response time is the sum of the time of the pilot valve's response, and the time required to displace the volume of oil needed to shift the slave spool. Consequently, the overall response time is dependent on the flow and *pressure* potential at the P port of the pilot valve. A typical 3/4" valve with an AC solenoid pilot shifts from center to end position in 40 m.s. at 700 PSI pilot pressure, with the time period dropping to 25 m.s. at 3000 PSI. However, for most applications, this time period is too fast for smooth system operation.

When flows in excess of 25 GPM are being handled at a relatively high pressure, the decompression shock at the time of valve shift has an important influence on smooth system operation. On valves designed to handle large flows, the "metering-notches," as discussed earlier in this chapter, become a major design consideration. However, even if the slave spool is notched sufficiently, shifting too fast may not allow enough time for pressure equalization to occur (see "Metering Notches").

In general, there are two accessories available for pilot operated directional valves, both of which slow down the shifting speed of the slave spool. This, in turn, tunes out the "water-hammer" associated with fast response.

NON-ADJUSTABLE PILOT ORIFICES

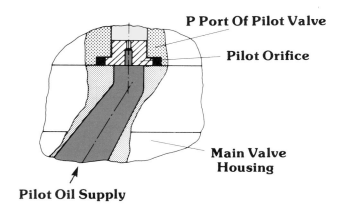

P Port Of Pilot Valve

Pilot Orifice

Main Valve Housing

Pilot Oil Supply

The simplest and most inexpensive method to lower the response time of the pilot operated directional control is to install a non-adjustable orifice in the P port of the pilot valve. This causes a meter-in flow control function, which slows the shifting of the slave spool equally in both directions. In general, a number of different orifice diameters are available to meet the need of various system requirements. Unfortunately, selection of the proper orifice requires some experience with the system, and may require some initial experimentation with different orifices.

SANDWICH MOUNTED FLOW CONTROLS

Another method of slowing the response time of the slave spool is to simply mount a sandwich type dual flow control

between the main valve and the pilot (see Chapter 3). The flow control is usually mounted in a meter-out orientation and allows independent shifting speed adjustment for both directions of spool shift. If the flow from the end caps is sufficiently restricted, this type of speed control not only eliminates "water-hammer," but it also allows for an adjustment of acceleration or deceleration for the actuator.

The adjustment adjacent to note 8 in the drawing influences the speed of the slave spool whenever it moves to the right. In effect, this controls both the time period required for the spring to return the spool to its center position, and the time required for pilot pressure to move the spool to its right-hand shifted position. Since the setting can be optimum for only one mode of operation, this adjustment must be a compromise. On the other hand, if you want only to control the shifting speed from center to either end position, the centering spring will center the spool at maximum speed (approximately 50-60 m.s.) if the flow control is mounted in the "meter-in" orientation.

One last consideration when you use the sandwich flow control to control shifting time is that severe restriction of the pilot flow will show up as a dwell period when energization of the solenoid causes no initial actuator response. The reason for this is that the severely restricted flow causes the slave spool to move slowly through its overlap. This time delay can be undesirably long, if the adjustment is not set properly.

STROKE LIMITER AND SPOOL POSITION INDICATORS

Early in this chapter (in our discussion of "Maximum Flow Rate for Directional Controls"), we showed how spool diameter and *spool stroke* affect the final maximum flow area in a shifted position. Consequently, a crude, but adjustable, flow control function can be achieved by incorporating an adjustable stroke limited on the slave spool. Although this flow control setting is not very sensitive, it can provide adequate speed control for many applications in one compact package. If speed control is required for both directions of actuator motion, both end caps can be replaced with stroke limiter covers. However, if speed control is desired only in one direction of operation, a spool position indicator can be installed in the opposite end cap. This facilitates the setting of the flow control by giving the operator a visual reference. Since most stroke limiters incorporate a static o-ring seal, adjustment should not be attempted while the end cap is pressurized.

HYDRAULICALLY OPERATED VALVES

Our discussion of pilot operated directional control has im-

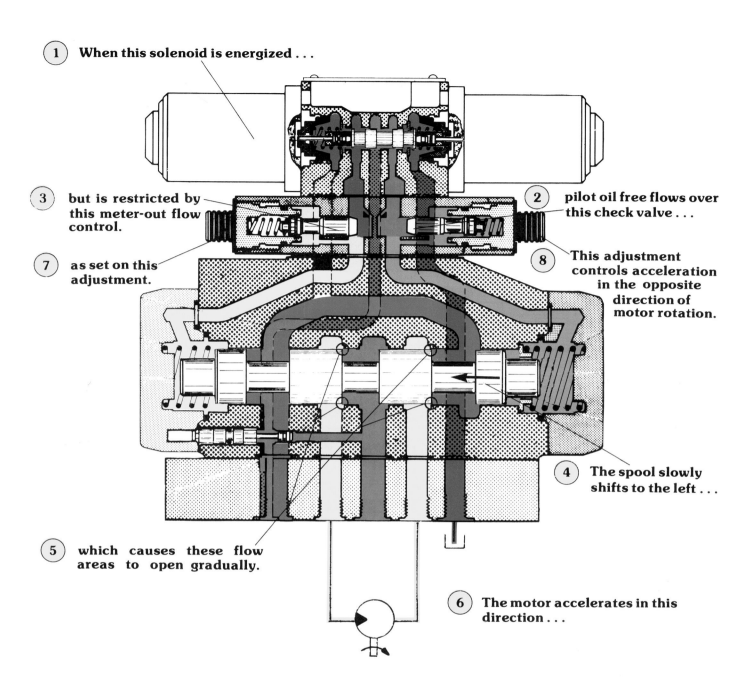

① **When this solenoid is energized . . .**

③ **but is restricted by this meter-out flow control.**

② **pilot oil free flows over this check valve . . .**

⑦ **as set on this adjustment.**

⑧ **This adjustment controls acceleration in the opposite direction of motor rotation.**

④ **The spool slowly shifts to the left . . .**

⑤ **which causes these flow areas to open gradually.**

⑥ **The motor accelerates in this direction . . .**

plied that the pilot valve always has solenoid actuators. However, it is not uncommon to replace the solenoid actuated pilot valve with one which has manual, mechanical or pneumatic operators. Notice that we have eliminated hydraulic actuators from the list.

If the method of operation is to be hydraulic, it would be repetitious to have a hydraulically piloted pilot valve operating a hydraulically piloted slave spool. Fortunately, a simple cover plate will allow us to hydraulically pilot the slave spool directly.

As shown in the cross-sectional illustration, the cover simply interconnects the X port with one spool end, while con-

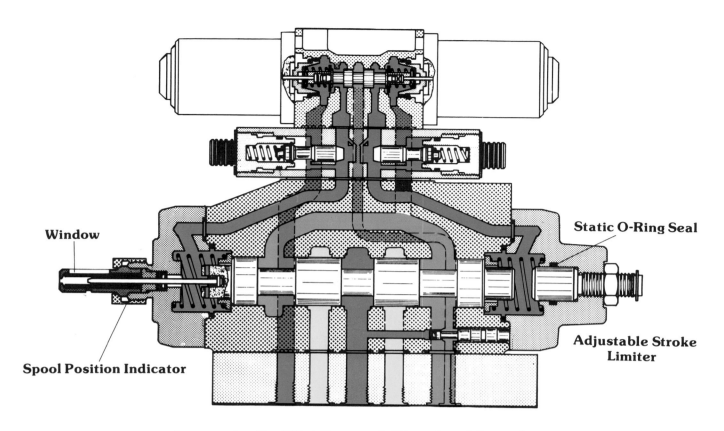

Window

Static O-Ring Seal

Spool Position Indicator

Adjustable Stroke Limiter

Accessories For Pilot Operated Directional Controls

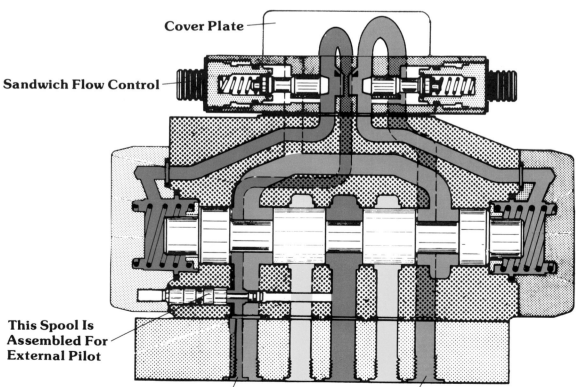

Cover Plate

Sandwich Flow Control

This Spool Is Assembled For External Pilot

Pilot Pressure Applied At This Port Shifts Spool To The Right

Pilot Pressure At This Port Shifts Spool To The Left

necting the Y port to the opposite side. The remote pilot connections are simply made through the X and Y ports in the subplate of the main valve. The slave spool can be hydraulically offset, spring offset, spring centered or hydraulically centered. Shifting speed can be adjusted by using a sandwich flow control between the main valve housing and the cover plate.

SYMBOL FOR PILOT OPERATED DIRECTIONAL CONTROLS

The pilot operated directional valve symbol, in its complete form, is a composite of two direct acting valve symbols. Needless to say, one symbol represents the pilot valve, while the second represents the slave spool's flow configuration.

Complete symbols, as used in our example of series circuits, are seldom used. Consequently, we will concentrate on the simplified versions.

Two Position Valves	
Simplified Symbol	Descriptions
	Two Position Hydraulically Offset Slave Spool With Spring Offset Single Solenoid Pilot Valve
	Two Postion Spring Offset Slave Spool With Spring Offset Single Solenoid Pilot
	Two Position Hydraulically Offset Slave Spool With Double Solenoid Two Position Pilot
	Two Position Hydraulically Offset Slave Spool With Double Solenoid Detented Pilot

Three Position Valves (Only Closed Center Conditions Are Shown)	
Symbol	**Description**
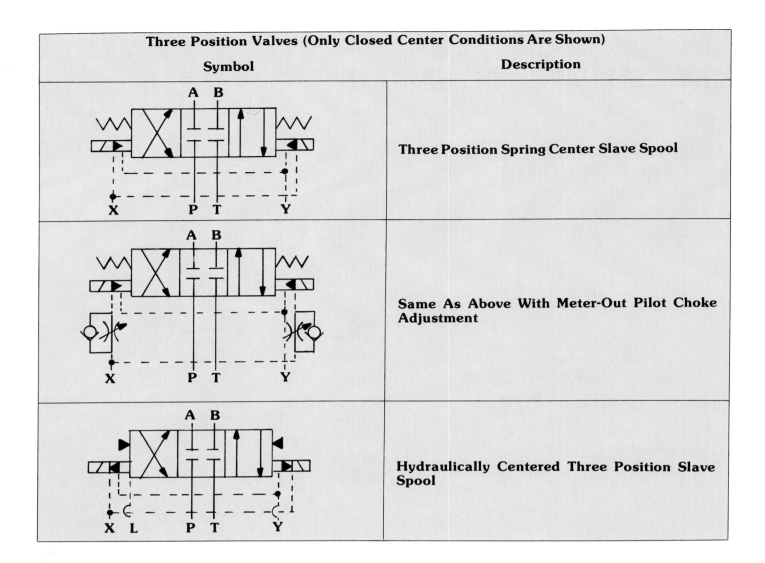	**Three Position Spring Center Slave Spool**
	Same As Above With Meter-Out Pilot Choke Adjustment
	Hydraulically Centered Three Position Slave Spool

APPLICATIONS FOR SPOOL TYPE DIRECTIONAL CONTROLS

In industrial applications, the type of directional control, its size, and the number of valves required are dictated by the work function(s) to be performed. Early in this chapter, we discussed two position valves and their intended applications. We have also shown that three position valves are quite popular, since you can obtain any required combination of flow paths when the valve is in the *center position*. Now that we have described the individual valve functions and their limitations, you should be able to develop any number of unique circuit applications.

Throughout this book, we have given examples of directional valve applications. For instance, Chapter 2 describes how the directional valve, when used in conjunction with a pilot operated relief valve, can provide system unloading and multiple pressure selection. We have also shown how the center position of the directional valve influences the braking ability of a counterbalance valve, and why it is necessary to incorporate *port* or cross port reliefs when using directional valves which block the actuator ports. Again, in Chapter 4, we have shown that the operating characteristics of a pilot operated check valve demand the selection of the proper directional valve center position.

In this chapter, we have outlined the flow paths made available by differently machined spools. We have discussed float center and regenerative center spool applications as pilots for spring centered and pressure centered pilot operated directional controls, respectively. We have also outlined the conditions for pilot operated, tandem center spool valves in series circuits. Since it would be impractical to cover the multitude of application examples possible for various spool types, the examples here will outline only a few of the less obvious applications and the associated complications.

PARALLEL CIRCUITS

When two or more directional valves are piped with a common pressure source (and tank return), they are said to be piped "in parallel." In selecting the directional valves for use in parallel circuits, you must remember that three position valve spools *must block their pressure* port in the center spool position. In addition, two position valves can be used in parallel circuits only if they are to control the direction of a cylinder which will "bottom-out." If these two points are not observed, the pump flow will simply *take the path of least resistance*. This path could be free flow to tank over the center position of an incorrectly selected three position valve. On the other hand, if a hydraulic motor has little or no load and is being controlled by a two position directional valve, it would be impossible to build pressure in the rest of the parallel circuit. A typical example of a two valve parallel circuit is shown in the following illustration.

In this circuit, the solenoid vented relief valve unloads the pump to tank whenever the actuators are not in operation. Its solenoid is electrically interlocked with solenoids one, two and three on the directional valves, so that it is energized

whenever one of the other three solenoids are actuated. Let us assume the machine cycle is as follows:

Solenoid 3 is actuated first, which causes cylinder B to "clamp" a work piece into position. Solenoid three remains energized, while solenoid 1 is actuated to extend the "punch" cylinder A. After punching is complete, solenoid 1 is de-energized, and cylinder A retracts. After full retraction of cylinder A, solenoid two is energized to unclamp the work piece. De-energization of solenoid 2 completes the cycle, and the solenoid relief vents pump flow to tank. Cylinder B is controlled by a "float center" spool so that the cylinder can be positioned manually during machine set up.

You will notice that both directional valves in this circuit have P port check valves. Check valve A holds cylinder A in its retracted position when the relief valve is vented. Check valve B is required to maintain clamping force while cylinder A is travelling through free air. It should be noted that the P port pressure insert for pilot operated valves can also be used as a P port check valve in this type of circuit. In parallel circuits, the P port check valve is not necessary for maintaining pilot pressure, since the main valve cannot be open center. It does, however, offer a compact and economical

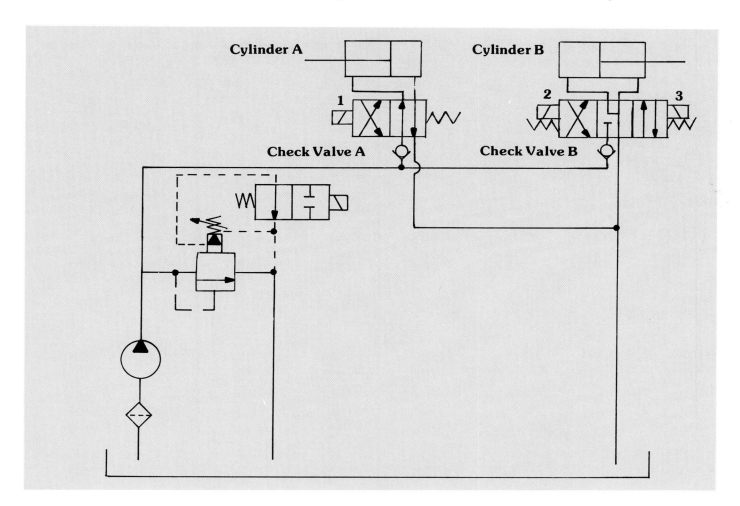

Circuit Schematic Of Two Valves In Parallel

alternative to piping a separate line mounted check valve.

REGENERATIVE CIRCUITS

In hydraulics, the word "regeneration" means using the flow of oil from the rod end of a single rod, double acting cylinder to supplement the pump flow being supplied to the blind end of the cylinder. Regeneration increases the speed at which the cylinder *extends*, and can be used in place of a larger pump. In general, regenerative circuits work best when the cylinder area ratio is close to 2:1. Although the regeneration principle can be made to work with small rod cylinders, it is evident that these cylinders, when used in a regenerative circuit, advance quite rapidly, but with very little force. Likewise, a small pump will extend the cylinder quickly, but may be too small to obtain satisfactory retraction speeds. Consequently, a 2:1 area ratio cylinder is generally used to optimize both speed and force. A typical example will now be examined.

One of the simplest methods of regeneration is achieved by using a two position 3-way directional valve. As shown, when the solenoid is de-energized, pump flow is connected to the rod end of the cylinder, while the blind end is con-

nected to tank. The cylinder will retract at the rate of: (formulas are explained in Chapter 1).

$$V = \frac{GPM \times 231}{A} = \frac{5 \times 231}{5.5} = 210 \text{ in./min.}$$

However, during retraction, the directional valve must also be large enough to handle the flow from the blind end of cylinder, which is:

$$GPM = \frac{A \times V}{231} = \frac{12.56 \times 210}{231} = 11.42 \text{ GPM}$$

When the solenoid is energized, pump flow is simultaneously directed to both ends of the cylinder. However, because the blind end of the cylinder has the larger area, it also has the larger force at equal pressure. The cylinder will extend, creating a flow of oil from the rod end port. Due to the piping, the rod end oil supplements the pump flow and passes through the directional valve to the blind end of the cylinder. Consequently, the directional valve must be capable of handling this combined flow. Although, at first glance, the flow calculations may appear to be complicated, using a logical approach will make the calculation of flow quite sim-

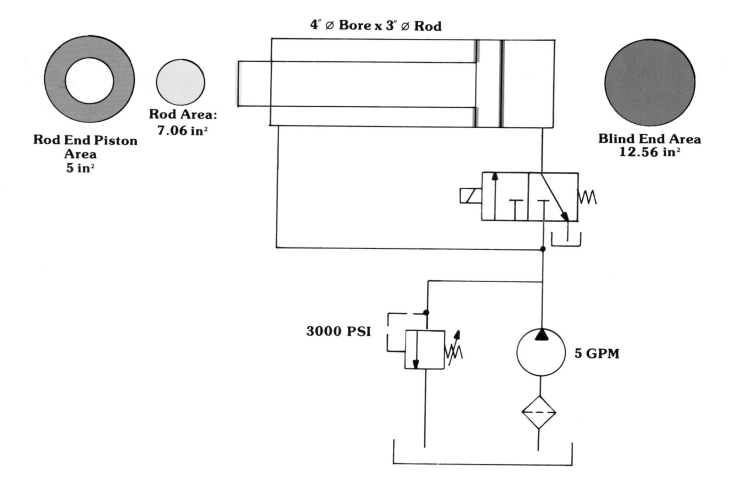

4″ ∅ Bore x 3″ ∅ Rod

Rod Area: 7.06 in²

Rod End Piston Area 5 in²

Blind End Area 12.56 in²

3000 PSI

5 GPM

ple.

Since no oil is lost as the cylinder extends, the oil which is forced out of the rod end can be thought of as filling an equivalent volume on the blind end. This means that the extra volume on the blind end side must be supplied by the pump. Geometrically, this volume is equivalent to that which is displaced by the rod. During regeneration, the cylinder bore has nothing to do with the cylinder speed, thus we can think of the cylinder as having a rod without a piston. Consequently, the cylinder extends at the rate of:

$$V = \frac{GPM \times 231}{A \ (rod)} = \frac{5 \times 231}{7.06} = 163.59 \ in./min.$$

Now that we know the velocity at which the cylinder extends, we can also calculate flow coming from its rod end.

$$GPM = \frac{A \times V}{231} = \frac{5.5 \times 163.59}{231} = 3.89 \ GPM$$

Consequently, the directional valve must handle the combined flow of 8.89 GPM (3.89 GPM + 5 GPM). Without a doubt, this is a relatively small valve, and is in proportion to other components in the system. However, if you go through the calculation using a 4" Ø bore × 1" rod cylinder with the same pump, plumbing and valve size must become considerably larger. The calculated solution to the cylinder's velocity is 1471 in./min., with a combined flow of 80 GPM! To achieve a 30 F.P.S. oil velocity, the nominal port size would be approximately 1" diameter. On the other hand, in the regenerative circuit with the 4" bore × 3" rod cylinder, the line size and valve could be as small as 3/8".

In regenerative circuits, the increase in speed is accompanied by a decrease in maximum output force capability of the cylinder during the regeneration portion of the cycle. Pressure only works on the effective area of the rod during regeneration. Consequently, regeneration is normally used only to move the cylinder to the work quickly. When the working position is reached, the circuit vents the rod end of the cylinder to tank so that fuel tonnage can be developed. Some of the directional valves which can be used to accomplish this function will be looked at.

REGENERATIVE CENTER SPOOL

The regenerative center valve spool produces three cylinder functions: regenerative forward, slow speed forward, and retract. In reference to the schematic illustration, the cylinder extends during regeneration when the valve is in its center position. When the valve is shifted to the left, slow speed and full tonnage result because the rod end of the cylinder is connected to tank. Likewise, when the valve is shifted to the right, the cylinder will retract.

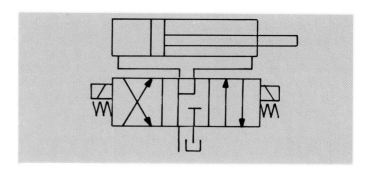

This spool type is generally used only in high cycling applications, and where the cylinder does not have to be stopped in midposition. It should be noted that the cylinder will only remain retracted if the left solenoid remains energized. Likewise, the pump flow cannot be unloaded by the directional valve.

SPOOL WITH REGENERATIVE END POSITION

The spool with a regenerative end advances the cylinder in regeneration when the right-hand solenoid is energized, and retracts the cylinder in the conventional manner, when the left-hand solenoid is actuated. The advantage that this spool offers is that the cylinder can be stopped in midstroke, since the valve has a closed center configuration. However, this spool alone cannot be used to advance the cylinder under full tonnage. The slow speed full tonnage cycle can only be accomplished if a second two position 4-way valve is added to the circuit.

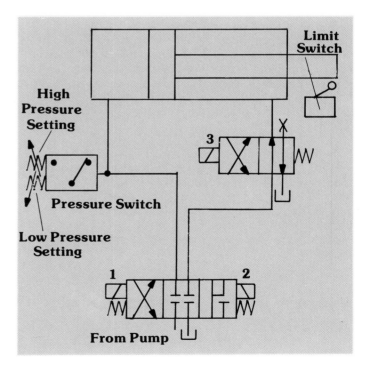

Four Function Regenerative Circuit

In this circuit, when solenoid 3 is not actuated, the cylinder will extend in regeneration when solenoid 2 is energized. Likewise, when only solenoid 1 is actuated, the cylinder will retract. Full tonnage, however, is developed in the slow speed mode when solenoids 2 and 3 are simultaneously energized. Of course, de-energization of all solenoids stops the cylinder in any position.

This circuit can be automated by energizing solenoid 3 by means of either a pressure switch or a limit switch. The pressure switch would be connected to the blind end side of the cylinder, and would automatically put the circuit into full tonnage when the predetermined load induced pressure has been reached. If the pressure switch were set properly, this changeover would occur just before the load resistance caused the cylinder to stall in regeneration. If load induced pressure fell below the *adjustable differential* of the pressure switch (see Chapter 8), the cylinder would automatically return to high speed regeneration. On the other hand, a limit switch can be used simply to take the cylinder out of regeneration at a preselected stroke.

There are many other methods available for accomplishing a regenerative circuit. However, for the purposes of this chapter, we only intend to discuss the use of directional valves, which are designed specifically for this purpose.

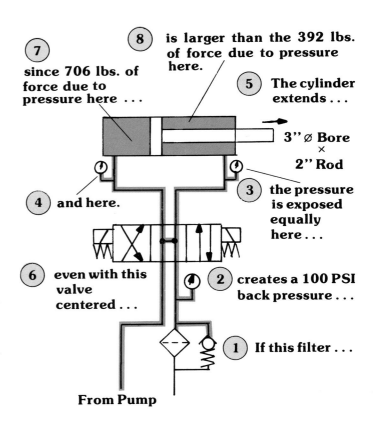

⑦ since 706 lbs. of force due to pressure here . . .

⑧ is larger than the 392 lbs. of force due to pressure here.

⑤ The cylinder extends . . .

3" ∅ Bore × 2" Rod

④ and here.

③ the pressure is exposed equally here . . .

⑥ even with this valve centered . . .

② creates a 100 PSI back pressure . . .

① If this filter . . .

From Pump

TANK PRESSURE AND OPEN CENTER SPOOLS

In a single valve circuit, the fully open center spool can be used to allow the actuator to "float", while, at the same time, it unloads the pump flow to tank. In other words, the functions of a float center and tandem center spool are combined. Although this spool works well with hydraulic motors, you must be careful in applying it to a single rod cylinder with differential areas. Likewise, the open center spool should never be used to replace a tandem center spool in a "series" circuit.

In the circuit shown, the open center valve back pressures both ends of the single rod cylinder. If the cylinder has little or no load, it will extend because the forces, due to pressure, are unbalanced. In the example, the cylinder would extend with a force potential of only 314 lbs. However, higher back pressure or larger differential areas in the cylinder could make this extension force considerably higher.

POPPET STYLE DIRECTIONAL CONTROLS

It is possible to apply the poppet style directional control whenever a leak free directional function is required. Likewise, because of its leak free sealing capabilities, it can

be used at extremely high pressures, even with low viscosity fluids. In fact, by manufacturing the component parts from stainless steel, the basic design can be used with pure water at operating pressures up to 7000 PSI. However, before proceeding to the actual valve construction and operation, we would like to point out a few basic differences between mineral oil and water hydraulics.

Examples Where Leak Free Directional Control Is Required

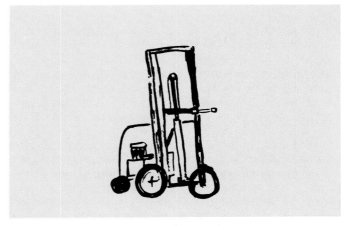

Fork Lift Truck

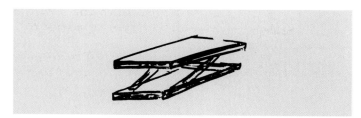

Scissor Lifts

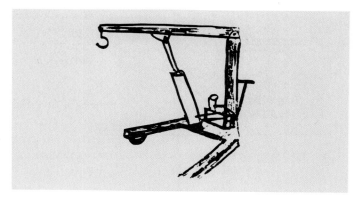

Workshop Crane

Fairground Carousels

WATER OR OIL HYDRAULICS?

The 1970's will be known as an era which evoked a need for change in industrial hydraulic systems. Oil hydraulics, a time proven method of power transmission, is becoming restricted in some areas of application for either economic or ecological reasons. Although oil hydraulics will maintain a strong foothold in the future of hydraulics, many manufactures are researching new component designs which are suitable for use in pure water hydraulic systems.

The poppet style directional control, as will be covered in this section, proves to be an economical and compact component for use with either oil or water. However, dynamic component designs for pressure control or pumping functions are more difficult to achieve. With these components, either the lack of lubrication or the inability to seal

pressurized water with a close tolerance fit is a problem which has not yet been overcome. Although high pressure water pumps are available today, they are 10 times the size of an equivalent oil hydraulics pump. The advent of pure water hydraulics will not be possible until component designs and materials are developed to overcome these problems compactly and economically.

To further understand the sealing of pressurized water with close tolerance fits, consider the following facts. First, if a typical mineral oil were to be chosen, it would have a viscosity of 150 SUS at 100° F. On the other hand, water at 100° F. has a viscosity which approaches 0 SUS. If we were to take the two fluids and try to hold pressure with a spool type directional control, the leakage rate with water would be approximately 40 times higher than it would be with oil. This clearly limits the application of spool valves in water hydraulic systems.

A second problem created for the spool design by the low viscosity of water is that high fluid velocity, out of necessity, accompanies the high leakage rate. This high velocity fluid quickly erodes the close fitting metal surfaces. In hydraulics, this erosion process is referred to as "wire drawing," most likely because of the appearance of the eroded surface. The quick deterioration of the metal surfaces produces a valve which can soon leak the entire output flow of the pump.

On the other hand, the advantages offered by water hydraulics cannot be discounted. For instance, with a typical mineral oil, as the temperature is raised from 32° F to 212° F, the viscosity changes from 3300 SUS to 46 SUS. This causes the system to react sluggishly at start-up, increasing its speed as temperatures warm up. Water's viscosity remains constant between 32° F and 212° F. This means that a water hydraulic system is virtually immune to fluctuation in speed because of temperature changes.

Apart from their technical or environmental advantages, water systems are also desirable where fire resistance is necessary. Typical examples are hot rolling mills, forging and extrusion presses, continuous casting machines, and furnace door applications. Other examples are machines on which the products being manufactured are inflammable, such as particle board presses, rubber vulcanizing presses and plastic injection molding machines.

BASIC POPPET VALVE DESCRIPTION

With a simple change in materials, the basic valve can be used for oil, oil-in-water emulsions, and water glycols. When the valve is to be used with mineral oil, the construction materials are steel functional parts with cast iron housings. For water glycols and oil-in-water emulsions, the housings are manufactured from steel, while the functional pieces are made of stainless steel. Valves for pure water usage use stainless steel materials throughout. Since poppets, seats

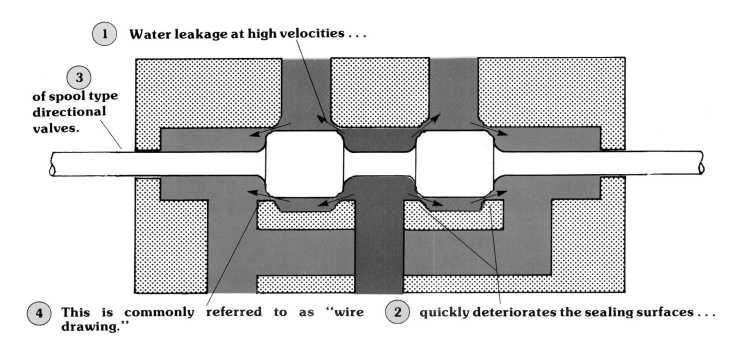

① **Water leakage at high velocities . . .**

③ **of spool type directional valves.**

④ **This is commonly referred to as "wire drawing."**

② **quickly deteriorates the sealing surfaces . . .**

Direct Operated Poppet Valves

BASIC OPERATION

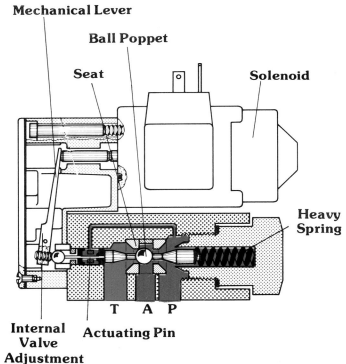

Single Ball, Normally Open 3-Way Valve

and sleeves are all interchangeable, the discussion will now cover the basic valve design without reference to materials or fluids used.

First, the basic poppet design lends itself quite well to a two position, three-way function. To perform a 4-way function, two three-way functions are combined. As will be shown, this can be accomplished by using a three-way valve sandwich. The basic valve is a solenoid direct operated model which can be used by itself for low flow applications (10 GPM maximum) or as a pilot valve for higher flows. As shown in the photograph, the solenoid actuator can also be replaced with various types of manual and mechanical operators.

The cross-sectional illustration of a normal open valve shows a single ball double seat arrangement of the internal pieces. The ball type poppet is held against the left-hand seat by a relatively heavy spring force. Pressure is opened to the A port, while the tank connection is blocked without leakage. When the solenoid is energized, the mechanical lever lifts the ball from the left-hand seat and presses it into the right-hand seat. This causes P to be blocked from A, and opens A to T. The valve displays open center crossover characteristics in that all ports are interconnected while the ball is being moved from one seat to the other.

External sealing of the actuating pin is achieved through the use of two u-cup seals which are constantly pressurized by the pressure at port P in the valve. Also, the mechanical lever is incorporated to give the solenoid a mechanical force advantage of 6:1. The ball at the lower end of the mechanical lever is necessary to eliminate a side loading which otherwise could be transmitted to the actuating pin.

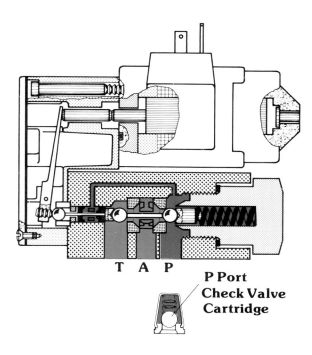

Two Ball, Normally Closed 3-Way Valve

The cross-sectional illustration of a normally closed valve shows it to be similar to a normally open valve in basic operation. However, in this assembly, the seats are reversed, and two balls are used in the moving member. The right-hand ball is held against the right-hand seat by the heavy spring force. This blocks P from A and opens A to tank. Energization of the solenoid presses the left-hand ball into its respective seat and also unseats the right-hand ball. The A port is connected to P and blocked from T in the shifted position.

In this flow pattern, it should be noted that the P and A ports are blocked by a check valve function. Therefore, sufficiently high pressure at port A could lift the poppet from its seat causing a free flow to port P. For this reason, a cartridge check valve can be installed in the P port of the main valve. This assures leak free sealing, even if A port pressure becomes higher than that at port P.

4-Way 2 Position Function

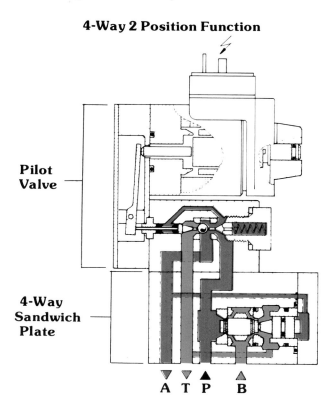

The 4-Way Sandwich Plate

The cross-sectional illustration shows that a sandwich plate is mounted between the three-way poppet valve and its subplate. When used with the normally open three-way poppet, the flow pattern is P to A through the pilot valve, and B to tank through the sandwich plate. If a normally closed pilot valve is used, the four-way function in the de-energized position is reversed, namely; P to B and A to T. For clarity, the de-energized and energized positions are represented in schematic form. Please note that the schematics are shown with a normally open pilot valve.

APPLICATIONS FOR DIRECT OPERATED POPPET VALVES

The sandwich plate is quite useful when a four-way two position function is required. However, it cannot be used to stop a cylinder actuator in midstroke. When a three position control valve function is required, two direct operated valves can be used. The following circuits are but a few examples.

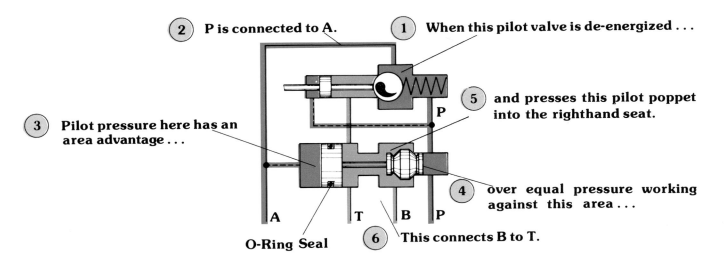

② P is connected to A.

① When this pilot valve is de-energized . . .

③ Pilot pressure here has an area advantage . . .

⑤ and presses this pilot poppet into the righthand seat.

④ over equal pressure working against this area . . .

⑥ This connects B to T.

O-Ring Seal

A T B P

De-Energized 4-Way Two Position

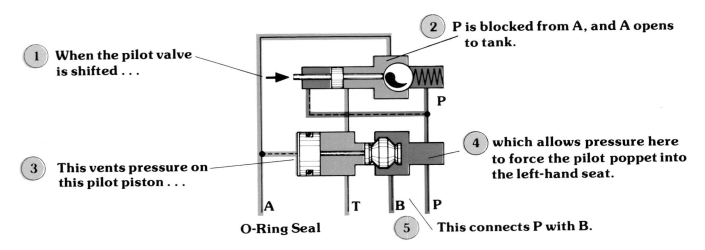

② P is blocked from A, and A opens to tank.

① When the pilot valve is shifted . . .

③ This vents pressure on this pilot piston . . .

④ which allows pressure here to force the pilot poppet into the left-hand seat.

O-Ring Seal

⑤ This connects P with B.

A T B P

Energized 4-Way Two Position

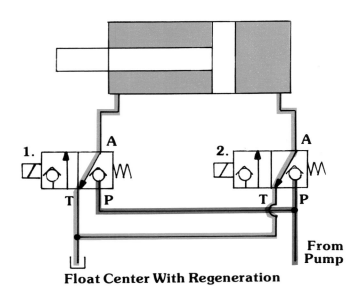

1. 2.

A A

T P T P

From Pump

Float Center With Regeneration

In this circuit, when both solenoids are de-energized, both ends of the cylinder are vented to tank through the A ports of the two normally closed three-way valves. This allows the cylinder to "float." Of course, pump pressure is blocked by the spring load poppet in the deactivated position.

When solenoid one is energized, pump flow is connected to the rod end of the cylinder, which causes it to retract. Likewise, the cylinder will extend when solenoid one is de-energized and solenoid two is actuated. It is interesting to note that if the two solenoids are simultaneously energized, pump pressure is directed to both sides of the cylinder. Assuming proper valve and cylinder size, the cylinder will advance rapidly in *regeneration*.

In this circuit arrangement of two normally open 3-way poppet valves, the cylinder is positively held in position by the cartridge P port check valves. With both valves deac-

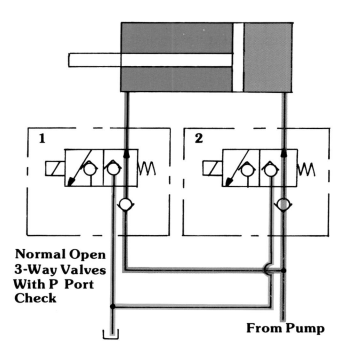

**Normal Open
3-Way Valves
With P Port
Check**

From Pump

Closed Center With Float Capability

**Exploded View Of A 2-Way Pilot Operated
Poppet Valve**

tivated, the pressure on the blind end of the cylinder is equal to the pressure setting of the main relief. However, the pressure at the rod end of the cylinder is intensified to the level needed to balance the forces on the unequal piston areas, assuming that there is no load on the cylinder. This is an important consideration, particularly when you use this circuit with larger rod cylinders.

In this circuit, unlike the previous one, when solenoid one is energized, the cylinder *extends* because its rod end is connected to tank. By de-energizing solenoid one and energizing solenoid two, the cylinder retracts. Simultaneous energization of both solenoids vents both ends of the cylinder to tank, which allows it to float.

TWO-WAY PILOT OPERATED POPPET VALVE

The two-way pilot operated poppet valve is similar to a pilot operated spool valve in that a direct operated poppet valve operates a slave poppet, which, in this case, is the two-way logic element. In this basic design, the main poppet rides inside an interchangeable bushing, which is sealed from the main housing by o-rings and Teflon back-up rings.

As shown in symbol form, the main flow passage from P to A is opened when the pilot valve vents the top of the main poppet. Likewise, the main flow passage is blocked when the pilot valve directs pilot pressure to the top of the logic element poppet (see Chapter 4 for a complete explanation of area ratios and basic logic element operation.) Like spool type pilot operated valves, pilot chokes can be installed to adjust the opening and closing speed of the main poppet. By adjusting the opening and closing time, shock due to decompression is minimized as the valve is operated. The valve can also be internally or externally piloted and drained.

PILOT OPERATED POPPET VALVES FOR DIRECTIONAL CONTROL

The logic element which was introduced in Chapter 4 can be used in conjunction with the direct operated poppet valve. In this manner, leak free directional control of high flow rates can be achieved with virtually any fluid (mineral oil, oil-in-water emulsions, pure water, etc.). Since a logic element performs only a two-way function, two or more elements must be combined to achieve three or four-way directional control.

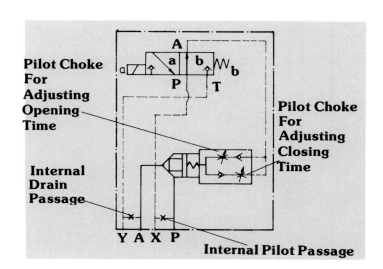

Pilot Choke For Adjusting Opening Time

Pilot Choke For Adjusting Closing Time

Internal Drain Passage

Internal Pilot Passage

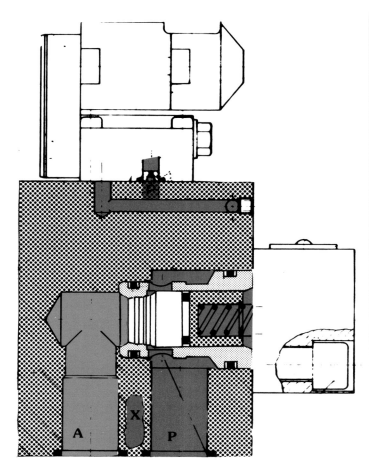

Cross-Sectional View Of A Two-Way Pilot Operated Poppet Valve

THREE-WAY PILOT OPERATED POPPET VALVE

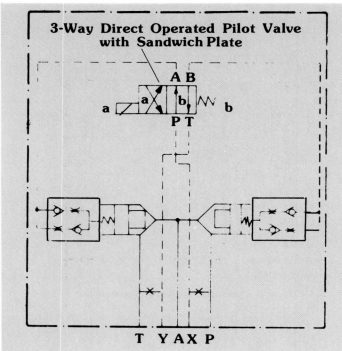

Symbol For A 3-Way Pilot Operated Poppet Valve

The three-way valve operates on the same principle as the two-way poppet valve, except for the fact that the main valve housing contains two logic elements. The piloting incorporates a four-way sandwich plate mounted between the pilot valve and the main valve housing. In this manner, the top side of one logic element can be vented to tank while the top side of the opposite element is pressurized, and vice versa, through the poppet pilot valve.

When a normally open three-way pilot valve is used, the pilot passages in the main valve housing are arranged so that P is open to A and T is blocked. Energization of the solenoid unloads the left-hand poppet, and pressurizes the top side of the right-hand logic element. This blocks P, and opens A to tank. During the shifting period, all ports are momentarily connected. This results in an open center crossover, similar to the one in a negatively overlapped spool valve (as previously discussed in this chapter).

THREE-WAY PILOT OPERATED POPPET VALVE WITH CLOSED CENTER CROSSOVER

In accumulator circuits and in some load holding circuits, the open center during crossover has an adverse effect on proper system operation. For this reason, it is sometimes necessary to use a pilot operated poppet valve with closed center crossover. As shown in the cross-sectional illustration, this is accomplished by replacing the two logic element cartridges

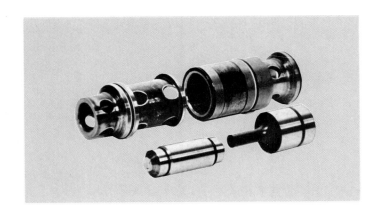

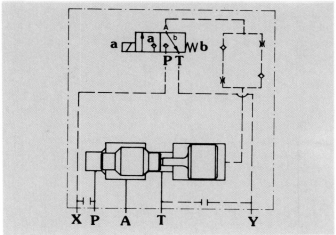

with a double end poppet with two seats.

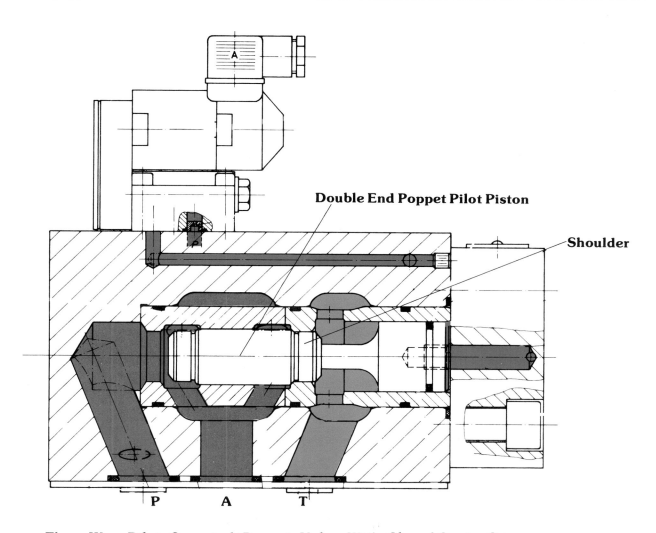

Three-Way Pilot Operated Poppet Valve With Closed Center Crossover

The cross-sectional illustration shows the orientation of the double end poppet and seat arrangement. The poppet position is determined by the prevailing pressure conditions on the pilot piston. This piston has a larger effective area than the exposed area of either of the poppets.

The main valve is piloted by a normally closed three way poppet valve. In the de-energized position of the pilot valve, the area behind the pilot piston (on the right-hand side) is vented to tank. Pressure at port P works over the effective area of the poppet nose, and causes it to shift to the right, as shown. Pressure in the P-A passage presses the opposite poppet into the right-hand seat, which positively seals the tank passage. When the solenoid is energized, pressure from port P pressurizes the right-hand side of the pilot piston. Since this piston has an area advantage, the double end poppet is pressed into the left-hand seat. The shifting speed of the double end poppet can be adjusted by incorporating the optional pilot choke flow controls.

The closed center crossover is achieved by the extended nose on each end of the double end poppet. This nose is closely fitted to the inside diameter of the seat. When the poppet moves from right to left, the first thing that happens is that the right-hand poppet is unseated. However, because the nose of the poppet is still extended into the seat, the main flow passage remains closed, except for a minimal

amount of leakage through the clearance fit. At approximately midstroke, the left-hand nose extension protrudes into the inside diameter of the left-hand seat, which blocks P from A. This occurs just before the nose of the right-hand poppet opens the A to T flow path. The net result is that the three ports are never interconnected during movement of the double end poppet. Of course, the function is identical when the spool moves to the right, which first blocks A from T, then opens P to A.

FOUR WAY PILOT OPERATED POPPET VALVE

The cross-sectional illustration shows that a 4-way pilot operated valve consists of a main housing with four logic elements and two direct operated poppet style pilot valves. For clarity, the operating modes are shown in schematic form as follows:

Cross-Sectional View Of A 4-Way Pilot Operated Poppet Valve

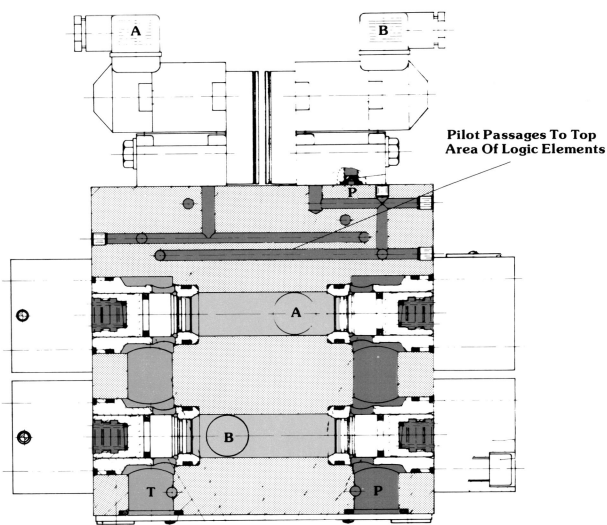

Pilot Passages To Top Area Of Logic Elements

PILOT PRESSURE REQUIREMENTS FOR PILOT OPERATED POPPET VALVES

The minimum pilot pressure requirements for pilot operated poppet valves are quite different from those for spool type directional valves. At this point, however, it would be repetitious to explain the opening and closing of the individual logic elements. Consequently, we ask that you review this information as it was presented in Chapter 4. The minimum pilot pressure requirements at port X can only be determined once the pressures at ports P, A, B and T are known. You must also consider the pilot pressure requirements for each portion of the machine cycle.

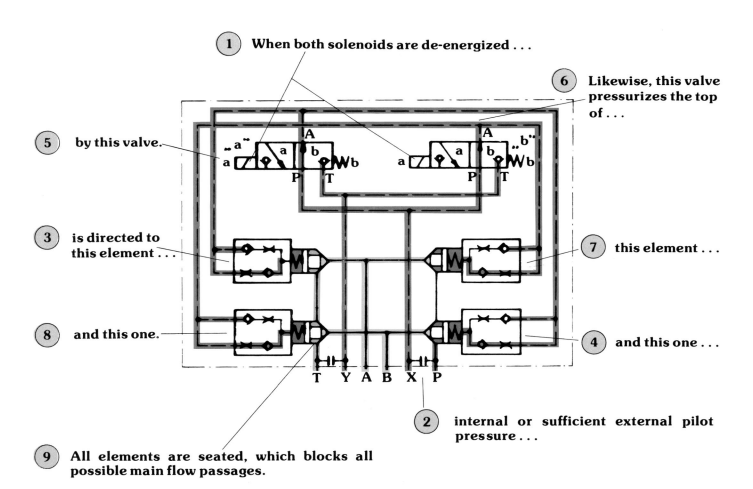

1. When both solenoids are de-energized . . .

6. Likewise, this valve pressurizes the top of . . .

5. by this valve.

3. is directed to this element . . .

7. this element . . .

8. and this one.

4. and this one . . .

2. internal or sufficient external pilot pressure . . .

9. All elements are seated, which blocks all possible main flow passages.

All Ports Blocked

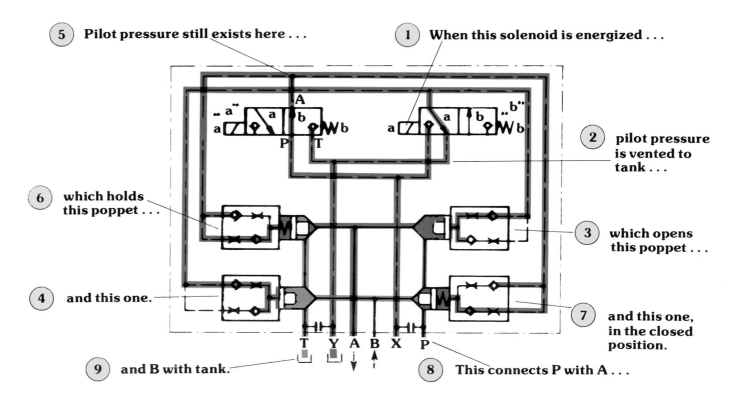

5. Pilot pressure still exists here . . .

1. When this solenoid is energized . . .

2. pilot pressure is vented to tank . . .

6. which holds this poppet . . .

3. which opens this poppet . . .

4. and this one.

7. and this one, in the closed position.

9. and B with tank.

8. This connects P with A . . .

P To A And B To T Flow Path

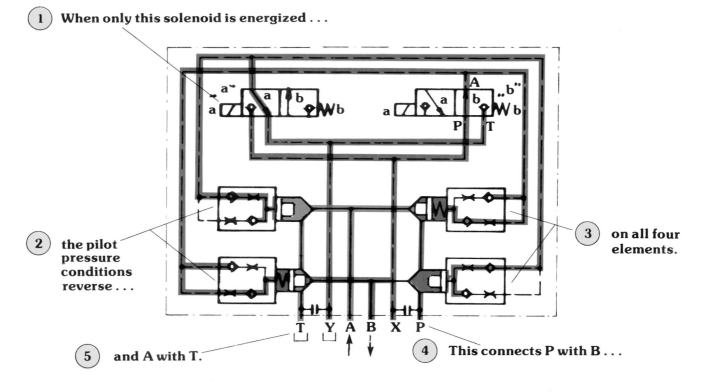

1. When only this solenoid is energized . . .

2. the pilot pressure conditions reverse . . .

3. on all four elements.

5. and A with T.

4. This connects P with B . . .

P To B And A To T

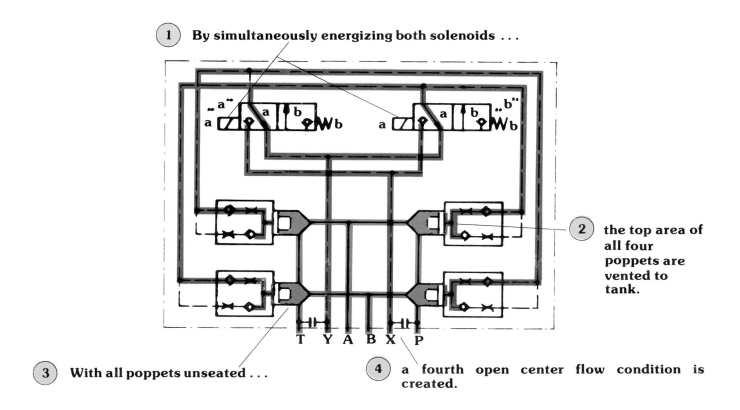

(1) By simultaneously energizing both solenoids ...

(2) the top area of all four poppets are vented to tank.

T Y A B X P

(3) With all poppets unseated ...

(4) a fourth open center flow condition is created.

CONCLUSION

In this chapter, we have attempted to explain the two most common methods of controlling direction of fluid flow in hydraulic systems: spool type and poppet style direction control. Most of the emphasis has been directed toward the sliding spool method of directional control, since this is by far the most popular. On the other hand, research in modern poppet valve design has developed a product with economic and technological feasibility. Among the poppet valve's strongest advantages is its leak free sealing capability and its ability to handle low viscosity fluids (even pure water) at high pressures. Your review of the material presented should give you an understanding of the following points.

SPOOL TYPE DIRECTIONAL VALVES

Starting with a very basic description of spool valve operation, we explained how a close fitting spool, which slides in a bore in the main valve house, blocks or opens flow passages. We also discussed the machining of various spool types, and how the valve's performance is affected by either positive or negative overlap. A description was also given of how Bernoulli flow forces affect the maximum performance

capability of the valve. The spool positioning method was also covered in detail for both direct and pilot operated valves.

With respect to direct operated valves, we have also covered the various methods of spool positioning. These included a two position valve with double actuators, and double actuators with detents or spring offsetting. Springs can also be used to provide a three position spring centered spool positioning. In addition, various types of valve actuators for providing shifting forces have been covered in detail. Actuator types include manual, mechanical, pilot operated, and electrical solenoids for use with either an AC or DC current. In addition, the description of solenoid actuators covered the advantages offered by either the air gap or wet pin design.

We have also described pilot operated directional valves for use in systems using higher flow rates. In describing the method of operation, we have shown how the slave spool is shifted by a command from a direct operated spool type pilot valve. The description included four methods of positioning the slave spool: two position hydraulic offset, two position spring offset, and three position valves which are either spring or pressure centered. The methods of converting from internal to external pilots and drains have also been presented. The special requirements of an internal pilot valve when you use spool types which unload pressure have been discussed, with various methods of maintaining minimum pilot pressure. In addition, the various accessories for pilot operated valves were explained. These included pilot chokes, stroke limiters and spool position indicators.

This chapter also included a discussion of symbolism for both direct and pilot operated directional valves. These symbols were used to outline the requirements of a number of various circuit applications. The application examples included series circuits, parallel circuits, three methods of obtaining regeneration, and the application precautions with open center spools.

POPPET STYLE DIRECTIONAL CONTROLS

The second part of this chapter was devoted to poppet style directional control. The advantages offered by the poppet design is that it allows one port to be sealed from another without leakage. Because of this leak free sealing, the poppet design can be used with pure water, since the problem of "wire drawing" is eliminated.

The direct operated poppet valve has a three-way flow pattern, and can be supplied in a normally open or a normally closed configuration. A sandwich plate is also available for converting the valve, so that it can be used to perform a two position 4-way function. In addition to solenoid operators, various manual and mechanical actuators are also available for direct operated poppet valves.

To accomplish leak free directional control for higher flow rates, the direct operated poppet valve can be used to pilot a main valve housing which incorporates one or more *logic elements*. Descriptions of two, three and four-way pilot operated poppet type directional valves have been covered.

For those of you who have been reading chapter by chapter, you have now been exposed to the major *valve* type components used in an industrial hydraulic system. In Chapter 6, we will turn our attention to the hydraulic pump. Selection of this single component can make or break a system design.

CHAPTER 6
HYDRAULIC PUMPS

In the design of any hydraulic system, proper pump selection will have a significant influence on overall system performance, operational efficiency, and cost. In regard to cost, it is important to understand that the initial acquisition is only one factor. Long range operating costs can make a burdensome expense of what seemed to be an inexpensive purchase. The expenditures which must be considered in evaluating the total cost of any system include: initial component and piping expense, continual cost for generating and dissipating unneeded power, and the money spent to obtain an acceptable noise level. This chapter is intended to familiarize you with the pump types available, so that you can make the proper selection for your particular system.

THE ENERGY INPUT

We said in Chapter 1 that the pump does not create energy, but that it *converts* energy into a form which can be utilized by the hydraulic system. Although pumps come in various shapes and sizes with uniquely different pumping mechanisms, their sole purpose is to convert the mechanical energy of the prime mover into hydraulic energy. They do this simply by *pushing* hydraulic fluid into the system.

In most industrial hydraulic systems, the *prime mover* is an electric motor. The rotary motion of the prime mover creates a flow of fluid from the outlet of the pump.

PRIME MOVERS

In the United States, industrial grade electric motors are available in syncronous speeds of approximately 860, 1140, 1750 and 3420 RPM (the nominal ratings of these motor's speeds are 900, 1200, 1800 and 3600 RPM). In general, the higher the electric motor speed, the lower is the cost of the electric motor for a given horsepower rating. However, the noise level and the maximum speed ratings of the pump should also be taken into consideration in selecting an electric motor. For this reason, most industrial hydraulic systems use either an 1140 RPM or a 1750 RPM electric motor.

Mobile hydraulic systems, on the other hand, usually use internal combustion engines as their prime movers. Since both diesel and gasoline engines have a variable speed output

(RPM), it is important that they do not drop below the minimum or exceed the maximum speed limit of the pump.

THE SIMPLE PUMP

The action of any hydraulic pump can be understood in terms of the operation of a simple hand operated pump. The basic pumping principle is that a captive volume increases in size during suction, then decreases to force the fluid out of the outlet port of the pump. Let us now consider how oil enters and leaves a hydraulic pump.

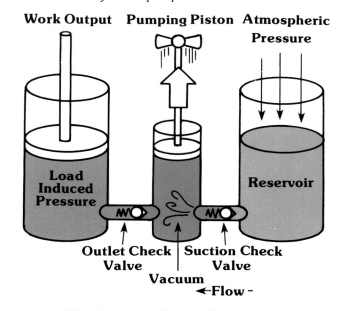

Simple Pump During Suction

The simplest hand operated pump consists of a pumping piston with a manual energy input, an oil reservoir, and two check valves. As shown in the illustration, when the pumping piston is pulled upward, a partial vacuum exists since an *increasing volume* is being created. This vacuum creates an unbalanced pressure condition so that atmospheric pressure (and/or head pressure of the oil, see Chapter 1) can push oil into the pumping cylinder by opening the suction check valve. While the pumping piston is being pulled upward, load induced pressure (and spring force) keeps the outlet check valve closed.

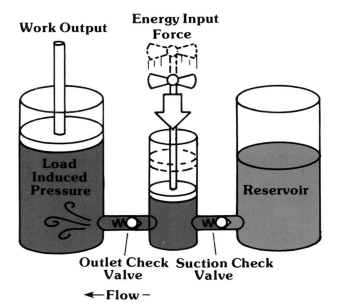

Work Output

Energy Input Force

Load Induced Pressure

Reservoir

Outlet Check Valve   Suction Check Valve

← Flow –

Simple Pump During Pressure Stroke

Once upward motion of the pumping piston ceases, the pump cylinder is filled with oil at nearly atmospheric pressure. When pressure in the pumping cylinder is close to the atmospheric pressure in the reservoir, the light spring force closes the suction check valve. Now, when the piston area is exposed to a downward force, a pressure is created in the captive fluid. Initially, as the downward force develops on the input piston, there is no flow, since the pressure in the pump cylinder is less than load induced pressure. However, the moment sufficient pressure is developed, the outlet check valve opens, transmitting flow and pressure (energy) to the output actuator.

Needless to say, the output flow of the hand pump is determined by the volume displaced during one stroke of the pumping piston, and the number of strokes per unit time. On the the other hand, the pressure capability is determined by the mechanical integrity of the pumping cylinder, and the maximum force potential.

RATINGS FOR HYDRAULIC PUMPS

In this book we will only concern ourselves with *positive displacement pumps*. A positive displacement pump delivers a relatively constant output flow, which, except for a small amount of leakage, is independent of the system's operating pressure. The pumping mechanism of a positive displacement pump always provides a mechanical seal between the inlet and the outlet of the pump. We will not consider centrifugal type impeller pumps, since they generally are not adequate for use in power transmission.

DISPLACEMENT

The size of a positive displacement pump is usually expressed in terms of the number of cubic inches *displaced* during one revolution of the drive shaft. As will be shown, most pumps have more than one pumping chamber. Consequently, the total displacement of the pump is the volume created by one pumping chamber multiplied by the number of chambers that pass the outlet porting during one revolution. Generally, displacement is represented in cubic inches per revolution.

Another common method of representing the size of a pump is to list its *nominal flow* at a specific drive speed. For instance, the variable volume vane pump (which will be discussed later in this chapter) is normally driven by a 1750 RPM electric motor. It is commonplace in the industry simply to refer to these pump sizes as 6 GPM, 8 GPM, 15 GPM, etc. The nominal pump rating does not represent an actual figure. A particular pump with a 8 GPM nominal rating at 1750 RPM may pump slightly more or less than 8 GPM depending on the load conditions. This brings us to another term: *volumetric efficiency.*

VOLUMETRIC EFFICIENCY

Theoretically, a pump which displaces 20 cubic inches per revolution will deliver 20 cubic inches of oil for each revolution of its input shaft. In reality, however, the actual pump output is reduced by two forms of leakage as pressure increases across the clearance fits of the pump. This leakage can be either crossport leakage, which means pressurized fluid flows back to the suction side of the pump, or in some pump designs, it can be leakage to the case or housing of the pump. Pumps which have case drain leakage ports simply allow pressurized fluid which passes through the clearance fits to collect in the housing and then free flow back to the reservoir through the case drain line. Of course, for a given clearance, the higher the outlet pressure (the higher the pressure drop across the clearance fit — Chapter 1), the greater is the leakage.

Volumetric efficiency is a percentage figure determined by dividing the actual flow by the theoretical flow value:

$$E_v = \frac{\text{ACTUAL FLOW}}{\text{THEORETICAL FLOW}} \times 100$$

If, for example, a pump size is stated as 10 in³/rev. at 1750 RPM, this pump should deliver:

$$\text{GPM} = \frac{\dfrac{10 \text{ in}^3}{\text{rev.}} \times \dfrac{1750 \text{ rev.}}{\text{min.}}}{231} = 75.75 \text{ GPM}$$

If the actual pump output at 1750 RPM is 69.5 GPM, the pump is said to have a volumetric efficiency of:

$$E_v = \frac{69.5 \text{ GPM}}{75.75 \text{ GPM}} \times 100 = 91.74\%$$

Because volumetric inefficiency does not cause mechanical work, the leakage flow produces heat. If the pump is operating at 2000 PSI outlet pressure, the rate of heat generation because of leakage is:

$$\frac{\text{BTU}}{\text{HR}} = 1.5 \times \text{GPM} \times \text{PSI} =$$
$$1.5 \times (75.75 - 69.5) \times 2000 = 18,750 \frac{\text{BTU}}{\text{HR}}$$

MECHANICAL EFFICIENCY

Another type of inefficiency is that produced by mechanical friction during operation of the pump. If the pump were to be delivering flow at zero pressure, then no force (torque) should be required. In Chapter 1 we have shown how the pressure relates to the torque of a rotational device, namely:

$$T = \frac{P \times D}{2\pi}$$

Where:
T = Torque (lb. − in.)
P = Pressure (PSI)
D = Displacement (in³/rev.)

If we again consider our 10in³/rev. pump operating at 2000 PSI, the *theoretical* torque would be:

$$T = \frac{2000 \,(10 \text{ in}^3/\text{rev.})}{2\pi} = 3183 \text{ (lb. − ins.)}$$

If we measure the actual torque required to drive the pump, we may find that at 2000 PSI, the actual input torque is 3360 (lbs. − ins.) (This would require the use of a dynamometer). The percentage of mechanical efficiency would be found by dividing the theoretical torque value by the actual torque required to drive the pump:

$$E_m = \frac{\text{THEORETICAL TORQUE}}{\text{ACTUAL TORQUE}} \times 100$$

For the example pump, the mechanical efficiency would be:

$$E_m = \frac{3183 \text{ (lb. − ins.)}}{3360 \text{ (lb. − ins.)}} \times 100 = 94.73\%$$

OVERALL EFFICIENCY

In the process of selecting a hydraulic pump, it is important that you compare the efficiencies properly. It is quite common for technical literature to list one type of efficiency but not the other. However, it is best to compare the pumps on an overall efficiency basis, which would include both volumetric and mechanical inefficiencies. Mathematically, the overall efficiency figure is simply the product of the two values. In our example, the overall efficiency of the pump would be:

$$E_t = \frac{E_v \times E_m}{100} = \frac{91.74\% \times 94.73\%}{100} = 86.9\%$$

Another way of determining the overall efficiency of a pump is to compare the theoretical power output with the actual power required to drive the pump. If the pump is actually pumping 69.5 GPM at 2000 PSI, the HP that would be available to produce useful work is:

$$HP_t = \frac{69.5 \text{ GPM} \times 2000 \text{ PSI}}{1714} = 81.09 \text{ HP}$$

However, if we use the actual torque required at the drive speed which we assumed to be 1750 RPM, we can calculate the actual horsepower input:

$$HP = \frac{T \times \text{RPM}}{63025} =$$
$$\frac{3360 \text{ (lb. − in.)} \times 1750 \text{ RPM}}{63025} = 93.29 \text{ HP}$$

Our overall efficiency is:

$$E_t = \frac{\text{THEORETICAL HP OUT}}{\text{ACTUAL HP IN}} \times 100 = \frac{81.09}{93.29} \times 100$$
$$= 86.9\%$$

This is the same efficiency we obtained by multiplying the volumetric and mechanical values of efficiency.

THE PRACTICAL SIDE OF PUMP EFFICIENCY

In order to explain the difference between volumetric, mechanical and overall efficiency, we have, more or less, shown the steps by which a pump manufacturer determines the efficiency of his pump. However, from the designer's standpoint, the problem is not how to determine (or calculate) pump efficiency. He must understand what these values mean, and how they will relate to his system.

If, for instance, you want to know the exact flow which can be expected from the pump, you must obtain from the manufacturer, *the volumetric efficiency for the pressure at which the pump will operate.* The actual output flow can then be calculated:

$$\text{Actual GPM} = \frac{(D) \times RPM}{231} \times E_v$$

Where D = theoretical displacement (in³/rev.)

On the other hand, if you want to determine the drive power required by the pump, the overall efficiency figure must be used. This is true because both leakage and friction turn input energy into heat. Since leakage inefficiency is already included in the E_t figure, the actual output flow is used for the GPM value. This eliminates including the volumetric efficiency twice in our calculations;

$$HP = \frac{GPM \times PSI}{1714 \, (E_t)}$$

For our example pump, the actual drive horsepower would be:

$$\text{HP Actual} = \frac{69.5 \, GPM \times 2000 \, PSI}{1714 \, (E_t)} = 93.3 \, HP$$
$$E_t = .869$$

If we are interested in determining the rate at which the pump generates heat, we simply subtract the theoretical HP output from the actual HP input. This difference in HP can then be converted into heat generated in BTU/HR:

a) $\text{HP (theoretical out)} = \dfrac{69.5 \, GPM \times 2000 \, PSI}{1714} = 81.1 \, HP$

b) $\text{HP (in)} - \text{HP (out)} = 93.3 - 81.1 = 12.2 \, HP$

c) $12.2 \, HP \times \dfrac{2545 \, BTU/HR}{1 \, HP} = 31,049 \, BTU/HR$

It is interesting to note that if we subtract from the total heat generation (31,049 BTU/HR) the heat generated by leakage as previously calculated (18,750 BTU/HR), we can find the amount of heat generated because of mechanical inefficiency; this value is 12,299 BTU/HR. You will find that the ratio between volumetric and mechanical efficiency changes with *pressure* and operating *speed.* At low pressure, volumetric efficiency is high, but mechanical efficiency is low. At high pressure, better lubrication increases the mechanical efficiency, but higher leakage decreases the volumetric efficiency. With respect to speed, mechanical efficiency is higher at low speeds. However, volumetric efficiency is highest at maximum speed. This is true because pump leakage is pressure dependent. Consequently, the leakage is a smaller percentage of the higher flow produced at high speed.

PRESSURE RATINGS FOR PUMPS

In Chapter 1 we introduced one of the most important concepts in industrial hydraulics: hydraulic pumps do not pump pressure. A pump simply creates a flow of fluid by overcoming any resistance to its output flow. If there is no resistance, then there is no pressure.

Consequently, the pressure rating of a pump is nothing more than a statement of the pump's mechanical integrity. It gives the designer a guideline as to the pressure at which the pump can operate without damage, so that he can select a pump which offers a reasonable service life. It is important to realize that a pump that is rated for 2500 PSI could easily produce 10,000 to 15,000 PSI if misapplied.

Most catalogue pressure ratings are the absolute maximum recommended operating pressures. For optimum pump life, it is recommended that you select a pump with a pressure rating higher than the operating pressure of your system. Operating a pump at a higher pressure than recommended will, at the very least, reduce its life expectancy. However, the more likely outcome is the catastrophic failure of the pump.

SHAFT ALIGNMENT AND PUMP MOUNTING

Offset Misalignment   **Angular Misalignment**

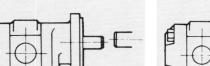 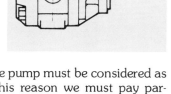

By nature of its application, the pump must be considered as a precision instrument. For this reason we must pay particular attention to the mounting and general installation of this component. Proper support and proper shaft alignment are two of the most important considerations.

APPLICATIONS OF FIXED DISPLACEMENT PUMPS

Before getting involved with the various types of fixed displacement pumps, we must clear up one area of possible confusion. A *fixed displacement* hydraulic pump is a positive displacement design in which the *amount of displacement cannot be varied.* At a given input RPM, the pump *must* deliver flow in an amount equivalent to its fixed displacement. On the other hand, a *variable displacement* pump is also a *positive displacement* design. However, with this type of pumping mechanism, the size of the pump's displacement can be changed easily. Variable displacement pumps will be covered in detail later in this chapter.

The amount of flow that is delivered by a *fixed displacement* pump can be changed only by changing the drive speed of the pump. Because there is no means of physically changing the pump's displacement, these pumps are generally less expensive and less complicated in design. However, since industrial systems usually use constant speed electric motor drives, the application possibilities of fixed displacement pumps are somewhat limited.

In Chapter 3 we have shown how flow control valves can be use to adjust speed in a hydraulic system. However, we have also shown how the flow control can be responsible for a considerable heat generation rate. In fixed displacement pump circuits, if the actuator(s) requires different flow rates during its operation, then the fixed displacement pump must be sized to deliver the highest flow. Unfortunately, when less flow is required at the lower operating speeds, the excess flow must be "dumped" over the relief valve at full system pressure. This unconditionally converts the unneeded energy into heat. For this reason fixed displacement pumps should only be used in constant speed applications, or in circuits in which speed control is very short in duration. Likewise, a fixed displacement pump should never be used to hold pressure on an actuator under static conditions.

Nevertheless, there are a multitide of applications where the fixed displacement pumps do the job and do it well. It is, however, imperative that the pump be sized precisely for the speed required. Normally, a fixed displacement pump will be adequate unless you answer "yes" to any one of the following statements.

Precautions must be taken if fixed displacement pumps are used under any one of the following conditions:
—System pressure must be maintained on a stalled actuator.
—The circuit operates over a broad speed range.
—The pump cannot be unloaded by the circuit design during idle periods.
—During a portion of the cycle, the actuator must be operated at a relatively low speed.

In summarizing the above, a fixed displacement pump has great potential for generating heat, if, for some reason, it is misapplied. For any system, it is the responsibility of the designer to calculate the heat generation (Chapter 1) during each portion of the cycle. If heating the system is not a problem, then the fixed displacement pump is adequate for the application. On the other hand, if it appears that a good deal of energy will be converted into heat, the designer may have to consider a variable displacement pump.

PUMP CLASSIFICATION

Today 99% of all hydraulic pumps fall into one of the three basic design classifications. They are: gear, vane, or piston pumps. Each major division can, in turn, be subdivided into specific pump types. In general, all three design classifications are applicable to fixed displacement pumps. However, only the vane or piston type can be used for variable displacement. We now wish to cover the most common designs as outlined in the pump classification chart. We will first discuss fixed displacement pumps and then cover variable pumps and their controls.

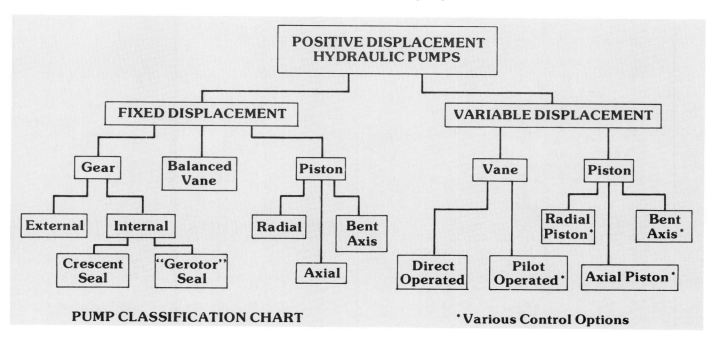

PUMP CLASSIFICATION CHART

*Various Control Options

THE EXTERNAL GEAR PUMP

The external gear pump is probably the oldest pump design which is still in use in modern hydraulic systems. The reason for this is that the basic design is rugged and is capable today of both high flow and high pressure. We will now take a closer look at the external gear pump design.

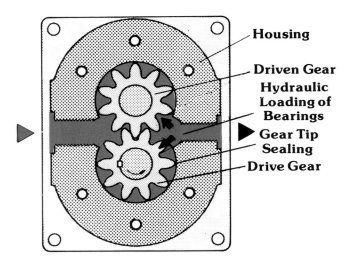

As shown in the cross-sectional illustration, an external gear pump is nothing more than a set of spur gears contained in a close fitting housing. You will notice that the bottom gear (in this illustration) is keyed to the drive shaft of the pump. As the *drive gear* is rotated by the prime mover, this gear meshes with and turns the *driven gear*.

If you look at this cross section from the point at which the drive shaft seems to protrude from the page, you can easily see that when the drive gear turns in a counterclockwise direction, the driven gear rotates in the clockwise direction.

The expanding and decreasing volume needed to produce a pumping action is created by the unmeshing and meshing of

the gear teeth. As the gear teeth on the left-hand side of the drawing separate, an expanding volume is created. This void causes a partial vacuum, so that atmospheric pressure can push oil into the pump's inlet. Once oil fills the space between adjacent pairs of gear teeth, the oil is carried around the outside of the two gears. During this transmittal of oil, the gear tips come in close proximity to the pump housing, effectively sealing and isolating the pressure and the suction sides of the pump.

Now, as the gear tips on the right-hand side of the drawing remesh, the oil is mechanically forced from the spaces between the gear teeth. This causes a flow of fluid from the outlet of the pump. The pump displacement is related directly to the number of teeth on each gear, and to the size of the spaces between adjacent pairs of teeth.

GEAR PUMP LEAKAGE

In general, most gear pumps do not have case drain leakage connections. Consequently, their volumetric inefficiency results totally from *crossport* leakage. The crossport leakage can take one of two possible flow paths.

The first path of possible leakage is that of pressurized fluid which passes between the housing and the gear tips. This, however, is the longer path, and the minor leakage path in closely fitted gear pumps.

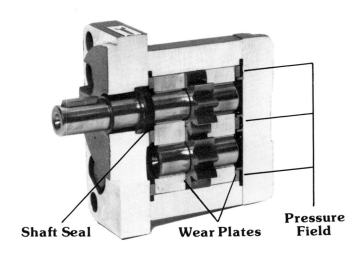

Typical Gear Pump (Cutaway)

If we now look at the pump from a side view, we can see the major leakage path. Physically, the suction and pressure sides of the pump are closest in the center of the pump housing. We must remember, however, that a clearance fit must exist if the gears are to rotate in the pump housing. This clearance will allow pressurized fluid to flow by the gear faces to the suction side of the pump.

High pressure gear pumps, on the other hand, are designed with *floating* wear plates (sometimes referred to as thrust plates). These two wear plates are located in the pump housing on either side of the gear faces. To facilitate pump start-up, the wear plates generally have bronze surfaces, and they are lightly mechanically loaded against the faces of the gears. As pressure is developed by the pump, it creates a hydraulic force, which tends to push the wear plates away from the gear faces. However, this hydraulic force is balanced by a pressure field created on the opposite side of one (or sometimes both, depending on the pump design) of the wear plates. The effective area of this pressure field is precisely designed so that a light hydraulic force always exists to load the wear plates against the faces of the gears. During operation, the plates self-adjust the pump clearance, according to the pressure level. Of course, the higher the system pressure, the higher is the hydraulic loading on the wear plates. The pressure loaded wear plates reduce leakage to a minimum without creating excessive mechanical friction. They also allow the pump to self compensate for wear.

EXTERNAL GEAR PUMPS ARE HYDRAULICALLY UNBALANCED

Although earlier gear pump designs were plagued with failure problems, modern gear pumps operate efficiently and quietly at high system pressures. The major cause of gear pump failure can probably be contributed to bearing failures. If you again refer to the cross-sectional illustration of this pump, you can see that high pressure is exposed unequally, considering the circumference of the gear. This high pressure is nothing more than a *force over an area*, and it causes a high mechanical loading on the shafts and bearings of the pump. For this reason, inexpensive gear pumps are usually limited to maximum operating pressures of 1500 PSI or lower.

On the other hand, gear pumps can be made to operate at high pressures (up to 4500 PSI), simply by providing them with a suitable bearing structure to support this hydraulic unbalance. High pressure gear pumps incorporate large diameter shafts which offer strength and allow for extra large bearings. Depending on pump design, these bearings can be either needle bearings or hydrodynamic (pressure lubricated) bushings.

OPERATING NOISE LEVEL

In the past, the gear pump has had an infamous reputation because of its high noise level during operation. This is a combination of mechanical noise caused by the meshing of the gear teeth, and, hydraulic noise created by the high frequency hydraulic pulsing due to the relatively high number of pumping chambers. Fortunately, computerized gear design and new manufacturing techniques have produced gear pumps which operate with very satisfactory noise levels. Therefore, the stigma which plagued the gear pump in the past is now being removed.

DIRECTION OF ROTATION

When specifying a gear pump for your system, you must be careful to order a pump with the proper direction of rotation. This precaution is necessary since most gear pumps cannot easily be converted from one direction of rotation to another. In fact, it may even require a separate "mirror image" housing to convert the direction of rotation for an external gear pump. Some of the reasons for this will now be considered.

Again, it is necessary to refer back to the cross-sectional illustration of the typical pump design. At first it may seem that the direction of rotation can be changed simply by changing the rotational input to the pump. In theory, this would reverse the mechanics of the pumping action, and simply require connecting suction and pressure lines to the opposite sides of the housing. However, this is not the case.

Most pumps which are capable of self priming have a larger inlet port than outlet. This facilitates use of the proper pipe diameter at the pump's inlet. Consequently, if only the direction of rotation is changed, the pump would try to pull its full displacement through the smaller port, while pumping the fluid out the larger port. This would not be desirable.

Another problem in changing the direction of rotation of an external gear pump is that most pumps do not have external drains. Since the pump case is not vented to tank, the low pressure sealing ability of the shaft seal must be internally connected to the suction side of the pump. If this is not done when the direction of rotation is changed, high pressure fluid would inevitably cause a failure of this seal.

Finally, pumps with pressure load wear plates may require totally different plates for the opposite direction of rotation. This is true because the pressure field created behind the plate is not symmetrical. In fact, it must be loaded more heavily on the pressure side than on the suction side of the pump. Rotating these pumps in the wrong direction would not provide adequate pressure loading of the wear plates.

INTERNAL GEAR PUMPS

Internal gear pumps cause a pumping action to occur in the same manner as the external gear pumps. That is, suction is caused as the gears unmesh, and flow from the pump's outlet as the gear teeth remesh. The major difference is that, with this design, one gear rotates inside the second gear. Today, internal gear pumps are offered in two different designs: the crescent seal, and the "Gerotor" design. A closer look will now be taken at these two different pumps.

CRESCENT SEAL INTERNAL GEAR PUMPS

Crescent Seal Gear Pump

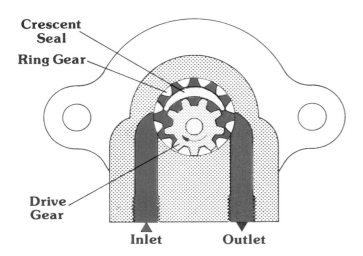

constant unmeshing of the gear teeth. The oil is then carried by the spaces between the teeth through the crescent sealing area to the high pressure outlet of the pump. Here the gear teeth remesh for the fluid to flow from the outlet of the pump. Sealing of the high pressure chamber from the pump's inlet is achieved by the close proximity of the crescent to the two gears on the top and the meshed gear teeth on the bottom (according to this drawing).

THE "GEROTOR" PRINCIPLE

The term *"Gerotor"* means generated rotor, and is the trade name for a very popular internal gear element.

The cross-sectional illustration shows a typical Gerotor element, which consists of a pair of gear shaped elements. The internal gear (or rotor) drives the outer gear in the same direction of rotation. This is identical to the internal gear pump with a crescent seal (clockwise rotation shown).

The inner Gerotor always has one less tooth than the outer element. The pumping chambers are formed by the adjacent pairs of teeth which are constantly in contact (except for clearance) with the outer element.

You will notice that, as the rotor is turned, its gear tips are accurately machined so that they precisely follow the contour of the outer element. The expanding chambers are created (on the left side of this drawing) as the gear teeth withdraw. The chamber reaches its maximum size when the female tooth of the outer Gerotor reaches top dead-center. Likewise, during the second half of the revolution, the spaces collapse, forcing fluid flow from the pump's outlet.

As shown in the operational cross section, the internal crescent seal gear pump consists of a small diameter internal gear, and an external *ring* gear. The inner gear is driven by the prime mover, in this example, in a clockwise direction. The internal gear meshes with and turns the ring gear in the same direction of rotation. In reference to the left-hand side of the illustration, oil is forced to enter the pump's inlet by the

ADVANTAGES OF THE INTERNAL GEAR DESIGN

The major advantage of any internal gear pump is that the gears mesh on an inside diameter. Rather than turning away from each other, the internal gear follows the ring gear

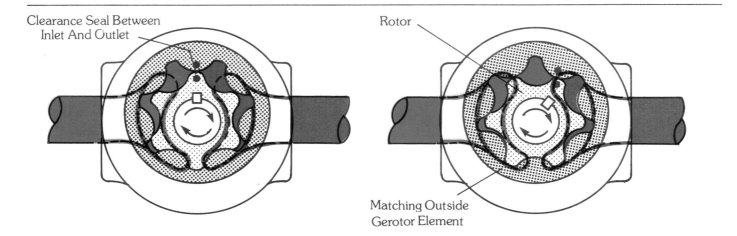

through more degrees of rotation. This means that the gears unmesh and remesh with a lower relative speed. This creates a smoother flow of fluid to and from the pump. On the suction side of the pump, this lower relative speed of the unmeshing of the gears means better pump filling. The lower fluid velocity allows the pump to start with more viscous fluids during cold start-up conditions. Likewise, the less radical meshing of the teeth at the pump's outlet means a smoother output flow, and, consequently, a lower operating noise level.

DISADVANTAGES OF INTERNAL GEAR PUMPS

Although high pressure internal gear pumps have been manufactured, most pumps are only capable of 1500 PSI maximum pressure. By studying the cross-sectional illustration, you will see that the internal gear pump, like the external gear design, operates under unbalanced pressure conditions. The internal gear can be provided with sufficient bearing capacity. However, the external (ring)gear presents a design problem.

Although the ring gear runs at a lower speed than the internal gear (more teeth cause a speed reduction), it is more difficult to support. Generally, the ring gear simply runs inside a close fitting bore in the pump housing. Lubrication and radial pressure balance are achieved by porting pressurized fluid between the outer gear and the pump housing. Because of the size of the gear and its geometry, this hydrodynamic bearing effect is usually only adequate for lower pressure operation (2000 PSI and below).

FIXED DISPLACEMENT VANE PUMPS

In the earlier years of hydraulics, the fixed displacement vane pumps gained wide acceptance over gear pump designs for two major reasons. First, because of manufacturing methods available at the time, gears were not able to be machined with a high degree of precision. This resulted in a gear pump

which produced considerable mechanical noise as the gear teeth meshed at high drive speeds. Second, the limited knowledge of manufacturing materials led to mechanical failure of the bearings and gear teeth. This failure was due to the high pressure unbalance of the basic gear pump design. For these reasons the fixed displacement "balanced" vane pump became quite popular. We will now take a closer look at how this pump functions.

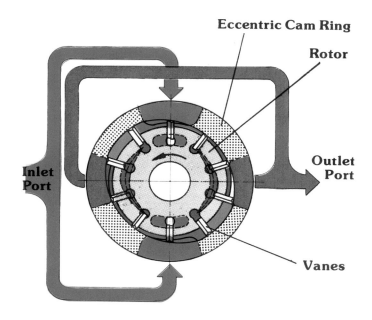

Fixed Displacement Balanced Vane Pump

As shown in the cross-sectional illustration, the basic vane pump consists of a rotor, an eccentric cam ring, and *vanes*. The rotor is either keyed or splined to the drive shaft, and is rotated by the prime mover. You will notice that the rotor has a number of radially machined slots which hold the *vanes*. Other than the rotor, drive shaft, and vanes, all parts, including port plates, are held stationary in the pump housing.

Initially, as the rotor is turned, centrifugal force causes the vanes to follow the contour of the eccentric cam ring. In this design an individual vane is fully extended and fully collapsed in its slot twice during each revolution. The expanding and decreasing volumes required for the pumping action are caused by the expanding and contracting volumes formed by the adjacent pairs of vanes.

The term *balanced* comes from the fact that the elliptical shape of the cam ring permits the use of two pressure outlets and two suction inlets. With a single pair of adjacent vanes, two pumping actions occur during one revolution of the drive shaft. Geometrically, the two pressure ports (and the two suction ports) are located directly opposite each other. In reference to the cross section, the hydraulic loading of the rotor and pump bearing to the right is offset by an equal hydraulic force to the left.

CARTRIDGE DESIGN

Today, many balanced vane pumps are of cartridge design. This simply means that the pumping elements (ring, rotor and vanes) are supplied as a self contained unit sandwiched between the two port plates. The housing of the pump holds the cartridge, and contains the drive shaft bearings and pipe

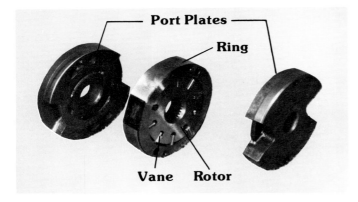

Port Plates — **Ring** — **Vane** **Rotor**

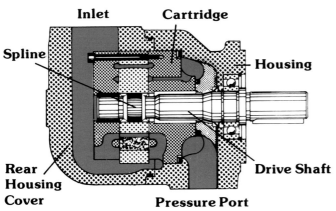

Inlet Cartridge Spline Housing Rear Housing Cover Drive Shaft Pressure Port

Typical Cartridge Vane Pump

connections. The cartridge design allows a worn out pump to be rejuvenated to new pump conditions in a matter of minutes, simply by replacing the cartridge. For a given pump housing, cartridges of several different displacements are available. This allows flexibility in matching the pump to the system.

FIXED DISPLACEMENT VANE PUMP SIZES

The fixed displacement balance vane pumps are offered in a variety of displacements, from less than 1 in³/rev. to over 20 in³/rev. At the pump's inlet, two expanding chambers are created simultaneously between the cam ring, rotor, and adjacent pairs of vanes. Inevitably, the size of these chambers determines the displacement of the pump. The chamber size is determined by the width of the cam ring and the stroke length of the vane. Consequently, the pump displacement is determined solely by the width of the cam ring and the shape of the elliptical surface.

DIRECTION OF ROTATION

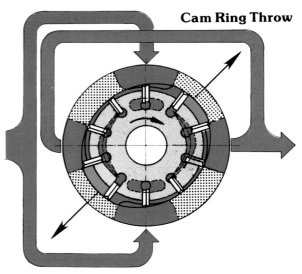

Cam Ring Throw

Clockwise Rotation

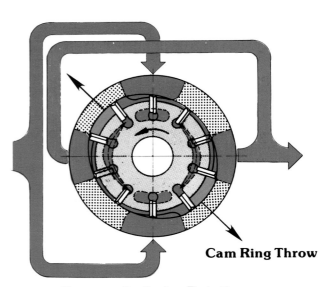

Cam Ring Throw

Counterclockwise Rotation

The fixed displacement balanced vane pump is normally field convertible from one direction of rotation to the other. The two assemblies shown should be viewed as if the pump shaft were protruding from the page. You can see that in both drawings, the port plates are oriented so that the suction inlets are on the vertical axis while the pressure outlets are on the horizontal axis. The difference is that the "throw" of the cam ring is to the top right and bottom left for a clockwise rotation pump. For a counterclockwise rotation, the throw is reversed with respect to the port plates, namely, upper left and lower right. In reference to this drawing, direction of rotation is changed simply by "flopping" the cam ring around the vertical axis. With some vane pump designs, the vanes must also be repositioned in their slots so that their "leading edges" follow the direction of rotation.

VANE TIP LOADING

The major cause of vane pump failure is wearing of the internal cam ring surface and the vane tip. Under normal operating conditions, vane pumps have extremely long life (over 25,000 hours). However, this life expectancy can be severely reduced by several adverse operating conditions. These include too high an operating pressure or speed, cavitation, contamination, and low quality hydraulic fluids. We will now study some of these conditions.

OPERATING PRESSURE

The major design difference between vane pumps of different manufacture is the method incorporated to load the vane tip against the inside surface of the cam ring. This is particularly true of vane pumps which are capable of operating at pressures higher than 1500 PSI.

Nevertheless, with any vane pump, the vane must be forced to follow the inside surface of the cam ring. If this were not the case, pressurized fluid could get between the vane tip and the cam ring and push the vane (against centrifugal force) into its slot in the rotor. This would mean that the pumping action would cease. For operating pressures of up to 1500 PSI, the single vane principle is generally used.

SINGLE VANES

Single Vane Principle

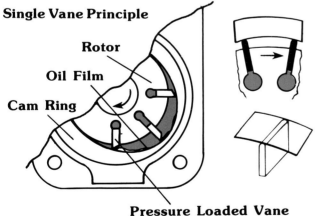

Pressure Loaded Vane

In reference to the illustration, as the vane is rotated through the pressure port area, the port plate exposes pressurized fluid underneath the vane. Pressure working over the rectangular area of the vane's base creates a force which assists centrifugal force. This holds the vane in an extended position against the cam ring.

However, during pressurization of the vane's base, mechanically, the vane is also being pushed back into the slot by the cam ring. This occurs as the captive volume is de-

creasing, forcing oil to flow from the outlet of the pump. Needless to say, the higher the operating pressure, the higher is the force required to collapse the vane. A point is reached at which the operating pressure becomes so high that excessive mechanical force is required. If the mechanical force becomes too high, the vane tip cuts through the oil film and comes in contact with the metal surface of the cam ring. This accelerates wear of both the cam ring and the vane tips.

DUAL VANE DESIGN

To alleviate the problems associated with the single vane design, high performance vane pumps incorporate *dual* vanes in each rotor slot. The purpose of the dual vanes is twofold. First, the two vane tips provide a double seal between pumping chambers. Second, the dual vane construction allows for a hydrostatic balancing of the vanes, thus reducing vane tip loading. Let us now look at how this hydrostatic balance is achieved.

Dual Vane Principle

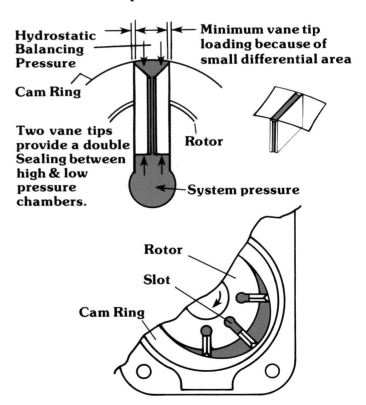

The illustration shows a typical dual vane assembly. Assuming clockwise rotation, you can see that the vanes are being collapsed in the slots causing a pumping action at the pump outlet. With this design, pressure at the base of the vane is channeled to the area between the two vane tips. This pressure field balances the pressure loading of the vane towards the ring, so that optimum vane tip loading is achieved at operating pressures up to 2500 PSI.

AVOID CAVITATION WITH VANE PUMPS

The vane pump is far more susceptible to damage by cavitation (see Chapter 1) than are gear pump designs. As a vane enters the suction area, it must extend from its previously collapsed position in the rotor. As the vane extends, oil fills the expanding chamber being formed at the base of the vane within the rotor. During this part of the rotation, the base of the vane is connected to the inlet of the pump, so that fluid is available for filling the void being created as the vane extends.

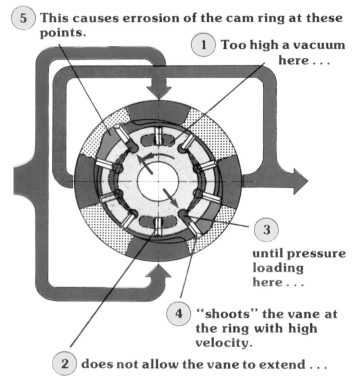

⑤ **This causes errosion of the cam ring at these points.**

① **Too high a vacuum here...**

③ **until pressure loading here...**

④ **"shoots" the vane at the ring with high velocity.**

② **does not allow the vane to extend...**

If an excessive vacuum exists at the pump's inlet, it also exists at the base of the vane. Damage occurs when the vane first loses contact with the ring during suction, and then is "fired" at the cam ring as it is rotated into the pressurized area. In general, this problem is non-existent with properly installed pumps.

SIDE CLEARANCE

Vane pumps and gear pumps share equal side clearance characteristics. With any of these designs, the rotating element is *sandwiched* between a combination of wear plates or port plates. Actually a port plate is nothing more than a wear plate with oil passages. In lower pressure equipment, these three elements operate with fixed clearances established during manufacture. As already discussed for the gear pump, higher performance pumps incorporate *pressure-balanced* wear plates which compensate for wear and reduce

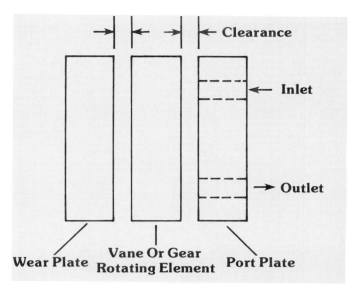

leakage to a minimum. We now will turn away from this basic pump concept and discuss the higher pressure capabilities of the piston pump design.

RADIAL PISTON PUMPS

The piston pump, in general, causes a pumping action simply be reciprocating a piston in a close fitting bore. In fact, the simple hand operated pump (explained earlier in this chapter) operates on the *"piston pump"* principle. Actually, a *radial piston pump* is nothing more than a number of mechanically operated "hand pumps" contained in a single housing. We now will discuss two different variations of fixed displacement radial piston pumps.

7 Piston Model

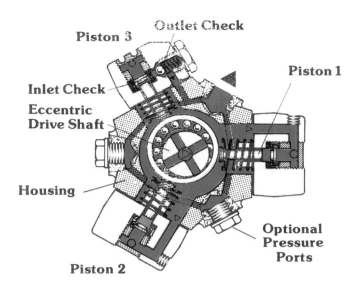

Piston 3
Outlet Check
Piston 1
Inlet Check
Eccentric Drive Shaft
Housing
Piston 2
Optional Pressure Ports

The cross-sectional illustration represents a typical radial piston pump. You can see that three *piston elements* are located in a symmetrical radial arrangement around the drive shaft. The supply of oil to the individual pistons comes from the center of the pump housing (green), while the pressure outlet is connected to a common pressure channel (shown in red). The pistons are actuated by the eccentric ball bearing on the drive shaft. The individual piston elements can actually be considered as three separate pumps, operated by a common eccentric drive. The pump can be driven clockwise or counterclockwise without modification, since either direction of rotation will cause the pistons to reciprocate in their bores. If we assume that the pump in this illustration is being driven in a counterclockwise direction, pistons 1, 2, and 3 will show us three separate pumping modes.

Piston number 1 is approaching the lower portion of the cam and is being retracted from the bore by its spring. A vacuum condition exists in the pumping chamber, and oil is drawn from the housing by flowing through the inlet check valve. To assure more complete filling of the piston element, oil is directed into the pump housing through axial and radial bores in the drive shaft. The radial bores, rotating at high speed, "sling" oil into the pump housing in the same way that a centrifugal pump would. This centrifugal pumping action increases the pressure in the case of the pump to a value slightly higher than atmospheric pressure. This *supercharging* assures better piston priming, which not only improves the suction characteristics, but also assists in lowering the operating noise level.

Piston number 2 is starting-up the ramp of the cam. The inlet check valve has closed, sealing the chamber, but pressure within the element is not yet equal to system pressure. At this point, pressure is developing in the fluid, but there is not sufficient mechanical force to cause flow. Needless to say, as the cam pushes harder on the piston, pressure will develop rapidly in the captive fluid.

Piston number 3 is approaching the end of its upward stroke. As the piston moves upward, fluid is forced to flow through the internal passages to the outlet of the pump. The outlet check valve (shown in the open position) will close as soon as the piston begins to retract into its bore. This positively seals the outlet from the inlet of the pump.

ISO — FLOW PUMPS

The cross-sectional illustration above shows a pump with all pumping elements connected to a common pressure outlet. Consequently, the displacement of the pump is determined simply by adding the displacements of the individual elements. Since optional elements are available with several different bore diameters, the displacement of the pump can be matched to the system simply by selecting the proper mix of pistons.

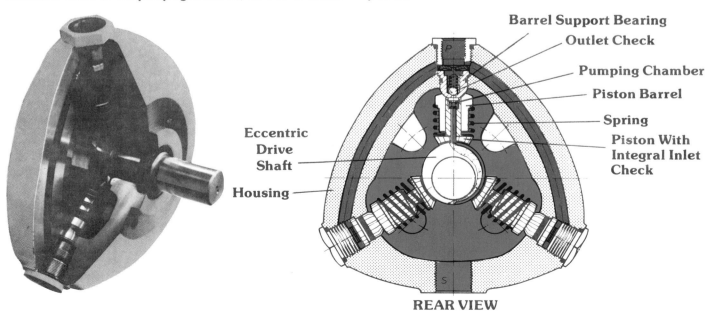

Eccentric Drive Shaft
Housing

Barrel Support Bearing
Outlet Check
Pumping Chamber
Piston Barrel
Spring
Piston With Integral Inlet Check

REAR VIEW

However, a second, even more unique feature of the radial piston pump, is that it can be supplied with several isolated pressure ports. The *ISO - flow* pump is nothing more than a modified housing which connects some of the pistons to one pressure port, while the other pistons are connected to a separate pump outlet. In fact, a three piston pump can be supplied with as many as three pressure ports, one for each piston.

The cross-sectional illustration (bottom of page 6-13) shows a modern radial piston pump design. Although similar in function to the design previously discussed, this particular pump offers somewhat higher performance characteristics, and is capable of lower operating noise levels.

The major design variation is that hydrodynamic bushings are used in place of ball bearings. In this bearing design, pressurized fluid from the pump's outlet is ported between the bearing surfaces. During operation, the shaft and bearing surfaces are actually separated by a film of oil, virtually eliminating metal to metal contact. In hydraulic pump application, these bearings have proven to exceed the life expectancy of either needle or ball bearings. They are also capable of supporting higher loads. To provide adequate protection during start-up conditions, the bearings are composed of a Teflon inpregnated bronze.

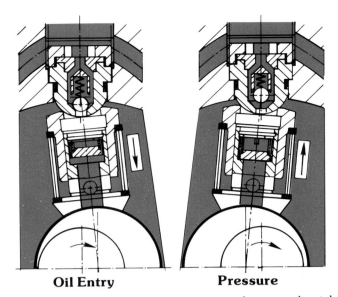

Oil Entry   **Pressure**

pumping chamber. The vacuum created opens the inlet check valve, allowing oil to enter this chamber. The base of the piston is exposed to the oil through a semi-annular groove machined into the eccentric cam.

Further rotation of the drive shaft causes the eccentric cam to push the piston back into the cylinder barrel. The inlet check valve closes, and pressure builds rapidly in the captive volume of the fluid. When the pressure in the captive fluid equals system pressure, the outlet check valve opens, allowing flow from the pressure port of the pump. As with any positive displacement pump, the higher the system pressure, the higher is the rotational torque requirement at the mechanical input to the pump.

FEATURES OF RADIAL PISTON PUMPS

The radial piston pump, in general, has the highest continuous pressure capability when compared with any other pump design. Today, radial piston pumps are available with continuous pressure ratings in the neighborhood of 10,000 PSI. However, they are not usually supplied in displacements larger than 0.5 cubic inches per revolution when they are required to operate at this extreme pressure level. It is important to realize that a 0.5 in³/rev. pump operating at 1750 RPM may only deliver 3.8 GPM, but requires a 25 HP electric motor for operating at 10,000 PSI.

The radial piston pump becomes absolutely necessary for systems operating at pressures above 5000 PSI. Typical applications include power supplies for hand tool operation (jacking cylinders, bearing pullers, crimpers), and high pressure clamp circuits for machine tools. In addition, the high pressure, low flow capabilities make the radial piston pump an ideal choice for holding pressure during a cure cycle on a hydraulic press. On the other hand, the radial piston pump is a highly efficient unit. Even at 10,000 PSI, typical pumps operate at over 93% volumetric efficiency, with

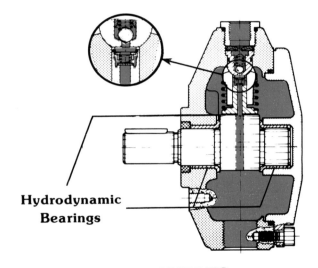

Hydrodynamic Bearings

OPERATING PRINCIPLES

The two previous cross-sectional illustrations show the general arangement of piston elements, eccentric drive shaft, housing, and bearing. As shown, the pistons are arranged radially to the eccentric drive shaft. Each piston element consists of a hollow piston with integral inlet check valve, a piston barrel support bearing with outlet check valve, and a spring.

As the drive shaft is rotated in a clockwise direction, the base of the piston is held in contact with the eccentric cam by the spring. The radius of this hydrodynamic bearing surface is equivalent to the radius of the eccentric cam. Downward motion of the piston causes an increasing volume in the overall efficiencies on the order of 86%. For this reason, radial piston pumps are also used on lower flow circuits when precise speed control is important (see Chapter 1).

PRESSURE AND FLOW RATINGS OF RADIAL PISTON PUMPS

In general, the displacement of a fixed displacement radial piston pump is determined by the piston diameter and stroke, assuming a given number of pistons. Although pumps are available with several different piston diameters, the highest pressure capabilities are obtainable only when using the smallest diameter pistons. In other words, as the piston diameter increases, the pump is capable of delivering higher flows, but at lower pressure limits. Over-pressurization of larger diameter pistons generally causes bearing failure in the pump.

PRIMING A RADIAL PISTON PUMP

In general, precautions should be taken during the initial start-up of any radial piston pump. A problem often occurs in starting a three piston pump, for example, because, in so doing, you are actually starting three separate pumps. The example which follows shows a three piston pump in which only two of the three pistons are pumping.

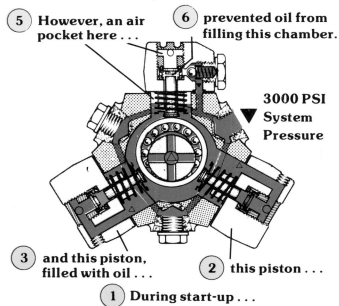

(4) **and are now pumping a flow of fluid against resistance in the system.**

(5) **However, an air pocket here . . .**

(6) **prevented oil from filling this chamber.**

3000 PSI System Pressure

(3) **and this piston, filled with oil . . .**

(2) **this piston . . .**

(1) **During start-up . . .**

In this example, during start-up, only two of the three pistons were primed, thus the pump was only producing 2/3 of its rated flow. The third piston received only air at its inlet, and during several reciprocations of the piston, the air pressure in

the pumping chamber was increased to a higher value. However, since air is compressible, the pressure could not reach a high enough level to open the outlet check against system pressure.

Once this condition is created, it is quite possible that the element will never prime. The air cannot escape over the outlet check, while at the same time air pressure is too high to allow oil entry over the inlet check. If precautions are not taken, the piston element will eventually fail, due to lack of lubrication. Fortunately, this problem is easily detectable and just as easily solved.

A pump which is operating with one or more of its pistons not primed is mechanically unbalanced. Since more torque is required to turn the drive shaft past the primed pistons, the unbalanced torque input creates excessive mechanical vibration and noise. The conditions are similar to those in an automobile engine which is not running on all its cylinders.

When you are starting a new installation with a radial piston pump, it is advisable for you to unload the outlet of the pump. In this manner, system pressure cannot build behind the outlet check valves, allowing the air to escape from the pumping chamber. If, after running the pump for several minutes in the unloaded condition, the problem is not solved (noise and vibration when operating under pressure), it may be necessary to bleed the unprimed piston elements individually.

In isolated instances, it sometimes happens that the outlet check valve cannot be opened by air pressure in the pumping element, even when the outlet of the pump is unloaded. This problem can be overcome by loosening the check valve access nut which will relax the spring force and allow the element to prime. The nut should be retightened as soon as all the air has escaped.

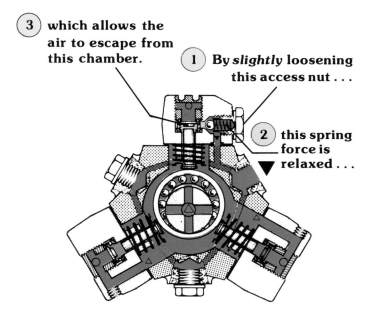

(3) **which allows the air to escape from this chamber.**

(1) **By *slightly* loosening this access nut . . .**

(2) **this spring force is relaxed . . .**

FIXED DISPLACEMENT IN-LINE AXIAL PISTON PUMPS

In-line axial piston pumps have gained wide acceptance because of their higher flow capabilities (over 100 GPM) at relatively high operating pressures (up to 5000 PSI). In this design, the pistons and cylinder barrel are parallel to the drive shaft. The cylinder barrel is a one piece unit and is bored to accept several closely fitted pistons. The number of pistons is determined by the actual pump design. However, there are usually the odd number of pistons: 5,7,9 etc. We make reference to the cross-sectional illustration for further descriptions of the operation.

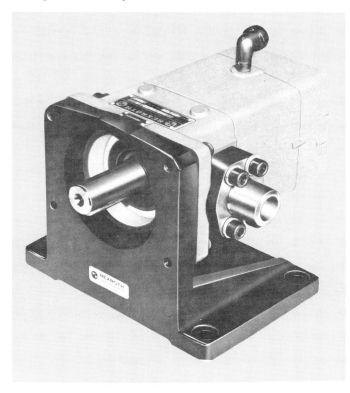

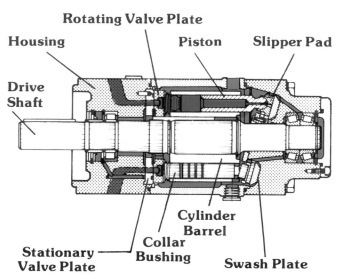

Housing — **Rotating Valve Plate** — **Piston** — **Slipper Pad**

Drive Shaft

Stationary Valve Plate — **Collar Bushing** — **Cylinder Barrel** — **Swash Plate**

The cross-sectional illustration represents a typical high pressure in-line piston pump. In this particular pump, nine pistons are contained in the cylinder barrel. The cylinder barrel is keyed to the drive shaft and is rotated by the prime mover. The pistons reciprocate in their bores, causing a pumping action, by following the inclined surface of the *swash plate*.

The swash plate in a fixed displacement pump is nothing more than a steel ring held at a fixed angle (typically 15°) in the pump housing. The dynamic bearing surface between the piston and the swash plate is created by a bronze *slipper pad*. The slipper pad has a ball and socket connection to the piston and is held against the swash plate by a retaining ring, which also rotates.

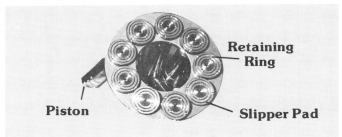

Retaining Ring

Piston

Slipper Pad

As the cylinder barrel rotates, it carries along each of the nine pistons. During exactly one half of a revolution, the pistons are pulled from their bores as the retaining ring causes the slipper pads to travel down the incline. Upon reaching its maximum extended position, the piston starts travelling up the incline, exerting force on the fluid in the cylinder barrel, forcing it to flow from the outlet of the pump. The *displacement* of a given pump is determined by the number of pistons, the piston diameter, and the length of the strokes. Of course, the steeper the angle of the swash plate, the longer is the piston stroke.

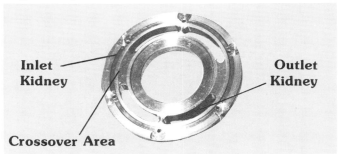

Inlet Kidney

Outlet Kidney

Crossover Area

Referring again to the cross-sectional illustration, you will notice that oil is ported to and from the cylinder barrel by the *valve plate*. The valve plate is nothing more than a flat surface (usually bronze coated steel) with two semi-circular *kidney* shaped openings. The two kidney shaped openings are connected through passages in the pump housing to the inlet and outlet ports of the pump. Depending on the angle of the swash plate and the direction of rotation, one kidney becomes the inlet port while the other becomes the outlet. The cylinder barrel rotates relative to the valve plate, pulling oil through the suction kidney as the pistons are retracting, and pushing oil from the cylinder barrel through the outlet kidney as the pistons are pushed back into their bores.

CASE DRAIN CONNECTIONS

The in-line axial piston, unlike the other pumps discussed previously, has a separate *case drain* port. In this pump, high pressure oil which leaks past the clearance fits of the pistons, and between the running clearance between the valve plate and cylinder barrel, collect in the case of the pump. Rather than leaking back to the suction side of the pump, the leakage oil is returned to the reservoir through a separate drain line. In general, the leakage oil provides a second function in that it lubricates bearings and other moving members in the pump. For this reason it is imperative that the housing of an in-line piston pump be filled with hydraulic fluid prior to starting the pump, and that the drain port be physically oriented upward to assure a permanently oil filled housing. In addition, the case drain line should be full sized and plumbed so as to prevent siphoning.

Remember: most in-line piston pumps should not operate with a case drain pressure higher than 5 to 15 PSIG.

PRESSURE LOADED CYLINDER BARREL

To assure high volumetric efficiency, the cylinder barrel must be pressure loaded against the surface of the valve plate. However, this pressure loading must be a precise balance, so that a lubricating film of oil can be maintained between the rotating cylinder barrel and the stationary valve plate. If we assume that the pump is instantaneously stopped, the pressure forces acting on the cylinder can be evaluated.

In any axial piston pump design, the cylinder barrel must necessarily be hydraulically loaded against the valve plate. This is simply accomplished by making the net area of ½ the

total number of piston bores slightly larger than the effective area of the pressure kidney. For clarity, if we think of the flow area between the piston bore and the valve plate as being plugged, it is easy to see that pressure in the cylinder works against the area created by ½ the total number of piston bores. This pressure force pushes the cylinder barrel against the valve plate on the pressure side of the pump.

The second force working on the cylinder barrel is related to the *area* of the kidney in the valve plate. This pressure field works against the face of the cylinder barrel, and creates a force to the left which tends to separate it from the port plate.

The optimum balancing of these pressure forces is achieved by designing the kidney area of the valve plate so that it has a less effective area than the pressurized area which loads the barrel against the plate. Needless to say, the higher the system pressure, the higher are the forces holding the cylinder barrel to the valve plate. This, however, does not necessarily mean that these two components will always maintain proper contact.

VALVE PLATE AND CYLINDER BARREL SEPARATION

If the pump is being operated at a higher than rated pressure, or in a system with high pressure spikes, it is not uncommon to have the cylinder barrel actually separate from the valve plate. This can cause *wire drawing* (Chapter 5) and/or mechanical damage to these critical surfaces in the pump.

To explain this phenomonen, we must again refer to the illustration which was used to explain the pressure loading of

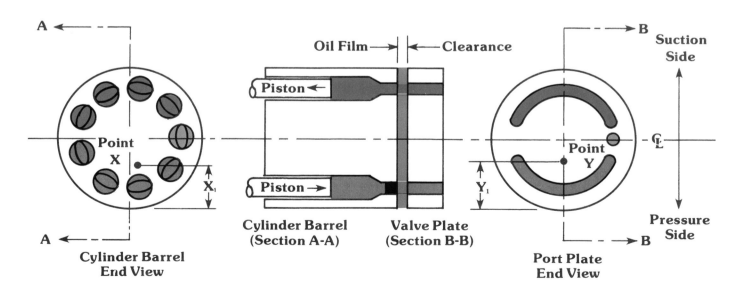

Pressure Loading Cylinder Barrel And Valve Plate

the cylinder barrel against the valve plate. The forces developed by the differential areas in the cylinder barrel work to the right, and hold the cylinder barrel to the valve plate. If the forces working simultaneously to the right are added together, the *resultant* (single) force to the right will act at point X at a dimension X_1 from the circumference of the barrel. Likewise, the resultant force of the kidney area can be thought of as a single force working at point Y to the left at dimension Y_1 from the circumference.

Unfortunately, it is difficult, if not impossible, to design a pump so that dimension X_1 exactly equals dimension Y_1. Since the two forces are out of alignment, a torque (Chapter 1) is created on the cylinder barrel. This mechanical imbalance must be supported by the drive shaft and bearing in the pump. Of course, too high an operating pressure or a pressure spike can cause mechanical flexing of the drive shaft, allowing separation of the surfaces.

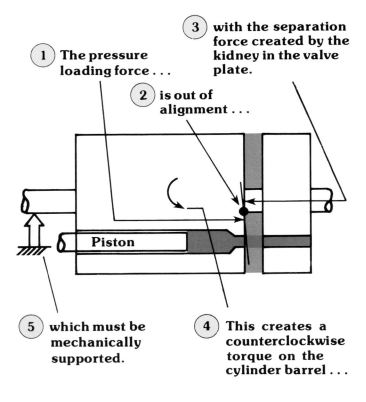

(1) **The pressure loading force . . .**

(2) **is out of alignment . . .**

(3) **with the separation force created by the kidney in the valve plate.**

Piston

(4) **This creates a counterclockwise torque on the cylinder barrel . . .**

(5) **which must be mechanically supported.**

Once separation occurs, the cylinder barrel cocks, bearing hard against the valve plate at the bottom and separating at the top (in reference to the drawing). The lubricating film is lost, and rotation causes scoring of the cylinder barrel and valve plate. Damage can also occur at the kidney area. Once the two surfaces separate, high pressure oil is blown into the case of the pump. This oil, travelling at a high velocity, can cause erosion of the metal surfaces. To avoid this type of damage, it is imperative that the pump not be operated above its pressure rating.

THE WEAK LINK OF IN-LINE PISTON PUMPS

In order to assure proper pump operation and satisfactory service life of the in-line piston pump, you must have a basic understanding of the slipper pad bearing design. Without this understanding, you might install and use the unit improperly, which would soon lead to a catastrophic failure. Basically, there are four operating conditions which cause failure of the slipper pad bearing. They are: operating with contaminated fluid, too much vacuum at the pump's inlet, excessive case pressure, and too high an operating speed.

Contaminated fluids not only accelerate wear of the valve plate and cylinder barrel, but more importantly, they cause blockage in critical lubrication passages. The principle of the slipper pad bearing is that the hydraulic force which pushes the piston towards the swash plate is offset by an equal pressure working in the opposite direction. In reference to the cross section, you will notice that a small hole through the piston's ball tip ports pressurized fluid between the slipper pad and the swash plate. The slipper pad is designed to have an effective area which precisely balances the pressure forces on the piston to the right.

(1) **If this passage clogs with contaminant . . .**

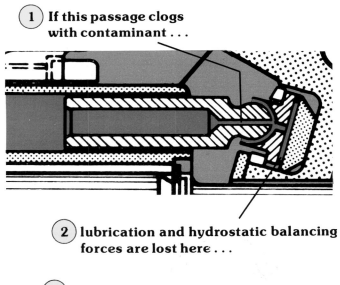

(2) **lubrication and hydrostatic balancing forces are lost here . . .**

(3) **which causes slipper pad failure.**

The relatively small holes in the piston keep the volumetric efficiency of the pump at a high level. If the pump were to be operated in a system with a high level of contaminants, "silting" clogs these small passages. This would lead to rapid failure of the slipper pad, because both lubrication and balancing forces would be lost.

High vacuum conditions can also lead to catastrophic failure of the pump. The in-line slipper pad pump, in general, requires better inlet conditions than any other hydraulic pump. The ball and socket joint which attaches the slipper pad to the piston, although excellent under compression, cannot withstand high tension forces. During suction, the retaining ring extracts the piston by pulling on the slipper pad. If the vacuum at the pump's inlet (see Chapter 1) is too high, the bronze slipper pad is simply pulled off the ball tip of the piston. Unfortunately, this cannot be detected by listening to the operation of the pump. The pump continues operating until it totally destroys the swash plate area.

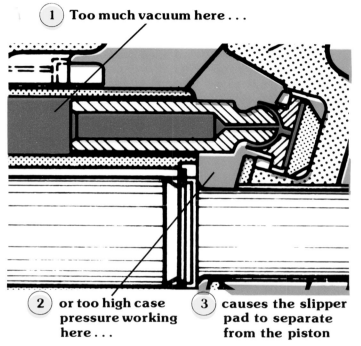

① **Too much vacuum here . . .**

② **or too high case pressure working here . . .**　③ **causes the slipper pad to separate from the piston**

Excessive case pressure has the same effect on the ball joint as does excessive vacuum at the pump's inlet. You can see in the cross-sectional illustration that these two conditions actually work together in damaging the pump. In other words, both case pressure and high vacuum resist extraction of the piston from its bore. Consequently, both forces must be overcome by the retaining ring pulling on the slipper pad, and, in turn, on the ball joint.

To avoid pump damage from either of the two previously mentioned reasons, it is advisable that both inlet and case drain conditions be optimized. In general, in-line slipper pad pumps should, at the very least, be mounted on an *L-shaped* reservoir so that the head pressure of the oil is available to force oil into the inlet of the pump. With pumps of large displacement, it may even be necessary to "*supercharge*" the inlet. This is typically achieved by mounting an internal gear pump of slightly higher displacement (115%) in series with the inlet of the in-line piston pump. A supercharge relief valve, normally set at an operating pressure of 150 to 300 PSI, is also necessary. The supercharge pump is normally started before start-up of the main pump.

On the other hand, it is also necessary to provide adequate case drain plumbing. The case drain line must be full sized,

and returned below the minimum oil level in the reservoir, with the shortest run possible. It is important that the case drain be connected individually, and not teed to any other return line. If a case drain heat exchange is to be used, it is of utmost importance that the heat exchanger be liberally over-sized in order to minimize back pressuring of the case. When plumbing the case drain, it is advisable that you use a male run tee, or another suitable fitting, at the case drain port. This will facilitate filling the case of the pump prior to start-up.

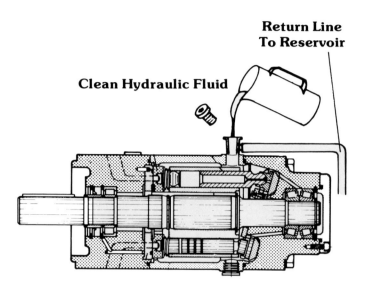

Return Line To Reservoir

Clean Hydraulic Fluid

Filling Pump Housing With Oil
Before Starting

Too high an operating speed can also lead to premature catastrophic pump failure. During each revolution of the shaft, a single piston must be moved from its fully collapsed position to its fully extracted position, and then back again. During each of the two reciprocating motions, the piston velocity changes from zero to maximum, and then back to zero, just before the direction of motion changes. Needless to say, the piston slipper pad and ball joint are subject to considerably strong acceleration and deceleration forces. In Chapter 1 we have shown that the *force* is equal to *mass* multiplied by *acceleration*. To limit the maximum force, the pistons in in-line slipper pad pumps are hollow, solely for the purpose of reducing the piston mass.

On the other hand, the acceleration of the piston is directly related to the drive speed of the input shaft. In other words, the faster the input speed, the higher is the acceleration and deceleration.

In the pump, acceleration of the piston in the retracted direction, and deceleration in the forward direction, causes a tension force on the ball joint. If this force is excessive, it can cause failure of the joint.

BENT-AXIS FIXED DISPLACEMENT PUMPS

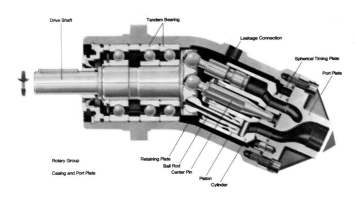

A more rugged axial piston pump is available in the bent-axis design. In general, this design is capable of higher flows, higher pressures, and higher operating speeds. This pump is also more suitable for self priming applications. Let us now take a look at how it works.

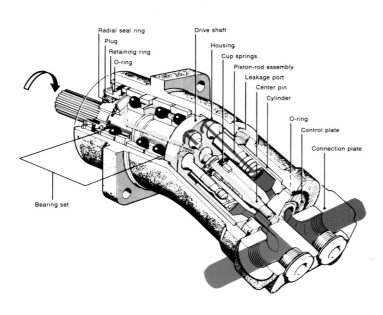

The cross-sectional illustration shows the general assembly of a fixed displacement bent-axis pump. In a bent-axis pump, the cylinder barrel turns with the drive shaft, but at a *bent-axis angle*. Piston rods connect the pistons to the drive shaft. You can see that the pistons reciprocate in their bores as the distance between the drive shaft flange and cylinder barrel changes. In reference to this view, as the shaft is turned in the direction of the arrow, the pistons on the left are being extracted from the bores, thus creating the inlet condition. As the pistons pass top dead center, they are pushed back into their bore, forcing an oil flow from the outlet of the pump.

TRANSFORMATION OF TORQUE INTO PRESSURE

One of the major advantages of bent-axis design pumps is that torque from the prime mover is transformed directly into the linear piston force. This linear force relates directly to system pressure. To further understand this concept, we must remember how torque develops pressure in an in-line piston pump.

In in-line designs, the torque input from the prime mover creates a force on the cylinder barrel which causes it to rotate. The cylinder barrel, in turn, transmits this force as a lateral force against the sides of the pistons. On the pressure side of the pump, this lateral force drags the slipper pad assembly up the ramp of the swash plate. Through this somewhat complicated transmittal of forces, an unwanted force is created, which tends to cock the piston in its bore. This accelerates wear, and increases the mechanical inefficiency of the pump. This problem is better explained in the illustration, which exaggerates the problem for the sake of clarity.

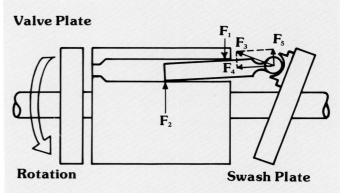

F_1 and F_2 = Torque transmittal to piston

F_3 = Reaction force of swash plates on piston

F_4 = Horizontal component of reaction force F_3 (develops pressure)

F_5 = Vertical component of reaction force (drag)

Force Diagram Of An In-Line Pump

Unlike the in-line piston pump, the bent-axis pump transforms torque directly into the linear force creating pressure. The torque from the prime mover works first on the ball joint connecting the piston rod to the drive shaft. The only resistance to the rotational force is that developed by system pressure over the area of the piston. This is true since the piston must be pushed into the bore if rotation is to occur. The force diagram is shown in the illustration. It is important

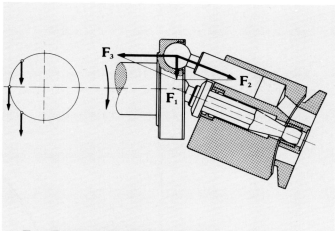

F_1 = Force created by torque

F_2 = Resultant force (develops pressure)

F_3 = Reaction force absorbed by bearings

Force Diagram Of A Bent-Axis Pump

to remember that the lateral side loading of the piston is not directly involved in creating a linear force on the piston. The piston rods do not transmit anymore torque than is necessary to cause acceleration of the mass of the cylinder barrel and to overcome the resistance of the barrel, spinning in an oil filled housing.

BETTER SUCTION CAPABILITIES

The bent-axis pump is far more suitable for use in self-priming applications than is the in-line piston design. To better understand this concept, you must consider several factors. They include the piston's capability to handle tension forces caused by vacuum at the pump's inlet, and the size of the inlet porting. Let us now examine these.

Earlier we explained how high vacuum can separate the slipper pad from the piston in in-line piston pump designs. This, however, is not a problem with bent-axis piston equipment. First, the piston is joined to the piston rod by a cold rolling process. As shown in the picture, this forms a close tolerance ball joint which is extremely suitable for transmittal of tension forces. In addition, the opposite end of the piston rod

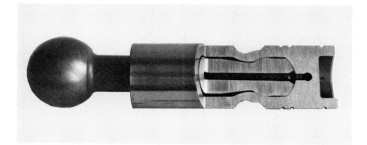

is a ball joint, which is bolted to the drive shaft flange with a retaining ring.

Working together, these two ball joints are quite strong, and can withstand considerable tension forces. Consequently, the bent-axis pump can develop high vacuum conditions in the cylinder barrel without fear of mechanical damage. In fact, a typical bent-axis pump can create a vacuum equivalent to nearly nine inches of mercury, and is capable of pumping a fluid viscosity of up to 4600 SUS during cold start-up.

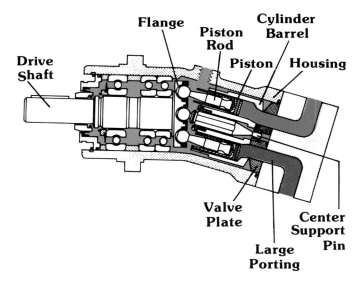

In considering self-priming applications, you will find that a second advantage is that the inlet porting can be made much larger than it can with an in-line piston design. In the cross-sectional illustration, the valve plate is located at the end of the *rotary group*. Unlike those in in-line piston pumps, the valve plate (and cylinder barrel) in this design can be much smaller in diameter, since a large drive shaft does

not pass through its center. As shown, this allows both the inlet and outlet *kidneys* to be located closer to the center of revolution. In turn, this offers several major benefits.

First, by locating the kidneys close to the center of revolution, the relative centripetal speed between the rotating cylinder barrel and the stationary port plate is considerably reduced. This has the result of minimizing the turbulence (resistance to flow) in the oil flow as it passes from the stationary valve plate into the rotating cylinder barrel, which improves filling of the pumping chambers.

The second advantage of locating the kidneys close to the center of revolution is apparent in the picture of the valve plate. You can see that each kidney has a wider cross-sectional flow area. Needless to say, this lessens the resistance to flow as oil enters the cylinder barrel, and also improves filling.

The third advantage is that the angle drilling of the passage to the cylinder barrel, creates a centrifugal force on the oil. In principle this centrifugal pump effect actually increases the pressure in the fluid. The increase in pressure is directly proportional to drive speed, and aids in filling the pumping chamber, particularly at higher RPM levels.

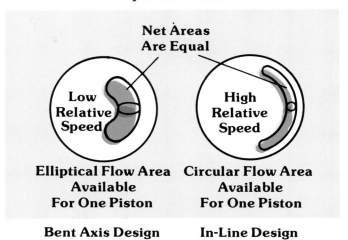

Bent-Axis Design Valve Plate And Cylinder Barrel

Let us go back for a moment to our previous discussion of hydraulic loading of the cylinder barrel to the valve plate for in-line piston pumps in order to consider a few important points. It is important to remember that the area of the kidney is precisely limited. We emphasize the word *precisely* because the area of the kidney produces a separation force which must be smaller in magnitude than the hydraulic loading force within the cylinder barrel. Consequently, a bent-axis piston design for a given size can have a wider flow area, but must have an equivalent kidney area. The drawing may be helpful in comparing the kidney shaped openings of the bent-axis and in-line piston pumps.

HYDRAULIC LOADING OF THE CYLINDER BARREL

In bent-axis design pumps, the proper cylinder port location can offer significant advantages in improving the suction characteristics of the pump. However, in moving the kidneys close to the center of rotation, the balancing of forces becomes somewhat more difficult (see "VALVE PLATE AND BARREL SEPARATION," as discussed for in-line piston pumps).

You can easily understand that moving the kidney area closer to the center of rotation increases the separation of the resultant forces which act on the cylinder barrel. Unless something can be done to compensate for the increased torque created on the cylinder barrel, valve plate separation will become more of a problem.

THE SPHERICAL VALVE PLATE

The spherical surface of the valve plate used in many bent-axis pumps prevents the possibility of port plate separation. However, instead of trying to hold the cylinder barrel in

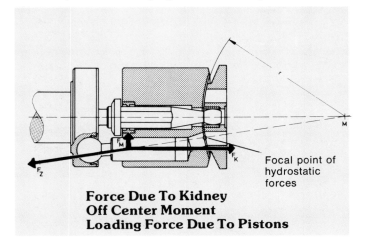

Force Due To Kidney Off Center Moment Loading Force Due To Pistons

position by sturdy shafts and bearings, the spherical port plate attacks this problem in a different manner. The theory behind the spherical port plate is that separation forces do exist. At some pressure peak, these forces can and will cock the cylinder barrel, no matter how sturdily it is supported. The spherical port plate simply self-compensates for the deflection caused by the unbalanced pressure forces.

The illustration shows the force diagram for a bent-axis design pump incorporating the spherical port plate design. First, you will notice that the connection between the cylinder bore and the port plate is drilled at an angle in order to locate the passage close to the center of revolution. As shown, the force due to the kidney area is further off center because of the drilling, but it works in a direction which is perpendicular to the tangent of the spherical surface. Second, the loading force due to the pistons works parallel to the axis of rotation in the direction shown, and is slightly larger in magnitude than the horizontal component of the force due to the kidney area. The off center moment is the vertical component of the kidney area force, and it is this force which must be supported by the center pin.

As operating pressures increase, this off center moment necessarily becomes larger in magnitude. However, if the moment becomes large enough to cause an elastic deformation of the center pin, the cylinder barrel will relocate on the spherical surface of the port plate.

RADIAL LOADING OF THE DRIVE SHAFT

In general, most hydraulic pumps do not have bearing structures sufficient to support radial loads on the input shaft. Consequently, if the application requires a gear, chain or V-belt drive for the pump, it is usually necessary to drive the pump with a jack shaft drive. The pillow block bearing supports the jack shaft and can absorb the radial forces, while torque is transmitted to the pump through the use of a flexible shaft coupling.

The bent-axis design pump is one of a few pumps in which radial loading of the drive shaft is permissible. In fact, if the direction of the radial force on the drive shaft is oriented properly, the external radial load will offset the internal bearing load due to the pumping mechanism. We ask, however, that you consult the manufacturer's recommendations before using any pump in this type of application.

VARIABLE DISPLACEMENT PUMPS

The variable displacement pump offers several advantages to the hydraulic circuit simply because the displacement (output flow) of the pump can be changed. This change of displacement can be accomplished simply through adjustment, or it can be totally automated and interfaced with computerized programming. We could not stay within the scope of this text if we were to discuss the exact operation of each control for all the different pump designs available. For this reason, we will discuss the mechanics involved in varying the displacement of vane and piston equipment. The actual control and its intended application will then be discussed as related to the variable displacement pump in general. Before we discuss the different types of pumps and controls, however, we must gain a basic understanding of the types of circuits in which the variable volume pumps can be used. Let us now compare the characteristics of the three different types of pump circuits, open, closed, and half-closed circuits.

OPEN PUMP CIRCUITS

The discussion in Chapter 1 involving the inlet conditions for hydraulic pumps was based on the assumption that the pump was to operate in an *open circuit*, even though this term was not actually used. In open circuit applications, the pump draws fluid from a reservoir and pushes this fluid into the hydraulic system. After passing through the control valve circuitry and the actuator, the fluid returns to the storage reservoir. The reservoir is sized so that it will hold a minimum of three times the volume which can be displaced by the pump in one minute. Typically, a thirty gallon per minute pump would be mounted on a 90 gallon reservoir.

A pump which is used in an open circuit pumps oil in only one direction. For this reason, it is normally supplied with a large diameter low pressure inlet port, and a smaller high pressure outlet. In open circuit design, the direction of the actuator's motion must be accomplished through the use of directional control valves.

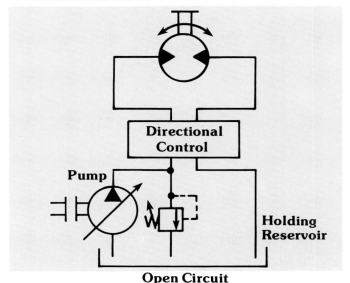

Open Circuit

The open circuit is by far the most popular. Its advantage is that, in this design, several different actuator functions can be performed simultaneously, if necessary, by a single pump. The reservoir's top plate can also be used as the foundation for building the entire hydraulic unit. In this type of self-contained system, oil conditioning can be optimized by proper reservoir design and use of the proper conditioning equipment. In fact, the only disadvantage to open circuit design is its relatively large size and weight, due to the large volume of oil required.

CLOSED PUMP CIRCUITS

The closed circuit design eliminates the need for a large storage volume of oil. Although this feature is more important to mobile equipment than it is to industrial machinery, there are a large number of closed circuit pumps used in industrial hydraulics. Even though this circuit requires special pumps (normally piston pumps) and pump controls, it does offer several advantages. Let us first look at how it works.

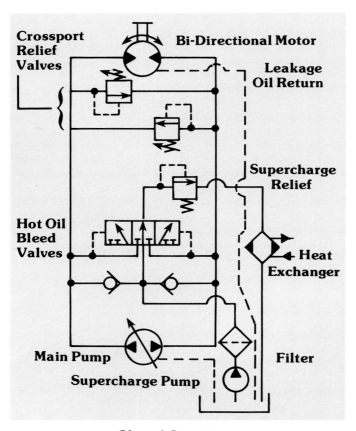

Closed Circuit

In this closed circuit design, a single hydraulic pump is used to drive a single hydraulic motor. The closed circuit has little or no significance for cylinder actuators which displace different volumes during extension and retraction. The reason for this is that the oil which passes through the motor actuator is returned directly to the low pressure side of the pump. For proper operation, the pump must receive the same quantity of oil at its inlet as it is pumping from its outlet.

The closed circuit is always used in conjunction with a smaller *supercharge* circuit. The supercharge circuit consists of a small fixed displacement pump (usually 15% of the displacement of the main pump), a small oil reservoir, and the necessary fiters and heat exchangers.

During operation, the main pump control can cause the pump's displacement to go *over* center, which means that the main pump can pump high pressure oil from either of its two main ports. In other words, it can cause a clockwise or counterclockwise flow of fluid through the *closed loop* plumbing. This, in turn, will allow the motor actuator to operate in either direction of rotation. The port which serves as the high pressure inlet to the actuator will determine the high pressure *leg*, while the low pressure *leg* will be determined by the actuator's outlet port.

The supercharge circuit always works on the low pressure leg of the main loop pumping freshly filtered oil into the loop through the make-up check valve network, while bleeding-off a percentage of oil through the hot oil bleed valve. This hot oil is then cooled by a heat exchanger and stored in the small reservoir before returning to the main system. The pressure in the low pressure leg is maintained at a value of between 100 and 300 PSI by the supercharge relief valve. The pressure setting of the supercharge relief is determined by the requirements of the pump and/or motor actuator, and the operating conditions of the system.

In closed loop circuits, pressure, flow, and directional control are all achieved by the controlling element of the pump. The crossport reliefs are incorporated only to protect the actuator from load induced pressure peaks. They cannot function as a main system relief valve, since this would, in short order, cause severe over heating of the circuit.

The advantages of a closed circuit pump system are that high horsepower systems are compact, and they operate with minimum amount of excess storage oil. The systems are highly efficient since the pump control must be designed to supply only the oil flow required by the actuator at the load induced pressure. The pump controls direction, acceleration, deceleration, and maximum speed and maximum torque of the motor actuator, thus eliminating the need for pressure and flow control components.

The major disadvantage of closed circuit systems is that a single pump can only operate a single output function. In addition, this type of *hydraulic drive* is *generally* usable only with motor actuators.

THE HALF-CLOSED CIRCUIT

In general, the features of half-closed circuitry are available only in a bent-axis design piston pump. The half-closed circuit is quite similar to the closed circuit except for the fact that it can be used with cylinder actuators with differential areas.

As shown in the simple circuit schematic during extension of the cylinder, the pump must create a larger flow from its left-hand port than is being returned to its right-hand port from the cylinder actuator.

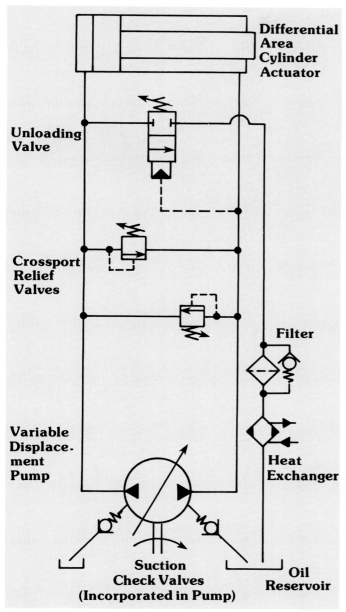

Half-Closed Circuit

The extra oil is drawn by the pump from the reservoir through the suction check valve, which is an integral part of the pump.

When the pump control causes the pumping assembly to go over center, flow is reversed and the cylinder begins retracting. During retraction, the differential area causes a larger flow than needed at the inlet of the pump. The excess flow is unloaded to the reservoir by means of the unloading valve. This unloaded flow to the reservoir provides for an oil exchange in the closed portion of the circuit, which allows for filtering and cooling of the fluid.

OPEN CIRCUIT DIRECT OPERATED PRESSURE COMPENSATED VANE PUMPS

Manifold Mounted Vane Pump

The open circuit pressure compensated vane pump is probably the most popular variable displacement pump used in industrial hydraulic systems. Because the direct operated variable volume vane pump is only available with a pressure compensated control, we must discuss the operation of the pump and it control as a single unit.

The cross-sectional illustration (page 6-26) shows the basic direct operated variable volume pressure compensated vane pump design. Unlike its fixed displacement counterpart, the variable volume model is not hydraulically balanced. In this pump design, the cam ring is round rather than elliptical in shape. As shown, the pump displaces fluid because the spring holds the cam ring in an eccentric position with respect to the rotor. Assuming that the pump shaft is being rotated in a clockwise direction (viewed from the shaft end), you can see that the vanes reciprocate in their slots as the rotor is turned. Because of the eccentricity of the cam ring, the vanes are collapsed in their slots on the right-hand side of this drawing, and extend as they are rotated past the suction kidney (shown in green) to the left. As the vanes rotate through the upper portion of the pump housing, they are again collapsed in their slots, forcing an oil flow from the outlet of the pump.

The reason the variable volume pump cannot be hydraulically balanced is that the pressure forces between the cam ring and the rotor are an integral part of the pump control. As the pump encounters a resistance to flow into the system, pressure builds at the pump outlet and between the rotor and the circular cam ring. Because of the geometry of the pump and the location of the pressure kidney, the resultant force due to this pressure pushes the cam ring up and to the right. When the horizontal component of the pressure force exceeds the force due to the spring, the cam ring moves to the right, toward a concentric position with

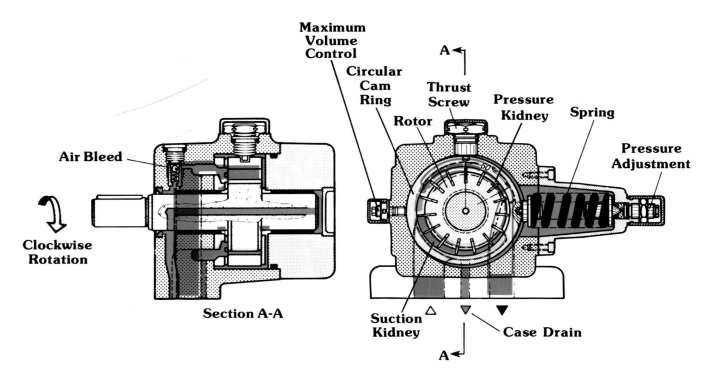

Section A-A

respect to the rotor. Needless to say, when the ring becomes concentric with the rotor, the pump ceases to deliver flow because the vane has no *throw*.

② **causes a force on the cam ring in this direction.**

④ **the cam ring moves to a concentric position . . .**

③ **When the horizontal component of this force over-comes this spring force . . .**

① **Pressure in the fluid here . . .**

⑤ **with respect to the rotor.**

MAXIMUM VOLUME CONTROL

The maximum volume control is nothing more than an adjustable mechanical stop which limits the eccentricity of the cam ring. As discussed for the fixed displacement vane pump, the pump's displacement is related directly to the throw of the vanes. In reference to the previous cross-sectional illustration, if we limit the eccentricity, we are also limiting vane throw, and consequently, the maximum displacement of the pump.

Generally speaking, the stroke limiter is intended for matching the pump to the flow requirement of the system in which it will operate. It is not intended for frequent flow (speed) adjustment. Should this be required, the stroke limiter can be replaced with a manual hand wheel adjustment option.

It should be noted that most stroke limiters are capable of adjusting the cam ring to nearly a no flow position. However, if the maximum pump flow is adjusted to less than 50% of the maximum flow capability of the pump, the volumetric efficiency will drop to undesirable levels. If, for instance, we consider a 10 GPM pump which displays a volumetric efficiency of 90% at 1500 PSI, the pump would effectively pump 9 GPM and leak 1 GPM from its case drain. If we now limited the stroke of this pump to 4 GPM maximum flow, we would find that the pump still leaks 1 GPM from its case drain at 1500 PSI. This is true because pump leakage is strictly determined by pressure and pump clearances. Of course, neither of these are effected by limiting the pump's displacement. Consequently, our 4 GPM pump which leaks 1 GPM displays a volumetric efficiency of only 80%. It would be far better, from an efficiency standpoint, to select a smaller 4 GPM pump for this application.

PRESSURE ADJUSTMENT FOR DIRECT OPERATED VARIABLE VOLUME VANE PUMPS

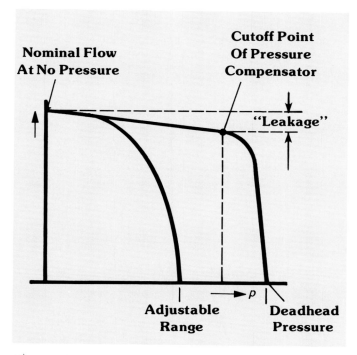

The graph represents a typical pressure versus flow relationship for a direct operated vane pump. It must be noted that the shape of this curve depends greatly on the spring selected for a given operating pressure. The initial, more gradual decrease in flow from minimum pressure to the point just prior to pump compensation is solely a function of internal pump leakage. Up to the cutoff point, the spring constant is stiff enough so that there is no spring displacement, hence no decrease in flow because of a change in the cam ring's eccentricity.

Spring displacement begins at the point where flow begins to drop off drastically with respect to rising pressure. The steepness of this drop off (or the pressure difference between maximum and minimum flow) depends on the stiffness of the spring. To cover different pressure requirements in the 0 −1500 range, four different springs are normally available. Since a single spring can only give optimum performance within a specific pressure range, it is important that you select the proper spring. The comparison indicates the proper spring selection for a typical 900 PSI operating pressure.

In this comparison, you will notice that the spring, which gives optimum performance at the 1500 PSI pressure, is inadequate for operating at 900 PSI. As this high pressure

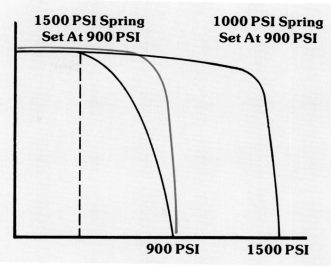

Comparison Of
1000 PSI And 1500 PSI Springs
When Set At 900 PSI

spring is adjusted for lower and lower operating pressures, the pressure span between cutoff and deadhead becomes broader. We must, of course, limit this pressure differential, since the output speed of the actuator(s) is drastically affected between cutoff pressure and deadhead pressure. If the pressure span is too great, pressure requirements of the system could allow the actuator to operate at a reduced speed between maximum flow and deadhead. Ideally, this should not occur in a pressure compensated system.

Generally speaking, the direct operated pressure compensated vane pump displays the best pressure versus flow curve when it is operated at the maximum pressure rating of the spring. When set at a lower pressure, the cutoff toward the deadhead portion of the curve becomes more gradual.

The spring should never be adjusted below 50% of its maximum pressure rating. If, for some reason, your system operates at a different pressure from that originally calculated, it is sometimes possible to simply exchange the spring. However, you must consult with the pump manufacturer, since pump clearances and timing of the port plate may also influence the operating pressure capabilities of the pump.

THE PILOT OPERATED PRESSURE COMPENSATED VANE PUMP

The pilot operated pressure compensated vane pump is similar to the direct operated model. It does, however, incorporate some unique features which allow for better performance characteristics, higher flows, and higher pressures. Since the pump is pilot operated, the design engineer can

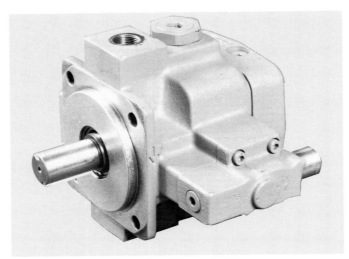

select from any number of pump controls. However, we will postpone discussion of the various controls until later in this chapter, and study this pump in conjunction with the basic pressure compensated control.

pilot valve. When system pressure overcomes the setting of the pilot spring, the larger control piston area is vented to tank. The small piston, which is still pressurized, is then able to push the cam ring into a concentric no-flow position. This position is then maintained until the system pressure is again reduced below the setting of the pilot spring. At this point, hydraulic loading of both control pistons is re-established, and the cam ring moves back to a flow position.

The pilot operated variable volume vane pump is suitable for higher pressure and higher flows than its direct operated counterpart. Generally speaking, direct operated pressure compensated vane pumps are limited to 1500 PSI operating pressure; and maximum flows of up to 20 GPM. Pilot operated versions, on the other hand, are capable of operating pressures of up to 2400 PSI, with flow capabilities as high as 60 GPM. You will notice that the pilot operated pump incorporates dual vane construction. In addition, the pump's volumetric efficiency is increased due to pressure loading of the wear plates. Since these features were discussed for fixed displacement pumps earlier in this chapter, they will not be covered again.

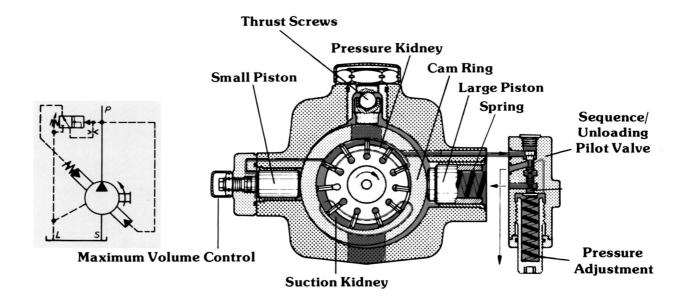

Maximum Volume Control

As shown in the cross-sectional illustration, the cam ring is sandwiched between two control pistons. The larger piston, on the right, has twice the effective area as the piston on the left, and is assisted by a light spring force (250-375 PSI). During start-up, this spring force holds the cam ring in an eccentric position, and the pump begins displacing fluid. As the pump meets a resistance to flow, the two control pistons and the end of the spool in the direct operated sequence/unloading valve are equally exposed to system pressure. As long as the spring setting of the pilot valve is not exceeded, pressure on the two pistons (with a 2:1 area ratio) keeps the cam ring eccentric to the rotor, and the pump displaces fluid.

System pressure is set by adjusting the spring force of the

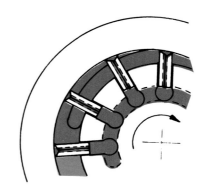

Dual Vane Construction

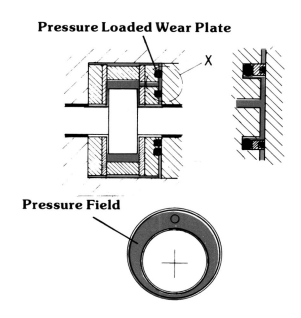

Pressure Loaded Wear Plate

X

Pressure Field

PERFORMANCE CHARACTERISTICS OF PILOT OPERATED VANE PUMPS

The pilot operated pressure compensated control displays much better pressure versus flow characteristics than does the direct operated version. The reason for this is twofold. First, the pump has higher volumetric efficiency because of the pressure loaded wear plates. Second, the pilot operated control is not directly influenced by a spring constant. We can easily see the improved performance when we compare the pressure versus flow curves for the two pumps.

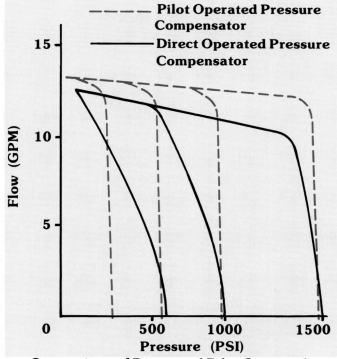

Comparison of Direct and Pilot Operated Pressure Compensated Vane Pumps

The graph consists of superimposed pressure versus flow characteristics of direct and pilot operated pressure compensated vane pumps. You will notice that both pumps are approximately the same displacement, since they both deliver nearly equal flows at low pressure. The comparison shows two major differences between these two pump designs. First, the effects of pressure loaded port plates and dual vane construction are readily apparent. The pilot operated pump has better volumetric efficiency characteristics than does the direct operated design. For this reason, there is less decrease in flow with increasing pressure, and the initial slope of the pressure versus flow graph for the pilot operated vane pump falls off more gradually.

The second advantage of the pilot operated pressure compensated vane pump is that its pressure versus flow curve is not affected by the pressure setting. The graph shows that it does not matter whether the pilot operated pump is set at 500 PSI or 1500 PSI. The pressure differential between the cutoff point and deadhead is always the same. For the same reasons that a pilot operated relief is not affected by pressure override (Chapter 2), the pilot operated pressure compensated vane pump has less pressure differential between cutoff and deadhead.

NOISE TUNING OF VARIABLE VOLUME VANE PUMPS

The variable volume vane pump (either direct or pilot operated) is probably the only pump which can be field adjusted for optimum noise level. The theory which we are about to explain applies to virtually all variable volume vane pumps. However, because this adjustment influences the pressure versus flow characteristics and can cause catastrophic pump failure, we are discussing the following procedure for educational purposes only. *You should consult the pump manufacturer prior to making any noise adjustments on your pump.* Let us now look at the theory of noise adjustment.

As the pump transfers oil from the suction to the pressure kidney, there is a point at which the volume of oil between adjacent pairs of vanes becomes captive. Also, during this crossover period, the captive volume can be made to decrease in size. By adjusting the amount of volume change, the *pressure* in the captive fluid can be made to equal the pressure in the system. Matching this *precompression pressure* with system pressure results in a smooth crossover, which results in extremely low operating noise levels. Obviously, this smooth crossover due to pressure match can be optimized only for one specific system pressure. Since most pumps are factory set at the maximum pressure rating of the pump, the noise adjustment must be field tuned for optimum noise level. This tuning is accomplished by *sight* adjustment of the cam ring thrust screw.

The cross-sectional illustration of a typical variable volume

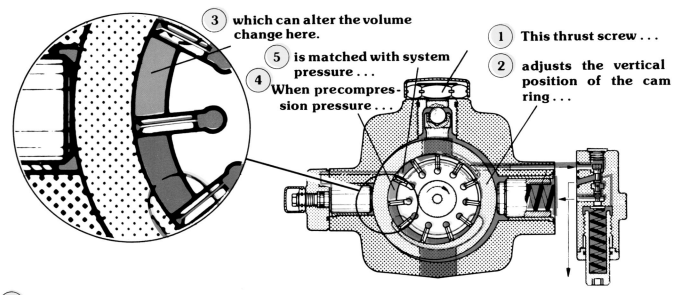

③ which can alter the volume change here.

⑤ is matched with system pressure . . .

④ When precompression pressure . . .

① This thrust screw . . .

② adjusts the vertical position of the cam ring . . .

⑥ there is no explosion or implosion of fluid.

Noise Adjustment For Variable Volume Vane Pumps

vane pump makes our explanation more graphic. As shown, the thrust screw does nothing more than adjust the vertical position of the cam ring with respect to the rotor and the port plate. This changes the cam ring's eccentricity in a vertical sense, which, in turn, adjusts the volume change during the crossover period. A clockwise rotation of the thrust screw (downward displacement of the cam ring) causes a more radical volume change, and, therefore, a higher precompression pressure. Turning the screw counterclockwise causes a decrease in precompression pressure by lessening the volume change.

Remembering that the ideal noise level is achieved when there is no explosion or implosion of the precompressed fluid, we can understand why the pump can be noisier in a flow condition than in deadhead, or vice-versa. Since noise adjustments are, out of necessity, a compromise, the thrust screw can be set with the pump in its *normal* operating mode. That is, if the pump operates a high percentage of the time in deadhead, the thrust screw can be adjusted in the no-flow condition of the pump. On the other hand, if the pump is more often pumping fluid at a lower pressure, the thrust screw can be set in a flow condition of the pump. This, however, will sacrifice the pump's optimum noise level when in the deadhead no-flow mode.

Finally, if we consider the fact that fluid is not compressible, we can understand the fact that very minute changes in the pre-compression volume drastically affect the precompression pressure. In discussing thrust screw adjustments, we are talking about only a *±60° rotation* of the thrust screw from the factory marked *center* position. Minimum to maximum adjustment should not exceed a 120° rotation. Radical over-adjustment will cause poor pressure versus flow characteristics and possible catastrophic failure of the pump.

ELECTRIC MOTOR SIZING FOR PRESSURE COMPENSATED PUMPS

Earlier in the chapter, we discussed the calculation of the horsepower needed to drive a hydraulic pump, namely:

$$HP = \frac{GPM \times PSI}{1714 \times E_t}$$

Where: GPM = Actual Flow Output
PSI = Maximum System Pressure
E_t = Overall Pump Efficiency

For any fixed displacement pump, you must calculate the horsepower for the full flow at maximum pressure, and then size the electric motor accordingly. This, however, is not necessarily mandatory with pressure compensated pumps.

The major advantage in selecting a pressure compensated pump is that the control produces only the amount of flow needed by the operating conditions of the system. In systems using flow controls to control actuator speed, the excess flow over the relief valve in a fixed displacement pump circuit is replaced with a pump control which simply does not generate an excess flow. Consequently, by eliminating this flow across the relief valve, the energy consumption and subsequent heat generation can be drastically reduced (estimating heat generation is discussed in Chapter 1).

The ability of the pump to produce full system pressure at no-flow unloads the electric motor in the same manner as does a fixed displacement pump when pumping full flow at no pressure. However, holding *pressure* at *no flow* offers definite advantages.

If we consider cylinder actuators, we find that the *duty cycle* often does not require full flow and full pressure simultaneously. In many applications, the cylinder first travels through "free air," then does its *work* on the load. After completion of the *work*, the cylinder may be required to maintain a *holding force* on the load, or it might be possible to retract the cylinder to its fully collapsed position. In either situation, maximum pressure and flow are required simultaneously only when the *work* is being done. During "free air" extension and retraction, there is virtually no load, and consequently, no pressure. If a holding force on the load is required, or if the cylinder is fully retracted, there is full pressure but no flow. In contrast to the fixed displacement pump, the pressure compensated pump draws very little horsepower. If the work portion of the cycle is short in duration, and sufficient time is available between consecutive *work* functions, we can "cheat" on the horsepower rating of the electric motor.

The most common electric motor for industrial hydraulic systems is the NEMA (National Electrical Manufacturers Association) design B. A three phase design B electric motor will produce a starting torque which is at least 200% of its maximum continuous running torque specifications. For short periods of time, it can produce up to 200% of its continuous torque rating before stalling, or dropping in speed. We must emphasize the word *short* because the higher than normal current in a motor which continuously operates above its rating will cause overheating and the eventual burn out of the electric motor. Let us now consider the capability of the electric motor in conjunction with the needs of the pressure compensated pump.

The graph shows a typical horsepower curve for a pressure compensated pump. The upper curve represents the flow

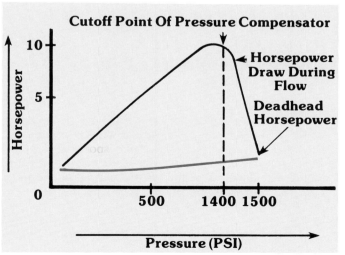

Horsepower-Pressure Relationships For A Pressure Compensated Pump

conditions of the pump, and shows that, for the flow rating of the pump, as the pressure increases, so do the horsepower requirements. Up to the cutoff point of the pressure compensator, this curve is identical to that of a fixed displacement pump. The difference is that when the pressure compensator, reduces pump displacement, the horsepower requirements drop off quickly to the lower limit. This lower limit is call *deadhead horsepower* (in red on the graph). It represents the mechanical and volumetric inefficiencies of the pump, and indicates the total amount of heat generated during no-flow conditions. If it were possible to make a pump with 100% efficiency, the deadhead horsepower would be zero.

More importantly, the graph indicates that the full 10 horsepower draw occurs only at a system pressure of 1400 PSI. In relation to our previously described cylinder actuator, the 10 horsepower demand on the electric motor would be required only during the *work* portion of the duty cycle. During the other portions of the cycle, a 10 horsepower electric motor would be operating considerably below its 10 horsepower rating. In consideration of the overload characteristics of the electric motor, it is acceptable design practice to use a smaller electric motor.

In this application, a 7½ horsepower electric motor would create the required torque to attain the 10 horsepower level with a 33% overload. Assuming a short enough work cycle, this overload would not seriously overheat the electric motor. Besides, if there is sufficient time between overload periods, the motor will be able to rid itself of the heat generated during the overload portion of the cycle. In fact, if the overload occurs only to get the pressure compensated pump over the "hump" of the pump's horsepower curve, the overload would normally be in the range of only 50 to 100 ms. This type of overloading occurs when the cylinder bottoms out after travelling through "free air" or after doing work at a rate below the horsepower rating of the electric motor.

At this point, however, we must refer you to your motor supplier for recommendations on satisfactory limits of electric motor overloading. There is no good rule of thumb which we can offer since there are too many variables which must be considered. The variables include ambient temperature, altitude of operation, motor design, and the service factor of the motor selected.

From an electric efficiency standpoint, electric motors are generally more efficient when operated at their full horsepower rating. An unnecessarily large electric motor may be less efficient in conserving electrical power than a motor which has been intentionally undersized.

In summary, undersizing the electric motor requires a complete understanding of the system duty cycle. Generally speaking, we can only consider this undersizing if the *cylinder actuator* overloads the system for brief time periods. Generally, we cannot consider undersized electric motors for use with hydraulic motor circuits which use pressure compensated pumps. The reason for this is that the hydraulic motor could conceivably operate at pressures and flows near the cutoff point of the pressure compensator for extended time periods. At this point on the curve, the pressure compensated pump would draw its maximum power from the electric motor.

VARIABLE DISPLACEMENT IN-LINE PISTON PUMPS

1 This control piston . . .

2 changes the position of this swashplate . . .

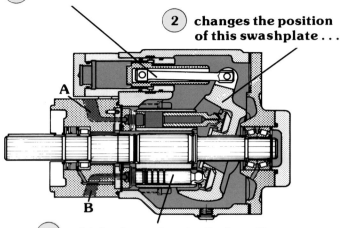

3 which alters the stroke length of the pistons.

4 This changes the displacement of the pump.

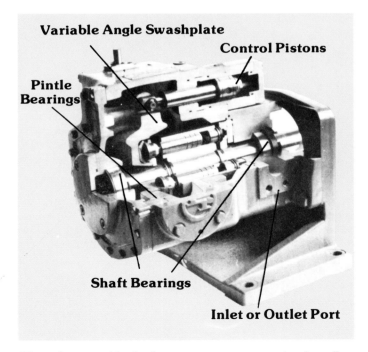

Variable Angle Swashplate

Control Pistons

Pintle Bearings

Shaft Bearings

Inlet or Outlet Port

The in-line variable displacement piston pump develops flow and pressure in the same manner as its fixed displacement counterpart, as was discussed earlier in this chapter. The major difference is that the angle of the *swashplate* can be changed rather than being at a fixed angle.

The housing of a variable displacement in-line piston pump has a yoke which is supported by pintle bearings. As shown, the yoke's position is controlled by a double acting single rod cylinder. The cross-sectional illustration shows the positioning cylinder in the fully extended position. In this position of the swashplate the pistons on the top are fully retracted, while the lower pistons are fully collapsed in their bores. Assuming clockwise rotation (when looking at the shaft end), the inlet would be port A, while the outlet would be port B.

The photograph of the cut-away pump shows the positioning cylinder at mid stroke. This positions the swashplate in the vertical position (perpendicular to the rotational axis). In this position of the swashplate there is no incline, and the pistons cease to reciprocate in their bores. This results in no flow, since the piston creates no displacement volume during rotation.

In using this pump in a closed loop circuit, you achieve flow reversal when the positioning cylinder is fully retracted. In this position, the piston on top of the pump would be fully collapsed, while the pistons on the bottom would be fully retracted in their bores. With the same direction of rotation, the flow direction is reversed.

The in-line piston pump can be used in either open or closed circuit applications. It is not generally recommended for half closed circuitry, since the suction characteristics of in-line piston pumps are, at best, marginal. For open circuit applications, the stroking cylinder incorporates a mechanical stop so that the displacement can be varied only on one side of center. Closed circuit controls, on the other hand, make use of the full stroke length of the positioning cylinder. This allows the pump's displacement to be infinitely varied for either direction of flow in the closed-loop circuit. Various controlling means will be discussed in general later in this chapter.

THE HYDROSTATIC TRANSMISSION IN-LINE PISTON PUMP

The in-line piston pump, as discussed up to this point, can be used either in open or closed loop applications. However, if a closed loop circuit is used, it is the responsibility of the design engineer to select the necessary components for proper closed circuit operation. The minimum components list includes: supercharge pump, supercharge relief, two make-up check valves, and two cross port relief valves. He must also choose the pump with the proper porting, so that both main ports can sustain high pressure operation. (Some in-line piston pumps are supplied specifically for open circuit application since they have a larger low pressure inlet port). Let us now take a look at the differences between a standard in-line piston pump and a *hydrostatic transmission* pump.

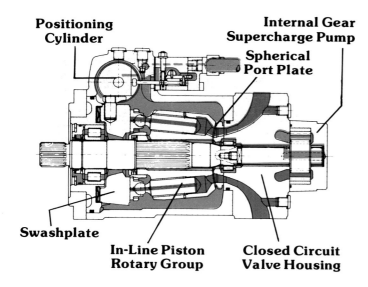

Positioning Cylinder

Internal Gear Supercharge Pump

Spherical Port Plate

Swashplate

In-Line Piston Rotary Group

Closed Circuit Valve Housing

Control Housing

Supercharge Relief

Cross Port Reliefs

Hydrostatic Transmission Pump

The *hydrostatic transmission* pump is designed specifically for closed circuit applications, because it includes all the necessary components within the main pump housing. As shown, the heart of this pump consists of a special variation of the basic variable displacement in-line piston rotary group. Apart from the main rotary group and its positioning cylinder, the hydrostatic transmission also includes an internal gear pump for supercharging the closed loop circuit. In addition, the supercharge relief, cross port reliefs, and make up check valves are incorporated in the closed circuit valve housing attached to the rear portion of the pump.

The hydrostatic transmission pump is designed primarily for hydrostatic drive on mobile equipment. For this reason, it must be sturdy enough to withstand the constant speed variations and relatively high drive speeds of internal combustion engines. Likewise, the drive shaft must be able to withstand the radial loading forces generated by gear or v-belt drives.

With respect to the rotary group, the major difference between this hydrostatic transmission pump and the standard

in-line piston design is that the pistons are at a slight angle to the axis of rotation rather than parallel to it. This slight angle (5°) uses the centrifugal force on the piston to its best advantage. We have already explained how too high a drive speed related to the mass of the piston can cause separation of the piston from its slipper pad. This also explains why the pistons on most in-line piston pumps are hollow. This design hydrostatic transmission pump is influenced differently because of its different geometry.

Because it is not hollow, the piston mass of the hydrostatic transmission is increased. Rotation of the drive shaft causes a centrifugal force on the piston which tends to retract the piston in its bore. The axial component of this force is applied on the slipper pad and ball joint, and tends to keep the slipper pad in contact with the swash plate. This allows the pump to operate at the high drive speeds of internal combustion engines without fear of damage to the slipper pad bearing.

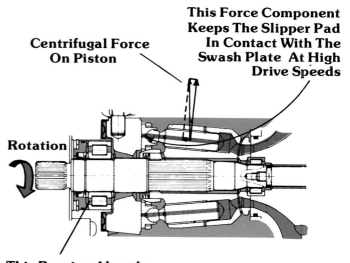

Centrifugal Force On Piston

This Force Component Keeps The Slipper Pad In Contact With The Swash Plate At High Drive Speeds

Rotation

This Bearing Absorbs Radial Shaft Loads

THE OPEN CIRCUIT BENT-AXIS PISTON PUMP

Open Circuit Bent-Axis Piston Pump

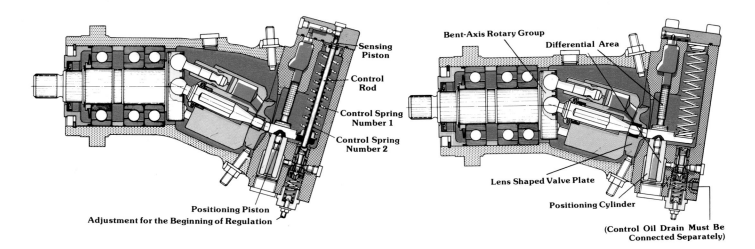

Constant Horsepower Control With 7°–25° Housing

Pressure Compensated Control 0–18° Housing

The cross-sectional illustration represents a bent-axis piston pump designed specifically for open circuit applications. It is quite similar to its fixed displacement counterpart, except for the fact that the cylinder barrel can swivel, which varies the displacement of the pump. You will notice that the piston stroke is related to the angle between the drive shaft and the cylinder barrel. Needless to say, when the cylinder barrel becomes parallel with the drive shaft, the pistons stop reciprocating in their bores. Depending on the pump control, the housing of this design pump can be supplied for two different stroke ranges, namely, 0° to 18° and 7° – 25°. The 0° – 18° housing allows the rotary group to be positioned in a no flow position, but has its maximum flow limited by the 18° swivel angle. The 7° – 25° housing allows slightly higher flow (large displacement because of longer piston stroke), but does not allow the pumping mechanism to achieve the no flow (zero angle) position.

The pump's displacement can be varied by using a *lens shaped port plate* which is connected to the positioning piston. You will notice that the positioning piston has two effective areas for pressure to act upon. The smaller area has approximately one half the *effective* area of the larger piston, and is constantly pressurized by system pressure. Assuming that the larger piston area is vented, the pressure working on this smaller piston has the ability to hold the pump in its maximum displacement position. When the control function being performed pressurizes the larger area, the pump is then swiveled back towards its no flow (or minimum flow) position.

Because of its design, this pump is capable of both high pressure (4600 PSI continuous, 5800 PSI intermittant) and

high flow (sizes available to 158 GPM at 1200 RPM). It also displays high volumetric and mechanical efficiencies. However, the real advantage of this type of pump is that it is specifically designed for open circuit, self priming applications. Let us now consider the features which make this a true *open circuit* pump.

THE LENS SHAPED VALVE PLATE

We have already discussed three of the basic reasons why a bent-axis pump should be selected for open circuit high pressure circuits. First, if the system must operate much higher than 2500 PSI, your selection of pumps is limited to one of the basic piston designs. Second, we have shown that the piston and rod assembly is stronger under suction than is the slipper pad used in in-line piston pumps. And finally, the spherical port plate offers less restriction to flow during suction than does the more complicated porting necessary in in-line piston equipment. The "lens" shaped valve plate makes these advantages, as previously discussed for fixed displacement pumps, available for the variable displacement designs.

As shown in the previous cross-sectional illustration, the lens shaped valve plate has two curved surfaces. One surface is the spherical surface, which mates to the cylinder barrel. The second curved surface is supported by the rear cover and allows the cylinder barrel to swivel through an 18° arc.

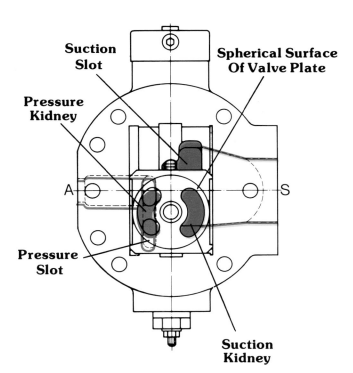

View Of The Rear Cover And Valve Plate From The Cylinder

If mounting the internally drained pump below the oil level is not feasible, the pump should be mounted with its suction port vertically upward. This allows the housing of the pump to be filled with oil prior to start-up, which aids in achieving proper sealing of the shaft. Needless to say, the suction line must be adequately sized so that the extra pipe fittings required for this type of mounting do not cause too much restriction to the inlet flow.

THE OVERCENTER BENT-AXIS DESIGN

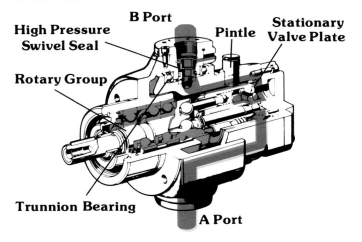

The cut-away illustration shows the front half of an overcenter bent-axis pump. Unlike the lens shaped port plate of the open circuit bent-axis pump, this unit uses the stationary valve plate, as already described for the fixed displacement unit. The difference is that the cylinder barrel, pistons and fixed valve plate are contained in a *swivel housing*. The swivel housing contains A and B port passages which communicate flow to the A and B port connections of the pump. As shown, the A and B ports are an integral part of the two trunnion bearings which support the swivel housing.

The lens shaped valve plate communicates flow from the suction port located in the rear cover to the cylinder barrel. As shown, the suction slot in the rear cover provides a full flow passage at any swivel angle. Pressurized flow passes from the cylinder barrel, through the pressure kidney and pressure slot, to the outlet port of the pump. This arrangement allows the pump to create a vacuum equivalent to 6 inches high without fear of pump damage.

Finally, it is important to mention the fact that this pump design does not require a separate case drain line. You will notice that leakage oil, which lubricates the bearings, is collected in the housing of the pump. Since the housing and suction inlet are inter connected, the leakage oil simply passes to the low pressure inlet of the pump. However, due to the fact that the housing and inlet port are inter connected, some mounting precautions are advisable.

In general, gear, fixed displacement vanes and any other pump type which internally drains its case to the inlet side of the pumping mechanism possess a potential problem when mounted on top of the oil reservoir. This problem stems from the fact that it may be easier for the pump to pull air through its shaft seal, than to lift oil from the reservoir. Even if the pump operates satisfactorily when new, slight wearing of the shaft seal can cause future service problems. For this reason, it is always advisable to mount internally drained pumps below the oil level in the reservoir. This, of course, maintains a positive *head pressure* within the housing of the pump (Chapter 1).

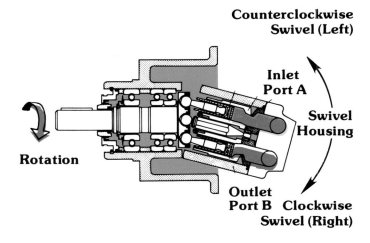

Top View Of An Overcenter Bent-Axis Pump

The cross-sectional illustration, from a top view, can be used to explain the method whereby the overcenter pump varies its displacement. As shown, the housing is *swiveled* in the clockwise direction to its maximum angle. In this direction, a right-hand rotation of the input shaft causes pump flow from port A to port B. Assuming constant drive speed, the pump will be producing its maximum flow. Now, if we started swiveling the housing counterclockwise towards the zero swivel angle, a reduction of flow would occur because the relative piston stroke would become less.

At the 0° swivel angle, the swivel housing and the drive shaft become parallel. In this position, there is no relative piston motion, and the pump stops delivering flow. If the swivel housing were to continue to move *overcenter* in the counterclockwise direction, a reversal of flow would occur. Of course, the larger the angle in the counterclockwise direction, the greater would be the flow. The following drawing and chart can be helpful in determining the direction of flow as related to swivel direction and direction of rotation.

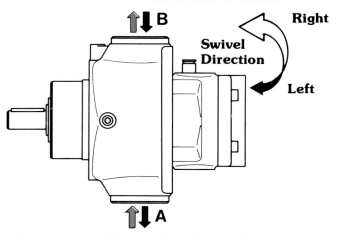

		Direction of Rotation	
		clockwise	counter - clockwise
Swivel Direction	right	A to B	B to A
	left	B to A	A to B

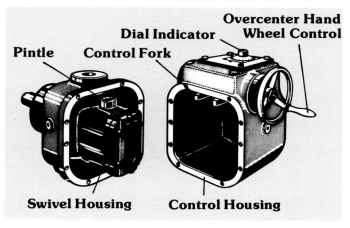

Pintle   Control Fork   Dial Indicator   Overcenter Hand Wheel Control

Swivel Housing   Control Housing

The overcenter pump, as shown up to this point, is incomplete in that the swivel housing is actually contained within the housing of the pump. The *control housing* is bolted to the rear of the pump. This encloses the swivel housing and provides the means of controlling its position. The drawing shows a pump with the simple hand wheel control. Independent of the type of control, the control housing contains a *fork* which mates with the pintle on the swivel housing. The control causes the fork to move in a horizontal sense, which in turn, adjusts the swivel angle of the pump.

The control housing provides an additional function in that it seals the entire pump. In this manner, leakage and lubrication oil collects in the pump housing and is returned to the hydraulic reservoir by a separate case drain line. Likewise, with this closed circuit type pump, it is imperative to fill the pump housing with oil prior to start-up.

THE HALF CLOSED CIRCUIT BENT-AXIS PISTON PUMP

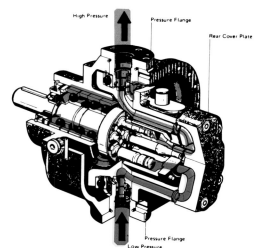

Swivel Housing Cover For Closed Circuit Operation

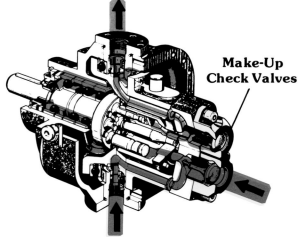

Swivel Housing Cover For Half Closed Circuit Operation

Earlier in this chapter, we have explained the difference between open, closed and half closed circuits. In a half closed circuit, the pump is not only required to create a flow of fluid from one service port to the other, but it must also *make-up* oil when the return flow is less than the output flow. This is easily accomplished by using bent-axis design overcenter pumps.

As shown in the cut-away illustration, a half closed circuit pump is nothing more than a closed circuit pump with make-up (suction) check valves installed on the rear cover of the swivel housing. The pump modification also includes a *control housing* with a large diameter suction port. Consequently, a pump for half closed circuit operation has three full size port connections, namely, two service ports for controlling the direction of flow in the closed portion of the circuit, and a full sized suction port for pulling the necessary make-up oil. Since the suction line is common to both the reservoir and the pump's case, a separate case drain line is not required. Depending on the requirements of the particular half closed circuit pump, full displacement can be drawn over the make-up check valve. You will notice that two check valves are necessary, one for each direction. The check which is not required for a particular direction of flow is simply held closed by system pressure.

VARIABLE DISPLACEMENT PUMP CONTROLS

Hydraulic pumps can be made to match the duty cycle of virtually any hydraulic system. They can conserve energy and avoid heating the system, since they supply only the required flow at a pressure level dictated by the load conditions. You can achieve this optimum transfer of energy simply by selecting a variable displacement pump with the proper control option.

Now that we have discussed the methods through which piston and vane pumps vary their displacements, we can discuss the control means available to alter the *flow* capability of the pump. We have previously covered the pressure compensator control in detail in conjunction with the variable displacement vane pump. Considering the fact that the same type of control is available for piston equipment, discussion of its merits would be repititious. At this point, it is more important for you to realize what the control does, rather than how the control operates with all the different pump designs. Likewise, you must remember to select the control to meet the circuit requirements of your system. Some controls are designed specifically for open circuit pumps, while others can be modified for use in either open, closed or half-closed circuits. We will begin our discussion of the various control options with the simple handwheel control.

THE HANDWHEEL PUMP CONTROL

The cross-sectional illustration shows a typical *handwheel* control which mechanically changes the displacement of the pump. The operation of this control is quite simple and easy to understand. You can see that a manual rotation of the handwheel will cause the threaded spindle to turn. The nut which is permanently attached to the positioning piston will travel along the threads of the spindle and cause the

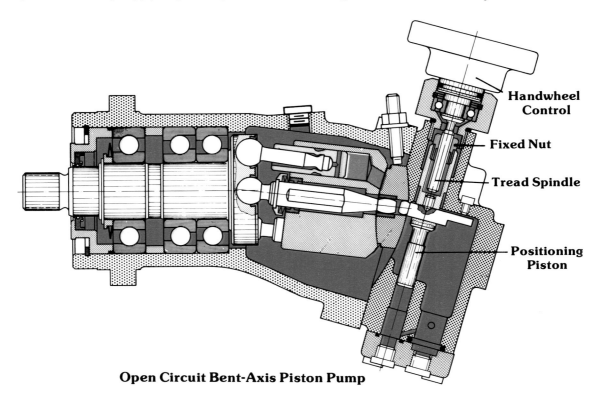

Handwheel Control

Fixed Nut

Tread Spindle

Positioning Piston

Open Circuit Bent-Axis Piston Pump

positioning piston to move up or down. This, in turn, will change the displacement angle between the cylinder barrel and the drive shaft.

The handwheel control is simple in design, which makes this control not only inexpensive to purchase, but also very reliable. Nevertheless, many design engineers overlook the benefits this type of control offers to the basic circuit design.

Whenever there is a requirement to adjust the speed of the actuator, it is commonplace to select a flow control valve (Chapter 3) for the system. However, we have shown in Chapter 1 that we must also concern ourselves with the heat generation caused by flow control components. In many cases, a handwheel controlled variable displacement pump could be used economically in place of a fixed displacement pump, used in conjunction with a flow control. It is usually better, from an energy conservation standpoint, to cause a change in the pump flow manually, rather than to alter the resistance to that flow, also manually.

The handwheel controlled pump, when used to vary system speed, proves the adjusted flow only at the pressure dictated by the load conditions. Although the pump must be used with a full flow relief valve, the relief valve will open only if the system is overloaded or stalled. It never has to bypass flow to tank during reduced speed operation. Consequently, heating of the system can be considerably reduced.

The handwheel control can be incorporated into either open, closed, or half-closed circuit pumps. In closed or half-closed circuits, the direction of the actuator is manually changed when the control causes the pump to go *overcenter*.

THE ELECTRIC MOTOR CONTROL

A variation of the simple handwheel control allows the thread spindle to be rotated by an electric motor drive. The electric motor control allows the pump's displacement to be changed more rapidly, and from a remote control station. Since the control is electrical, there is virtually no limit on the distance between the control station and the pump. By incorporating cam operated limit switches, the pump control can easily be adapted to programmable or timed sequence operation.

The cross-sectional illustration shows an electric motor control for a bent-axis design overcenter pump. The electric motor works through a two-stage gear reduction and causes rotation of the thread spindle. Rotation of the spindle causes an axial motion of the fork assembly. Remember, the fork connects with the pintle on the swivel housing, which, in turn, causes a change in the pump's displacement.

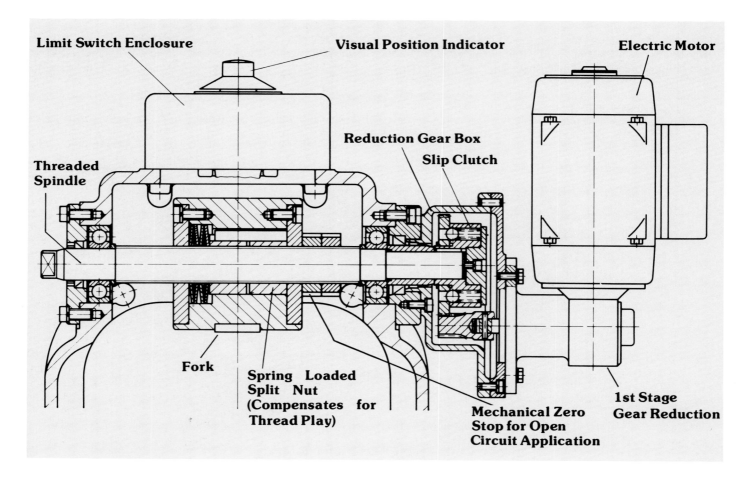

The bi-directional electric motor allows the position of the pump's swivel housing to be varied infinitely from zero displacement to maximum, in either flow direction. The stroking time is related to the RPM rating of the electric motor and to the gear ratio. Electric motor and gear ratio combinations are available for a multitude of swivel times. They range from 13 seconds to over 6 minutes. The motor is protected from overload by the slip clutch, which is built into the reduction gear box. In this way, there is no damage if the motor is left running after the pump has reached its maximum displacement.

In designing the electrical circuit, you can equip the electric motor control with a number of cam operated limit switches (double pole single throw), a potentiometer, or both, mounted on the same pump. The limit switches and/or the potentiometer serve as a feedback of the pump's swivel position to the electrical circuit. Rotation of the cam mechanism is accomplished by a rack and pinion drive which senses the position of the fork assembly.

THE CONSTANT HORSEPOWER CONTROL

The constant horsepower control (sometimes referred to as a horsepower limiter control) is intended for use with a prime mover which drives the pump at a constant speed. The prime mover can be either an electric motor or an internal combustion engine with a speed governor. The purpose of the pump control is to keep the prime mover working at its maximum torque capability, or better still, at a constant horsepower level. Remember:

$$HP = \frac{T \times RPM}{5252}$$

Where: T = Torque in lb.-ft.

To draw constant horsepower from the prime mover, the pump must maintain the mathematic product of flow and pressure at a constant value. This means that if the flow output is high, the operating pressure must be low. Likewise, when pressure increases, flow must decrease. Since the operating pressure level of a system is dictated by the load conditions, the flow must vary with changes in load induced pressure if we want to maintain the product of flow and pressure at a constant value.

The constant horsepower control senses the load induced pressure in the system and regulates pump displacement accordingly. The pump control holds the pump at its maximum displacement until the pressure level reaches the point at which regulation begins. During regulation, the pump supplies as much flow as possible for the input power available.

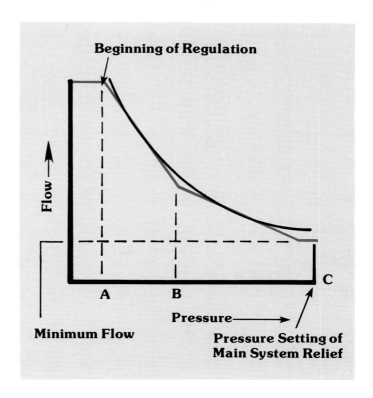

The graph shows the pressure and flow relationships for a constant horsepower control. The black (curved) line represents the theoretical constant horsepower relationship between flow and pressure, while the red line depicts the actual characteristics of the pump control. In reference to the graph, the pump is at full displacement until pressure A is reached. The slight slope of the curve between zero pressure and point A represents only a loss in flow because of pump leakage. Once regulation begins, the pump flow decreases quickly as pressure increases from point A to point B. Further increase in pressure (between point B and C) decreases pump flow more gradually until the control reaches the minimum flow valve.

The pump control must be used with a main system relief valve capable of relieving this minimum pump flow. Once the end of regulation is achieved, the slightest increase in system pressure will open the relief valve and bypass the minimum pump flow to tank. Needless to say, if load induced pressure drops, the control will follow the curve in the reverse direction (toward maximum flow). You can see that the two straight lines, which represent the actual pressure versus flow curve of the pump, closely approximates the actual horsepower curve.

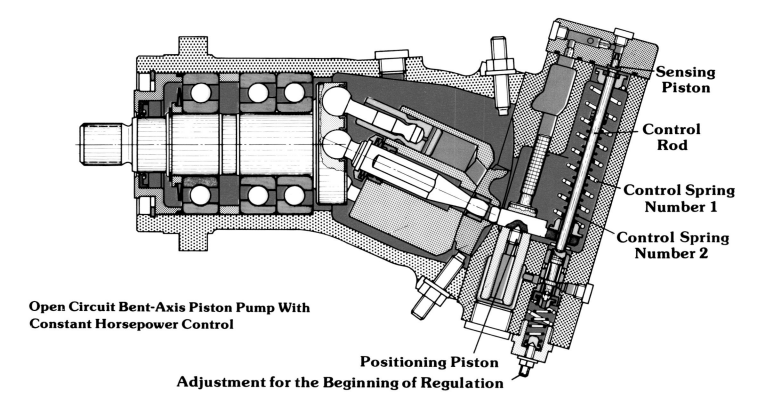

Open Circuit Bent-Axis Piston Pump With Constant Horsepower Control

Sensing Piston

Control Rod

Control Spring Number 1

Control Spring Number 2

Positioning Piston
Adjustment for the Beginning of Regulation

The cross-sectional view of a bent-axis design open circuit pump can be used to explain the operation of any constant horsepower control. During start-up, control spring number 1 holds the pump on full displacement and the pump begins delivering a flow of fluid to the system. As the flow encounters resistance, system pressure builds on the small area of the positioning piston which holds the pump on full displacement, and on the small piston sensing the pressure in the system. As long as system pressure working over the area of the sensing piston is not high enough to move the pilot spool against the small spring (which establishes the beginning of regulation), the large area of the positioning piston (orange) will be vented to the pump housing (green) through the pilot spool.

When system pressure exceeds the pressure setting for the beginning of regulation, the sensing piston will push on the control rod and shift the pilot spool. The pilot spool will then direct system pressure (red) to the large area of the positioning piston (orange). Under this condition, the area differential of the positioning piston will cause the pump to begin destroking.

Destroking of the pump will cause control spring number 1 to be compressed, which, in turn, will increase the mechanical force on the control rod and the sensing piston. When spring force balances the force due to pressure working over the area of the sensing piston, the pilot spool will modulate the pressure on the large diameter of the positioning pistons. In this way, the pump will destroke only to the point at which the spring force of control spring number 1 will balance the hydraulic force on the sensing piston. Consequently, control spring number 1 establishes the slope of the initial pressure versus flow curve of the pump.

When the pump destrokes to approximately 50% of its maximum displacement control, spring number 2 begins being compressed. This further increases the pressure needed on the sensing piston to cause displacement of the pilot spool. The second, more gradual, slope of the pump's pressure versus flow characteristics is shaped by the combined force of the two control springs.

Variable Volume Vane Pump With Similar Constant Horsepower Control

THE LOAD SENSING CONTROL

The load sensing control is becoming quite popular in modern hydraulic systems. Its advantage is that it conserves energy and virtually eliminates heat problems in the hydraulic system. The control operation is based on the principle that

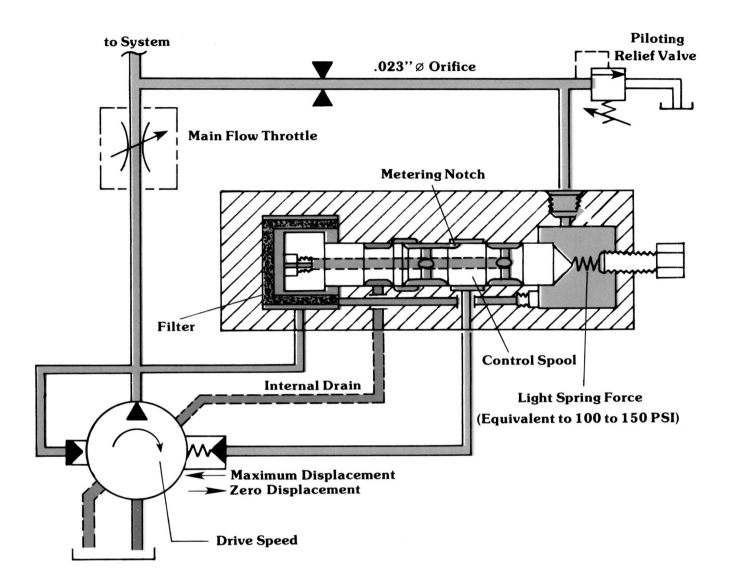

if there is a constant pressure drop maintained across an orifice, there will also be a constant flow. For this reason, the explanation of the load sensing control will more or less parallel our explanation of the pressure compensated flow control as discussed in Chapter 3. The illustration shows a typical load sensing control.

In this illustration, we are highlighting the pilot control spool of a variable volume vane pump with a load sensing control. The pilot control spool functions much like the *hydrostat* in a

pressure compensated flow control valve. You will notice that the left-hand area of the spool has the same effective area as that on the right. The spool is held to the left by a light spring force (equivalent to approximately 150 PSI). The left-hand area of the spool senses the inlet pressure of the main flow orifice, while the opposite end of the spool (spring end) senses the pressure at the outlet of this orifice. Consequently, the forces which act on the pilot spool are balanced when the pressure at the orifice's outlet is approximately 150 PSI (spring force) lower than the inlet pressure.

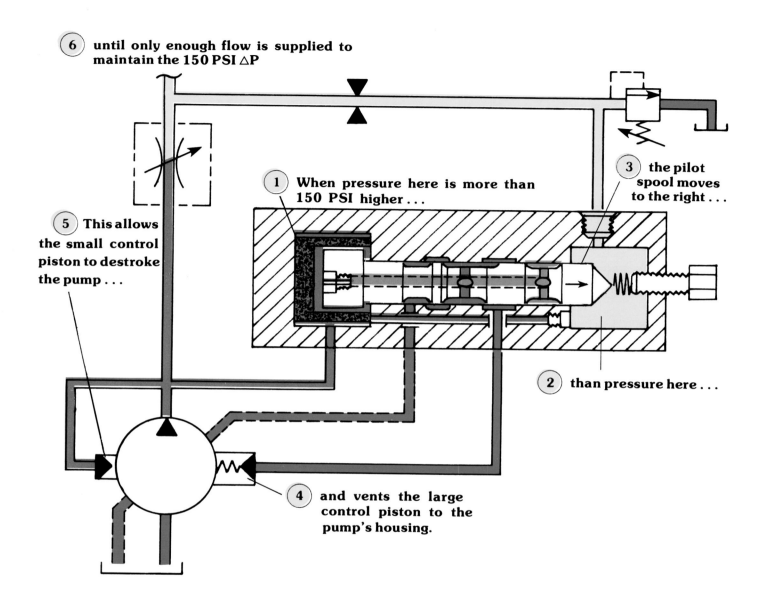

6 until only enough flow is supplied to maintain the 150 PSI △P

1 When pressure here is more than 150 PSI higher . . .

3 the pilot spool moves to the right . . .

5 This allows the small control piston to destroke the pump . . .

2 than pressure here . . .

4 and vents the large control piston to the pump's housing.

Destroking

The first illustration shows the pump in equilibrium, delivering just enough flow so that the pressure loss across the main flow orifice is at the 150 PSI value. If we assumed that a reduction in load were occurring at the actuator, we would immediately see a loss in the load induced pressure which was being fed back to the right-hand spool area. With this loss in equilibrium of forces, the pilot spool would move to the right. As shown in the illustration, the pump destrokes

(reducing its displacement) when the spool vents the larger control spool area to the housing of the pump.

Now, considering the fact that the pump control reestablishes equilibrium conditions at the lower load induced pressure, let us look at what will happen when the load increases.

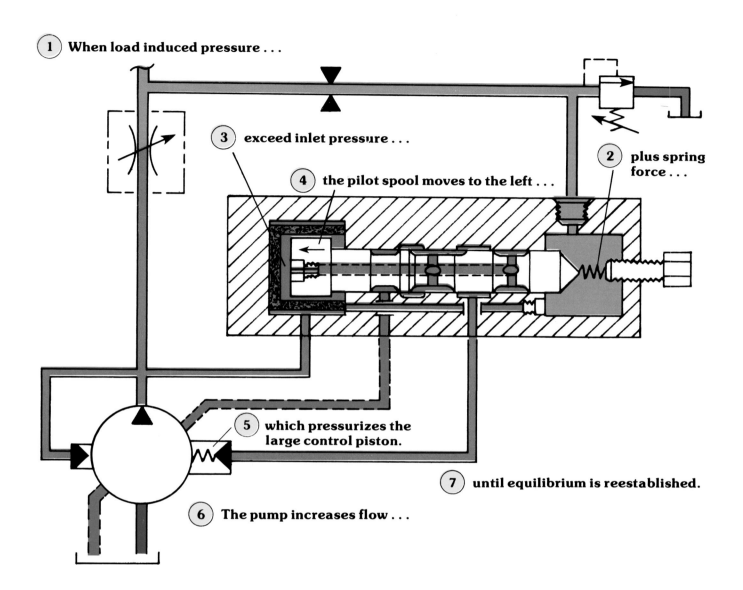

1. When load induced pressure . . .

3. exceed inlet pressure . . .

4. the pilot spool moves to the left . . .

2. plus spring force . . .

5. which pressurizes the large control piston.

7. until equilibrium is reestablished.

6. The pump increases flow . . .

As load induced pressure increases downstream of the orifice, the system will slow down if the pump is not able to increase the pressure at the inlet of the orifice. However, the increase in load induced pressure increases the pressure forces acting on the pilot control spool to the left. As the spool moves to the left, it upsets the previous established equilibrium condition, and loads the larger control piston with system pressure. This causes the pump to increase its displacement. The pump increases its output flow until the resistance to this flow creates a pressure at the inlet of the main flow orifice which is 150 PSI higher than the pressure at its outlet.

The small pilot relief, which is incorporated in the load sensing control circuit, provides a very important function. Its purpose is to limit the maximum feedback pressure to the pump control. When load induced pressure exceeds the setting of this relief valve, the valve opens and limits the maximum force available for pushing the pilot spool to the left. The moment the pressure at the outlet of the pump exceeds the limited load induced pressure plus spring force, the pilot spool moves to the right. This causes the pump to go into *deadhead*. The pump *pressure compensates* and provides only the flow required to maintain system pressure. The .023″ orifice stabilizes the pump control by limiting the amount of flow in the pilot circuit. If too much flow potential were to be exposed to the piloting relief valve, the pressure override characteristic would adversely affect the proper operation of the pump.

A less obvious feature of the load sensing control is that it will provide a constant flow regardless of the input drive speed. In a fixed displacement pump, an increase in its drive speed will also cause an increase in its flow output. If a restriction were to be placed downstream of the pump, the higher flow with higher drive speed, would necessarily require a higher pressure drop across the orifice.

In a variable volume pump (with load sensing control), an increase in RPM will also tend to cause increased flow. However, the moment the increase in flow occurs, there will be a higher pressure at the inlet of the main flow orifice. The control will sense this increase in pressure on the left-hand area of the control spool (discussed previously), and cause the pump to destroke. If the drive speed decreases, the loss of flow at the main orifice inlet will cause a loss in control pressure. This will allow the load induced pressure plus spring force to move the pilot spool to the left. This, in turn, will cause the pump to increase its displacement to the point at which pressure equilibrium is reestablished at the main flow orifice.

When you are selecting a pump with load sensing control for use in applications with variable drive speeds, be sure that the pump is sized so that the maximum flow will be supplied at the minimum drive speed. The pump will then decrease its displacement automatically as drive speed increases.

ELECTRONIC PROPORTIONAL CONTROL

Generally speaking, electronic control is probably the fastest technological field in existence today. The advent of the microprocessor has changed the way of doing things on both a personal (hand held calculator, for example) and industrial level. In fact, most of the "confidential research and development" now being conducted by industry is in some way related to electronic control.

One of the major advantages of using a hydraulic system for the transfer of energy is the ease and accuracy with which it can be interfaced with electronic control. Unfortunately, information on this subject is complete enough to fill the pages of another text. In addition, new products and methods in this field are being introduced on a daily basis. For these reasons, we must limit our discussion to a typical pump control intended for interfacing with electronics. We must ask the interested reader to consult the manufacturer's technical data in order to keep up with this ever expanding technology.

You will find that in almost all electronic interfaces, a *proportional solenoid* or a *torque motor* converts a D.C. electric signal into a force output. Both of these components operate on a constant D.C. voltage, and their force output increases with increased current. A typical proportional solenoid, for instance, operates on a 24V D.C. voltage and varies its force output in the control range of 150 ma to 700 ma.

The cross-sectional illustration represents a pump control

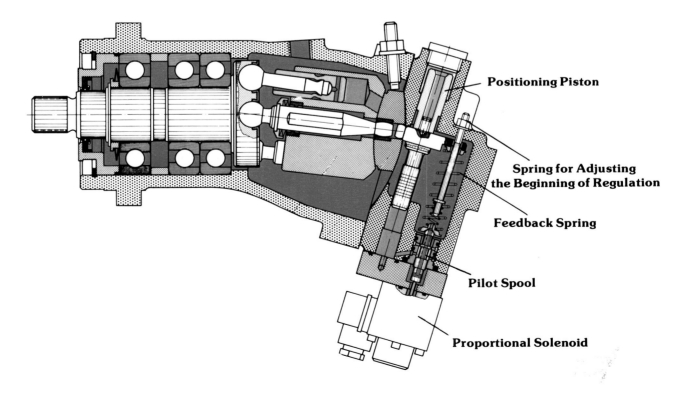

Positioning Piston

Spring for Adjusting the Beginning of Regulation

Feedback Spring

Pilot Spool

Proportional Solenoid

which uses a proportional solenoid to vary pump displacement. The pump responds from minimum to maximum displacement proportional to the current of a 24V D.C. command signal. The displacement of the pump is shown in the minimum position with no electrical signal supplied to the solenoid. The pump is held in this position by the force of the feedback spring and system pressure working over the smaller area of the positioning piston.

As a D.C. current is supplied to the proportional solenoid, the solenoid pushes on the pilot spool with a specific force. When the current, and, therefore, the force, is high enough to move the pilot spool against the small spring (which adjusts the beginning of regulation), pilot pressure is exposed to the large diameter of the positioning piston. Because of the area difference of the positioning cylinder, the pump begins stroking towards maximum displacement. However, stroking of the pump also causes the feedback spring to be compressed, which increases its force. When feedback spring force exceeds the limited force of the proportional solenoid, the spool will be moved back to its original position. This will cause the large diameter of the positioning piston to be disconnected from the pressure source and vented to tank.

The net result is that the pilot spool modulates the pressure on the large area of the positioning piston, so that the precise balance of feedback spring force and proportional solenoid force is maintained. The pump stays at this displacement position until the current supply is changed, which changes the force output of the proportional solenoid.

The control, as described, can be used to change the velocity of the output actuator, while the maximum force (or torque) output would be controlled by a separate pressure control piped into the hydraulic circuit. There are, however, many other variations of pump controls which use a proportional solenoid to adjust both displacement and the maximum pressure capability of the pump. For instance, the load sensing control, as previously discussed, is available with the adjustment of both the main flow orifice and the pilot relief established by two proportional solenoids. This allows both velocity and force output of the hydraulic system to be interfaced with electronic controls.

THE HYDRAULIC CYLINDER CONTROL

The hydraulic cylinder control, as shown in our discussion of variable displacement pumps, is the basis for varying the displacement of virtually all piston equipment. The pilot control varies pump displacement simply by determining the pressure and flow condition for the *adjusting cylinder* (positioning piston). With most pumps that use a positioning cylinder for varying the pump displacement, one control variation is simply to provide port connections to the positioning cylinder. The control of the pump displacement can then be determined by a pilot control circuit designed to meet the requirements at hand. This control can be as simple

as a two position control, using a two position four-way directional control, or it can be as sophisticated as a control cylinder which is positioned by a four-way directional servo valve.

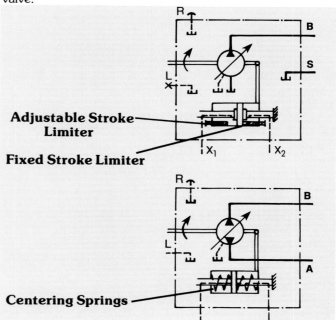

The circuit schematics show two variations of the cylinder controlled variable displacement pump. The top schematic is for use in open circuit applications, while the bottom schematic represents a pump for closed loop overcenter operation. The controls are quite similar, except for the fact that the overcenter pump incorporates centering springs, while the open circuit pump has a fixed stroke limiter which prevents the pump from going overcenter.

Although the operation of this type of control is quite simple and needs no further explanation, there are some precautions concerning it which should be observed. First, the pressure and flow requirement must be calculated using the same method described for any double acting hydraulic cylinder (Chapter 1). Normally, the control cylinder size is determined by the size of the pump with which it is used. This, of course, influences the piston *area*, which is the determining factor for both the flow and the pressure requirements. Second, you will notice that the schematics represent a pump control which uses a double rod cylinder. In this pump design, the cylinder rod is permanently attached to the pump housing. The pump's displacement is changed when the cylinder housing swivels the displacement mechanism. With other pump designs, the stroking cylinder may only have a single rod. With these designs, you must consider the area differential and its influence on both flow and/or pressure intensification.

Finally, you will find that there are several optional features offered for use with cylinder controlled pumps. The options include adjustable stroke limiters, centering or single acting return springs, and limit switches or potentiometers for feedback of the pump's displacement position to the electrical control circuit.

THE MECHANICAL SERVO CONTROL

The mechanical servo control can be used with a mechanical cam system for automatic operation, or it can be used to manually change the pump's displacement. This control is essentially a power assist, similar in operation to the automotive power steering unit. The control takes a low level force input and uses hydraulic flow and pressure to amplify the force, while at the same time obtaining a desired positioning of the pump's displacement. A simplified explanation of the operation is shown in the illustration.

rected to the cylinder so that it moves back to the null position. Because the pilot spool is machined with *zero overlap* (Chapter 5), precise displacement positioning is obtained.

The mechanic servo control is normally supplied with separate pressure and tank connections for the control. To prevent damage to the pilot spool or servo stem, the proper pilot pressure and flow must be supplied to the control. In addition, the pilot oil supply circuit must be operating before an attempt is made to reposition the servo system.

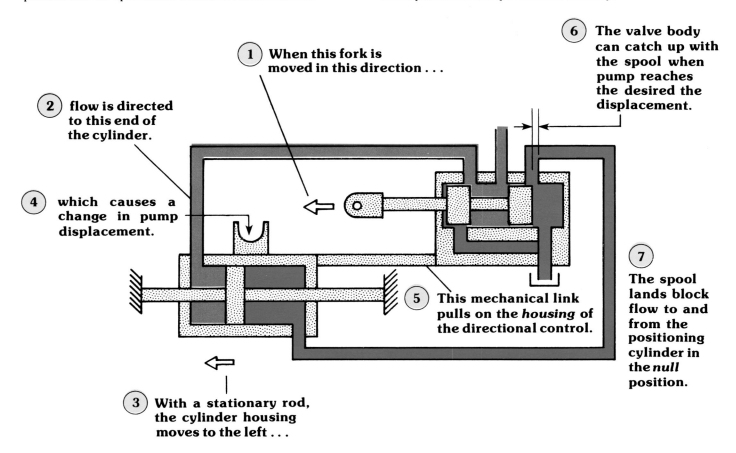

1. When this fork is moved in this direction . . .

2. flow is directed to this end of the cylinder.

4. which causes a change in pump displacement.

3. With a stationary rod, the cylinder housing moves to the left . . .

5. This mechanical link pulls on the *housing* of the directional control.

6. The valve body can catch up with the spool when pump reaches the desired the displacement.

7. The spool lands block flow to and from the positioning cylinder in the *null* position.

The diagram shows the basic operating principle of any mechanical servo system. The control positions the pump's displacement as determined by the position of the servo stem. You can easily see that if the stem is repositioned to the right, pressure and flow would cause the positioning cylinder to follow the motion of the piloting spool. It is important to note that, during operation, the pump is held precisely in the *null* position determined by the servo stem. Even if leakage by the pilot spool causes the positioning cylinder to drift, the control will self-compensate for this unwanted motion. The slightest drifting of the positioning cylinder causes the directional valve to open. Flow is then di-

THE PILOT PRESSURE RELATED CONTROL

The pilot pressure related control simply changes the pump's displacement directly proportional to the pilot pressure signal received by the control mechanism. In its simplest form, the control is not unlike the proportional solenoid. The only difference is that the variable force of the solenoid working on the control spool is replaced with a variable pressure working on the area of the pilot spool. The similarity of operation is shown in the following cross-sectional illustration.

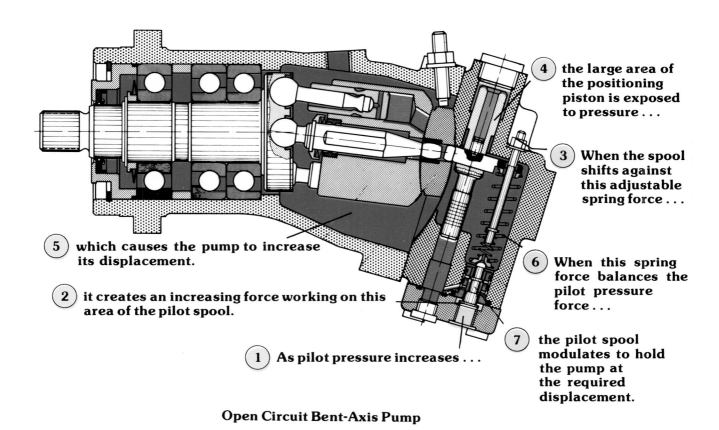

4 the large area of the positioning piston is exposed to pressure . . .

3 When the spool shifts against this adjustable spring force . . .

5 which causes the pump to increase its displacement.

2 it creates an increasing force working on this area of the pilot spool.

6 When this spring force balances the pilot pressure force . . .

1 As pilot pressure increases . . .

7 the pilot spool modulates to hold the pump at the required displacement.

Open Circuit Bent-Axis Pump

In this control, the pump displacement is linearly adjusted in proportion to the pilot pressure supplied to the pilot port connection. The typical control pressure range is 150 PSI, with the beginning of regulation being adjustable over the range of 30 to 725 PSI.

THE PILOT PRESSURE RELATED CONTROL FOR OVERCENTER PUMPS

The pressure related control for use with overcenter pumps is somewhat more sophisticated, but it performs the same basic function: it varies pump displacement in accordance with a pilot pressure signal. Because the pump strokes overcenter, two pilot pressure ports are provided, one for each direction of flow. A typical remote control pilot circuit for a closed circuit pump is shown in the illustration.

The illustration shows the typical arrangement of the component parts which make up a proportional hydraulic remote control. Although at first glance, this control looks somewhat complicated, it is actually quite simple in operation.

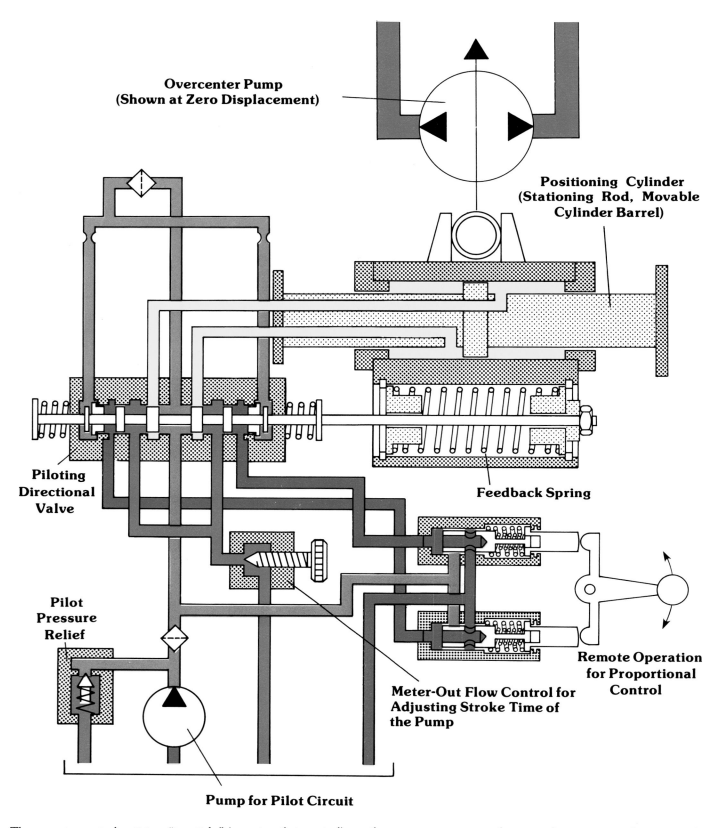

Overcenter Pump
(Shown at Zero Displacement)

Positioning Cylinder
(Stationing Rod, Movable Cylinder Barrel)

Piloting Directional Valve

Feedback Spring

Pilot Pressure Relief

Remote Operation for Proportional Control

Meter-Out Flow Control for Adjusting Stroke Time of the Pump

Pump for Pilot Circuit

The remote control unit is a "joystick," (remote pilot control) which allows the operator to control pilot pressure in proportion to the position of the hand lever. A close look at the valve shows that it is nothing more than two direct operated three-way pressure reducing valves contained in a single housing. When the joystick is in the neutral position, the spring force on both spools is relaxed. As shown, this unloads the pilot circuit to tank.

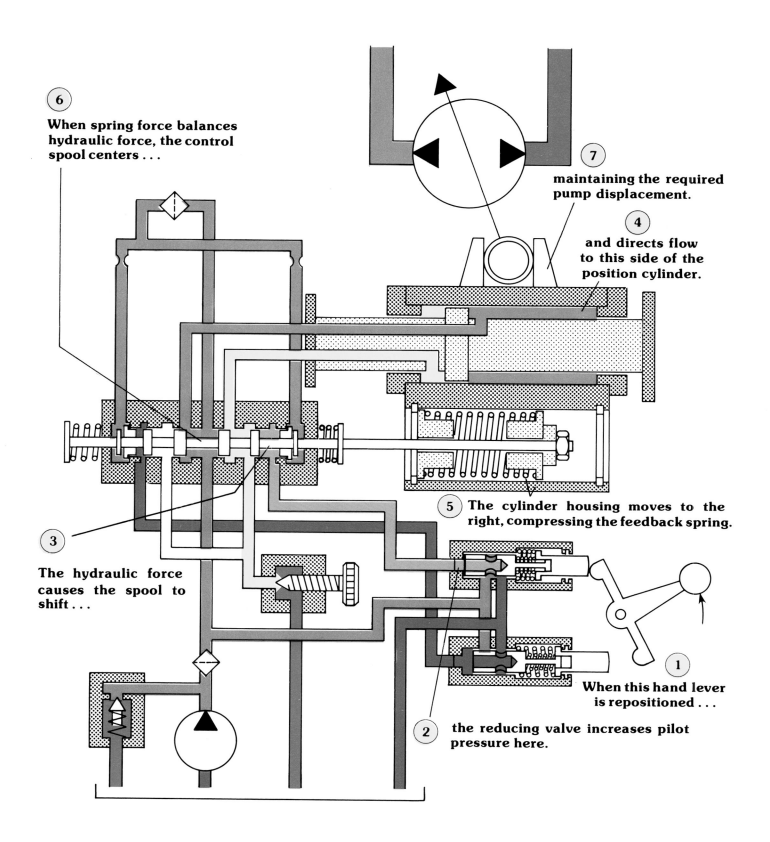

6 When spring force balances hydraulic force, the control spool centers . . .

7 maintaining the required pump displacement.

4 and directs flow to this side of the position cylinder.

3 The hydraulic force causes the spool to shift . . .

5 The cylinder housing moves to the right, compressing the feedback spring.

1 When this hand lever is repositioned . . .

2 the reducing valve increases pilot pressure here.

When the pilot circuit is unloaded, there is no pilot pressure on either end of the directional valve spool. Consequently, there is no hydraulic force causing the spool to shift. As shown, under these conditions, the pump is held in its zero displacement position. If leakage across the control spool allows the position cylinder to drift, the position error is transmitted to the control spool. This "feedback" is accomplished by the mechanical link between the feedback spring and the control spool. The error feedback causes the control spool to shift, thus allowing flow to and from the positioning cylinder. Let us now take a look at how proportional variable displacement is achieved.

HYDRAULIC PROPORTIONAL CONTROL OF PUMP DISPLACEMENT

The illustration indicates the stroking of the pump to one side of center. You will notice that the operation is identical for the reverse direction of stroke. When the pump is operating in the opposite direction, downward motion of the joystick will cause pressure to build on the left end of the control spool. Flow will then be directed to the left side of the stroking cylinder, with the pump displacement varied proportionally to the pilot pressure. Compression of the feedback spring will push the spool to its center position when the equilibrium between spring force and hydraulic force is achieved.

The control is designed so that the relationship between pilot pressure and pump displacement is perfectly linear. A typical control varies the pump displacement from zero to full as the pilot pressure varies between 100 to 580 PSI. As shown in the graph, the pump does not respond to pilot pressures of

less than 100 PSI. This prevents the resistance to flow in the pilot circuit, when unloaded, from inadvertently shifting the pump.

THE CONSTANT HORSEPOWER OVERRIDE FOR THE OVERCENTER PILOT PRESSURE RELATED CONTROL

The pressure related control, as discussed up to this point, can be provided with an optional constant horsepower override. This horsepower override protects the prime mover from being overloaded by either fluctuations in the work load, or by a heavy-handed operator. The horsepower override works on the principle of modifying the control signal at either of the pilot pressure supply ports, in relation to the pressure at the outlet of the main pump. (For a complete description of the constant horsepower control principle, please refer to the discussion of this control earlier in this chapter.)

The hardware which accomplishes this horsepower override is essentially made up of a variable pressure direct operated relief valve and two pressure equalizing sleeves assembled on either end of the pilot control spool.

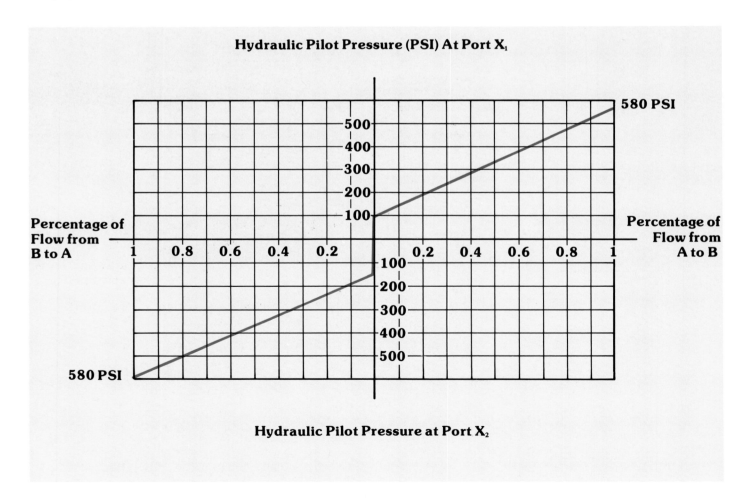

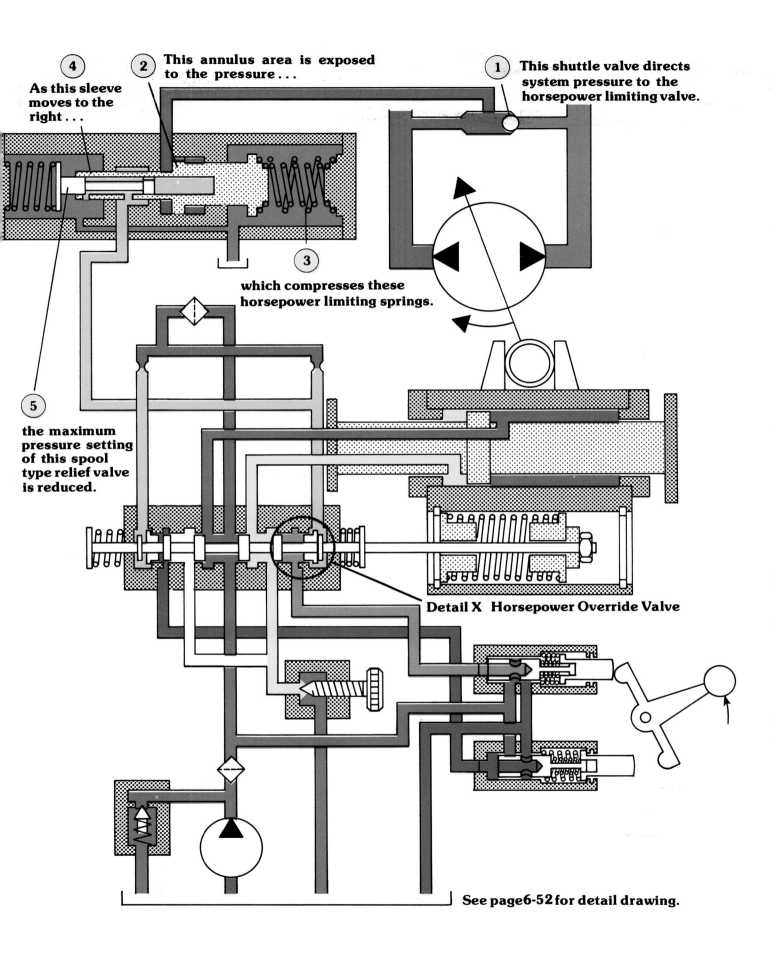

4 As this sleeve moves to the right . . .

2 This annulus area is exposed to the pressure . . .

1 This shuttle valve directs system pressure to the horsepower limiting valve.

3 which compresses these horsepower limiting springs.

5 the maximum pressure setting of this spool type relief valve is reduced.

Detail X Horsepower Override Valve

See page 6-52 for detail drawing.

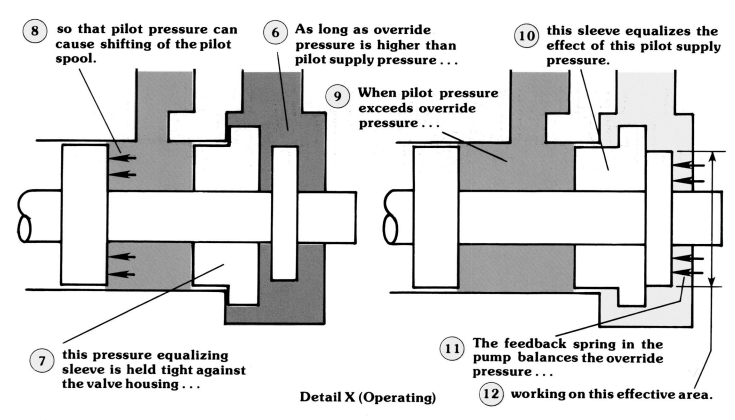

(8) so that pilot pressure can cause shifting of the pilot spool.

(6) As long as override pressure is higher than pilot supply pressure . . .

(9) When pilot pressure exceeds override pressure . . .

(10) this sleeve equalizes the effect of this pilot supply pressure.

(7) this pressure equalizing sleeve is held tight against the valve housing . . .

Detail X (Operating)

(11) The feedback spring in the pump balances the override pressure . . .

(12) working on this effective area.

OTHER USES FOR THE PILOT PRESSURE RELATED CONTROL

The pilot pressure related control as shown, varies pump displacement proportional to manual remote control valves. These remote control valves are available in a variety of hand lever and foot pedal operators to fit the application at hand.

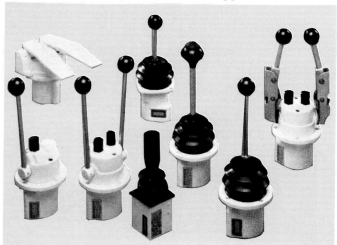

The control, as discussed, is but one of many possible applications. The possible uses of a pump control which varies pump displacement directly proportional to a pilot pressure signal are actually limited only by the imagination of the design engineer. The method of generating the command pressure signal is irrelevant as long as it is not effected by pressure fluctuations in other parts of the circuit. With this in

mind, the designer can design a pilot circuit for controlling the pump to meet virtually any system requirement.*

*The application of this control is more completely discussed in the Rexroth publication, "Pilot Pressure Related Control On Variable Displacement Hydraulic Pumps and Motors," by Graham Scott, Senior Applications Engineer.

SYMBOLS FOR HYDRAULIC PUMPS

Representation of the fixed and variable displacement pump is quite simple. The pump is shown as a circle with one or two outward pointing arrows indicating the direction of flow possibilities of the pump. Variable displacement is indicated simply by a diagonal arrow, which is superimposed on the circle. A dashed line is used to indicate that the pump has an *external* case drain line. It should not be used to indicate pumps which are internally drained.

Unfortunately, representation of the pump control is somewhat more complicated. In fact, with pilot operated controls, the pump control can become a complete circuit schematic in itself.

In the following chart, we list first the standard symbols for fixed and variable displacement pumps. We then attempt to show a representative cross section of the various pump controls.

SYMBOL	EXPLANATION
	Fixed Displacement Open Circuit Pump
	Fixed Displacement Closed Circuit Pump (Bi-Directional Rotation)
	Variable Displacement Pump for Open Circuit With Separate Case Drain Connection (No Control Indication)
	Variable Displacement Overcenter Pump for Closed Circuit With Case Drain (No Control Indicated)
	Variable Displacement Overcenter Pump for Half Closed Circuit (No Control Indicated)
	Variable Displacement Pump, Open Circuit, With Pressure Compensator Control, and Separate Case Drain

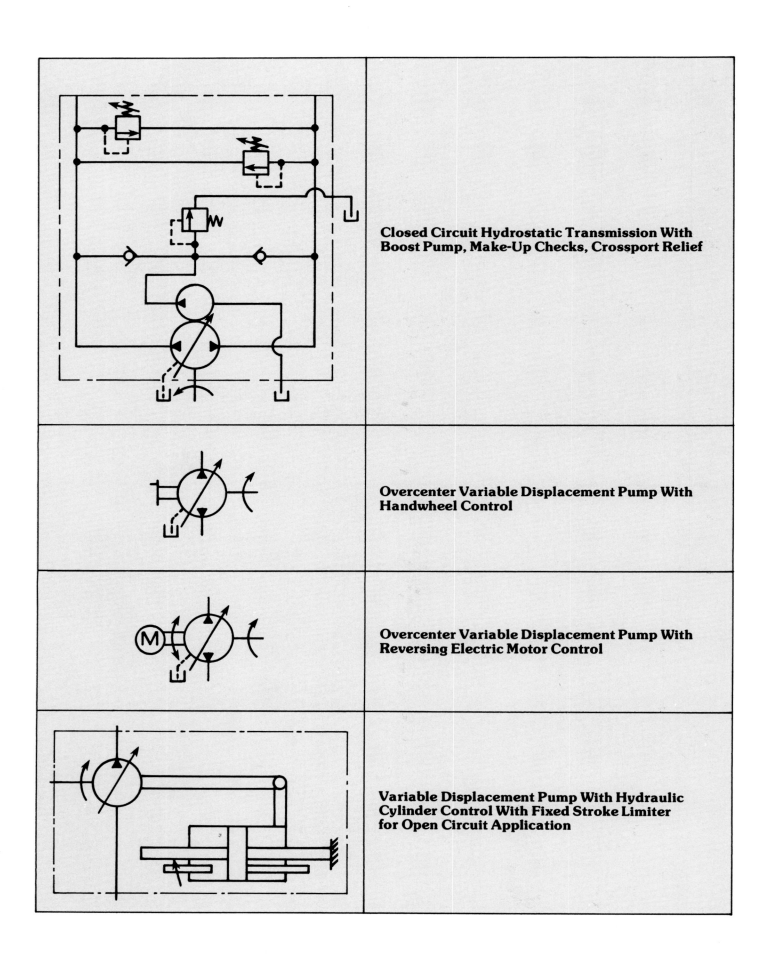

Closed Circuit Hydrostatic Transmission With Boost Pump, Make-Up Checks, Crossport Relief

Overcenter Variable Displacement Pump With Handwheel Control

Overcenter Variable Displacement Pump With Reversing Electric Motor Control

Variable Displacement Pump With Hydraulic Cylinder Control With Fixed Stroke Limiter for Open Circuit Application

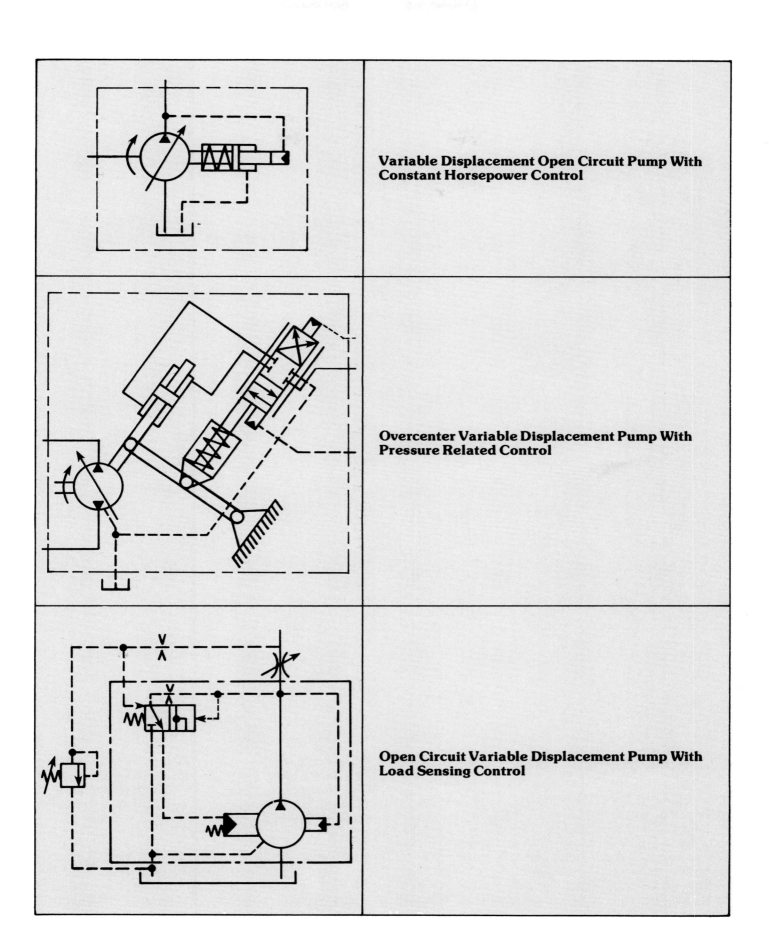

Variable Displacement Open Circuit Pump With Constant Horsepower Control

Overcenter Variable Displacement Pump With Pressure Related Control

Open Circuit Variable Displacement Pump With Load Sensing Control

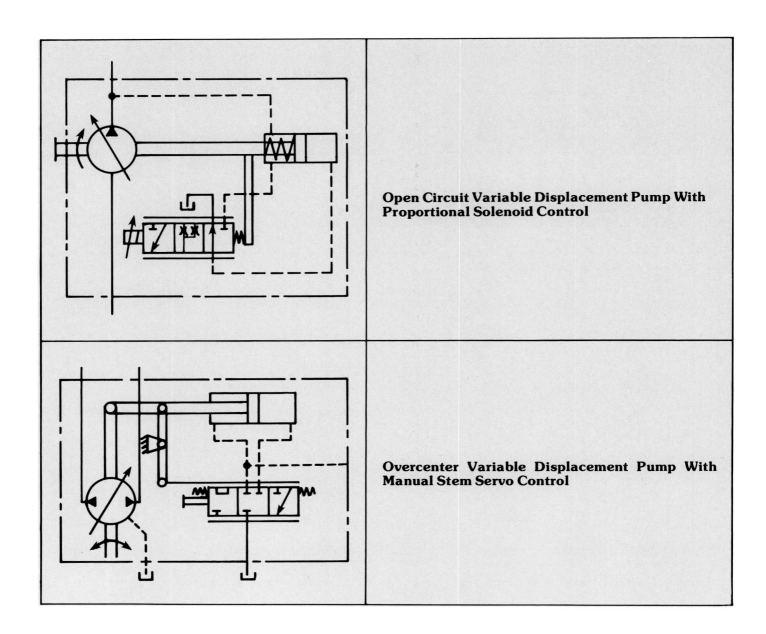

Open Circuit Variable Displacement Pump With Proportional Solenoid Control

Overcenter Variable Displacement Pump With Manual Stem Servo Control

CONCLUSION

This chapter has been devoted to an explanation of the major pump designs used in industrial hydraulic systems, beginning with a very basic explanation of how a pump converts the energy of the prime mover into hydraulic energy. For a very basic understanding of any hydraulic pump, the reader should know the meanings of the following terms. Without a basic knowledge in this area, it would be difficult to compare pumps in order to make a proper selection for the system requirements at hand. The terms are:

Displacement
Nominal Flow
Volumetric Efficiency
Mechanical Efficiency
Overall Efficiency

Pump Pressure Rating
Positive Displacement
Fixed Displacement
Variable Displacement

Any variety of hydraulic pump available today can be put into one of three general categories: gear, vane, or piston. If the pump is a variable displacement design, it must either be a vane or piston pump, since gear pumps are available only in the fixed displacement version.

FIXED DISPLACEMENT PUMPS

We have defined the parameters for using fixed displacement pumps. Generally speaking, the system must operate at a more or less constant speed, as determined by the maximum flow capability of the pump. Likewise, it is important to remember that any fixed displacement pump has the capability of wasting energy and of severely overheating the system, if, for some reason, it is misapplied. Nevertheless, when properly used, the fixed displacement pump can provide adequate service for a multitude of operating requirements. To assist the designer in the selection of the proper fixed displacement pump, we have discussed and compared the features and operating characteristics of external gear, internal gear, "Gerotor," balanced vane, radial piston, in-line piston, and bent-axis design piston pumps.

VARIABLE DISPLACEMENT PUMPS

Efficient use of our energy resources has become an important topic for discussion in all facets of our life, both at home and on the job. Today, engineers are evaluating the power consumption of new machines and appliances, looking for ways to reduce their energy demands to the lowest possible levels.

The use of variable displacement pumps is playing a greater part in modern hydraulic systems. The variable displacement pump has been instrumental in overcoming the stigma that hydraulic systems are inherently inefficient. This old line of thinking is quickly being replaced by an awareness and utilization of components providing higher efficiency, better performance and superior control.

The single most important advantage of the variable displacement pump is that heat is not generated by *moving* oil around the circuit when no work is being done. Even when a fixed displacement pump is unloaded, energy is converted into heat, simply because the oil is in motion. Likewise, during operation, oil must be diverted, restricted, or removed from the system at a high pressure level. Many times, this pressure level is considerably higher than the actual pressure required to do the *work* during most of the cycle. On the other hand, the variable displacement pump can be made to produce only the hydraulic energy required to do the work. It can also be made to produce this energy *only when it is needed* to cause the required motion of the load.

Our discussion of variable displacement pumps began with a description of the three types of pump circuits: open, closed, and half-closed circuits. We then discussed the mechanics involved in varying the displacement of vane, in-line piston, and bent-axis piston pumps.

A great deal more could be said of variable displacement pump controls than has been outlined in this chapter. We have, however, described the more common controls which are more or less standard to industrial pumps. With an understanding of the information presented in this chapter, the design engineer should be well on his way to determining the operation and application of any variable displacement pump control.

CHAPTER 7
ELECTRONICALLY CONTROLLED
PROPORTIONAL VALVES

SERVO VALVES VS. PROPORTIONAL VALVES:

There is a misconception that servo valves and proportional valves are so closely related that one can be used in the place of the other. This is not true: servo valves are different than proportional valves, and each has a particular use.

Servo Valves: are usually used in closed loop systems. A servo valve has feedback built into the system. Feedback is part of the closed loop system which monitors the machine or processes and feeds a signal back to the valve which controls it.

Proportional Valves: are usually used in open loop systems. This means there is no feedback, it is controlled by the operator or a process controller, or there is a fixed setting for the valve.

Servo Valves: are extremely accurate, generally better than a 1% error factor.

Proportional Valves: are not as accurate as servo valves, generally not better than a factor of 3% error.

Servo Valves: are faster in response when compared to proportional valves, generally between 60 to sometimes as high as 400 Hz.

Proportional Valves: are generally low in response, usually below 10 Hz.

Although the use of servo valves can be justified for extremely accurate control and high dynamic capabilities, proportional valves may be used anywhere directional and flow control valves are normally used.

DISADVANTAGES OF SERVO VALVES

1. High cost: by comparison to proportional valves.
2. The complexity of a servo valve demands far more auxiliary equipment, most of it being electronics. Proportional valves, by comparison, require a minimal amount of electronics.
3. Contamination: servo valves are more dirt sensitive,

while proportional valves, on the other hand, are far more tolerant of contamination.

FORCE CONTROLLED SOLENOIDS

It was only through the development of the proportional solenoid and the perfection of simple dirt resistant valves, that proportional valves made a significant breakthrough in the hydraulic system design. The performance of a proportional valve not only depends on its electronic requirements and unique hydraulic features, but also on the proportional solenoid as well.

There are two types of proportional solenoids, one being a stroke controlled solenoid (which will be discussed later) and the other being a force controlled solenoid. Force controlled solenoids are modified DC solenoids providing linear adjustable forces, by simply altering the current signal to the solenoid (see Figure 1).

Proportional force solenoids are of the wet pin DC type which appear similar to a conventional DC solenoid, with a modified internal construction optimizing the linearity of the solenoid. When a conventional DC solenoid is energized, the plunger travels its full distance creating a constant output force. A force controlled solenoid operates on the principle that solenoid force output is linear to the current supplied. This linearity of force output to current, works effectively over a stroke of approximately 0.060" (1.5mm).

The easiest way to comprehend a force controlled solenoid is from the force travel curve (Figure 2).

Considering that a given amount of current creates a given force, the force travel curve demonstrates this linear relationship at various current levels. When current is supplied to the solenoid and held constant, solenoid force also remains constant over a stroke output of approximately 0.060" (1.5mm). For example, when a 200 mA signal is elevated to 400 mA the force increases, but remains constant over the same stroke output of approximately 0.060" (1.5mm). Maximum force output for force controlled solenoids lies between 12 to 14 lbs.. Since adjustable forces can be achieved over a small

Figure 1

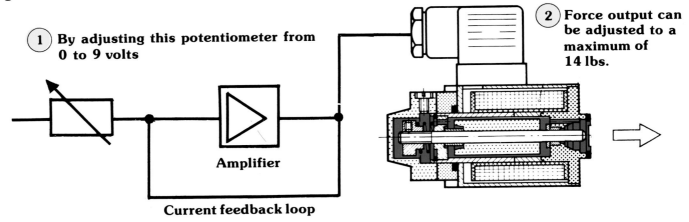

① **By adjusting this potentiometer from 0 to 9 volts**

② **Force output can be adjusted to a maximum of 14 lbs.**

Amplifier

Current feedback loop

stroke, installation dimensions for the solenoid do not become too great; therefore, the solenoid is compatible to pilot operated proportional pressure controls, directional control valves, and some variable displacement pump controls (Chapter 6). Also, since the solenoid is a wet pin there is a removable screw to bleed any air that may become trapped.

Figure 2

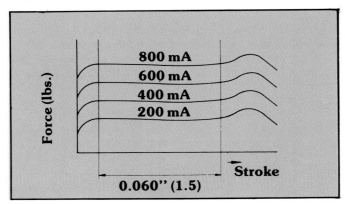

Force (lbs.)

800 mA
600 mA
400 mA
200 mA

Stroke

0.060" (1.5)

PROPORTIONAL PRESSURE RELIEF VALVES

Proportional pressure relief valves perform essentially the same function as those of manually adjusted pilot operated types. The major difference between the two, is that the spring adjustment assembly in the pilot head is replaced by a force solenoid.

As mentioned previously in our discussion of force solenoids, the solenoids maximum force lies between 12 to 14

lbs. This force is sufficient to enable an adjustable force to hold a small direct operated relief valve poppet in a seated position.

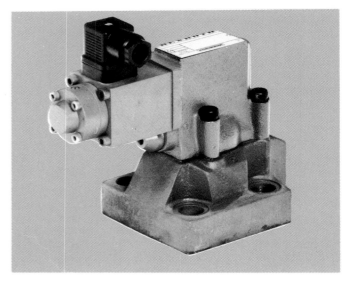

As shown in the crossection, (Figure 3) when the valve is supplied with an input signal the solenoid provides a direct force on the pilot poppet. Pilot pressure is fed internally from passage C working through orifice 1.2 on the nose of the pilot poppet and on top of the main poppet. As long as pressure does not exceed the force of the proportional solenoid the main poppet remains in a closed position, due to the main poppet being of equal area and incorporating a light spring. Pressure works equally above and below the main poppet with the light spring allowing for a slightly greater downward closing force.

When system pressure exceeds the setting of the proportional solenoid, the pilot poppet opens establishing a pilot flow from passage C through port Y to tank. This allows a decay in pressure above the main poppet felt by orifice 1.1. At the same time, the main poppet opens allowing oil to pass

Figure 3

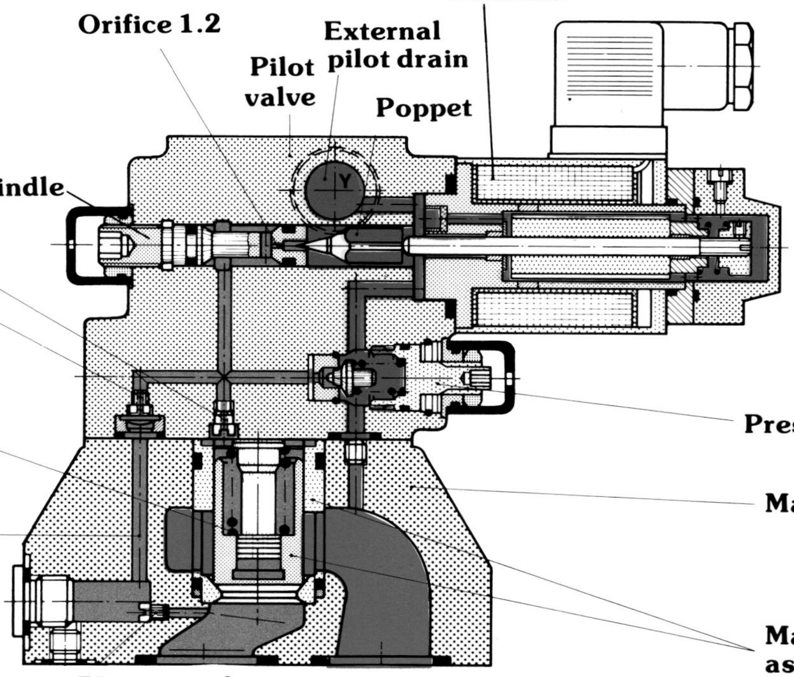

Labels on figure: Orifice 1.2, Pilot valve, External pilot drain, Proportional solenoid, Poppet, Spindle, Orifice 1.3, Orifice 1.1, Orifice 1.2, Passage C, Pressure relief cartridge, Main valve, Main poppet assembly

△ X ▲ A ▽ B

from port A (pressure port) to port B (tank port).

The main poppet is a small low mass poppet which allows for minimal stroke during opening, meaning the valve reacts quickly. The sleeve is manufactured with three radial holes drilled symmetrically around it to allow for a divergent flow characteristic when the valve opens. The result is a much quieter valve.

Unlike a conventional pilot operated relief valve, (where the maximum pressure rating of the valve is effectively established by the force of the spring in the pilot head), the maximum pressure rating for a proportional pressure relief valve is established by the seat area of the pilot poppet. Considering the solenoid provides an adjustable force of up to 14 lbs., a larger seat results in a lower maximum adjustable pressure rating of the valve. The resultant pressure force therefore has to work over a larger area on the nose of the pilot poppet, thus requiring less pressure to push it open.

Likewise, a smaller seat results in a higher pressure rating of the valve since the resultant pressure force must now work over a smaller area on the nose of the pilot poppet. It takes a greater amount of pressure to push the pilot poppet open.

The sensitivity of the proportional solenoid requires that the pilot head be externally drained directly back to tank from port Y. If the pilot head is internally drained, back-pressure can develop causing erratic operation of the valve.

With the help of the electronic amplifier the pressure setting of the valve can be either gradually increased or decreased accordingly. Also, solenoid force can be quickly or frequently adjusted during machine operation. Adjusting time; or the time it takes to go from one valve setting to the next, with respect to the signal received from the amplifier, is in a range from 50 ms to 150 ms depending on valve size.

If power is lost to the valve, solenoid force immediately falls off, allowing oil to pass from port A or port B. To protect the system from high unexpected solenoid forces, (such as those caused by electronic failure or high current peaks), a maximum pressure relief valve can be built into the pilot head of the valve. This can be accomplished by using a standard spring and poppet assembly which can be mechanically adjusted just slightly above the maximum desired system pressure. It should also be mentioned, that many times a relief valve is needed for very small flow rates. By removing the pilot head and using it as an electronically adjustable direct operated relief valve, the pilot head alone can handle flows up to about one half a gallon per minute.

PROPORTIONAL PRESSURE REDUCING VALVE

Proportional pilot operated pressure reducing valves are similar to proportional pilot operated pressure relief valves, in

that they are electronically adjustable and incorporate a force solenoid. The main valve assembly is the same as a manually adjusted pilot operated pressure reducing valve, with the pilot head being the same as the proportional relief valve. The maximum pressure rating of the valve is therefore determined by the seat diameter of the pilot poppet as is the relief valve.

When the valve (Figure 4) is supplied with an input signal the force of the proportional solenoid directly operates on the pilot poppet. As long as the force of the solenoid holds the pilot poppet closed the pilot oil remains in a static condition.

Pressure is transmitted through passage 9, and works above and below the main spool. Since the main spool is of equal area, a force balance is created because of the equal pressures. With a hydraulic balance on the main spool, a light spring force keeps the main spool in an open position. Oil is thus able to flow unrestricted from the primary port B, to the secondary port A. When pressure in the secondary port exceeds the force of the proportional solenoid, the pilot poppet opens allowing oil to drain from the top of the main spool via port Y to tank. This establishes a pressure drop on orifice 6 and 7 which unbalances the forces on the main spool. The main spool then moves upward reducing the flow area from B to A (due to the radial drillings in the main spool and sleeve) and creating a secondary reduced pressure in port A. The main spool then modulates to maintain pressure in port A at the setting of the proportional solenoid.

With the help of the amplifier, solenoid force can be quickly and/or frequently adjusted during machine operation. Adjustment time (or the time it takes to go from one valve setting to the next with respect to the signal received from the amplifier) is in the range of 100 ms to 300 ms depending on the size of the valve.

Solenoid force can also be gradually increased or decreased. This results in either a gradual increase or decrease in pressure as required.

For maximum protection, a manually adjusted relief valve can be fitted in the pilot head. As with the proportional pressure relief valve, the pilot head should be externally drained directly back to tank.

**Reducing Valve With
Secondary Control (Figure 4)**

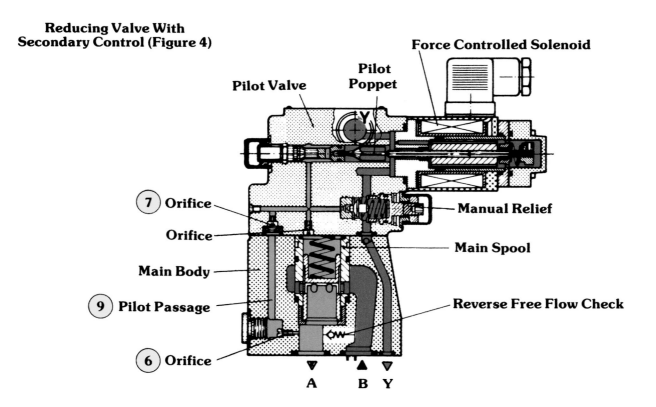

PRIMARY CONTROLLED REDUCING VALVE

An electronically adjustable proportional pressure reducing valve with a pressure compensated flow controller fixed in the pilot head, is capable of maintaining precise pressure settings at its highest flow rating (Figure 5).

Since the main spool of a pressure reducing valve acts as a regulating orifice, at high flow rates, flow downstream of the orifice is more turbulent. To make the valve more precise at higher flow rates, the pilot oil is taken from the primary port rather than the secondary port; thus preventing turbulent flow from influencing the valve's setting (See Chapter 2).

As in the previous discussion of the proportional pressure reducing valve, as long as solenoid force keeps the pilot poppet closed, the valve will remain open allowing oil to flow from inlet port B, through the main spool, to the secondary port A. This open position is maintained by feeding oil from the primary port B through passage C and through the pressure compensated flow controller to the top (spring loaded side) of the main spool. The desired system pressure is thus maintained on top of the poppet, thereby giving an unrestricted flow path from port B to A since the main spool and sleeve are in alignment due to the radial drillings in both.

When pilot pressure exceeds the force of the proportional solenoid, the pilot poppet opens. A constant pilot flow is established by the pressure compensated flow controller and oil drains from port Y to tank. This creates a regulated pressure above the main poppet.

When pressure in the secondary port A exceeds spring force plus pilot pressure, the main spool moves upward creating a secondary reduced pressure, and modulates as required.

If pressure in the secondary port builds too high during a static condition, the overload protection will open allowing oil to return to the pilot head, thus preventing pressure build-up due to leakage.

Both types of proportional pressure reducing valves can be built with reverse free flow checks.

PROPORTIONAL DIRECTIONAL VALVES

Proportional 4-way directional control valves are the most versatile of all proportional valves. The valve itself looks similar to that of a conventional directional valve, but with the spool configuration being designed specifically to provide precise metering in both the inlet and outlet sections of the valve. Not only does the valve have the ability to meter oil in both directions, but when applied correctly, pressure drops on both sides of the valve remain relatively equal. This allows for good controllability of cylinders and motors. Many times acceleration, deceleration and counterbalancing can be

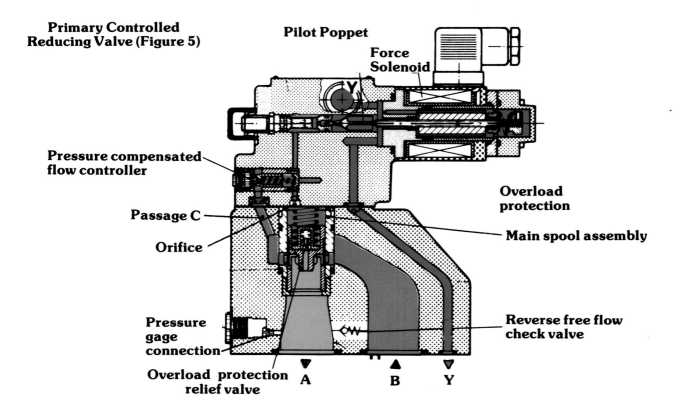

Primary Controlled Reducing Valve (Figure 5)

Pilot Poppet

Force Solenoid

Pressure compensated flow controller

Passage C

Orifice

Pressure gage connection

Overload protection relief valve

Overload protection

Main spool assembly

Reverse free flow check valve

A   B   Y

7-5

achieved with just one proportional directional valve, when interfaced with the required electronics. With conventional valving, such controllability is sometimes not possible even with as many as seven valves. It is not only the required electronics that give the proportional directional valve this capability, but its spool as well, which plays a big part in its overall operation.

PROPORTIONAL VALVE SPOOLS

Due to modern precision machining methods, the radial clearance between the proportional spool and the inside bore diameter of the valve housing is approximately 3 to 4 microns (.00012" to .00016"). Although all spool valves have internal leakage, at this close tolerance between the spool and inside bore diameter, leakage is kept to a minimum. This also allows for spool overlap to be kept to a minimum.

Spool configurations for 4-way proportional valves are basically simple in construction and easy to apply. As previously discussed, the spools are designed specifically to provide metering in both directions.

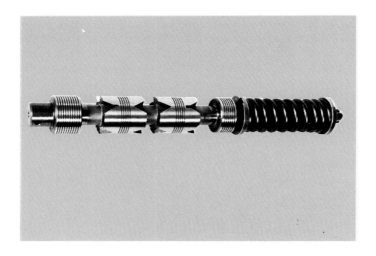

Figure 4 shows a closed center spool. The metering notches are provided by machining triangular grooves on the spool lands, often referred to as "control grooves". Each land has eight control grooves cut symmetrically around it, providing equal flow areas in both directions.

When the spool is moved in either direction, the specially designed control grooves never move fully free from the annuli, thereby always retaining a metering function. As in the condition of conventional directional valves, the spool first moves through a deadband and then completely opens, to virtually eliminate metering. Although all proportional spools are positively overlapped precisely 11%, compensation has been made in the amplifier to reduce this to a minimum. The spool is normally used to control motors or cylinders (with

cylinder ratios close to 1:1). Since it is an equal area spool, the pressure drops from ports P to B, A to T or from ports P to A, and B to T stay fairly equal giving good controllability.

Figure 5 shows a restricted center spool which gives a restricted flow path from P to A and B, with T blocked. The restricted center position is achieved by machining square metering notches on both P port spool lands. This allows about 3% metered oil of the full flow rating of the spool. The spool is normally used in motor applications providing the necessary make-up oil in the center position, which may be needed due to motor leakage or any suction that is created if the motor is brought to a sudden stop. Other than the modified center position, the spool construction and operation is the same as the closed center spool.

Figure 6 shows a 1:1 restricted center spool. This spool gives a restricted flow path from ports A and B to T with P blocked. Once again the square metering notches provide 3% metered oil while in the center position. The spool is normally used with single rod cylinders with an area ratio close to 1:1. Since all spool valves have some leakage, oil that leaks from port P when the valve is centered, can drain from ports A and B to tank. This eliminates the risks of cylinder extension and pressure intensification. When this spool is used for overhung loads, some type of counterbalance or pilot operated check valve must be used.

A regenerative closed center spool is shown in Figure 7. The right outside land contains no control grooves, therefore blocking B to T when the spool is moved left.

A regenerative spool (see Figure 8) with a restricted center allows oil to bleed from ports A and B to T with P blocked. The right spool land being extended with a square metering notch cut into it, provides the metered oil from B to T when centered. When the spool is moved to the left, B to T is blocked.

2:1 SPOOLS

When selecting the proper proportional spool for cylinders with area ratios close to 2:1, one must always make a careful decision.

A 2:1 cylinder's rod end delivers only half the amount of flow of that received at the blind end; the blind end delivers twice the amount of flow received at the rod end. If an equal area closed center or restricted center spool is used to control a 2:1 cylinder, the pressure drop across the valve in both directions can become fairly unequal. This can lead to cylinder control problems. To avoid this, a closed center or restricted center spool can be chosen with a reduced flow area giving one half the flow area on one side of the spool, as that of the other side (see Spool Chart on Page 7-9).

The photograph shows how this reduced flow area is achieved. By eliminating half of the control grooves on one land, the flow area is one half of that of the other land. This keeps the total pressure drop across the valve fairly equal

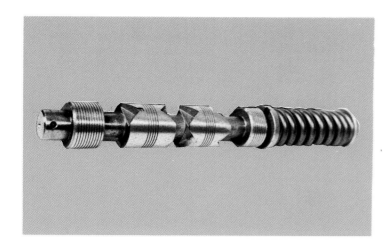

maintaining good controllability of 2:1 cylinders.

Pressure drop calculations for 2:1 cylinders will be shown later in this text, as well as cavitation effects and braking pressure when a 1:1 spool is used with a 2:1 cylinder.

3-WAY PROPORTIONAL PRESSURE CONROL VALVE

Before presenting the pilot operated proportional directional control valve, let us first discuss the pilot head for this valve. In order to understand the total pilot operated proportional directional control valve assembly, one must first have a complete understanding of the pilot head, which is essen-

Figure 4

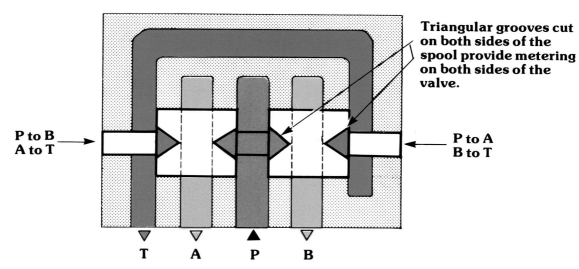

P to B
A to T

Triangular grooves cut on both sides of the spool provide metering on both sides of the valve.

P to A
B to T

T   A   P   B

Figure 5

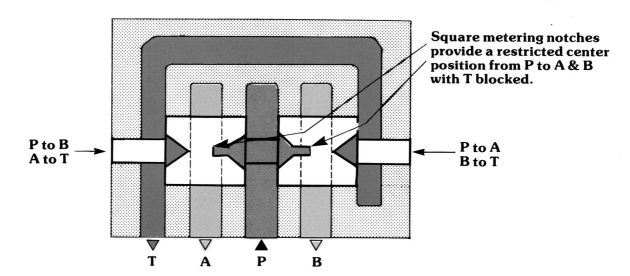

P to B
A to T

Square metering notches provide a restricted center position from P to A & B with T blocked.

P to A
B to T

T   A   P   B

Figure 6

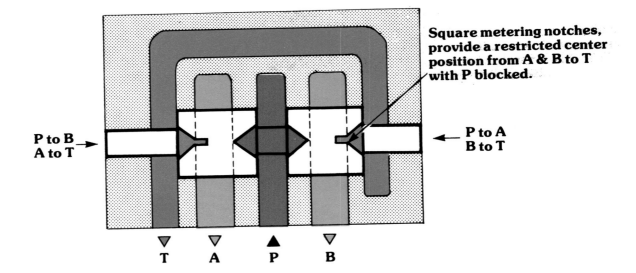

Square metering notches, provide a restricted center position from A & B to T with P blocked.

P to B
A to T →

← P to A
B to T

▽ T   ▽ A   ▲ P   ▽ B

Figure 7

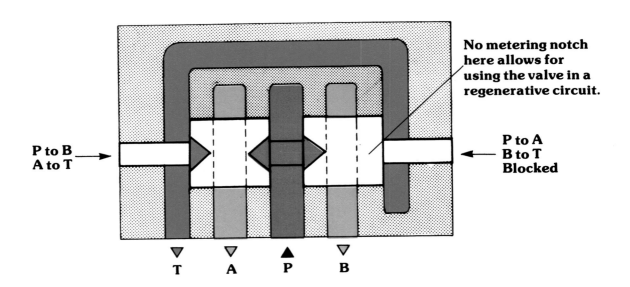

No metering notch here allows for using the valve in a regenerative circuit.

P to B
A to T →

← P to A
B to T
Blocked

▽ T   ▽ A   ▲ P   ▽ B

Figure 8

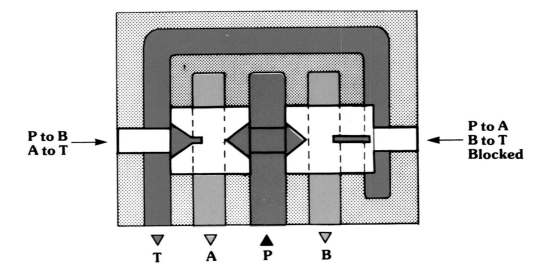

P to B
A to T →

← P to A
B to T
Blocked

▽ T   ▽ A   ▲ P   ▽ B

FLOW PATHS AVAILABLE FOR 3 POSITION PROPORTIONAL SPOOLS

	CLOSED CENTER	P → A = Q, B → T = Q P → B = Q, A → T = Q	Motor or Cylinder Spool (With cylinder area ratio close to 1:1)
	CLOSED CENTER	P → A = Q, B → T = Q/2 P → B = Q/2, A → T = Q	Cylinder Spool (With cylinder area ratio close to 2:1)
	CLOSED CENTER	P → A = Q/2, B → T = Q P → B = Q, A → T = Q/2	Cylinder Spool (With cylinder area ratio close to 2:1)
	CLOSED CENTER	P → A = Q, B → T Blocked P → B = Q, A → T = Q	Regenerative Spool
	RESTRICTED CENTER P → A and B T Blocked	P → A = Q, B → T = Q P → B = Q, A → T = Q	Motor Spool
	RESTRICTED CENTER A and B → T P Blocked	P → A = Q, B → T = Q P → B = Q, A → T = Q	Cylinder Spool (With cylinder area ratio close to 1:1)
	RESTRICTED CENTER A and B → T P Blocked	P → A = Q, B → T = Q/2 P → B = Q/2, A → T = Q	Cylinder Spool (With cylinder area ratio close to 2:1)
	RESTRICTED CENTER A and B → T P Blocked	P → A = Q/2, B → T = Q P → B = Q, A → T = Q/2	Cylinder Spool (With cylinder area ratio close to 2:1)
	RESTRICTED CENTER A and B → T P Blocked	P → A = Q, B → T Blocked P → A = Q, A → T = Q	Regenerative Spool

tially two 3-way proportional pressure reducing valves. A simplified diagram of a 3-way proportional pressure reducing valve is show in Figure 9.

Figure 9

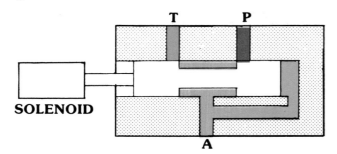

When the solenoid is supplied with an input signal, a corresponding force is created, shifting the spool to the right. This action opens port P to outlet port A allowing oil to pass to its required function. At the same time pressure building in port A is fed back to the opposite end of the spool applying a counterforce to that of the solenoid force. When pressure in port A builds up high enough to equal the force from the solenoid, the spool centers and goes to a no-flow condition. If pressure in port A overcomes solenoid force, the spool shifts left allowing oil to pass to tank until equalibrium is achieved between the two forces, once again allowing the valve to return to a no-flow condition. This is basically representative of the actual pilot head. The only difference is the valve incorporates two proportional force solenoids, and consists of a special 3-piece spool arrangement.

Figure 10

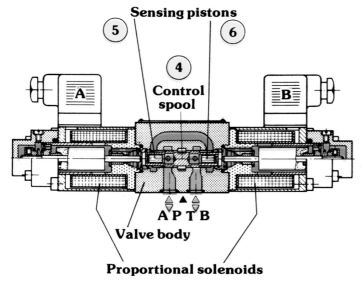

Solenoid force operates directly on this 3-piece arrangement (see Figure 10), which consists of a control spool (4) with a sensing piston (5 and 6) in each end of the spool. Both sensing pistons are free to move in each end of the control spool.

If solenoid B receives an input signal, the force of the solenoid pushes directly against sensing piston 6 which pushes the control spool to the left. This allows oil to flow from port P to A and causes a pressure build-up in port A. At the same time, two radial drilled holes in the control spool allow pressure in port A to feed through the drilled hole furthest to the left, thus acting on sensing piston 5. Since the piston is free to move in the end of the control spool, the pressure pushes the piston out against solenoid A. The pressure force between piston 5 and the control spool work against the force of solenoid B. When pressure in port A increases (to a point where it corresponds to the force of solenoid B), the control spool is moved to the right, closing off the connection from P to A, while holding pressure in port A constant. If the force of solenoid B is reduced, the pressure in port A pushes

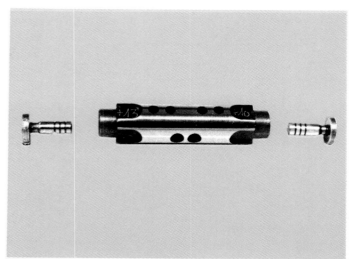

the spool even further to the right. Oil can then drain from A to T until pressure is reduced to where it once again corresponds to the force of the solenoid. If a signal is provided to solenoid A, the process reverses with port P opening up to Port B.

PILOT OPERATED PROPORTIONAL DIRECTIONAL VALVE

Now that the 3-way proportional pressure control valve has been discussed in its entirety, emphasis will now be placed on the total pilot operated proportional directional control valve assembly.

Electronically adjustable pilot operated proportional/directional valves can be either internally or externally piloted from port X. Pilot pressure requirements must be carefully considered. To ensure full opening of the main spool under all operating conditions, a minimum pilot pressure of 435 PSI is required at the pilot valve's inlet. Also, if the valve is internally piloted and the system operates above 1450 PSI, a sandwich mounted pressure reducing valve must be mounted between the main valve and the pilot section. This

serves to protect the pilot section since its maximum operating pressure at port P is limited to 1450 PSI.

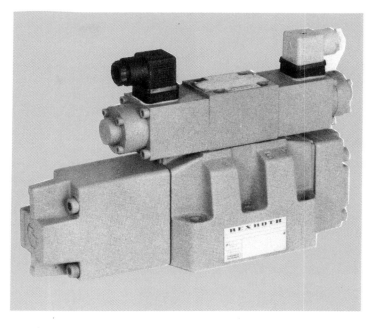

In Figure 11 when both solenoids are deenergized, the main spool (closed center 1:1) is held in its center position by a pretensioned push-pull spring assembly. The push-pull

Figure 11

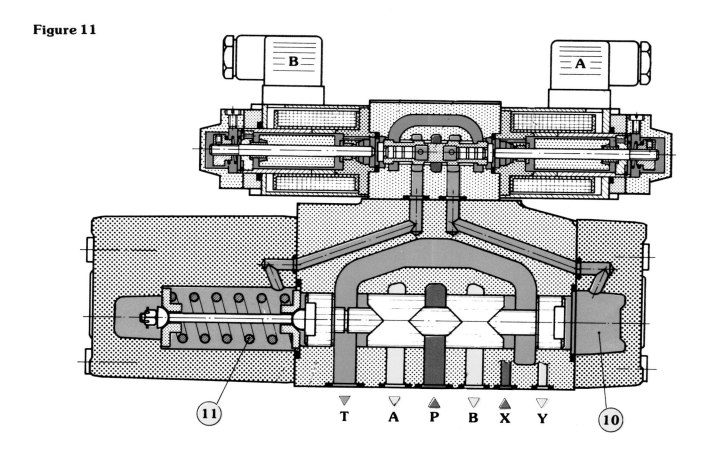

spring assembly is fixed to one end of the spool by means of a rod, with the spring held between two retaining plates, allowing the rod to move freely through the retaining plates. A pressure signal in pilot chamber 10 moves the spool to the left, compressing the spring against the outer cavity of the end cap; or it can be said that a pressure signal in chamber 10 moves the spool to the left pushing on the spring assembly. A pressure signal in pilot chamber 11 moves the spool to the right compressing the spring against the valve housing or pulling on the spring assembly. The spool is "spring centered" until pilot pressure in one of the end caps is sufficient to move the spool to a metering position. The maximum pilot pressure needed in either chamber to cause full movement of the spool is 365 PSI. When solenoid B receives its maximum signal, the solenoid develops 14 lbs. of force and moves the control spool to the right allowing a 365 PSI pressure signal to develop in chamber 10. At the same time, the main spool is moving left a proportional distance to the pressure signal developed by the force solenoid.

Not until the force of the solenoid corresponds to that of the pressure in chamber 10, does the pilot valve hold constant pressure in the pilot chamber. The main spool then maintains a set position which in this case, would cause the spool to travel its full distance. Since the spool moves in proportion to the input signal to solenoid B, the control grooves open progressively to give an increasing flow from P to A and B to T. If a signal is received at solenoid A, the process reverses and the main spool moves to the right allowing oil to pass from P to B and A to T.

Adjustable forces are achievable by the amount of signal supplied, making it possible for various spool positions to be set. Since the control grooves are triangular in shape to provide metering, each time a particular spool position is set a particular orifice is created. Various speeds for motors and cylinders can therefore be set, by the desired amount of signal directed to the valve. With the help of the electronic amplifier, a time controlled movement of the spool can provide smooth starting and stopping of loads. If, for example, the pilot operated proportional directional valve just described were used to accelerate a load to a constant velocity and then decelerate the load to a stop, with a time controlled movement of the spool and the precise metering of the spool, this would be accomplished very smoothly.

Let us consider solenoid B as requiring a 100% signal to determine the set point. When solenoid B receives a 100% signal the signal can be increased with the help of the electronics, from 0 to 100% in a given time rate. This means the force of the solenoid is gradually increasing and a pressure signal is gradually developing in the pilot chamber. At the same time the main spool is proportionally moving from its center position to its set point providing a progressive opening of ports P to A and B to T and accelerating the load to a constant velocity. When decelerating the load to a stop, solenoid B is deenergized decreasing the signal from 100% to zero in a given time rate and proportionally moving the spool back from its set point to its center position bringing the load smoothly to a stop. It should be clear as the signal increases from 0 to 100% or decreases from 100% to 0 that

the spool is also responding to the increasing or decreasing time controlled signal. So, the rate for which the signal is set determines the rate at which the spool reaches its set point. The amount of signal determines the final set point of the valve or the final spool position; which allows us to conclude that:

1. The amount of signal determines the final spool position.
2. With the help of the amplifier, a time controlled signal determines how fast or how slow the spool is going to reach its set point, directly corresponding to acceleration and deceleration.
3. The spool provides metering in both directions.

HYDRAULICALLY OPERATED PROPORTIONAL DIRECTIONAL VALVE

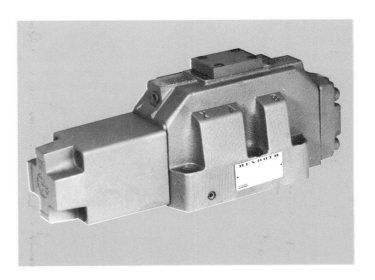

Many applications require the control of a proportional directional valve, but for various reasons designers do not want the electronics involved. A direct pilot operated proportional directional valve without electronics can be used if simple direct control is all that is needed. Its main valve assembly is exactly the same as the electronically controlled pilot operated directional valve. The only difference is, the pilot head is replaced with a connecting plate (see Figure 12).

Instead of having an electronically controlled proportional valve, it becomes a hydraulically controlled proportional directional valve, requiring external pilot pressure.

The connecting plate connects pilot ports A to Y and B to X. Providing pilot pressure at port X causes movement of the spool to the right to give a flow path from P to B and A to T. Pilot pressure at port Y causes the spool to move left giving a

Figure 12

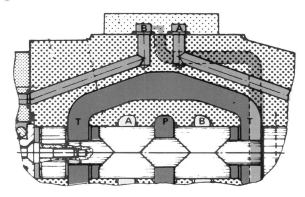

Figure 13

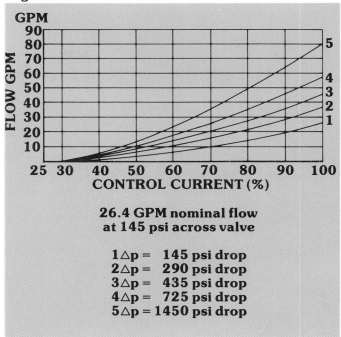

26.4 GPM nominal flow
at 145 psi across valve

$1\triangle p = \quad 145$ psi drop
$2\triangle p = \quad 290$ psi drop
$3\triangle p = \quad 435$ psi drop
$4\triangle p = \quad 725$ psi drop
$5\triangle p = 1450$ psi drop

flow path from P to A and B to T. Movement of the spool is proportional to a pilot pressure between 21 and 365 PSI.

Common pressure controls used to provide pilot pressure are joysticks, footpedals, and pressure reducing valves. (see description & photograph on pages 6-47 and 6-52). Any of these can be mounted away from the main valve, providing easy installation in control consoles and test areas.

TYPICAL OPERATING CURVES FOR PROPORTIONAL DIRECTIONAL VALVES

To provide full control of proportional directional control valves, both the inlet and outlet must be continually metered. In order to achieve good resolution, the maximum possible spool stroke must be utilized. Various nominal flow ratings are available for each particular valve size, and this is made possible by either increasing or decreasing the size or number of the control grooves.

Along with each nominal flow rating, an operating curve has been developed, making sure that the intended use of the spool allows for maximum controllability.

Shown in the operating curve (Figure 13) is a flow to input control current percentage relationship for a 26.4 GPM nominal spool. As an example, let us consider the following. When a 26 GPM flow rate is required, and the valve must operate from a closed condition to a fully open condition, looking at the curve for 100% control current and a flow rate of 25 GPM, the total pressure drop across the valve is 150 PSI. This would mean a pressure drop of 75 PSI from P to A and 75 PSI from B to T, thus utilizing the full spool stroke of the valve. If, however, only a 10 GPM flow rate were required and the same 26.4 GPM nominal spool were used, looking back at the curve at 70% control current, the valve is already passing 10 GPM at 150 PSI pressure. Anything beyond 70%

control current does not effectively utilize the full spool stroke. The valve would virtually pass 10 GPM unmetered providing little or no controllability at that end of the curve. A smaller spool would be needed to give full control.

The curve clearly demonstrates that the purpose of using proportional directional valves is to provide control. In order to provide full control, there must be metering, meaning there must be pressure drop across the valve. The example just given does not consider load conditions. A more detailed explanation of these curves is covered later in Chapter 9.

SPOOL MOVEMENT WITH STEPPED INPUT SIGNAL

When predicting the maximum cyclic rate and load condition of a particular circuit, it is sometimes necessary to consider the physical limiting factor(s) of the valve(s) being used. Although the natural frequency of the system (and therefore the maximum acceleration rate), more often than not becomes the limiting factor, it is important to familiarize yourself with the response characteristics of the valve. (Natural frequency will be explained later in Chapter 9). This is particularly true when process controllers or computers are used to control the time relationships between component functions. By being able to predict a dependable valve response characteristic, computerized control can repetitively anticipate the required starting point of a function. The computer or a controller is then able to start the valve, prior to the occurance of a required function. In this way, deadband is eliminated and cycle rates can be improved.

Figure 14

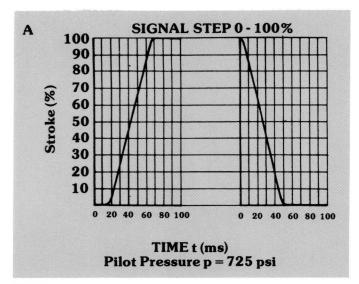

SIGNAL STEP 0 - 100%

Stroke (%)

TIME t (ms)
Pilot Pressure p = 725 psi

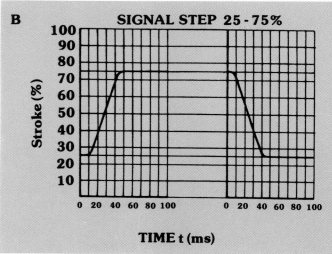

SIGNAL STEP 25 - 75%

Stroke (%)

TIME t (ms)

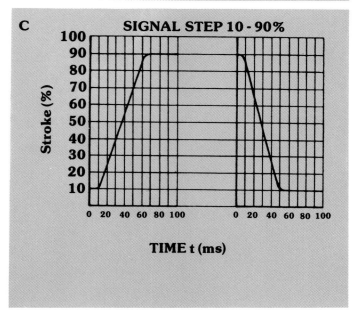

SIGNAL STEP 10 - 90%

Stroke (%)

TIME t (ms)

Figures 14 A, B and C show the fastest possible movement of the spool from one position to another, assuming a stepped (immediate change) input from the electronic amplifier. Figure A shows a change in command from 0 to 100% on the left of the graph and a change in signal from 100% to 0 on the right. Figures B and C are similar, however Figure B shows a 50% stepped signal change (25% to 75%) and Figure C shows an 80% change in command (10% to 90%). It is important to note that the above Figure 14 graphically represent the valve's reaction to a single change in input signal. They show the time required in milliseconds for the valve to reach a desired position, assuming an immediate command to go to that position. This time requirement introduces phase lag in the system which is important when considering a cyclic change in command.

In Figure A the graph shows that the signal for the valve to go from 0 to 100% must endure for approximately 80 milliseconds in order to have the valve achieve 100% opening. Likewise, when the signal is taken away, no new command can be introduced for at least 70 milliseconds if the valve is to fully close. In other words, approximately 150 milliseconds are required to achieve a complete cycle. This means:

$$\frac{1 \text{ cycle}}{150 \text{ milliseconds}} \text{ X } \frac{1000 \text{ ms}}{\text{sec}} = 6.6 \text{ cycle/sec.}$$

Consequently, the fastest the valve can be cycled and achieve 100% response is 6.6 cycles per second. If the signal changes cyclically at a faster rate, the valve can no longer keep up with the command. For instance if the signal is changing at ten cycles per second, the 0 to 100% command to the valve tells the valve to open. The valve, however, may only achieve 50% opening before it gets a new command to close.

FREQUENCY RESPONSE CURVES

In order to further explain the frequency response characteristics of the valve we must first discuss the terms used to describe these measurements of performance.

Frequency: The number of times any action occurs in a given measure of time. More specifically when frequency is assigned in units of Hz, we are speaking of the number of cycles per second. As used in this text, we are referring to the frequency in Hz of the command signal.

Amplitude Response: Is a ratio of output change to input change. Amplitude response is measured in db (decibels).

Decibels: Is the $\log_{10}$ of the ratio of output change to input change. Logarithms are used in order to condense numbers.

Example 1: Input change: 100%
Measured output change: 50%

$$\text{Amplitude Response (db)} = \log_{10} \frac{50\%}{100\%} \times 10 = -3db$$

The negative sign indicates that the output is becoming less since the $\log_{10}$ of a fractional number is negative.

Example 2: Input change: 100%
        Output change: 100%

$$\text{Amplitude Response (db)} = \log \frac{100}{100} \times 10 = 0db$$

Phase lag: The time required for the output to recreate the command of the input. In cyclic occurrences this is normally measured in degrees (refer to Figure 15).

Figure 15

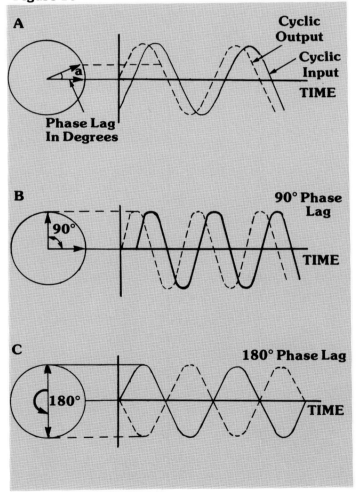

NOTE: At 180° of phase lag the system goes into instability. This is due to the fact that the output does exactly the opposite of the command. In other words, as the command grows larger the output grows smaller and vice versa.

Figure 16

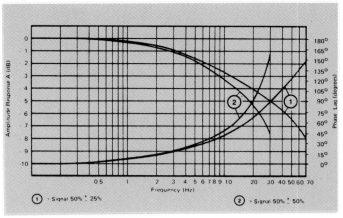

Figure 16 shows a typical frequency response curve for a proportional (or servo) valve. In this graph the top curve (descending curve) shows the relationship between amplitude response and frequency. Curve 1 shows a ± 25% change assuming a 50% input (50% opening P→A and B→T). Curve 2 shows a 50% signal which varies to a high of 100% and a low of 0% cyclically. For this particular valve at an amplitude -3db (50% output) the frequency response is 10 Hz. It is important to note that the industrial standard for representing valves has been placed at the -3db level. The curves clearly indicate, that as the signal comes faster and faster, the amplitude of spool motion in the valve becomes less and less.

The bottom curves in Figure 16 show the relationship between phase lag and frequency. Phase lag as measured in degrees is shown on the right vertical axis of the graph. As the signal increases in frequency the ability of the valve to keep up becomes less and less; in other words the phase lag becomes greater. In comparing curve 1 and 2 (variations in the amount of signal change as previously discussed), it takes considerably longer (more degrees of phase lag) for the spool to catch up as the amount of required spool motion is increased.

ELECTRONICALLY CONTROLLED DIRECT OPERATED PROPORTIONAL DIRECTIONAL VALVES

Up to this point two types of proportional directional valves have been discussed; electronically controlled pilot operated directional valves and hydraulically controlled proportional directional control valves. A third type used for lower flow ranges than those just mentioned is an electronically controlled direct operated proportional directional valve (see Figure 17).

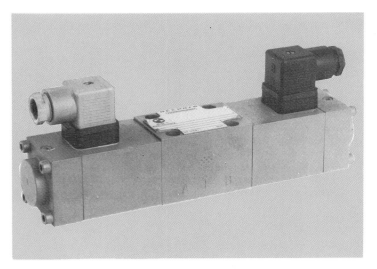

STROKE CONTROLLED SOLENOIDS

Figure 18

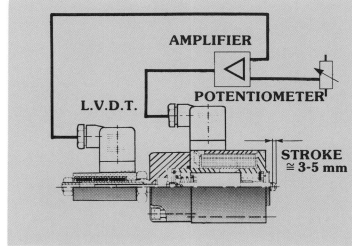

Basic construction of the valve is similar to the 3-way proportional pressure control valve. Both possess force solenoids, but with this third type of valve, the 3-piece spool assembly is replaced with a proportional spool. In this case, when either one of the solenoids receives an input signal, the force from the solenoid operates directly on the spool.

When both solenoids are deenergized the spool is held in its center position by two return springs. If solenoid A receives an input signal, the spool is moved to the right a proportional distance to the signal, allowing oil to progressively flow from P to B and A to T. The same holds true for solenoid B, except the spool moves left against the spring force allowing oil to progressively flow from P to A and B to T.

A proportional solenoid with a built-in positional transducer, sometimes referred to as a LVDT (linear variable differential transformer), is called a stroke controlled solenoid. (See Figure 18). The primary reason these solenoids were developed was to improve valve performance. This was made possible through the LVDT which provides electrical feedback allowing the stroke of the solenoid to be measured more accurately.

Figure 17

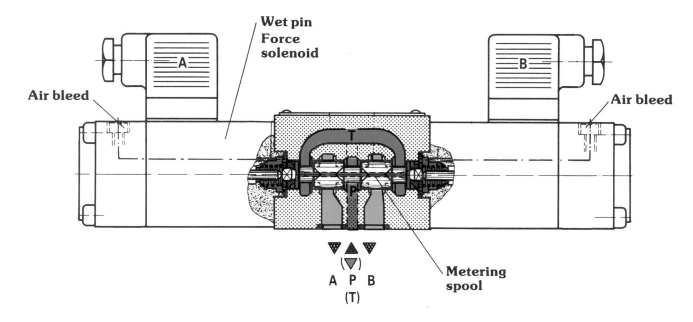

When a proportional solenoid first receives an input signal causing it to respond, a certain percentage of error is generated if direct operation of a process is required. Such would be the case with a directly controlled spool stroke of a directional valve. Since the LVDT is built into the end of the proportional solenoid, it measures what the actual spool position is, and then feeds back a signal to the amplifier. The input signal and feedback signal (or actual value) are then compared electronically in the amplifier. From these two values a corrected signal is generated back to the solenoid to compensate for any error generated. This results in the flow forces on the spool (being counteracted), maintaining a very accurate spool position (orifice flow area).

DIRECT OPERATED PROPORTIONAL DIRECTIONAL VALVE WITH FEEDBACK

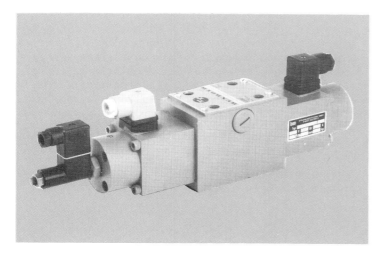

So far discussion about proportional directional valves has been solely based on directional valves with force controlled solenoids. Proportional directional valves that incorporate positional feedback can be directly operated with a high degree of accuracy.

Figure 19 shows a direct operated proportional valve, stroke controlled, with its spool held in center between two centering springs. When solenoid A receives an input signal the spool is moved to the right opening ports P to B and A to T. When solenoid B receives an input signal, the spool moves to the left opening up ports P to A and B to T. The LVDT being mechanically linked to solenoid A is capable of movement ± .117 in. for either direction of the spool. Thus when either solenoid receives a particular input signal the spool moves a corresponding distance. This causes the core of the LVDT (since it is mechanically linked to solenoid A) to move out of equalibrium, which induces a signal and feeds it back to the amplifier relaying to it the actual spool position. The input signal and feedback signal (or actual value) is then compared electronically in the amplifier. From these two values a corrected signal is generated and fed to the solenoid giving a definite position of the spool. If feedback is lost the spool will return to its center position. This safety feature is built into the amplifier.

The main spool, similar to that in the pilot operated proportional directional valve, has control grooves cut into it giving a progressive flow action. Unlike the pilot operated directional there is no need for pilot pressure since the valve is directly operated.

It also should be mentioned that stroke controlled directionals are the most accurate of all proportional directional valves but have one small drawback, their size. A D02 valve size is the largest available at a nominal flow rating of 16 GPM at 150 PSI drop across the valve, whereas pilot operated proportional directionals are available in a D10 valve size with a nominal flow rating of 137 GPM at 150 PSI drop. Stroke controlled proportional directionals could be made larger to handle more flow; however, there is the problem of higher flow forces being generated at higher flow rates. With

Figure 19

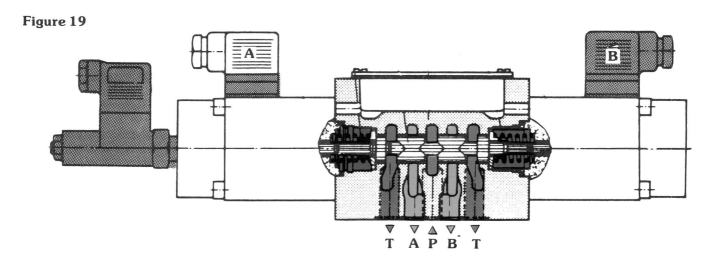

T A P B T

the solenoid acting directly on the spool, the solenoid would have to become very large to counteract the generated flow forces. Although the electrical feedback would try to maintain spool position, the solenoid would eventually run out of force.

DIRECT OPERATED PROPORTIONAL RELIEF VALVE

Direct operated pressure relief valves are poppet type valves

which are electronically adjustable with an LVDT for positional feedback. (See Figure 20.)

The pressure setting of the valve is directly proportional to the input signal. When the proportional solenoid receives an input signal, the stroke of the solenoid pushes directly on a pressure pad. This in turn pushes on a compression spring with the spring pushing on the poppet. The actual position of the pressure pad is then determined by the LVDT feeding a signal back to the amplifier. The feedback signal and input signal are then compared electronically sending a corrected signal back to the solenoid. A definite position of the pressure pad is then maintained. A very accurate spring tension is also maintained which accounts for very accurate pressure settings.

When pressure exceeds the setting of the spring, the poppet opens allowing oil to flow from the pressure port through the spring chamber to the tank. As with the pilot operated proportional pressure relief valve, the pressure setting can be gradually increased or decreased with the help of the amplifier.

Since the pressure can be set very accurately, the valve is used extensively in injection molding applications where injection pressure accuracy is critical. It also can be used as a pilot control for logic elements and pressure relief valves. Maximum flow capabilities are limited by the various pressure ranges, since seat diameter decreases with increased pressure capability.

If power is lost, solenoid force is reduced to zero and the valve's pressure setting is dependent only on the unloading characteristics of the valve.

Figure 20

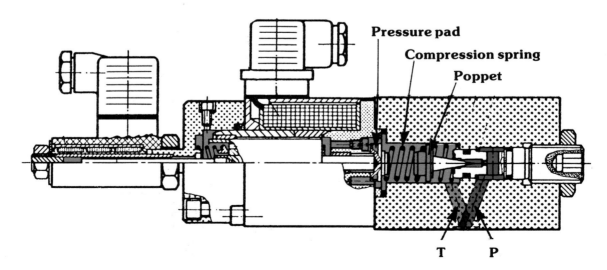

PROPORTIONAL PRESSURE COMPENSATED FLOW CONTROL VALVE

Proportional flow control valves are pressure compensated 2-way valves with the main control orifice being electronically adjustable.

Similar to conventional pressure compensated flow control valves, a proportional pressure compensated flow control valve maintains a constant flow output by keeping the pressure drop across the main control orifice constant. The proportional valve, however, is different in that the control orifice has been modified to work in conjunction with a stroke controlled solenoid.

The 2-way proportional pressure compensated flow control valve consists of an electrically adjustable control orifice which is in series with a pressure reducing valve spool called a hydrostat (see Figure 21.) The hydrostat is placed before the main control orifice and is held in its open position by a light spring. If the input signal to the solenoid is zero, the main control orifice remains in a closed position by means of a light spring force. When the solenoid receives an input signal, the stroke of the solenoid operates directly on the control orifice moving it downward against the spring to an open position, thus allowing oil to pass from A to B (Figure 22.) At the same time the LVDT, as discussed in previous sections, provides the necessary feedback to maintain position. In this case the LVDT is providing feedback to maintain a very accurate orifice setting. Pressure compensation is achieved by feeding a pilot passage from the front of the control orifice to one end of the hydrostat and feeding a pilot passage beyond the control orifice to the opposite end of the hydrostat, assisted by the spring. Load induced pressure at the outlet port or pressure deviations at the inlet port are therefore compensated for by the hydrostat, resulting in a constant output flow.

Figure 22

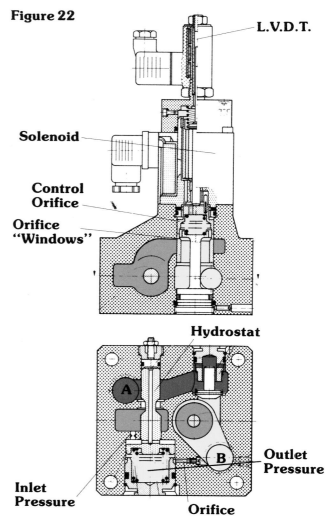

Figure 21

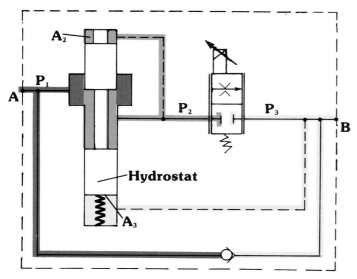

Time controlled opening and closing of the orifice is made possible with the help of the amplifier. For reverse free flow, a check assembly is built into the valve to give a free flow path from B to A.

Proportional flow control valves can also be provided with either linear or progressive flow characteristics. The input signal range is the same for both, except the progressive flow characteristic gives a finer control at the beginning of orifice adjustment.

If power or feedback is lost, solenoid force reduces to zero and the spring pushes the orifice closed. Also, when power is supplied and the feedback polarity is reversed, by mistake, the orifice remains in its most open position.

PROPORTIONAL FLOW LOGIC VALVE

Proportional flow control logic valves are electrically adjustable flow controls that fit into the standardized logic valve cavity. The cover and cartridge are assembled as a single unit, with the cover consisting of a proportional force solenoid and pilot controller (see Figure 23). When an electrical signal is put into an electronic amplifier, the solenoid and controller adjust the pilot pressure supplied from the "A" port side, to change the spool position. The position is then fed back to the amplifier by a linear variable differential transformer (LVDT). This maintains the desired orifice condition for flow from the "A" side to the "B" side of the element. The proportional logic valve is available with either linear or progressive flow characteristics which are adjusted by a 0 to 6 volt or a 0 to 9 volt command signal.

The valve is relatively unaffected by changes in the system pressure; so it can open and close the orifice in the same amount of time. This maximum time can be changed on the amplifier card by adjusting a built-in ramp generator. The amplifier can be used in a variety of ways. An external poten-

tiometer can make the orifice remotely adjustable while the maximum spool acceleration is still limited by this internal ramp, or a limit switch can be used to turn the ramp on and off. In the event of a power failure, the element will return to its normally closed position.

Figure 23

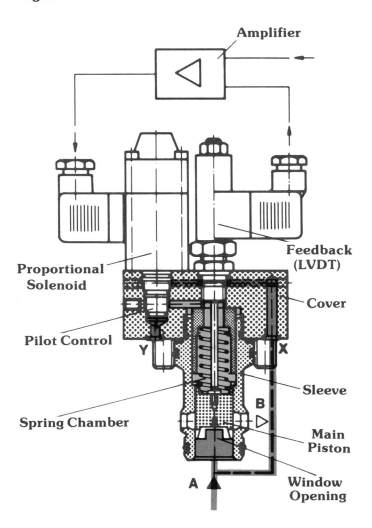

PROPORTIONAL VANE PUMP

The proportional vane pump is a variable volume vane pump which, in principle, has the control operation of a load sensing control (Chapter 6). The pump, therefore, provides a constant output flow as long as there is constant pressure drop across an orifice. Furthermore, when comparing this pump to a standard vane pump with load sensing, both the main throttle orifice and pressure relief valve (which is used for the pressure compensation stage) can be electronically set for flow and pressure control rather than manually setting these adjustments.

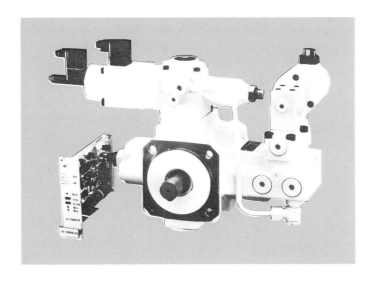

BASIC PUMP OPERATION

The cam ring of the variable volume vane pump (see Figure 24) is held between two control pistons. The larger piston

is assisted by a light spring force which has twice the effective area of the smaller piston, therefore, during start-up the spring force holds the cam ring in an eccentric position allowing the pump to displace fluid. System pressure works on both pistons and as long as the larger piston is not vented to tank, the pump will maintain an output flow. As soon as the larger piston is vented to tank, the smaller piston which is still pressurized, pushes the cam ring in a concentric position providing a no flow condition until system pressure is re-established over both pistons. (For a more detailed explanation on variable volume pumps refer to Chapter 6.)

CONTROL OPERATION

The output flow of the pump is directed through the electronically settable orifice which for any particular setting of the orifice, the pressure drop is maintained constant by the load sensing pump control. The control spool in the pump control works much like a hydrostat in a pressure compensated flow control valve. The control spool (bottom spool in Figure 25) senses pressure at both the inlet and outlet of the proportional orifice. The outlet sensing side of the spool is assisted by an adjustable spring force which is normally set at approximately 150 PSI. The setting of this spring force

Figure 24

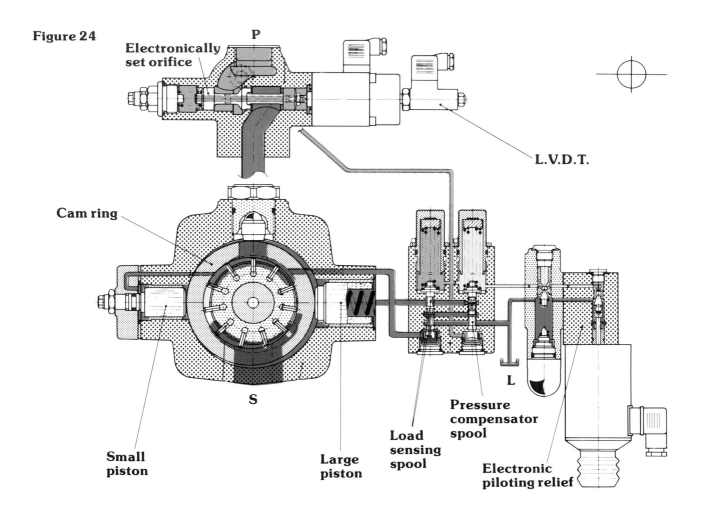

Electronically set orifice

P

Cam ring

L.V.D.T.

Small piston

Large piston

Load sensing spool

Pressure compensator spool

Electronic piloting relief

S

L

Figure 25

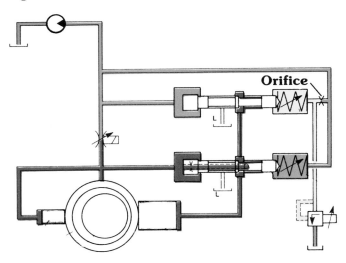

Orifice

determines the pressure drop across the main orifice. By adjusting this differential pressure, an exact flow can be achieved for a given electronic input signal.

Since the control spool is of equal areas at both ends, it modulates to maintain a balance between inlet pressure exposed on the left side and outlet pressure plus spring force on the right. When the orifice is moved in a closing direction, or where there is a loss in load induced pressure, a tendency exists where inlet pressure tries to exceed outlet pressure plus spring force. This cannot happen since the higher inlet pressure pushes the control spool to the right partially unloading the pump's larger control piston. In this way pump flow decreases until inlet pressure again balances outlet pressure plus spring force. Conversely, if the proportional orifice is opened, or if load induced pressure increases, inlet

pressure at the orifice is no longer sufficient. This, however, unbalances the spool so that it moves left loading the pump control piston. The pump flow increases until the resistance to flow at the main orifice reestablishes the modulating pressure balance on the control spool. Due to the fact that the electronically selected flow is influenced by only the orifice area, and the constantly maintained pressure drop, ($GPM = CA \sqrt{\Delta P}$), the pump's volumetric efficiency does not influence the desired flow selection.

PROPORTIONALLY ADJUSTED PRESSURE COMPENSATION

The electronically settable pressure control, and pump's pressure control spool (top spool is Figure 25) works in a manner identical to the electronic proportional relief valve discussed previously. As long as load induced pressure working over the effective area of the pilot poppet does not exceed the adjusted solenoid force, there is no pilot flow, hence there is no ΔP on the orifice located adjacent to spring chamber (in reference to Figure 25). A pressure balance then exists on this spool and the spring force keeps the spool to the left in a "pump loaded" position. When load induced pressure exceeds the setting of the proportional relief valve, the pilot flow across the fixed orifice creates a pressure imbalance on the top control spool. The spool snaps to the right thus pressure compensating the pump.

PROPORTIONAL PRESSURE RELIEF VALVE

The proportional pressure relief valve is direct operated, and is controlled by a force solenoid. The desired amount of signal to the solenoid determines the maximum pressure at which the pump compensates. Likewise, the minimum pressure at which the pump compensates is determined by the setting of the spring adjustment on the pressure control

Figure 26

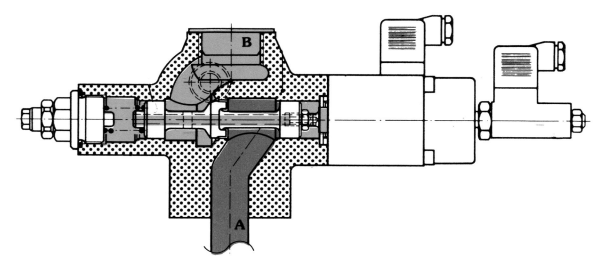

B

A

spool. This generally is set at a low pressure for proper operation of the pump control. The pilot valve can handle flows up to 3.2 GPM which is more than sufficient for draining oil from the control section of the pump. Sandwiched directly beneath the electronic proportional valve, is a mechanically adjustable pressure relief valve. Similar to the proportional pilot operated relief valve with maximum pressure protection, this valve can be adjusted slightly above the setting of the proportional force solenoid. In the case of power failure or high current peaks, there is always maximum protection provided for the pump. The sensitivity of the solenoid requires that the tank port be run separately back to tank, avoiding any back-pressure that otherwise might develop in the valve.

ELECTRONICALLY ADJUSTABLE MAIN ORIFICE

The main orifice (Figure 26) is a spool type variable orifice controlled by a proportional solenoid with an LVDT for positional feedback. The orifice is shown in a closed condition. As the desired amount of signal is increased, the solenoid pushes directly on the spool which is counteracted by a light spring at the opposite end. If power or feedback is lost, the force of the spring pushes the spool back to a closed condition. At each position of the spool the orifice proportionally opens allowing the output flow of the pump to pass from port A to B.

For maximum protection of the pump, a quick acting mechanically adjustable relief valve can be obtained in the housing of the orifice. This is fitted just before the inlet side of the orifice (A side) so that high pressure peaks can be avoided.

PROPORTIONAL PRESSURE CONTROL SYMBOLS (WITH FORCE SOLENOIDS)

SYMBOL		DESCRIPTION
Without Maximum Pressure Protection	**With Maximum Pressure Protection**	**Electronically Adjustable**
		Direct Operated, Pressure Relief Valve, (Pilot head)
		Pilot Operated, Pressure Relief Valve, Internal Pilot, External Drain
		Pilot Operated, Pressure Relief Valve, External Pilot, External Drain
		Pilot Operated, Pressure Reducing Valve, External Drain
		Pilot Operated, Pressure Reducing Valve, External Drain, Reverse Free Flow Check

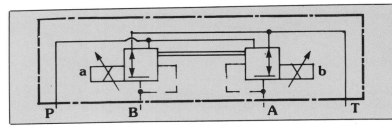

3-Way Pressure Reducing Valve (Pilot head for pilot operated directional valves)

PROPORTIONAL DIRECTIONAL VALVE SYMBOLS (WITH FORCE SOLENOIDS)

SYMBOL	DESCRIPTION
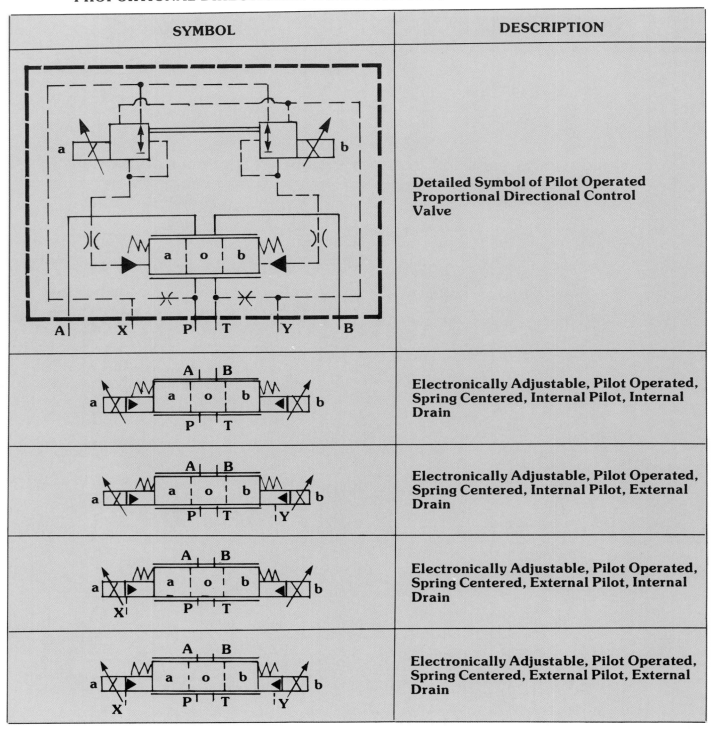	**Detailed Symbol of Pilot Operated Proportional Directional Control Valve**
	Electronically Adjustable, Pilot Operated, Spring Centered, Internal Pilot, Internal Drain
	Electronically Adjustable, Pilot Operated, Spring Centered, Internal Pilot, External Drain
	Electronically Adjustable, Pilot Operated, Spring Centered, External Pilot, Internal Drain
	Electronically Adjustable, Pilot Operated, Spring Centered, External Pilot, External Drain

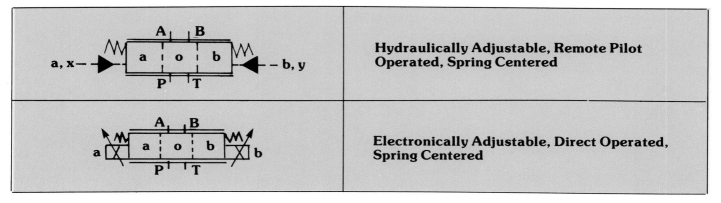

SYMBOL	DESCRIPTION
	Electronically Adjustable, Direct Operated Pressure Relief Valve, with Feedback
	Electronically Adjustable, Pressure Compensated Flow Control Valve, with Feedback of Main Flow Orifice Setting
	Electronically Adjustable, Direct Operated Directional Valve, with Feedback of Spool Setting
	Electronically Adjustable Flow Logic Valve, with Feedback of Flow Orifice Setting

PROPORTIONAL VALVE SYMBOLS (WITH POSITIONAL FEEDBACK)

SYMBOL	DESCRIPTION
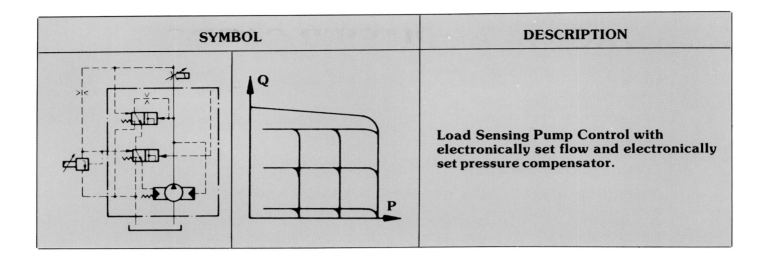	**Load Sensing Pump Control with electronically set flow and electronically set pressure compensator.**

CHAPTER 8
ELECTRONIC AMPLIFIER CARDS

ELECTRONICS

In order to operate any proportional solenoid, two major electronic devices are needed: an amplifier and a power supply. The electronic amplifier, often referred to as an amplifier card, provides the driving current to the proportional solenoid and interfaces the control signal. The power supply converts 120 volts AC power to 24 volts DC power which is needed for the card, (see Figure 1).

For each particular proportional valve there is a specific amplifier card that is needed to operate the valve. The following discussion will be based solely on these amplifier cards.

Figure 1

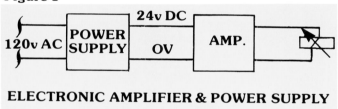

ELECTRONIC AMPLIFIER & POWER SUPPLY

To clarify the different types of amplifiers, the first one to be discussed will be referred to as a Type VT-2000. It is primarily used for controlling pilot operated proportional pressure relief and pressure reducing valves. Other uses are to control single solenoid two position pilot operated proportional directional valves as well as proportional pumps and motors, all possessing force solenoids.

Amplifier Type VT-2000 being the simplest in internal electronic circuitry, also requires the least amount of wiring. Figure 2 is a functional block diagram of the VT-2000.

The user should mainly concern himself with how to wire the card and how to use the card adjustments in conjunction with the valve, rather than be overly concerned with the internal electronic circuitry of each block. The diagram shows an input and output side where all external wiring takes place. Anything in between these two lines, designated by the dashed lines, is already on the amplifier card. Beginning with the input side; this is where power is supplied and where a command signal must be provided. When supplying power to the card a specific polarity must be observed, meaning the positive lead from the power supply must be connected to the proper terminal on the card as must be the negative lead. If these leads are accidently switched, internal damage to the

Figure 2

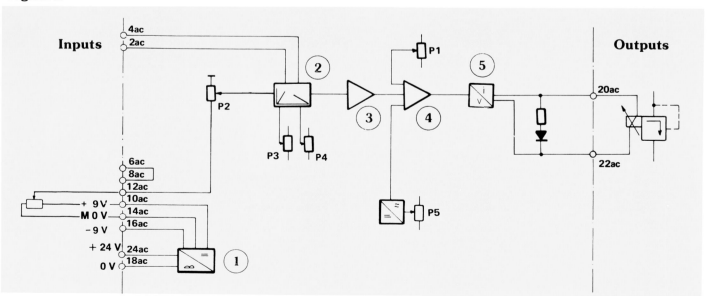

card generally does not occur due to the input being diode protected; however, the card will obviously not be able to operate properly.

In order to operate the valve, a low level command signal must be provided on the input side. This is achieved by providing reference voltage terminals +9V, 0V, −9V, at the points where either a switch or potentiometer can be added. The potentiometer is preferred more often than the switch because it is an electrical device that can provide an adjustable command signal by simply turning a knob. Looking at the output side, terminals are provided for wiring to the force solenoid. Also, only one force solenoid can be controlled by the amplifier at one time.

INTERNAL CIRCUITRY

As was stated previously, anything between the dashed lines is already on the card. Each block in the diagram represents a specific function.

As power is supplied to the card (terminal 24 ac (+), terminal 18 ac (−)), the first block it encounters is voltage filtering and regulation (1). Since the supply of the 24V DC is not necessarily consistently smooth or steady, voltage regulation is used to provide a fixed known level of voltage (designated by terminals 10 ac (+9V), 14 ac (0V), and 16 ac (−9V)) which is used for the rest of the circuitry. Voltage regulation also provides stability with respect to temperature to keep the card accurate over a wide temperature range: as ambient temperature varies, the set point on the card will not vary.

From these known levels of voltage referred to earlier as reference voltage terminals, a potentiometer or switch can be wired, providing the required command signal. Looking back at Figure 2 a potentiometer is shown wired to the card. One leg of the potentiometer is connected to terminal 10 ac (+9V), the other leg of the potentiometer is connected to terminal 14 ac (0V) with the wiper or output of the potentiometer connected to terminal 12 ac. This provides a command signal range from 0 to +9V which can be adjusted by turning the potentiometer.

As the signal proceeds from 12 ac, the second block it encounters is called a ramp generator (2). The input command signal goes into the ramp generator and comes out as a linear change with respect to time. This is the generator's sole function. The most important thing to remember about the ramp generator is the signal from the generator does not change in magnitude, it reproduces the magnitude of the input at a given time rate. In other words, if the input goes from 0 to 100%, the output goes from 0 to 100% but at a given time rate. Likewise, when the input goes from 100% to 0 the output goes from 100% to 0 at a given time rate. The ramp generator will not allow the output to move any faster than the ramp adjustment setting. Ramp adjustments will be discussed later.

The output of the ramp generator then proceeds to the next

block, which is the matching amplifier (3). This is basically an amplification stage.

The fourth block is a summing amplifier (4). This block adds together three signals; one signal from the dither oscillator, a signal from adjustment P1, and the input signal. The dither oscillator generates a modulating signal in order to minimize solenoid hysteresis. The other signal from P1 is a pilot or bias current setting.

The last block is a power or output amplifier (5) which has two basic functions. First, it is responsible for amplifying the signal up to the power level needed to drive the solenoid. Secondly, it provides current feedback to continue stable operation over changes in coil temperature and wiring losses.

AMPLIFIER ADJUSTMENTS

Every amplifier card has a number of adjustments on it that need to be set for proper operation of the valve. These are most often referred to as presets which are actually multiturn potentiometers.

ADJUSTMENTS P3 AND P4

As previously mentioned, the ramp generator can be adjusted. A VT-2000 has two ramp adjustments: one is designated P3 for setting the ramp up time (or the time it takes for an increasing signal), and one is designated P4 which is for setting the ramp down time (or the time it takes for a decreasing signal). Having two separate ramp adjustments, independent ramp times can be set. If, for example, the situation calls for the use of a proportional pressure relief valve and a slow pressure build-up is required with quick unloading of a pump, by setting P3 for a slow ramp up time the maximum pressure setting of the valve can take as long as 5 seconds. By setting P4 for a fast ramp down time, the pump can be quickly unloaded. Likewise, P3 can be set so pressure builds up quickly and P4 can be set so the pump unloads slowly.

Figure 3

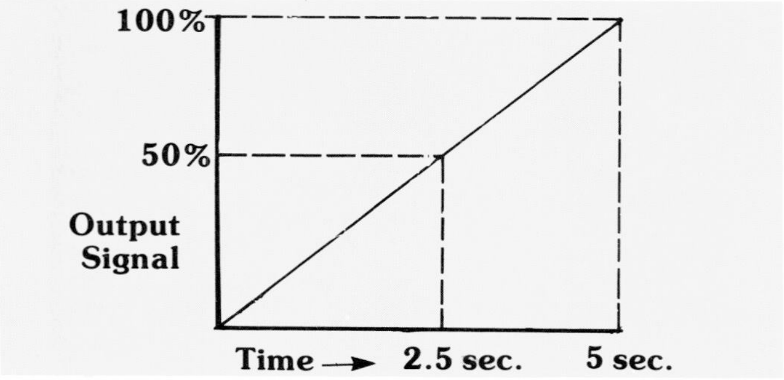

Acceleration, deceleration; and decompression can be achieved through the use of the ramp generator. The given ramp time range for the amplifier card is from 0.1 second minimum to 5 seconds maximum. The maximum 5 second time limit, however, is achievable only by providing a full +9 volt signal to the input of the ramp generator. If a signal is provided lower than +9V, the ramp time will not be achieved in the full 5 seconds as intended. Figure 3 demonstrates this relationship more fully.

At 100% signal a maximum ramp time of 5 seconds is achieved. By changing the input signal to 50% and keeping the ramp time set at its maximum value, the ramp time reduces to the change in signal. It also should be mentioned if no ramp time is required, terminals 4 ac and 2 ac can be bridged by either a jumper wire or a switch. By jumping 4 ac and 2 ac the signal bypasses the ramp generator completely. This means the output follows the input, or the valve will respond directly to the potentiometer setting.

PRESETS P1 AND P2

Figure 4

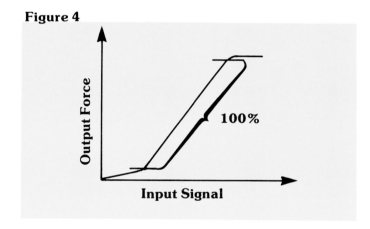

The force out of a proportional valve is linear only over a particular range (Figure 4). Proportional valves are designed to work over this linear range and anything below the nonlinear point on the curve becomes unpredictable. To overcome this, preset P1 (which is a bias current setting) adds a signal to boost the input signal to that useable linear portion of the curve. This allows the force output of the valve to work only over this useable linear range. Because this amplifier is not exclusively used for proportional pressure relief valves, and because this nonlinear point differs for other components that require the use of this amplifier card, P1 is capable of adjusting a bias current from 0 to 300 mA. To further demonstrate this point, a performance curve for a proportional pressure relief valve is given in Figure 5.

From the figure it can be seen that a portion of the curve is called dead range or deadband. Dead range is where the setting of P1 is of the utmost importance. For example, if P1 is set at zero and a potentiometer is used to provide the com-

Figure 5

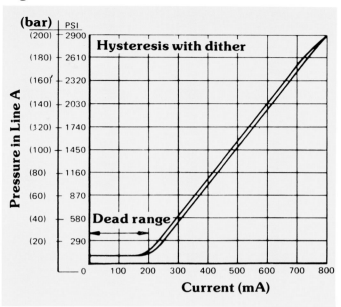

mand signal, as the potentiometer is turned the valve will not build pressure until the point is reached where the signal provides approximately 180 mA. The signal must first travel through the dead range before the valve responds. In order to boost the input signal to its proper starting point, P1 has to be adjusted to provide approximately 180 mA signal. In this way, when one first begins to turn a potentiometer, the valve immediately starts to build pressure. (P1 would be set at approximately 180 mA only assuming the lowest set pressure related to flow is about 100 PSI.)

To set the maximum pressure of the valve, preset P2 must be used. P2 is a maximum current limitation adjustment, which is accessible on the front face of the card. P2 can be adjusted to limit the command signal, so if the full pressure range for the proportional pressure relief valve in Figure 5 is desired and assuming P1 is set for 180 mA, P2 would have to be set for its maximum value of 800 mA. If a lower pressure setting of the valve is required, P2 can be adjusted accordingly (Figure 6). Also, since current is directly related to the pressure setting of the valve, pressure in the system can be adjusted by presets P1 and P2 while reading the pressure gauge at the same time. 180 mA signal directly corresponds to approximately 100 PSI on the curve just as 800 mA directly corresponds to 2900 PSI. The same holds true for any other limits that are desired. For example, if a particular application calls for a maximum pressure of 2500 PSI and the minimum pressure setting of the valve related to flow is 150 PSI, the lower and upper limits can once again be established by setting P1 and P2. P1 would be adjusted to set the lower 150 PSI limit with P2 being adjusted to set the upper 2500 PSI limit. Also with the use of a potentiometer, the valve would be capable of variable adjustment between 150 to 2500 PSI without exceeding the upper limit.

Another thing that must be considered when adjusting P1

and P2 is the fact that P1 adds a signal to boost the input signal; therefore, the setting of P1 adds to the setting of P2. If P1 is set at zero, and P2 is adjusted for some maximum pressure, then P1 is adjusted to its minimum pressure setting. The maximum pressure setting of the valve will increase by the setting of P1 (see Figure 7); therefore, it is necessary to first establish P1 and then set P2 for its maximum value. This is accomplished by keeping the command signal at zero and setting P1 for the required bias current. P2 can then be set by setting the command signal at 100% and setting the maximum current as desired. The following curves will illustrate these conditions more fully.

Figure 6

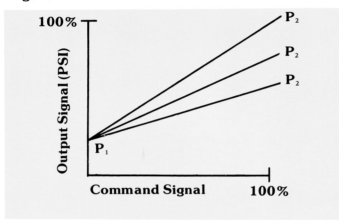

When P1 is set for its minimum bias current, P2 can be increased or decreased to the maximum current desired without changing the bias current setting. Relating this to the proportional pressure relief valve, and knowing P2 sets the maximum current level or maximum pressure, the maximum pressure can be increased or decreased without changing the minimum pressure setting of the valve.

Figure 7

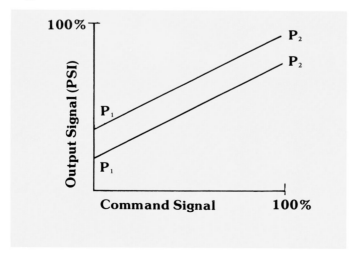

Changing the setting of P1 when P2 is already set for its maximum pressure, changes the entire setting of the valve. When P1 (the bias current) is increased, it can be seen from Figure 7 that the range or span stays the same, but the range is at increased lower and upper limits. The pressure, for example, would increase from a minimum pressure of 100 PSI to a minimum pressure of 200 PSI. If the maximum pressure of the valve was originally set for 2500 PSI, it would also increase 100 PSI so that the final setting would be 2600 PSI.

PRESET P5

Preset P5 is the adjustment for the dither oscillator mentioned earlier. P5 is preset at the factory and does not need to be adjusted.

HYSTERESIS

For any man-made device there is a certain percentage of error. The amount of error for proportional valves is expressed as the hysteresis (%) of the valve and for most good proportional valves does not exceed 6% (±3%). Knowing what the hysteresis of the valve is, a direct relationship can be made as to the accuracy of the valve. If the hysteresis of a particular proportional valve is less than 3%, it can be said that the accuracy of the valve is better than 3% error.

There are various reasons for hyteresis in proportional valves, but the primary cause is friction, such as solenoid, spool, and poppet friction. For example, hysteresis for a proportional valve can be defined as the difference in output signal when the input is increased to a set point and then decreased from a higher value to that same set point. Relating this to the spool position of a proportional directional valve, hysteresis can be defined as the difference in the spool position when approaching the set point from two different directions (see Figure 8).

The "repeatability" of a proportional valve is another term often referred to when describing the valve's dynamic characteristics. Repeatability is a measure of exactness with which motion or position can be duplicated. It can also be defined as the error in the output when approaching the set point in the same direction. In other words, if one shifts a proportional directional valve twice in the same direction, the valve will not return to the exact same position both times. Repeatability is very often one half of hysteresis and will never be worse than hysteresis.

To help reduce hysteresis it was mentioned earlier in the internal circuitry section that the dither oscillator provides a modulating signal in order to minimize valve hysteresis. The following curves (Figure 9) of a proportional pressure relief valve demonstrate the difference between a valve with hysteresis and one without.

Figure 8

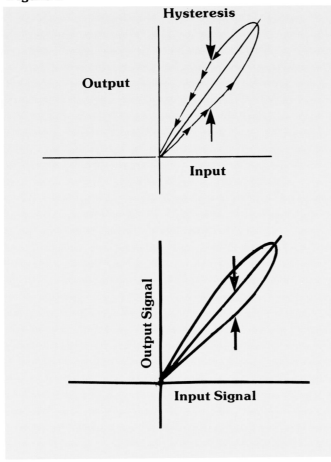

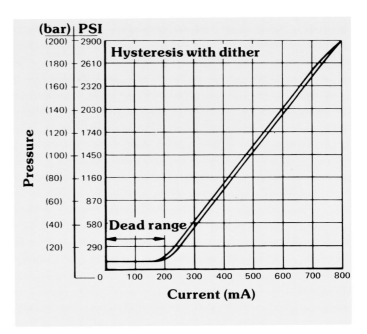

Although all electronic amplifiers have this dither feature built-in, the curves clearly demonstrate that there can be

Figure 9

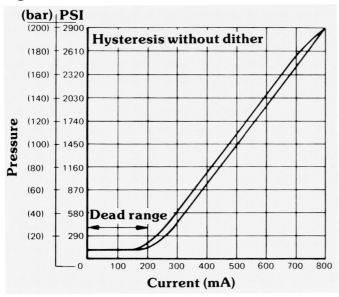

quite a substantial difference in pressure settings when a dither signal is excluded. With a dither signal the difference between an increasing pressure setting and decreasing setting is about ± 2.5%. Without the dither signal the difference is about ± 4.5%.

TYPICAL WIRING SCHEMES FOR VT 2000 CARDS

The following diagrams demonstrate some typical wiring schemes for proportional pressure control valves.

For simple on-off control a single pole double throw switch can be used to provide the required command signal (Figure 10). The switch is shown in the off condition; therefore, the minimum pressure setting of the valve is dependent on P1. When the switch is thrown to provide the command signal, the valve builds pressure to its maximum limit dependent on the setting of P2, and the time it takes depends on the setting of P3 for ramp up time. When the switch is thrown back to provide zero signal, the valve decreases in pressure dependent on the setting of P4 which is the ramp down time. This is one of the simplest wiring schemes for achieving a single maximum pressure setting when a controlled time of the setting is required.

The most common wiring scheme to provide a variable command signal quickly and conveniently, is through the use of a potentiometer (see Figure 11). It was mentioned earlier that a potentiometer provides a variable command signal by simply turning a knob. A potentiometer, when excited by DC or AC voltage, provides a proportional voltage versus displacement relationship. The output signal of the potentiometer is linear

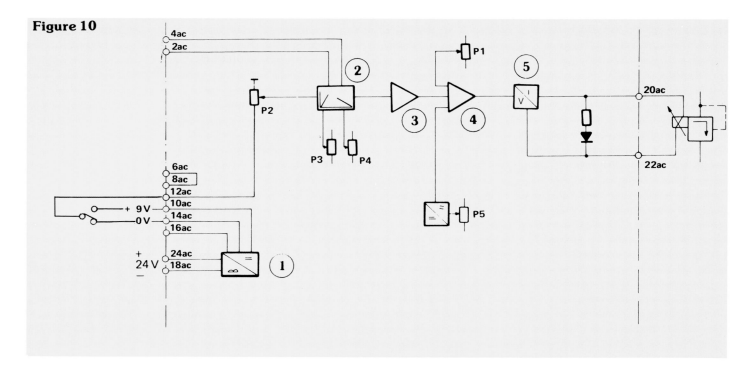

Figure 10

to the rotation of the potentiometer. As shown in the diagram, the external potentiometer allows the operator to have full control of the pressure range of the valve as long as P2 is set for its maximum current. Since P2 is in series with the potentiometer, P2 can determine the maximum pressure limit, whereas the potentiometer can be adjusted to whatever pressure is required but not in excess of P2's setting.

Also, if the ramp generator is turned off, the operator can control how fast pressure increases or decreases by how fast

he turns the potentiometer. When the ramp generator is on, it does not matter how fast the potentiometer is turned because the ramp generator will allow the signal to reproduce only at the time set. Obviously, one can turn the potentiometer slower than the ramp setting. This arrangement is very useful in test areas since the potentiometer can be mounted in a remote location away from the test with the option of controlling pressure with or without the ramp time. It also should be mentioned that the external potentiometer should have a resistance of no lower than 500 Ω or no higher than 5000 Ω.

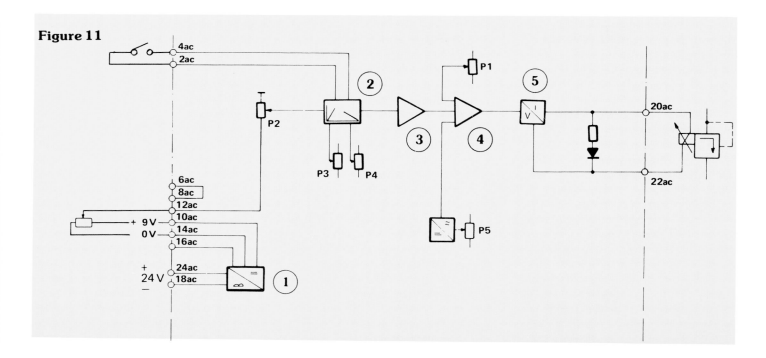

Figure 11

DIGITAL PRESSURE SELECTION

To cycle back and forth from a number of different pressure settings, and to maintain these settings without having to hand adjust a potentiometer each time a different pressure setting is required, the following wiring scheme can be used (Figure 12).

From the diagram it can be seen that there are four potentiometers in parallel and four switches in series. Each potentiometer or preset can be adjusted separately to provide a particular command signal, which in turn can provide four separate pressure settings. It also should be noted that since the switches are wired in series, an order of priority is present. If sw-1 is thrown to provide a signal from P1 and then sw-2 is thrown to provide a signal from P2, switch sw-2 will have priority and the signal from sw-1 will have nowhere to proceed to since sw-2 broke that part of the circuit. Switch sw-4 will have the highest priority; therefore, if sw-4 is thrown to provide a signal from P4 it does not matter what position any of the other switches are in. The signal from P4 will always proceed first. Although four potentiometers are shown wired in parallel, as many as ten potentiometers may be wired in parallel with ten separate switches wired in series to provide various command signals. The important thing to remember when wiring potentiometers in parallel, is that the minimum resistance to provide the low level signal must not be any lower than 500 Ω. Kirchoff's Law for resistors wired in parallel states: "the total resistance is the reciprocal of the combined resistance which equals the sum of the reciprocals of each individual branch."

$$\frac{1}{R_T} = \frac{1}{R_1} + \frac{1}{R_2} + \frac{1}{R_3} + \ldots$$

If, for example, the four potentiometers in the diagram each have a resistance of 5000 Ω the total resistance can be calculated from Kirchoff's Law.

$$\frac{1}{R_T} = \frac{1}{5000\ \Omega_1} + \frac{1}{5000\ \Omega_2} + \frac{1}{5000\ \Omega_3} + \frac{1}{5000\ \Omega_4}$$

$$\frac{1}{RT} = \frac{4}{5000\ \Omega}$$

$$R_T = \frac{5000\ \Omega}{4} = 1250\ \Omega$$

The four potentiometers in parallel have a total resistance of 1250 Ω, which is well above the required 500 Ω minimum. It can easily be seen that if more than ten potentiometers are wired in parallel, the minimum of 500 Ω is exceeded.

$$\frac{1}{R_T} = \frac{1}{5000\ \Omega_1} + \frac{1}{5000\ \Omega_2} + \frac{1}{5000\ \Omega_3} \ldots + \frac{1}{5000\ \Omega_{11}}$$

$$\frac{1}{R_1} = \frac{11}{5000\ \Omega}$$

$$R_T = 455\ \Omega$$

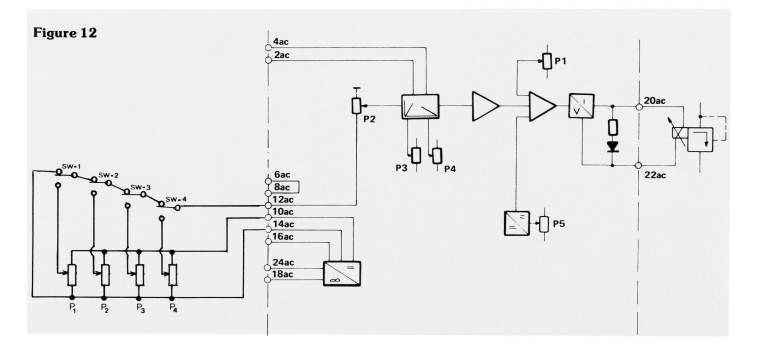

Figure 12

Ten potentiometers wired in parallel each having a resistance of 5000 Ω would equal 500 Ω, the exact minimum requirement. These three wiring schemes are just a few of the possible schemes that can be applied.

ELECTRONIC AMPLIFIER (VT-3000)

The second type of amplifier which will be discussed is a VT-3000 amplifier card. It is exclusively used to control pilot operated proportional directional control valves and electronically controlled hydrostatic transmissions.

Amplifier Type VT-3000 basically operates the same as the VT-200 except that it is built to provide a signal to two proportional force solenoids and has some added internal circuitry providing additional application uses.

Referring to the figure 13, anything between the dashed lines is already on the card. External wiring of switches, potentiometers, and solenoids is done at the numbered terminals.

INTERNAL CIRCUITRY

In reference to Figure 13, + 24 volts DC power must be supplied to the card (terminal 32 ac (+) and terminal 26 ac ( )). The first block it encounters is voltage regulation and filtering (1). This is the same voltage regulation block that the VT-2000 card has. It provides a smooth steady fixed level of known voltage designated by terminals 20 c for +9 volts, 20 a for 0 volts, and 26 ac for −9 volts, to provide a signal to the next block which is the ramp generator (2). The added presets P1, P2, P3 and P4 and relays d1, d2, d3 and d4 must be used. For ease of explanation, these presets and relays will be discussed later. At this point, let us imagine that a signal is provided ± 9 volt terminals through any one of the four presets P1 to P4 to the input of the ramp generator. As with the VT-2000, the signal goes into the ramp generator and comes out as a linear change with respect to time. The major difference is that instead of having separate ramp times for up and down, the generator

Figure 13

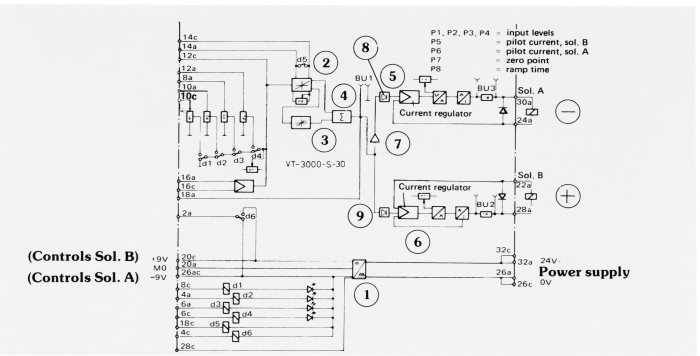

only has one ramp time for setting the speed with which the spool opens and closes. This relates directly to accelerating and decelerating times for the load. Since the signal can be controlled, the valve is controlled as to how fast or slow and how far to open or close. In this way smooth stopping and starting of the load is achieved. These conditions will be discussed later as will typical acceleration and deceleration curves.

The output of the ramp generator then proceeds to the next block which is called the function generator (3). The function generator is an added function which compensates for deadband in proportional directional valves. The primary causes for deadband in proportional directional valves can be linked to three sources:

1. Solenoid friction.
2. Spring bias; springs to hold proportional spools in their center position are under compression and these forces have to be overcome.
3. Spool overlap, which as stated previously, is precisely 11% for all proportional spools.

To show more fully what the function generator does, the following condition will be considered. If the function generator was not included in the amplifier circuitry and a proportional directional was shifted in both directions, it would take a significant amount of input signal before the valve would produce an output flow in either direction (see Figure 14).

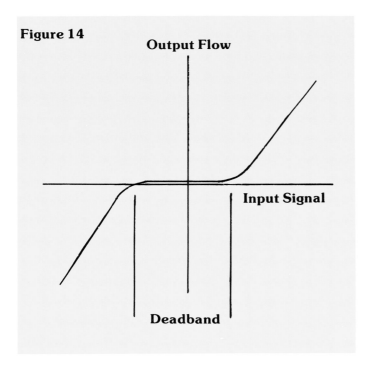

Figure 14

Output Flow

Input Signal

Deadband

The reasons for this considerable amount of signal being needed are those just mentioned: solenoid friction, spring bias, and spool overlap (11%), which together create a significant amount of deadband around zero.

In a more practical sense, if a potentiometer is used to pro-

vide the command signal and one turns it, nothing will happen until the point is reached where the potentiometer provides enough signal to overcome this amount of deadband. This is obviously not a good condition and the function generator compensates for this deadband by abruptly jumping the input signal up to the linear portion of the curve (see Figure 15).

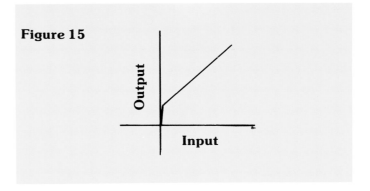

Figure 15

Output

Input

The rest of the card basically operates similar to the VT-2000 with block number (4) being the summing unit for adding the signal from the ramp generator and function generator. Block numbers (5) and (6) are the power amplifiers for solenoids A and B. It is important to note that unlike the VT-2000, negative and positive voltage (0 to ± 9V) must be provided in order to shift a 3 position 4-way proportional valve in both directions. In other words, to operate solenoid A, a negative voltage command signal must be provided, and to operate solenoid B a positive voltage command signal must be provided. The inverter stage (7) and diodes (8 and 9) allow for the positive and negative voltage's direction control.

1. Diode 8 allows positive voltage through.
2. Diode 9 allows positive voltage through.
3. Inverter stage changes negative voltage to positive voltage.

When a negative command signal is provided, diode 9 rejects it since it only allows a positive signal through in the direction of the arrow. The inverter changes negative voltage to positive voltage allowing it to pass through diode 8 to operate solenoid A. Likewise, when a positive command signal is provided, the inverter changes positive voltage to negative voltage so that diode 8 rejects it and the signal proceeds through diode 9 to operate solenoid B.

PRESETS AND RELAYS

From the lower part of the diagram it can be seen that there is a section of relays indicated by a rectangular box ([⊿]), numbered from d1 to d6. Also shown are the contacts of each particular relay which are also numbered from d1 through d6 in various locations throughout the amplifier. To energize any particular relay, 24 volts DC must be supplied to terminals 8 c, 4 a, 6 a, 6 c, 18 c and 4 c. This can be done by coming directly off terminal 28 c (terminal 28 c is a 24 volt

DC terminal) to a switch (or switches) and connecting the output of the switch to the particular relay terminal (see Figure 16).

In series with each relay d1 through d4 is a light emitting diode (LED) indicating when the relay is energized. These are numbered d1 through d4 on the front face of the card.

Moving to the upper part of the diagram, four adjustable presets (which are accessible on the front of the card) are numbered P1 through P4 and are used to limit the ± 9V signal. Also accessible on the front of the card is P8 which is used to set the ramp time.

PRESETS P1 - P4

In order to provide the command signal; any one of the relays d1 through d4 must be energized. In reference to Figure 16 it should be noted that the contacts of relays d1 through d4 are in series just below each preset P1 though P4. As was discussed earlier for the VT-2000, when switches or contacts are wired in series, the one having the highest priority (when activated) will always allow the signal to pass through regardless of the other contacts being activated.

In this case preset P4 has the highest priority. When relay d4 is energized, LED d4 comes on, and contact d4 breaks from the series wiring sequence and connects with the output of preset P4, thus allowing the signal to proceed to the input of the ramp generator and then through the rest of the card to

its required solenoid. When relay d4 is de-energized, the LED goes off and the signal decreases to zero. Likewise, when relay d3 is energized, LED d3 comes on and contact d3 connects to the output of P3 allowing the signal to proceed through the card to its required solenoid. The priority chain continues on respectively with preset P2 corresponding to relay d2 and LED d2. Preset P1 is lowest in priority and corresponds to relay d1 and LED d1.

The simple wiring scheme in Figure 16 below shows how these presets and relays work in relationship with a 3 position 4-way proportional directional control valve. First, one should notice that a wire is connected from 20 c to 10 c to provide a +9 volts and a wire is connected from 26 ac to 10 a to provide −9 volts. (Remember positive voltage is required to operate solenoid B and negative voltage is required to operate solenoid A). By energizing relay d1, contact d1 pulls in sending a signal through the card to solenoid B moving the proportional spool from its center position to a distance set by P1. In this case P1 can be said to be set to provide +9 volts, thereby allowing the spool to travel its full distance in one direction. By de-energizing relay d1 the spool travels back to its center position. When relay d2 is energized contact d2 pulls in sending a signal to solenoid A moving the spool in the opposite direction, a distance set by P2. Likewise, the spool returns to its center position when relay d2 is de-energized. One must also remember that presets P1 and P2 can be adjusted to limit the ± 9V value thus limiting the spool stroke. If other settings of the value are required, presets P3 and P4 can be used. Typical wiring schemes showing all the presets in use will be discussed later.

Figure 16

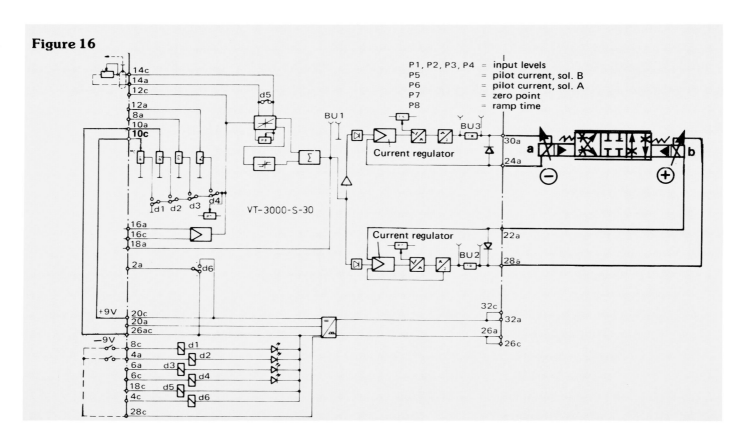

P1, P2, P3, P4	= input levels
P5	= pilot current, sol. B
P6	= pilot current, sol. A
P7	= zero point
P8	= ramp time

RAMP ADJUSTMENT - P8

The VT-3000 amplifier card only has one ramp setting (P8) which is usually settable within a range of .03 to 5 seconds. The spool opening and closing time is therefore controlled by the setting of P8 if required. In the example just given, if the ramp time is set for its maximum value of 5 seconds and relay d1 is energized, the signal will increase from 0 to 100% in 5 seconds moving the spool from its center position to its set point in 5 seconds. Likewise, when d1 is de-energized the signal will decrease from 100% to 0 in 5 seconds and the spool will move from its set point back to its center position.

If no ramp time is required, relay d5 can be energized which closes contacts d5 by bypassing the ramp generator completely, or terminals 14 c and 14 a can be bridged with either a switch or jumper wire. If an external time potentiometer is needed, it can be connected to 14 a and 14 c, but the potentiometer of the card must be adjusted to its maximum ramp time, so as not to allow the possibility of the external potentiometer exceeding a time longer than that of the potentiometer on the card.

If, for example, the ramp setting on the card is set for 50% and the external time potentiometer is at its maximum time setting, the signal will take the path of least resistance and the desired time value will not be achieved. It is therefore necessary to keep the ramp setting at its maximum time value when using an external time potentiometer. Also, if a preset is changed in value from 100% signal to a lower value, and the ramp time is held constant, the ramp time automatically reduces. When selecting an external time potentiometer the rating of the potentiometer should be 500K Ω.

PRESETS 5, 6 AND 7

Presets 5 and 6 are bias current settings and as with the VT-2000, they add a signal to boost the input signal to that useable linear portion of the curve. Unlike the VT-2000, these are already set at the factory for Series 30 cards and do not need to be adjusted. Preset P7 is a zero point, and is also set at the factory needing no adjustment. These three presets are not accessible on the front face of the card.

CHANGEOVER CONTACT D6

By energizing relay d6 the changeover contact can be used to provide negative or positive voltage at any of the presets P1 through P4. A typical wiring diagram of this contact in use will be shown later.

ADDITIONAL INPUTS

For control systems having analog outputs, terminals 16a and 16 c should be used. Terminal 12 c can be used for an input for electrical joysticks.

One of the simplest ways to achieve bi-direction for a pro-

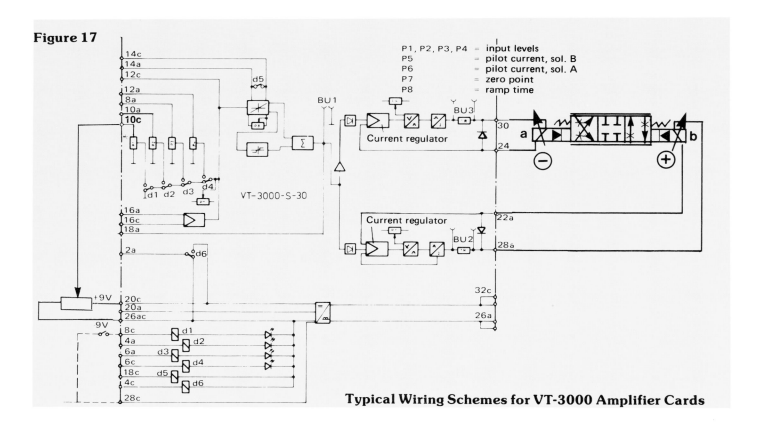

Figure 17

P1, P2, P3, P4 = input levels
P5 = pilot current, sol. B
P6 = pilot current, sol. A
P7 = zero point
P8 = ramp time

Typical Wiring Schemes for VT-3000 Amplifier Cards

portional directional valve and to establish various spool positions quickly and conveniently, is through the use of an external potentiometer (Figure 17).

By connecting the potentiometer to 20 c for +9 volts, 26 ac for −9 volts, and the wiper to any one of the preset terminals (in this case it is 10 c for P1) the operator has control of the valve in both directions. P1 would determine the maximum spool travel in both directions.

TWO SPEEDS FORWARD, TWO SPEEDS REVERSE

Many applications require a proportional directional valve and cylinder to accelerate a load to a constant velocity, then decelerate it to a slower speed, and finally reverse the process to start the cycle over again. With the use of the VT-3000 card and a few added electrical devices, this can be accomplished rather easily (see Figure 18).

Knowing that there are four adjustable presets on the card and two different speeds are required in each direction, a sequential order has to be established when selecting the presets. If the application calls for an automatic cycle, this can be accomplished by using external latching relays and establishing the relay logic accordingly. This can be seen more clearly in Figure 18. First, two presets are wired to provide positive voltage and the other two are wired to provide negative voltage, thereby giving two forward speeds and two reverse speeds when selected. Secondly, a typical relay logic diagram has been included with four limit switches to provide the necessary logic to the amplifier card.

Starting with the relay logic diagram, when the operator presses the start button and assuming the cylinder is sitting directly on top of the first limit switch (LS-1) which is nor-

mally open, relay 1-CR will latch in, closing contact 1-CR and energizing internal relay d3. This then closes contact d3 allowing the cylinder to accelerate forward to a speed set by preset P3. The cylinder proceeds forward until it closes limit switch LS-3 which in turn energizes relay 3-CR and opens normally closed contact 3-CR. Relay 1-CR is de-energized allowing the cylinder to decelerate to a slow speed forward, since the only relay on the card now energized is d1, with its preset P1 set for some minimal value. Once the cylinder reaches limit switch LS-4, relay 4-CR energizes closing contact 4-CR, energizing relay d4 and allowing the cylinder to accelerate in the reverse direction to a speed set at preset P4. The cylinder proceeds in the reverse direction until it closes limit switch LS-2, which energizes relay 2-CR and drops out relay 4-CR. At the same time relay d2 energizes decelerating the load to a creep speed at a minimal setting of P2. When the cylinder reaches limit switch LS-1, the cycle repeats itself.

Another important characteristic of the cycle is the ramp setting. Since there is only one ramp setting, all acceleration and deceleration values are the same. (See the Velocity Vs. Time graph Figure 19).

When setting the ramp time for an automatic cycle it generally takes some fine tuning in order to achieve smooth acceleration and deceleration rates.

THREE SPEEDS FORWARD, ONE REVERSE

Another typical wiring scheme used many times in machine tool applications is shown in Figure 20. With three of the presets wired for +9 volts three different speeds can be set in the forward direction and the other preset wired for −9 volts can provide one speed in the reverse direction.

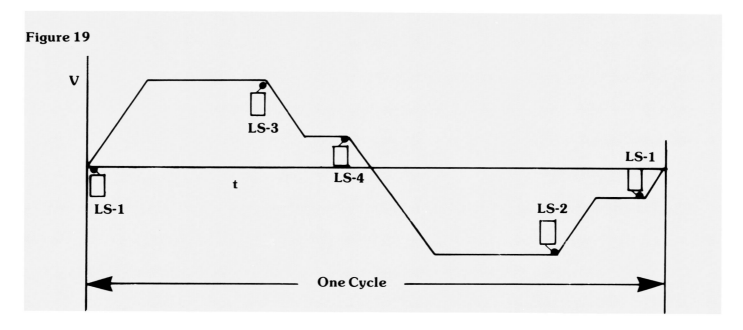

Figure 19

Figure 18

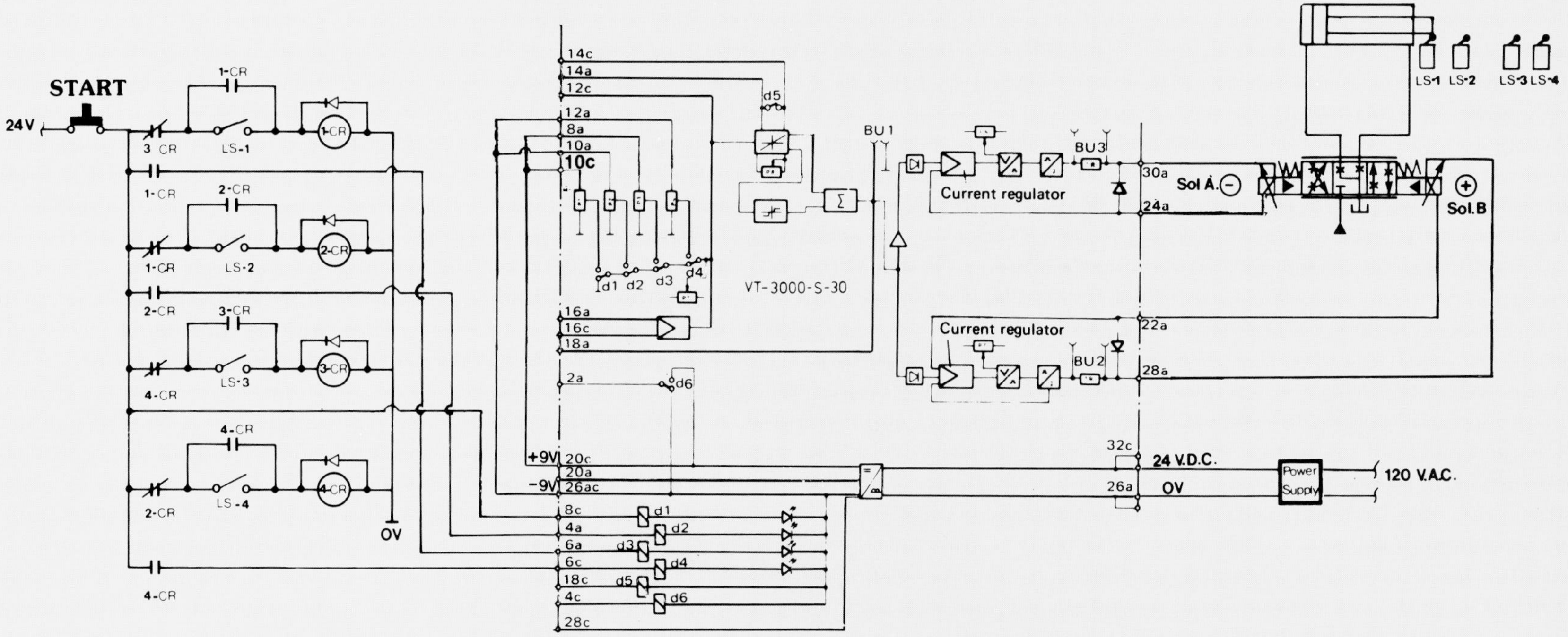

Two Speeds Forward; Two Speeds Reverse

Figure 20

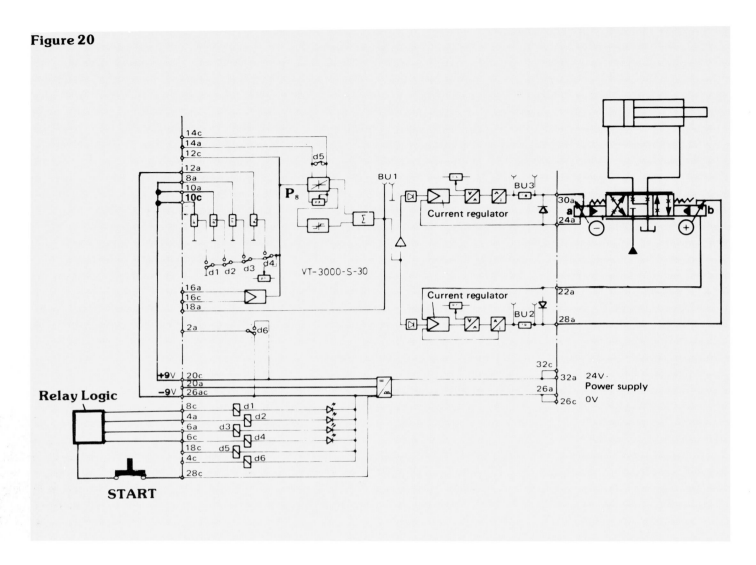

A typical velocity vs. time graph for this example is shown in Figure 21. By setting one of the presets for a high valve, fast or rapid traverse speed can be achieved. By setting another preset for a lower value, a feed speed can be achieved and by setting the last preset to a minimal value, a very slow cutting speed can be achieved. Once the cylinder comes to the end of its stroke it retracts quickly to start the cycle over again. The ramp is fine tuned to achieve smooth speed change and reversal.

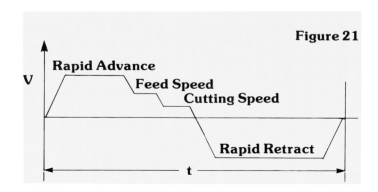

Figure 21

FOUR SPEEDS FORWARD, FOUR SPEEDS REVERSE, USING CHANGE OVER CONTACTS

From Figure 22, it can be seen that contact d6 is tied directly to the +9 and −9 voltage lines and incorporates a separate terminal enabling it to be wired to any one of the preset terminals. By energizing relay d6, the contact switches from negative voltage to positive voltage and back again when de-energized. The example shown demonstrates a 4-way proportional directional valve controlling a hydraulic motor and the card is wired to all four presets from the changeover contacts. It should be fairly obvious that if each preset is adjusted for a different value, four different speeds can be obtained in either direction, since there would be a different spool position at each preset value. The direction can be changed by use of the changeover contacts. These are just a small fraction of possible wiring schemes which can be applied to 4-way proportional directional valves. The wiring scheme to be used is dependent upon the application and the type of cycle to be accomplished.

Figure 22

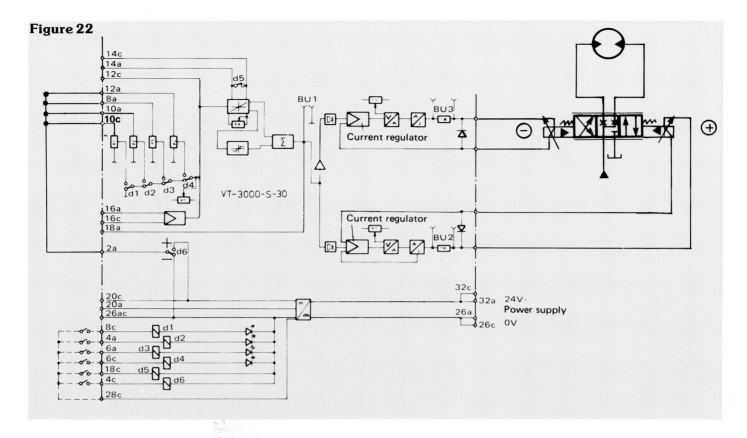

VT-3000-S-30

Current regulator

Current regulator

Power supply

ELECTRONIC AMPLIFIER VT-3006

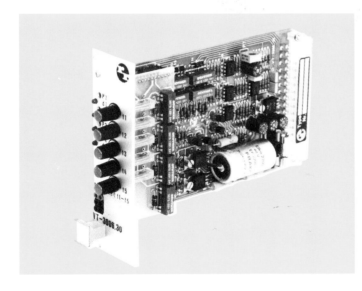

The VT-3006 (Figure 23) is the same type of amplifier card as the VT-3000 amplifier card except it has five ramp settings (instead of one) which are all accessible on the front face of the card. Looking at the figure it can be seen that an additional board of relays has been added as well as the ad-

ditional board of ramp adjustments. The added relays are in parallel with the relays needed for P1 through P4. Anytime relays d1 are energized, contacts d1 pull in, meaning the set point depends on P1 and the ramp time depends on the ramp setting P11. If relays d2 are energized contacts d2 pull in, and the set point depends on P2 with the ramp time dependent on the ramp setting P12. In other words, the priority chain remains the same for the ramp adjustments as it does for P1 through P4. Whenever relays d4 are energized, preset P4 and ramp setting P14 will have the highest priority.

Since each preset P1 through P4 can be set for a different ramp time, acceleration and deceleration rates can be established separately for each preset. When all presets are de-energized the valve returns to its center position bases on the ramp time setting of (P10).

ELECTRONIC AMPLIFIERS VT-5001—5004

Electronic amplifier Types VT-5001 through 5004 are used to control pressure, directional and flow control valves with an LVDT mounted on one proportional solenoid. The following amplifier types correspond to the respective proportional valves.

VT-5001 — for single solenoid direct operated proportional directional valve (D01 mounting)

Figure 23

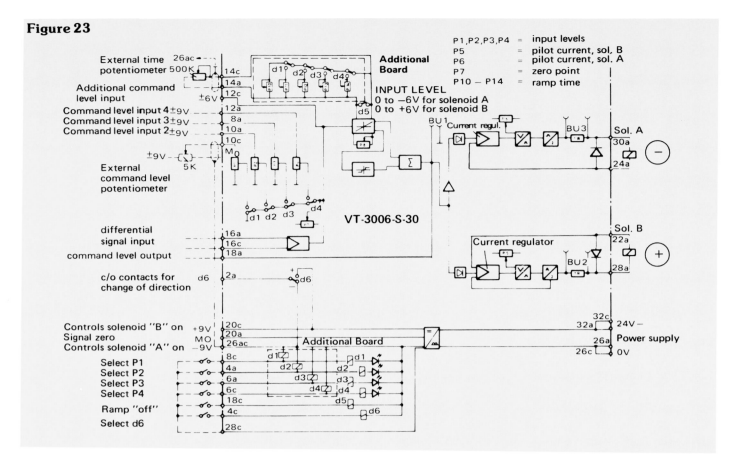

INTERNAL CIRCUITRY

Although block diagram for the VT-5001 through 5004 is the same for all, there are some minor differences (not shown) between each card type. It is, therefore, important to use the correct card for a particular valve.

There are basically two major differences between the Series 3000 and the Series 5000 card now being presented. The Series 5000 has cable break detection and it has some additional circuitry to compensate for the feedback on the valves (see Figure 24).

ELECTRONIC AMPLIFIER VT-5006

The electronic amplifier Type VT-5006 (Figure 25) is used to control direct operated proportional directional valves having two proportional solenoids and a LVDT for positional feedback.

The amplifier is the same as the VT-3000, except it has the added circuitry for cable break detection and the feedback as was just discussed for the VT-5001 through 5004 amplifier.

VT-5002 — for single solenoid direct operated proportional directional valve (D02 mounting)

VT-5003 — for direct operated proportional pressure relief valves

VT-5004 — for proportional pressure compensated flow control valves

Figure 24

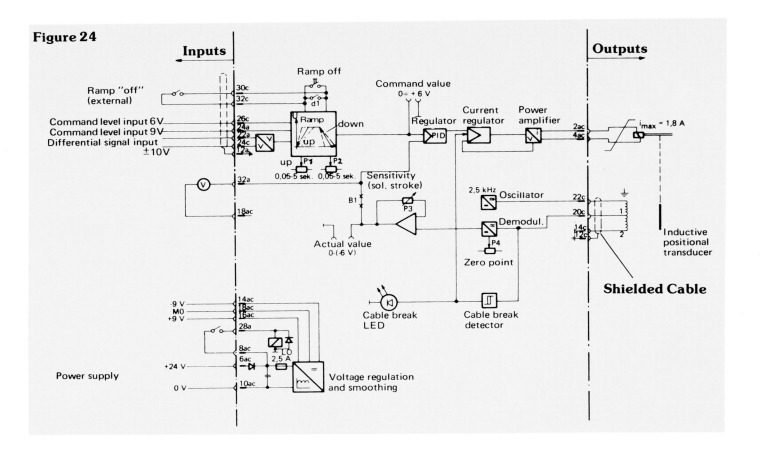

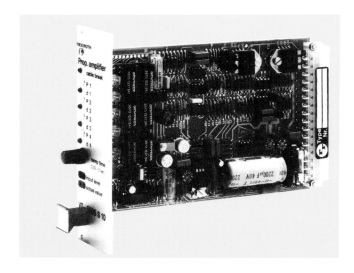

The presets and relays can be used the same as they are with the VT-3000. The only significant difference is that unlike the VT-3000 the command signal must be negative in order to energize solenoid B and positive to energize solenoid A. If these solenoid leads are wired incorrectly the spool moves hard over and the valve fully opens.

Starting with the added circuitry for the feedback, there are four new blocks presented. A P.I.D. regulator, matching amplifier, oscillator, and demodulator are all needed to ensure the proper positioning of the orifice or spool.

The output of the ramp generator serves as the input to the proportional, integral, differential regulator in which a comparison is made to the actual position. This is made possible by the oscillator which is a separate circuit within the amplifier, generating a signal at a definite frequency within desired limits to the LVDT on the particular valve. The LVDT then sends a signal back to the amplifier, corresponding to the position of the orifice or spool The signal is then received by the demodulator which recovers the intelligence from the signal and delivers a voltage signal proportional to the position of the orifice or spool through the matching amplifier to the P.I.D. regulator. At this point, a comparison is made in the P.I.D. as was previously mentioned resulting in a corrected signal back to the solenoid maintaining a very accurate orifice or spool setting. The matching amplifier (which is preset at the factory) limits the stroke of the spool, and influences both the accuracy and stability of the valve.

The cable break detector monitors the lines to the LVDT and is connected internally to the current regulator. If feedback is lost because of a break in a wire or due to an unconnected wire, the cable break detector switches the current regulator off, which in turn cuts off power to the solenoid. A light emitting diode (LED) on the front plate of the amplifier will turn on at the same time indicating a cable break. In the case of the direct operated directional valve and flow control valve

Figure 25

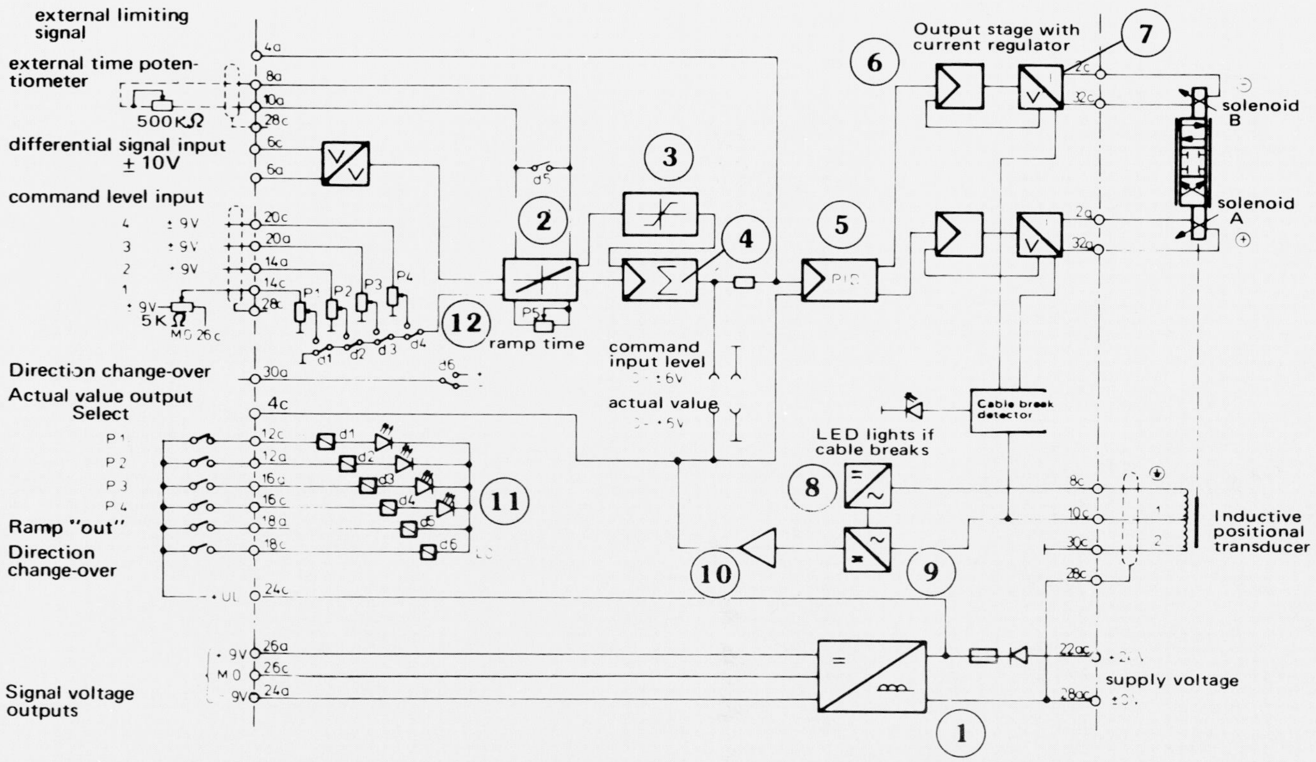

The card contains:

1. Voltage regulation and filtering
2. Ramp generator
3. Function generator
4. Summing unit
5. P.I.D. regulator
6. Current regulator

7. Power amplifier
8. Oscillator
9. Demodulator
10. Matching amplifier
11. Relays with LEDs
12. Presets

with feedback, a broken cable results in both valves falling in a closed position. When feedback is lost to the direct operated relief valve, it fails in an open condition preventing any pressure to build.

The Series 5000, as with the 2000 and 3000 Series, has:

1. Voltage regulation and filtering.
2. Current regulator for stabilizing the output.
3. Power amplifier.
4. Ramp generator with separate ramp up and down times, for use in setting spool or orifice opening and closing times, or for setting the pressure controls' increase or decrease pressure times.

ADJUSTMENTS

The only adjustments on the front face of the amplifier are for setting the ramp up and down times and one switch for turning the ramp off.

FEEDBACK CONNECTOR AND WIRING

It is of the utmost importance that the terminal designated with the ground symbol ($\perp$) on the feedback connector be wired properly.

The wiring sequence is as follows: pin number 1 on the plug connects to terminal 20 c, pin number 2 on the plug connects to terminal 14 c on the card, and pin (⏚) on the plug connects to terminal 22 c, not to a chasis ground (reference Figure 24).

ELECTRONIC AMPLIFIER TYPE VT-5000

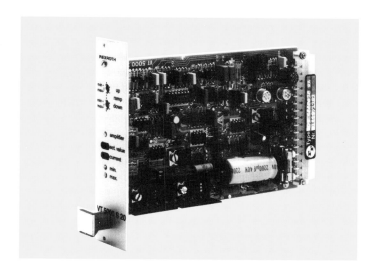

Electronic amplifier Type VT-5000 Figure 26 is used for controlling proportional variable volume vane pumps. The amplifier is unique in the respect that it incorporates a circuit to control a stroke controlled solenoid and a circuit to control a force solenoid. Relating this to the proportional vane pump, the top half of the amplifier provides a signal to the main orifice which has the stroke controlled solenoid and the bottom half provides a signal to the relief valve which has the force solenoid.

INTERNAL CIRCUITRY

The top half of the circuit contains:

1. Proportional, integral, differential regulator
2. Current regulator
3. Pulse width generator
4. Power amplifier
5. Oscillator, for feeding the LVDT
6. Demodulator, for generating the feedback signal
7. Matching amplifier, for limiting the stroke of the main orifice

The bottom half of the circuit contains:

1. Current regulator
2. Pulse width generator
3. Power amplifier

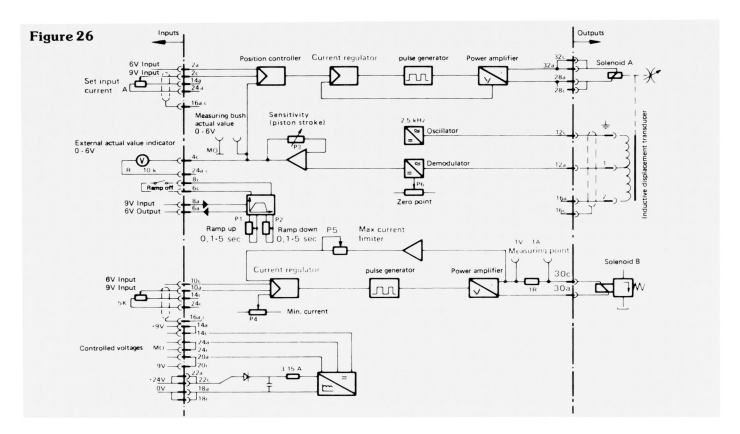

Figure 26

The amplifier also contains voltage regulation and filtering, and a ramp generator. Reference voltage terminals provided from the voltage regulation and filtering block allow for potentiometers to provide the required command signal to operate solenoid A and B.

The ramp generator is separated from both circuits, and is provided with an input and output terminal where it can be wired for either setting the ramp times for the main orifice or the ramp times of the relief valve.

PRESETS

P3 is an adjustable preset which is used to set the maximum current to the main orifice, and is accessible on the front face of the card. Although the orifice still can be remotely adjusted by a potentiometer, it will never exceed this value P3.

Presets P4 and P5 function in the same manner as do P1 and P2 for the VT-2000 amplifier. P4 is a minimum current setting and is used to establish the minimum pressure setting of the valve or the minimum pressure at which the pump compensates. P5 is a maximum current setting and is used to establish the maximum pressure setting of the valve or the pressure at which the pump compensates. Like the VT-2000, the minimum pressure setting of the valve is additive to the maximum pressure setting, therefore, P4 should always be set first.

RAMP ADJUSTMENTS

There are two ramp adjustments which can be used to separately set how fast the orifice opens and closes, or they can be used to separately set how fast the proportional pressure relief valve increases and decreases pressure. The ramp generator can be used for either solenoid A or B, but cannot be used for both solenoid A and B at the same time.

WIRING THE RAMP GENERATOR

Since the ramp generator is separated from both circuits, external wiring must be done to include the generator for whatever solenoid it is intended to be used with. If the ramp generator is intended to be used with solenoid A (main flow orifice) and remote control is desired for both solenoid A and B by the use of two potentiometers, the potentiometer that operates the main flow orifice (solenoid A) must be connected from the wiper of the potentiometer to the 9 volt input terminal of the ramp generator. The output of the ramp generator is 6 volts and this is designated by a 6 volt output terminal which must be connected to the 6 volt input terminal 2 a. The main flow orifice (solenoid A) would then be capable of variable adjustment plus the ramp generator could be set to control orifice opening and closing times.

The other potentiometer used to control solenoid B, would

have its wiper connected directly to the 9 volt input terminal 10 a. Variable adjustment of the pump compensator would then be achievable. If it is desirable to use the ramp generator for both solenoid A and B, a relay may be used to switch back and forth to operate the ramp generator as desired for a particular solenoid, or a second card with multiple ramps can be incorporated.

TEST POINTS

Figure 27   COMMAND
SOL. B
SOL. A

On the front face of the VT-3000 Series cards there are three sets of test points (Figure 27). One set is for reading the command signal and the other two are for reading coil current, solenoid B and A respectively.

Placing a voltmeter across the two command test points enables one to read the command signal just after the summing amplifier. (Command test points are marked BU-1 in the diagram.) If it appears an internal relay may not be working properly, the command test points can be used. For example, by energizing each particular internal relay on the card and measuring the voltage across the command test points, one can find out which relay on the card is not working.

Coil current test points are marked BU-2 in the diagram for solenoid B and BU-3 for solenoid A. Since 1 mA = 1 mV (1 ma × 1 Ω = 1 mV) the signal actually being measured is voltage, therefore, when using the coil current test points, a voltmeter should also be used. If for example the voltmeter reads .5 volts this is directly proportional to 500 mA. A high impedance voltmeter is needed to measure the range of less than 1 volt and it is generally best to use a digital voltmeter.

For VT-5000 Series cards two sets of test points are accessible on the front face of the card for measuring the command signal and the feedback signal.

SHIELDING

Since the input signals for all VT amplifiers are low current signals they are subject to radio frequency interference. The most common way to alleviate this problem is to use shielded wire. Shielded wire is a combination of wire(s) that has a protective guard around it which helps to eliminate the intrusion of other outside signals.

It is usually used when the potentiometer is mounted a few feet from the card, or if the card is mounted in a console and the potentiometer is mounted on top of the console with other electrical devices in the console (such as relays or anything that can produce magnetic or electrostatic fields). Shielded wire should also be used for wiring the LVDT on stroke controlled solenoids. It is important to remember when wiring with shielded wire, that it should only be grounded on one end. If both ends of the shielded wire are grounded, the shield has no effect. In fact, it may even pick up interference making the problem worse.

DRY CIRCUIT SWITCH

Anytime a switch is used to provide the ± 9V signal, a dry circuit switch should be used. Since the ± 9V signal is low level, any dirt that may accumulate around the contacts of a standard switch can cause corrosion. After a short period of time the contacts corrode and the switch will no longer be useable. Dry circuit switches are designed to work at these low level signals: their contacts are flashed with a gold coating to prevent contamination. It should be noted that shielded wire and dry circuit switches are needed only for the low level +9 or −9 volt signal. Dry circuit relays are also available.

POWER SUPPLIES

When selecting a power supply for an amplifier card the absolute limits should not drop below a minimum of 22 volts or a maximum of 27 volts. The most common type of power supply used to provide power to the amplifier is a 24 volt DC ± 10% regulated power supply. Although unregulated power supplies may also be used, one must be aware of the problems that can occur. The more an unregulated power supply is loaded, the greater the voltage drop is. Likewise, the output voltage is proportional to the input voltage, which can also affect the variable being controlled. Another problem with unregulated power supplies is if 24 volts are required for a load condition, once the load is removed a variation in voltage occurs which can cause the 24 volts to go beyond the maximum 27 volt limit, may times leading to the destruction of the card. With the regulated power supply, the output stays at about 24 volts DC even with changes in load. It is, therefore, more desirable to use the regulated power supply. It also should be mentioned that if more than one amplifier is to be used with one power supply, one must carefully check the rating of the power supply to ensure that it is large enough to handle the power capacity of the amplifiers.

CARD HOLDER

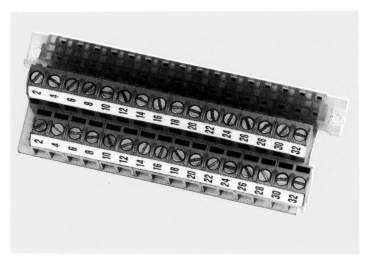

Every amplifier card (with the exception of one type) has a 32 pin connector permanently attached to the end of it. With the connector being permanently attached, the card can be plugged directly into a card holder which possesses two rows of terminals for wiring. Each row contains 16 terminal connections with one row marked "a" and the other row marked "c", each row being evenly numbered from 2 to 32. This allows the user to do all the wiring directly to the card holder so that anytime a card has to be replaced it can be done without rewiring. Consequently, if a terminal is marked with ac, either a or c both can be used for a wiring connection. If, however, two terminals are labeled for one connection, both terminals must be used. This is important because each terminal has a limited current carrying ability.

If a different card is intended to be used with a previously wired card holder, one must make sure the necessary wiring changes are made, as terminal connections for different amplifier cards may not directly correspond to each other. Not only does the card plug directly into the card holder but there are guide rails as well as two fastening screws to hold the card firmly in place.

CARD RACK

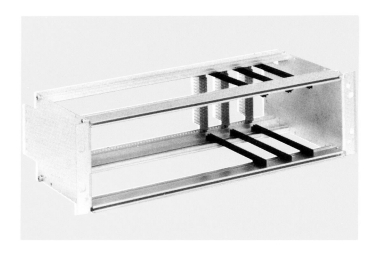

If a number of amplifier cards are required, rather than mounting each amplifier card to an individual card holder, a card rack can be used which is capable of holding a number of amplifier cards in one frame. All wiring can then take place at the back of the card rack to wire wrapped terminal connections as needed, this eliminating an excess of terminal connections as well as keeping the cards in a neat orderly

fashion when mounting in a console. The rack is made with divisions, allowing for the cards to be equally spaced when required.

AMMETER TEST BOX

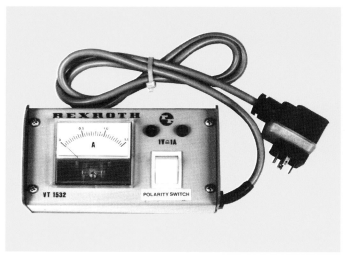

For conveniently testing solenoid current, an ammeter box which has a scale from 0 to 1.5 amps can be used. It has a special adapter plug enabling it to be quickly sandwiched between the solenoid and solenoid plug. Since the plug can only be hooked up one way it also incorporates a polarity button so that current can be measured for both solenoids for 4-way proportional directional valves. The ammeter test box is also effective during start-up and trouble shooting to ensure that power is being supplied to the solenoid or solenoids.

CHAPTER 9
DESIGN CONSIDERATIONS &
VALVE ANALYSIS

When designing for any 4-way proportional valve system, especially when cycling heavy masses quickly, there is one very important design factor that must be considered. This is known as the natural frequency of the system. From the physical laws of motion, the formula for undampened natural frequency is:

$$\omega o = \sqrt{\frac{C}{M}}$$

ωo = **Natural frequency**
C = Spring constant
M = Moving mass = w/g

The spring constant for a hydraulic system can be directly related to the oil volume trapped between the 4-way proportional valve and the actuator. The moving mass is the weight of the total load, plus the weight of the oil, divided by gravity.

Gravity = 32.2 ft./s²

The natural frequency of a hydraulic system is expressed in Hz. It is dependent on the mass and the oil volume trapped between the valve and the actuator. With this information one can determine how fast a load can be accelerated and decelerated without causing instability and subsequent damage to the system. To clearly demonstrate this point we will first look at a simple system, which has a weight attached to a spring. The natural frequency of the system is dependent on the spring constant and the mass.

This frequency can be mathematically calculated and in effect tells us how fast this weight can be moved back and forth without having the weight directly opposing the input to the spring. For example, the input to the spring-mass system could be someone's hand moving the spring-mass system up and down a certain distance (Figure 1). As long as the spring is moved much more slowly than the natural frequency of the total spring-mass system, the weight will follow the movement of the spring. There will be very little difference between the movement of the spring and weight. The faster the input or hand movement to the spring, the more the weight lags behind. If the input to the spring is at the same frequency of the total spring-mass system, as one moves his hand (the spring-mass system) down, the weight moves up. Likewise, as his hand moves up, the weight moves down. The weight would be in direct opposition to the movement of the spring. This results in the system performing a function opposite of what is required. This is called instability or resonance. To put this in perspective with regard to a hydraulic system, the natural frequency can be calculated (as previously mentioned) and the factor which determines instability is the acceleration and deceleration time. Trying to accelerate and decelerate high inertial loads too quickly, can cause the cylinder or motor to be unstable. This also creates shock waves in the plumbing, which leads to external system leakage.

It is possible to increase the spring constant of the system by keeping the valve as close to the actuator as possible, thus reducing the oil volume trapped between them. This will allow higher acceleration and deceleration rates due to a stiffer spring. If, however, too high of an acceleration is chosen, the actuator will have an irregular movement, regardless of the higher natural frequency. If the natural frequency is too low, the system will oscillate.

Figure 1

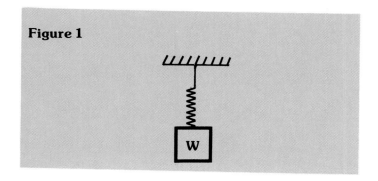

Figure 2

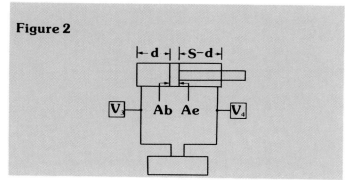

Now let us consider how we calculate the natural frequency of a differential cylinder and how we then determine the acceleration time.

The first thing that must be established is the spring constant. The designer must be cautious when the spring constant is at its minimum value, which means the natural frequency is at its lowest value. This is the worst case of the spring constant and one must design around it.

C_{min} must be established. C_{min} however, is related to some distance of the cylinder travel. A formula to calculate this distance has been developed for differential cylinders. The origin of this formula is given below:

In order to determine the distance at which the spring constant is at its minimum value, the maximum value was first established by determining the spring constant when the cylinder was first fully retracted and then fully extended.

When the cylinder is fully retracted the bulk modulus formula can be applied, $(S = 0)$.

$$\beta = \frac{Vo \times \Delta P}{\Delta V}$$

$$\frac{\Delta P}{\Delta V} = \frac{\beta}{Vo}$$

ΔP = Change in pressure (lb/in^2)
ΔV = Change in volume (in^3)
Vo = Original volume (in^3)
β = Bulk modulus (in/lb^2)

Bulk Modulus Formula: The bulk modulus of a fluid is a measure of the change in volume which occurs when the pressure on the fluid is changed. The magnitude depends on the bulk modulus of the fluid, the original volume and the amount of pressure change.

$$\Delta P = \frac{\Delta L}{A_b}$$

$$\Delta V = \Delta S \times A_b$$

ΔL = Change in load force
ΔS = Change in stroke
A_b = Area of blind end

The change in load is influenced by the acceleration force $(F = mA)$

By substitution:

$$\frac{\Delta L / A_b}{\Delta S \times A_b} = \frac{\beta}{Vo}$$

$$\frac{\Delta L}{\Delta S \times A_b^2} = \frac{\beta}{Vo}$$

From $F = -Kx$:

$$C = \frac{\Delta L}{\Delta S} = \frac{A_b^2 \times \beta}{Vo}$$

$$C = \frac{A_b^2 \times \beta}{Vo}$$

The bulk modulus formula dictates the amount of pressure change for a given compression (or decompression). This pressure change is created by the acceleration forces $(F = mA)$.

To define the oil volume (reference Figure 2):

$$Vo = V_3 = A_p \times L_1$$

V_3 = Pipe volume blind end of cylinder (in^3)
A_p = Area of pipe or tube (in^2)
L_1 = Length of pipe or tube between valve & actuator on blind end (in)

$$C = \frac{A_b^2 \times \beta}{V_3} \quad \textbf{Blind End constant (When fully retracted)}$$

The volume in the cylinder, the bulk modulus, and the volume between the valve and actuator on the rod end side must also be considered since the proportional valve meters both in and out.

$$V_4 = A_p \times L_2$$

$$V(cyl) = A_e \times S$$

$$C_{1\,max} = \frac{A_b^2 \times \beta}{V_3} + \frac{A_e^2 \times \beta}{V_4 + (A_e \times S)}$$

V_4 = Pipe volume rod end of cylinder (in^3)
A_e = Effective area of rod end (in^2)
S = Stroke (in)
L_2 = Length of pipe between valve and actuator on rod end (in)
$C_{1\,max}$ = Constant when fully retracted

Likewise, when the cylinder is fully extended, the constant is defined as:

$$C_{2\,max} = \frac{A_b^2 \times \beta}{V_3 + (A_b \times S)} + \frac{A_e^2 \times \beta}{V_4}$$

$$C_{2\,max} = \textbf{Constant when fully extended.}$$

The distance at which the spring constant is at a minimum was then derived from:

$$\frac{dc}{ds} = 0 \qquad C' = 0$$

$$\textbf{when } C' > 0$$

From the derivitive, this distance then equals:

$$d = \frac{\dfrac{(A_e \times S) + V_4}{\sqrt{A_e^3}} - \dfrac{V_3}{\sqrt{A_b^3}}}{\dfrac{1}{\sqrt{A_e}} + \dfrac{1}{\sqrt{A_b}}}$$

The graphic solution would appear as follows:

Figure 3

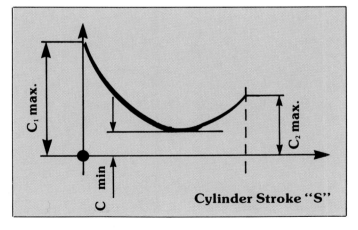

Cylinder Stroke "S"

$$C_{min} = C_1 + C_2 \text{ at stroke length "d"}$$

$$C_{min} = \frac{A_b^2 \times \beta}{V_3 + (A_b \times d)} + \frac{A_e^2 \times \beta}{V_4 + A_e(S - d)}$$

$$V_3 + (A_b \times d) = V_1$$

$$V_4 + A_e(S - d) = V_2$$

$$C_{min} = \frac{A_b^2 \times \beta}{V_1} + \frac{A_e^2 \times \beta}{V_2}$$

$$V_1 = \textbf{Oil volume on blind end side (in}^3\textbf{)}$$

$$V_2 = \textbf{Oil volume on rod end side (in}^3\textbf{)}$$

The natural frequency for the differential cylinder would then be:

$$\omega_o = \sqrt{\frac{C_{min}}{M}}$$

$$\omega_o = \sqrt{\frac{C_1}{M} + \frac{C_2}{M}}$$

$$\omega_o = \sqrt{\frac{\dfrac{A_b^2 \times \beta}{V_1} + \dfrac{A_e^2 \times \beta}{V_2}}{M}}$$

$$\omega_o = \sqrt{\frac{A_b^2 \times \beta}{V_1 \times M} + \frac{A_e^2 \times \beta}{V_2 \times M}}$$

As calculated above "ω_o" is the natural frequency in radians per second (rad./sec). From a theoretical view "ω_o" can now be used to determine the time needed for acceleration. From experience (Figure 4), however, we must consider other capacitances of the system. (e.g. hoses, mechanical components, etc.) As proven by application examples, we find that the useable acceleration is better estimated by dividing the calculated natural frequency by 3. Naturally, this is a simplified estimate which has been proven to give ample accuracy for most systems. This simplification avoids a complex mathematical analysis, which would require variables which are difficult, if not impossible to determine. Therefore; to calculate the useable acceleration:

$$\omega = \frac{\omega_o}{3} \textbf{ (rad./sec.)}$$

To obtain the natural frequency of the system in hertz (hz) we must divide by 2π.

$$F = \frac{\omega}{2\pi} \textbf{ (hz)}$$

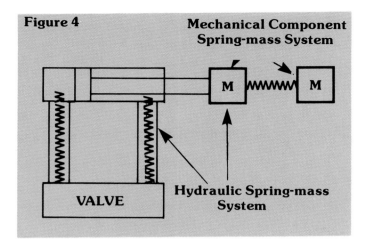

Figure 4

Mechanical Component Spring-mass System

VALVE

Hydraulic Spring-mass System

Likewise; from "ω" (rad/sec) we can also find the time constant "T". This is the time period required for one oscillation.

$$T = \frac{1}{\omega} \text{ (sec.)}$$

As described in the following text, the time required for acceleration is based on this time constant. Generally, for stable acceleration, the time allowed must be a minimum of 4 to 6 times the time period for one oscillation. The mechanics involved are better described in Figure 5.

$$T_b = 6 \times T$$

T_b = **Time allowed for acceleration (Figure 6)**

T = **Time period for one oscillation**

Figure 5

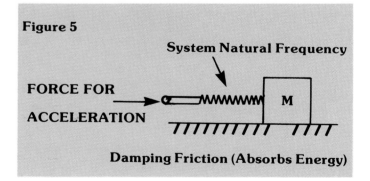

System Natural Frequency

FORCE FOR ACCELERATION

M

Damping Friction (Absorbs Energy)

During the acceleration of any mechanical system (Figure 5) the available force input is split into three parts. First a percentage of the force is used to cause the actual acceleration ($F = mA$). Second, a percentage of the force goes toward compressing the natural frequency of the system ($F = Kx$). Finally, some force is used in overcoming frictional forces

and other dampening factors. For vertical loads we must also overcome the weight of the load.

For extremely low levels of force and therefore low levels of acceleration, the incoming force has a magnitude much lower than the compressive spring force of the system's natural frequency. For these conditions the final velocity is predictable based solely on the low acceleration rate and the desired change in velocity. If, however, we attempt to provide more and more input force, in order to accelerate the mass faster and faster, we reach a point where the spring (system's natural frequency) cannot transmit this force. In other words, as the input force is increased, more of this force is used in compression of the spring while a limited maximum force is transmitted through the spring to cause acceleration. For maximum cycle rate from the system at hand, we try to supply sufficient force to accelerate the mass without supplying additional forces which only excite the natural frequency of the system (compress the spring). The ideal maximum acceleration is achieved when the extra force absorbed by the spring can be quickly dampened by the frictional forces (dampening factors of the system). If the spring forces are excessive when compared to dampening forces, an unstable oscillation is created.

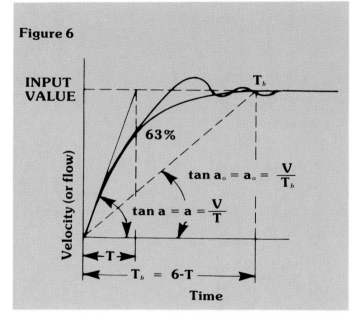

Figure 6

INPUT VALUE

Velocity (or flow)

63%

$$\tan a_o = a_o = \frac{V}{T_b}$$

$$\tan a = a = \frac{V}{T}$$

T

$$T_b = 6 \text{-} T$$

Time

In reference to the graphic analysis of the maximum acceleration (Figure 6), the limiting acceleration is based on a time constant as derived from the following formula:

$$V_f = V_d (1 - e^{T/\tau})$$

V_f = **Actual velocity**
V_d = **Desired velocity**
e = **Irrational number = 2.72**
T/τ = **Time constant based on number of time periods**

This formula shows that during the first time period the maximum velocity achievable is 63% of the desired final velocity. During the second time period the velocity reaches 86% of the desired, the third, fourth, fifth and sixth time period are 95, 97, 99 and 99+% respectively.

By allowing six time periods for acceleration a smooth exponential increase to final velocity is achieved. If only four time periods are provided for acceleration, there is a critically dampened oscillation which occurs prior to achieving the final velocity. With less than four time periods an unstable oscillation is created which typically cannot be tolerated. It is interesting to note that it does not matter what the acceleration rate is, the mechanical system always reaches 63% of the desired velocity in the first time period. Likewise, it achieves a stable constant velocity in the sixth time period.

On the practical side, this information is important when selecting the system pressure, and it is necessary when establishing the maximum pump flow. These considerations will be dealt with in the following example. In the actual system, however, the maximum acceleration is adjusted by starting with maximum ramp time.

During machine operation the ramp time is gradually decreased until the instability point is reached. By adjusting the ramp time to the point just before instability (approximately six time constants) maximum acceleration and therefore maximum production can be achieved without shock.

At this point, therefore, it is best to look at a conventional application, where a proportional directional valve is used to accelerate a load to a constant velocity and decelerate to a stop, then retract in the same manner to start the cycle over again. Also, assuming the amplifier used has one ramp setting, the acceleration and deceleration times will be the same.

Parameters known:

The application requires that a 1000 lb. horizontal load be moved in 1 second a distance of 30 inches and the cylinder size is 1-1/2" bore, by 1" rod.

The natural frequency must be calculated first so that the time to accelerate can be determined, and from this the maximum velocity can be determined.

w	=	1000 lbs.
A_b	=	1.76 in^2
A_e	=	.98 in^2
S	=	30 in.
β	=	2.0×10^5 lb/in^2
Tube size	=	**3/4" O.D.** $\times$ **.065"**

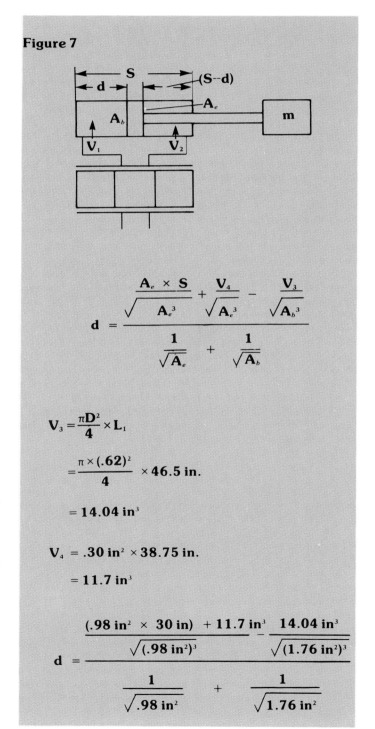

L_1	=	Length of pipe on blind end = 46.5"
L_2	=	Length of pipe on rod end = 38.75"

Since the following information is known, and as was stated earlier, by designing around a C_{min}, "d" can be determined (Figure 7):

Figure 7

$$d = \frac{\sqrt{\dfrac{A_e \times S}{A_e^3}} + \sqrt{\dfrac{V_4}{A_e^3}} - \sqrt{\dfrac{V_3}{A_b^3}}}{\dfrac{1}{\sqrt{A_e}} + \dfrac{1}{\sqrt{A_b}}}$$

$$V_3 = \frac{\pi D^2}{4} \times L_1$$

$$= \frac{\pi \times (.62)^2}{4} \times 46.5 \text{ in.}$$

$$= 14.04 \text{ in}^3$$

$$V_4 = .30 \text{ in}^2 \times 38.75 \text{ in.}$$

$$= 11.7 \text{ in}^3$$

$$d = \frac{\dfrac{(.98 \text{ in}^2 \times 30 \text{ in}) + 11.7 \text{ in}^3}{\sqrt{(.98 \text{ in}^2)^3}} - \dfrac{14.04 \text{ in}^3}{\sqrt{(1.76 \text{ in}^2)^3}}}{\dfrac{1}{\sqrt{.98 \text{ in}^2}} + \dfrac{1}{\sqrt{1.76 \text{ in}^2}}}$$

$$d = 20 \text{ in}$$

The natural frequency can then be calculated (Figure 7):

$$\omega_0 = \sqrt{\frac{A_b{}^2 \times \beta}{V_1 \times M} + \frac{A_e{}^2 \times \beta}{V_2 \times M}}$$

$$\begin{aligned} V_1 &= V_3 + A_b \times d \\ &= 14.04 \text{ in}^3 + 1.76 \text{ in}^2 \times 20 \text{ in} \\ &= 49.05 \text{ in}^3 \end{aligned}$$

$$\begin{aligned} V_2 &= V_4 + A_e\,(S - d) \\ &= 11.7 \text{ in}^3 + .98 \text{ in}^2\,(30 \text{ in} - 20 \text{ in}) \\ &= 11.7 \text{ in}^3 + 9.8 \text{ in}^3 \\ &= 21.50 \text{ in}^3 \end{aligned}$$

$$\omega_0 = \sqrt{\frac{(1.76 \text{ in}^2)^2 \times 2.0 \times 10^5\,\frac{\text{lbs}}{\text{in}^2} \times 32.2\,\frac{\text{ft}}{\text{sec}^2} \times 12\,\frac{\text{in}}{\text{ft}}}{49.05 \text{ in}^3 \times 1000 \text{ lbs.}}} +$$

$$\sqrt{\frac{(.98 \text{ in}^2)^2 \times 2.0 \times 10^5\,\frac{\text{lbs}}{\text{in}^2} \times 32.2\,\frac{\text{ft}}{\text{sec}^2} \times 12\,\frac{\text{in}}{\text{ft}}}{21.05 \text{ in}^3 \times 1000 \text{ lbs}}}$$

$$\omega_0 = \sqrt{\frac{4840}{(\text{sec})^2} + \frac{3512}{(\text{sec})^2}}$$

$$\omega_0 = 91.4\,\frac{\text{radians}}{\text{second}}$$

The useable acceleration lies at about one third of the natural frequency

$$\omega = \frac{\omega_0}{3} = \frac{91.4}{3} = 30.46\,\frac{\text{rad}}{\text{sec}}$$

The acceleration time can then be calculated,

$$T = 1/\omega$$
$$T = 1/30.46 = .032 \text{ sec}$$

This, however, only determines the time in which the amplitude (velocity) reaches about 63% of its desired final value as was mentioned previously. The acceleration time is proportional to the final desired speed; therefore, a factor or 6 × is used to allow for an acceleration stabilizing time. Using this factor of 6 for a proportional valve system has proven that this time for acceleration and deceleration lies outside the unstable region.

Therefore, the acceleration stabilizing time would be:

$$T_b = 6 \times T$$
$$T_b = 6 \times .032 = .20 \text{ sec}$$

From this acceleration time, the maximum velocity can be determined in terms of stroke. From V_{max}, acceleration rate, acceleration force, acceleration pressure and the required flow rate can then be determined (Figure 8).

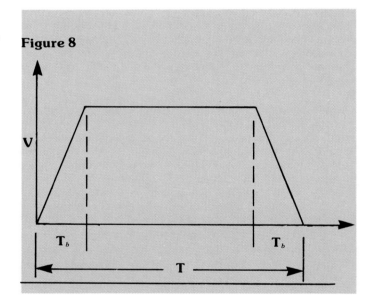

Figure 8

$$S = \frac{V_{max}\,T_b}{2} + \frac{V_{max}\,T_b}{2} + V_{max} \times (T - 2T_b)$$

$$V_{max} = \frac{S}{(T - T_b)}$$

$$V_{max} = \frac{30 \text{ in}}{1.0 - .20} = 37.5\,\frac{\text{in}}{\text{sec}} \times 60\,\frac{\text{sec}}{\text{min}} = 2250\,\frac{\text{in}}{\text{min}}$$

Therefore:

$$A_{max} = \frac{V}{T_b} = \frac{37.5 \text{ in/sec}}{.20 \text{ sec}} = \frac{187 \text{ in}}{\text{sec}^2} \quad \text{or} \quad \frac{15.6 \text{ ft}}{\text{sec}^2}$$

Acceleration force would be:

$$F = ma = \frac{w}{g} a = \frac{1000 \text{ lbs } 15.6 \text{ ft/sec}^2}{32.2 \text{ ft/sec}^2} = 485 \text{ lbs}$$

Frictional Force:

$$F = \mu N = .58 (1000) = 580 \text{ lb}$$

$$F_t = 580 \text{ lb} + 485 \text{ lb} = 1065 \text{ lbs}$$

Acceleration pressure at the blind end would equal:

$$P = \frac{F_t}{A_b} = \frac{1065 \text{ lbs}}{1.767 \text{ in}^2} = 605 \text{ PSI}$$

Acceleration pressure at the rod end would be:

$$P = \frac{F_t}{A_e} = \frac{1065 \text{ lbs}}{.982 \text{ in}^2} = 1085 \text{ PSI}$$

The flow rate required would be:

$$Q_b = \frac{V_{max} \times A_b}{231} = \frac{2250 \text{ (in/m)} \times 1.76 \text{ in}^2}{231}$$

$$Q_b = 17.2 \text{ GPM}$$

$$Q_r = \frac{V_{max} \times A_e}{231} = \frac{2250 \text{ (.982)}}{231} = 10.0 \text{ GPM}$$

Since the cylinder has an area ratio close to 2:1, the valve selected should also have a spool area ratio of 2:1. From the calculations that will be shown later in the text, the pressure drops can be determined and the valve can be selected. If the valve were moved closer to the cylinder, and the natural frequency would be recalculated, it could be seen that the natural frequency would increase. This would then allow for higher acceleration and deceleration rates, thus allowing for a faster cycle rate. This is shown in the following example. It also should be mentioned that if pump flow was determined without considering the accelerating time, the required one second cycle time would not be achieved.

NATURAL FREQUENCY FOR MOTORS

Figure 9

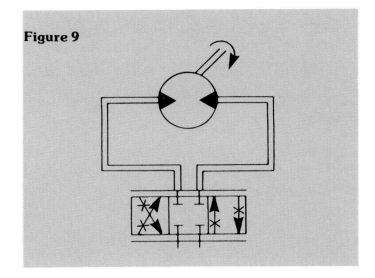

From the physical laws of motion:

$$\omega o = \sqrt{\frac{C}{I}}$$

ωo = **The natural frequency**
C = **Spring constant of the oil**
I = **Moment of inertia of the mass**

NOTE: Since the mass moment of inertia for rotary movement depends on the object being rotated, an example for one particular application will be shown. The effect of the proportional valve being mounted a substantial distance from the motor will also be shown in this example.

Figure 10

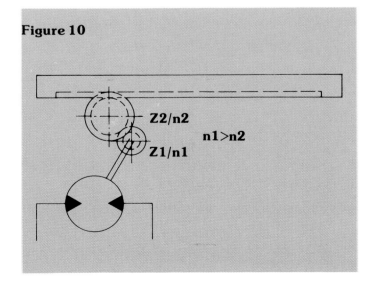

Z2/n2
n1>n2
Z1/n1

In a molding machine, the movement of prepared molding boxes to the molding line is carried out by a proportional directional valve operating a hydraulic motor which operates a carriage having a specific gear ratio. It is desired to move a load weighing 8100 lbs to a linear velocity of; $V_{max} = 3.28$ ft/s and then stop within 1.5 ft.. Therefore the required acceleration would be:

$$a = \frac{V^2}{2S} = \frac{(3.28 \text{ ft/s})^2}{2 (1.5 \text{ ft})} = 3.56 \frac{\text{ft}}{\text{sec}^2}$$

The parameters of the system are as follows:

$W = 8100$ lbs.

Gear Ratio $= i = \dfrac{Z_2}{Z_1} = \dfrac{38}{17}$

Displacement of motor $= 6.7$ in^3/rev
Desired speed of motor $= 272$ RPM
Tube inside diameter $= 1/2''$
Tube length $= 32$ ft.

$$\omega_0 = \sqrt{\frac{C}{I}}$$

$$C_t = C_1 + C_2$$

$$C_r = 2 \times \left[\frac{\left[\frac{D}{2\pi} \right]^2 \times \beta}{V_1} \right]$$

$V_1 = $ Trapped oil volume per side (in^3)
$D = $ Volume of the motor (in^3)
$\beta = 2.0 \times 10^5$ lb/in^2
$I_r = $ Mass moment of inertia

$$V_1 = A_p \times L + \frac{D}{2}$$

$A_p = $ Area of pipe
$L = $ Length of pipe

$$V_1 = \frac{\pi (.5)^2}{4} \times 393 \text{ in} + \frac{6.7 \text{ in}^3}{2}$$

$V_1 = 77$ in^3 $+ 3.4$ in^3

$V_1 = 80.4$ in^3

Mass moment of Inertia

$$I = \frac{w}{g} \times r^2$$

$$I_r = \frac{I}{i^2}$$

$W = 8100$ lbs
$r = 2.3$ in or $.2$ ft

$$I_r = \frac{\frac{w}{g} \times r^2}{i^2} = \frac{8100 \text{ lb}/32.2 \text{ (ft/s}^2) \times (.2 \text{ ft})^2 (17)^2}{(38)^2}$$

$$I_r = 2.1 \frac{\text{lb-ft}}{\text{sec}^2}$$

The natural frequency for rotary motion is:

$$\omega_0 = \sqrt{2 \times \frac{\left[\frac{D}{2 \times \pi} \right]^2 \times \beta}{V_1 \times I_r}}$$

$$\omega_0 = \sqrt{2 \times \frac{\left[\frac{6.7 \text{ in}^3}{2 \times \pi} \right]^2 \times 2.0 \times 10^5 \text{ lb/in}^2}{80.4 \text{ in}^3 \times 2.1 \frac{\text{lb-ft}}{\text{sec}^2} 12 \frac{\text{in}}{\text{ft}}}}$$

$$\omega_0 = 14.9 \text{ sec}^{-1}$$

$$\omega = \frac{\omega_0}{3} = \frac{14.9}{3} = 4.96 \text{ sec}^{-1}$$

$$T = \frac{1}{\omega} = \frac{1}{4.96} = .202 \text{ sec}$$

Acceleration Time

$$T_b = T \times 6 = .202 \times 6 = 1.21 \text{ sec}$$

Acceleration Rate

$$a = \frac{V_{max}}{T_b} = \frac{3.28 \text{ ft/sec}}{1.21 \text{ sec}} = \frac{2.71 \text{ ft}}{\text{sec}^2}$$

It was stated previously that the required acceleration was to be 3.56 ft/s^2. The calculations show that a maximum acceleration of 2.71 ft/s² is all that is available if smooth running is to be achieved. In order to achieve a higher acceleration, the natural frequency of the system must be increased.

To increase the natural frequency of the system, the valve can be placed closer to the motor which in turn reduces the volume of oil trapped between the motor and valve. This gives a stiffer spring and allows for higher acceleration and deceleration rates.

If the system is recalculated with a tube length of 3.5 ft,

Trapped Oil Volume V_1

$$V_1 = A_p \times L + \frac{D}{2}$$

$$= \frac{\pi (.5 \text{ in})^2}{4} \times 42 \text{ in} + \frac{6.7 \text{ in}^3}{2}$$

$$= 11.6 \text{ in}^3$$

Natural Frequency ω_0

$$\omega_0 = \sqrt{2 \times \frac{\left[\frac{D}{2\pi}\right]^2 \times \beta}{V_1 \times I_t}}$$

$$\omega_0 = 40.9 \text{ sec}^{-1}$$

Achievable Acceleration

$$\omega = \frac{\omega_0}{3} = \frac{40.9}{3} = 13.65 \text{ sec}^{-1}$$

$$T = \frac{1}{\omega} = \frac{1}{13.65 \text{ sec}^{-1}} = .073 \text{ sec}$$

Acceleration Time

$$T_b = T \times 6 = .439 \text{ sec}$$

Acceleration Rate

$$a = \frac{V_{max}}{T_b} = \frac{3.28 \text{ ft/s}}{.439 \text{ sec}} = 7.47 \text{ ft/sec}^2$$

With the reduced oil volume between the motor and the valve, a recalculated acceleration rate of 7.47 ft/s² now allows the load to be accelerated at 3.56 ft/s² without the system going into instability.

Calculation of Natural Frequency in Hydraulic Cylinders
Double Rod Cylinders

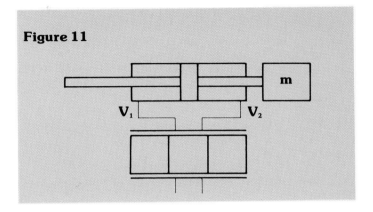

Figure 11

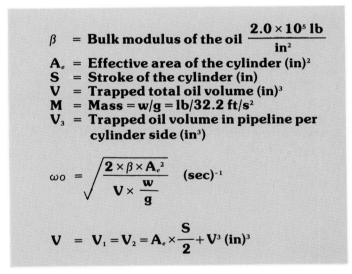

β = Bulk modulus of the oil $\frac{2.0 \times 10^5 \text{ lb}}{\text{in}^2}$
A_e = Effective area of the cylinder (in)²
S = Stroke of the cylinder (in)
V = Trapped total oil volume (in)³
M = Mass = w/g = lb/32.2 ft/s²
V_3 = Trapped oil volume in pipeline per cylinder side (in³)

$$\omega_0 = \sqrt{\frac{2 \times \beta \times A_e^2}{V \times \frac{w}{g}}} \quad (\text{sec})^{-1}$$

$$V = V_1 = V_2 = A_e \times \frac{S}{2} + V^3 \text{ (in)}^3$$

A double rod cylinder is at its minimum frequency when it is in midstroke, S/2 (Figure 11).

ACCELERATION AND DECELERATION CURVES

The following curves illustrate acceleration and deceleration time and distance for linear acceleration. They may be used to make close estimates of required acceleration rates or they can serve as a final check to see if previous acceleration calculations are correct. Referring back to the example, where the acceleration time was determined from the natural frequency for a 2:1 cylinder, the acceleration time was .20

seconds, the acceleration rate was 15.6 ft/s² and the velocity was 3.2 ft/s. The accelerating/time curve (Figure 12) shows that a suitable acceleration will be realized in a time of .20 seconds to obtain a velocity of 3.2 ft/s, proving that the calculations completed earlier are correct. If, however, we arbitrarily pick a velocity and assume we can accelerate in a particular time period, it can also be seen from the curves that uniform acceleration will not be achieved. For example, if it is desired to accelerate at 9.8 ft/s² in under .25 seconds to a velocity of 3.3 ft/s, the desired velocity will not be achieved. The curve also shows that if a very low acceleration rate is desired, a very long acceleration time is required. This can be established by the ramp setting on the amplifier. Ramp settings range from .03 seconds to 5 seconds, which is more than sufficient for setting acceleration and deceleration rates.

$$s = \frac{v^2}{2_a}$$

$$s = \frac{(37.5 \text{ in/s})^2}{2 \times 187 \text{ in/s}^2} = 4.0 \text{ in or } .33 \text{ ft}$$

When these values are graphically analyzed, linear acceleration is assumed (see Figure 13). This distance can also be used as a starting point as to where limit switches or proximity switches should be set. These switches are the electrical devices that are physically activated by the cylinder when the acceleration or deceleration point is reached; therefore it is desirable to set them as close to the actual deceleration point as possible.

Figure 12

Deceleration and Acceleration Time for Constant Acceleration

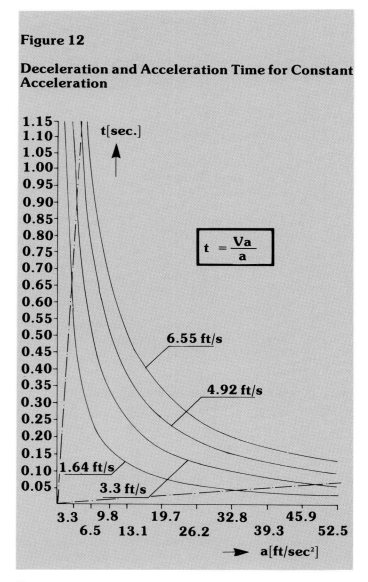

Figure 13

Deceleration and Acceleration Distance for Constant Acceleration (Deceleration)

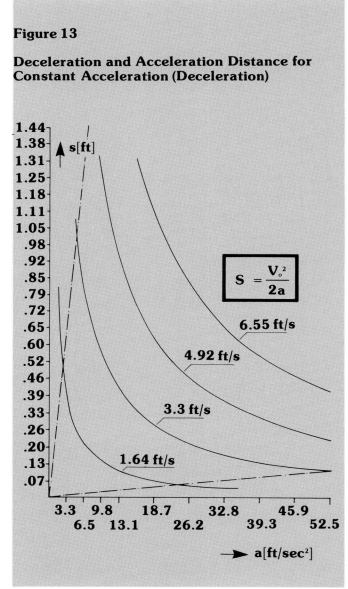

To determine the acceleration distance the linear acceleration distance curve (Figure 13) may be used. Referring back to the previous example, the acceleration distance is:

VALVE ANALYSIS

The calculations for the natural frequency of the system is only part of the design procedure that must be considered. In actuality, the natural frequency calculations may only need to be considered if a fast cycle time must be predicted in the design stage. When accuracy is the prime consideration, such as slow and smooth movement of a load, the natural frequency calculations may be considered only on an estimated basis.

The following information will be in regard to the two main types of proportional spools (1:1 and 2:1 spools) and the effects they have on overrunning loads and resistive loads. From this information a precise analogy may be made as to the proper selection of the valve. This is the final design procedure when considering a proportional valve, whether the natural frequency is calculated or estimated.

The calculations that follow have been worked through step by step to show the designer their origin. The resulting formulas have been charted at the end of this section to provide an easy reference guide for the user.

OVERRUNNING LOADS

Systems requiring a 2:1 cylinder should use a spool with a 2:1 area ratio. It was mentioned in Chapter 7 that a 2:1 spool is machined to give half the flow area on one land as compared to the other land. To further clarify this point, let us mathematically approach the reasoning behind why a 2:1 spool should be used with a 2:1 cylinder.

All proportional spools have the ability to meter-in and meter-out. Because of this orifice function, the equation for flow through an orifice applies (Figure 1).

$$Q = CA\sqrt{\Delta P}$$

Where Q = **Flow across the orifice (GPM)**
C = **Discharge coefficient**
A = **Area of the orifice (in^2)**
ΔP = **Pressure drop across the orifice (lb/in^2)**

At first glance, it may seem that extensive calculations would have to be done to determine the pressure drop across the valve; however, considering the load conditions of the system the calculations become rather easy. The first condition that can be satisfied is the orifice equation. This will be satisfied for a 2:1 spool and then for a 1:1 spool to show the adverse effects they cause when they are used with 2:1 cylinders.

Figure 1

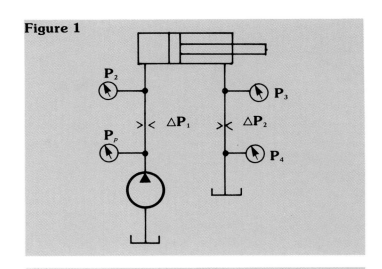

Figure 2

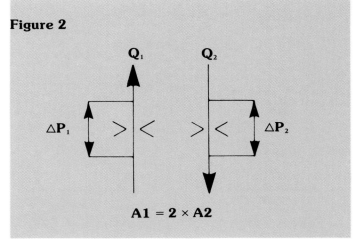

$$A1 = 2 \times A2$$

For a 2:1 cylinder with a 2:1 spool Q_1 = will always be double of Q_2's value (Figure 2).

$$A_1 = 2 \times A_2, \text{ or } A_2 = \frac{A_1}{2}$$

Since there are two orifices

$$Q_1 = CA_1\sqrt{\Delta P_1}$$
$$Q_2 = CA_2\sqrt{\Delta P_2}$$

We can set them equal to each other:

$$A_2 = \frac{A_1}{2} \text{ or } 2A_2 = A_1$$

Therefore:

$$A_2 = \frac{Q_2}{\sqrt{\Delta P_2}} = \frac{Q_1/\sqrt{\Delta P_1}}{2}$$

$$\left[\frac{Q_1}{2Q_2}\right]^2 = \frac{\Delta P_1}{\Delta P_2}$$

with a 2:1 flow relationship:

$$\Delta P_1 = \Delta P_2$$

The pressure drop will be fairly equal on both sides of the valve, giving good controllability for 2:1 cylinders.

For 2:1 cylinders with 1:1 spools however:

Figure 3

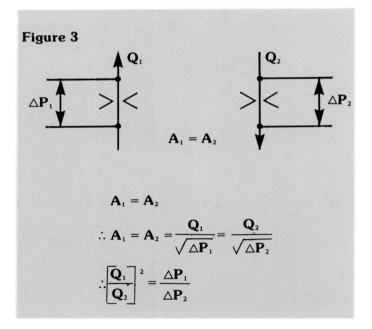

$$A_1 = A_2$$

$$\therefore A_1 = A_2 = \frac{Q_1}{\sqrt{\Delta P_1}} = \frac{Q_2}{\sqrt{\Delta P_2}}$$

$$\therefore \left[\frac{Q_1}{Q_2}\right]^2 = \frac{\Delta P_1}{\Delta P_2}$$

with a 2 to 1 flow relationship:

$$4\Delta P_2 = \Delta P_1$$

When using a 2:1 cylinder with a 1:1 spool area ratio (Figure 3), ΔP_1 is four times greater than ΔP_2. This can cause considerable problems if the required back-pressure on the rod end of the cylinder must be greater than 1/4 of system pressure. A vacuum can be created since the blind end of the cylinder will not completely fill with oil. To see this in more detail we will consider a condition where there is a 1000 lb. overrunning load, and a 1:1 spool with a 2:1 cylinder (Figure 4). This relates directly to the method used to determine the pressure drops across the valve as was previously mentioned.

Figure 4

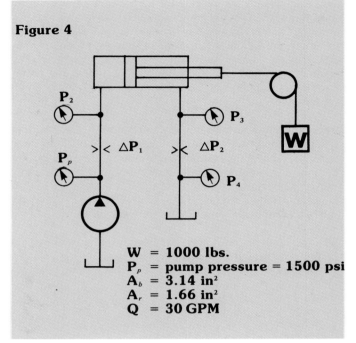

W = 1000 lbs.
P_p = pump pressure = 1500 psi
A_b = 3.14 in²
A_r = 1.66 in²
Q = 30 GPM

Based on Newton's Law a force balance must exist at constant velocity. If we let "F" represent the total net load (Assuming no friction F = W in this example) we can write:

$$P_2A_b + F = P_3A_r$$

$$P_3 = \frac{P_2A_b + F}{A_r}$$

We can also state:

$$\Delta P_1 = P_p - P_2$$

and

$$\Delta P_2 = P_3; \text{ assuming } P_4 = 0$$

Likewise the Pressure drops; (Based on P_2 and P_3 pressures), must also satisfy the orifice equation; which for a 1:1 spool is:

$$\left[\frac{Q_1}{Q_2}\right]^2 = \frac{\Delta P_1}{\Delta P_2}$$

From the above, by substitution and solving for P_2 the formula becomes:

$$P_2 = \cfrac{P_p\left[\dfrac{Q_1}{Q_2}\right]^2 - \dfrac{F}{A_r}}{\dfrac{A_b}{A_r} + \left[\dfrac{Q_2}{Q_1}\right]^2}$$

For the example Problem (Figure 4):

$$P_2 = \cfrac{1500\,\text{PSI}\left[\dfrac{15\,\text{GPM}}{30\,\text{GPM}}\right]^2 - \dfrac{1000\,\text{lbs}}{1.66\,\text{in}^2}}{\dfrac{3.14\,\text{in}^2}{1.66\,\text{in}^2} + \left[\dfrac{15\,\text{GPM}}{30\,\text{GPM}}\right]^2}$$

$$P_2 = -106\,\text{PSI}$$

Note: The minus sign indicate a vacuum would have to be created on the blind side of the cylinder. Since $P_p = 1500$ PSI the maximum ΔP_1, can be is:

$$\Delta P_1 = P_p - 0 = 1500\,\text{PSI}$$

The above calculation show that to satisfy the flow balance ΔP_1 would have to be:

$$\Delta P_1 = 1500 - (-106\,\text{PSI})$$

$$\Delta P_1 = 1606\,\text{PSI}$$

This of course is not possible!

EXAMPLE PROBLEM USING A 2:1 SPOOL

(Reference Figure 4):

$$P_3 = \frac{P_2 A_b + F}{A_r}$$

$$\Delta P_1 = P_p - P_2$$

$$\Delta P_2 = P_3$$

From the orifice calculation completed previously for 2:1 spools

$$\left[\frac{Q_1}{2Q_2}\right]^2 = \frac{\Delta P_1}{\Delta P_2}$$

By substitution; and solving for P_2 the formula becomes:

$$P_2 = \cfrac{P_p\left[\dfrac{2 \times Q_2}{Q_1}\right]^2 - \dfrac{F}{A_r}}{\dfrac{A_b}{A_r} + \left[\dfrac{2 \times Q_2}{Q_1}\right]^2}$$

For the example problem (Figure 4):

$$P_2 = \cfrac{1500\left[\dfrac{2 \times 15\,\text{GPM}}{30\,\text{GPM}}\right]^2 - \dfrac{1000\,\text{lbs}}{1.66\,\text{in}^2}}{\dfrac{3.14\,\text{in}^2}{1.66\,\text{in}^2} + \left[\dfrac{2 \times 15\,\text{GPM}}{30\,\text{GPM}}\right]^2}$$

$$P_2 = 309\,\text{PSI}$$

The cylinder does not pull a vacuum.

$$\Delta P_1 = P_p - P_2$$

$$\Delta P_1 = 1500 - 309$$

$$\Delta P_1 = 1191\,\text{PSI}$$

Since $\Delta P_2 = P_3$ and P_2 is now known

$$P_3 = \Delta P_2 = \frac{P_2 A_b + F}{A_r}$$

$$\Delta P_2 = \frac{309\,(3.14) + 1000\,\text{lbs}}{1.66\,\text{in}^2}$$

$$\Delta P_2 = 1182\,\text{PSI}$$

The valve would now be capable of keeping the load from

overrunning and from keeping the system from creating a vacuum. With a total pressure drop across the valve of 2373 PSI, however, the spool stroke would still have to be considerably limited.

Refering to the performance curve for the valve, at 70% control current and 30 GPM the total pressure drop across the valve is 1450 PSI (Figure 5). The calculated pressure drop was 2373 PSI. This means, to obtain the 30 GPM flow requirement at a 2373 PSI total pressure drop, control current would have to be limited to much less than 70%. Since a small orifice is required at this considerably high ΔP, very little of the spool stroke would be used. Also the resolution of the valve at this high ΔP will not be as good as if it were in the range of 1450 PSI and below, at the required flow rate. The load should be counterbalanced. This will be discussed later in this text.

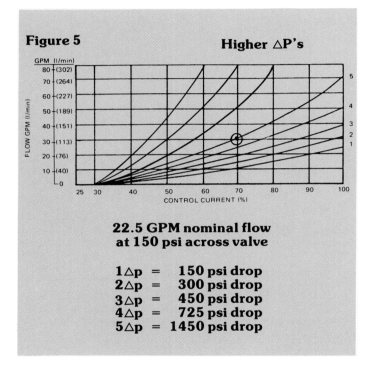

Figure 5   **Higher ΔP's**

22.5 GPM nominal flow at 150 psi across valve

$1\Delta p$	=	150 psi drop
$2\Delta p$	=	300 psi drop
$3\Delta p$	=	450 psi drop
$4\Delta p$	=	725 psi drop
$5\Delta p$	=	1450 psi drop

RESISTIVE LOADS

Now that the conditions for 1:1 and 2:1 valves have been satisfied for overrunning loads, we will look at how 1:1 and 2:1 valves are affected by a resistive load (Figure 6).

By summing forces, P_2 can be solved . . .

$$\Sigma F = P_2 A_b - (P_3 A_r + F)$$

$$P_2 = \frac{P_3 A_r + F}{A_b}$$

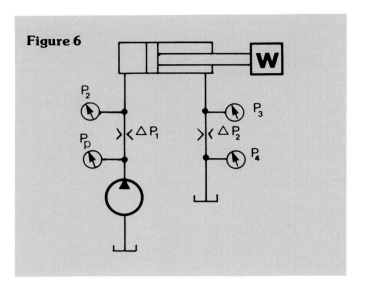

Figure 6

For a 1:1 valve . . .

$$\frac{\Delta P_1}{\Delta P_2} = \left[\frac{Q_1}{Q_2}\right]^2$$

$$\Delta P_1 = P_p - P_2$$

$$\Delta P_2 = P_3 - P_4^{\;0}$$

By substituting and solving for P_3 the formula becomes:

$$P_3 = \frac{P_p - \dfrac{F}{A_b}}{\left[\dfrac{Q_1}{Q_2}\right]^2 + \dfrac{A_r}{A_b}}$$

Likewise, for 2:1 valves with resistive load the formula is:

$$P_3 = \frac{P_p - \dfrac{F}{A_b}}{\left[\dfrac{Q_1}{2 \times Q_2}\right]^2 + \dfrac{A_r}{A_b}}$$

Using the same parameters as before for a 2:1 valve with a resistive load:

$$P_3 = \frac{1500\ \text{PSI} - \dfrac{1000\ \text{lbs}}{3.14\ \text{in}^2}}{\left[\dfrac{30\ \text{GPM}}{(2)(15)\ \text{GPM}}\right]^2 + \dfrac{1.66\ \text{in}^2}{3.14\ \text{in}^2}}$$

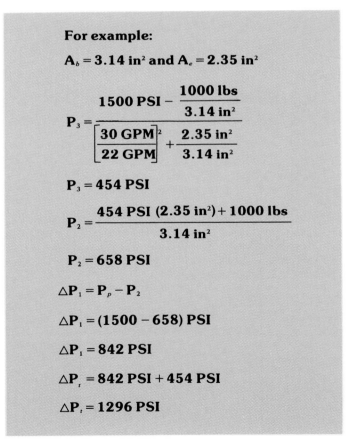

$$P_3 = 777 \text{ PSI}$$

Since $\triangle P_2 = P_3 = 777 \text{ PSI}$

$$P_2 = \frac{P_3 A_r + F}{A_b}$$

$$P_2 = \frac{777 \text{ PSI } (1.66 \text{ in}^2) + 1000 \text{ lbs}}{3.14 \text{ in}^2}$$

$$P_2 = 729 \text{ PSI}$$

$$\therefore \triangle P_1 = P_p - P_2$$

$$\triangle P_1 = 1500 - 729$$

$$\triangle P_1 = 771 \text{ PSI}$$

$$\triangle P_t = \triangle P_1 + \triangle P_2$$

$$= 771 \text{ PSI} + 777 \text{ PSI} = 1548 \text{ PSI}$$

The total pressure drop across the valve is 1548 PSI. To obtain this 1548 PSI pressure drop, and to use the maximum possible spool stroke, the optimum valve size would have to be selected from the operating curves. It is important to remember, that each direction and load condition will indicate an optimum valve size. The final selection of the valve will be the best compromise of all possible operating conditions. In comparing all the operating curves for each valve size for a 2:1 spool, the best choice for this operating condition is a 22.5 GPM 2:1 spool for a 30 GPM required flow rate and a total pressure drop of 1548 PSI across the valve.

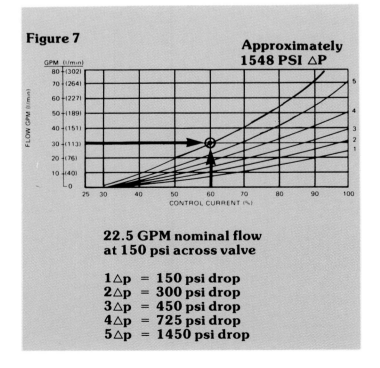

Figure 7

Approximately 1548 PSI $\triangle P$

GPM (l/min)

FLOW GPM (l/min)

CONTROL CURRENT (%)

22.5 GPM nominal flow at 150 psi across valve

1 $\triangle p$ = 150 psi drop
2 $\triangle p$ = 300 psi drop
3 $\triangle p$ = 450 psi drop
4 $\triangle p$ = 725 psi drop
5 $\triangle p$ = 1450 psi drop

VALVE SIZING CONSIDERATIONS DURING RETRACTION

At 30 GPM and a pressure drop of 1548 PSI approximately 60% control current is needed to establish the required total pressure drop. This is only considering one direction. If we recalculate the pressure drops in the other direction, and assuming it is desired to retract the cylinder as fast as possible, one must be careful that the flow and pressure drop requirements do not exceed the rating of the valve size-selected since the blind end flow will be double that of the rod end flow. The actual pressure drop in the retraction mode in this particular example would become quite high at 60 GPM return flow. Not all applications, however, require that the cylinder be retracted quickly. This means the valve size presented would be more than adequate if the retraction mode speed were not a major factor. If the cylinder must be retracted as fast as possible, a larger 2:1 valve may have to be selected. Not much of the spool stroke would be utilized in the extension mode, however, the amplifier presets can easily be set to give the required speed.

For a cylinder with an area ratio that is close to 1:1, the formula for a 1:1 valve is used. The parameters remain the same except for the cylinder area ratio.

For example:

$$A_b = 3.14 \text{ in}^2 \text{ and } A_e = 2.35 \text{ in}^2$$

$$P_3 = \frac{1500 \text{ PSI} - \dfrac{1000 \text{ lbs}}{3.14 \text{ in}^2}}{\left[\dfrac{30 \text{ GPM}}{22 \text{ GPM}}\right]^2 + \dfrac{2.35 \text{ in}^2}{3.14 \text{ in}^2}}$$

$$P_3 = 454 \text{ PSI}$$

$$P_2 = \frac{454 \text{ PSI } (2.35 \text{ in}^2) + 1000 \text{ lbs}}{3.14 \text{ in}^2}$$

$$P_2 = 658 \text{ PSI}$$

$$\triangle P_1 = P_p - P_2$$

$$\triangle P_1 = (1500 - 658) \text{ PSI}$$

$$\triangle P_1 = 842 \text{ PSI}$$

$$\triangle P_t = 842 \text{ PSI} + 454 \text{ PSI}$$

$$\triangle P_t = 1296 \text{ PSI}$$

A total pressure drop of 1296 PSI was calculated. Referring to figure 8, which is an operating curve for a 13.2 GPM spool (nominal flow rating) with a 150 PSI drop across the valve.

At 30 GPM and a calculated pressure drop of 1296 PSI; approximately 90% of the spool stroke can be utilized. For 30 GPM the calculated pressure drop of 1296 PSI will fall between curve 4 and 5.

Figure 8

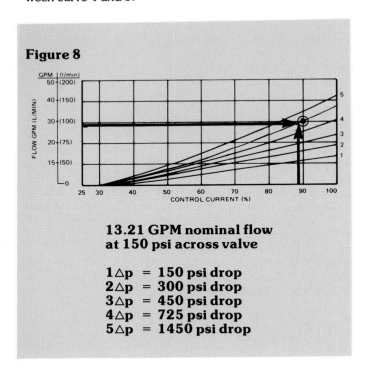

**13.21 GPM nominal flow
at 150 psi across valve**

$1\triangle p$ = **150 psi drop**
$2\triangle p$ = **300 psi drop**
$3\triangle p$ = **450 psi drop**
$4\triangle p$ = **725 psi drop**
$5\triangle p$ = **1450 psi drop**

COUNTERBALANCING WITH PROPORTIONAL VALVES

Proportional valves used to control a vertically acting load with a cylinder which has an area ratio close to 1:1 can use a direct operated counterbalance valve.

Although the proportional valve provides metering, the pressure drop needed at the required flow rate to keep the load from overrunning may become quite high. Both the pull of the load and the push of the pump, must be taken as a pressure drop across the valve.

For example, consider a down acting cylinder (Figure 9) with a 8.29 in² blind end and a 6.80 in² rod end which must vertically move a 5000 lb. load. Flow requirements are 40 GPM and pump pressure is set for 1200 PSI. Using the formula for overrunning loads (1:1 valve):

$$P_2 = \frac{P_P\left[\dfrac{Q_2}{Q_1}\right]^2 - \dfrac{F}{A_r}}{\dfrac{A_b}{A_r} + \left[\dfrac{Q_2}{Q_1}\right]^2}$$

$$P_2 = \frac{1200\ \text{PSI}\left[\dfrac{33\ \text{GPM}}{40\ \text{GPM}}\right]^2 - \dfrac{5000\ \text{lbs}}{6.8\ \text{in}^2}}{\dfrac{8.29\ \text{in.}^2}{6.80\ \text{in}^2} + \left[\dfrac{33\ \text{GPM}}{40\ \text{GPM}}\right]^2}$$

$$P_2 = 43\ \text{PSI}$$

$$\triangle P_1 = P_p - P_2$$

$$\triangle P_1 = 1200 - 43$$

$$\triangle P_1 = 1157\ \text{PSI}$$

$$P_3 = \frac{F + P_2 A_b}{A_r}$$

Figure 9

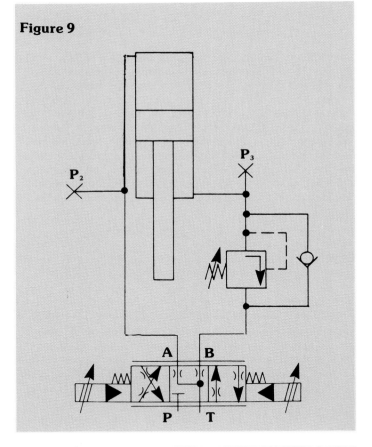

$$P_3 = \frac{5000\ \text{lbs} + (43\ \text{PSI})\ 8.29\ \text{in}^2}{6.80\ \text{in}^2}$$

$$P_3 = 787\ \text{PSI}$$

$$\triangle P_t = 1157\ \text{PSI} + 787\ \text{PSI}$$

$$\triangle P_t = 1947 \text{ PSI}$$

A loop pressure drop of 1947 PSI was calculated with no counterbalance valve. If we look at the particular pressure curve for the proportional valve used, the loop drop is fairly high for the valve.

Figure 10

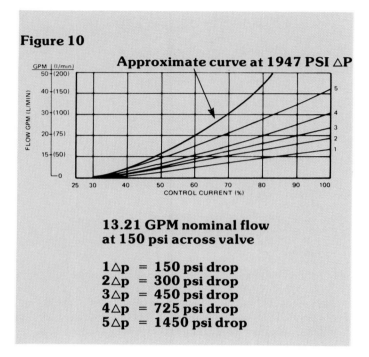

Approximate curve at 1947 PSI △P

13.21 GPM nominal flow at 150 psi across valve

1△p = 150 psi drop
2△p = 300 psi drop
3△p = 450 psi drop
4△p = 725 psi drop
5△p = 1450 psi drop

By using a direct operated counterbalance valve, better resolution of the valve can be obtained. It may seem that the counterbalance valve should be used directly between the rod end of the cylinder and the proportional valve (Figure 11), however, there are disadvantages to this. The setting of the counterbalance valve would be the pressure force over the cylinder's piston area needed to keep the load suspended. Also, we must remember that the proportional valve adds resistance downstream of the counterbalance valve. The spring chamber of the valve is therefore increased to whatever the pressure drop is over the proportional valve from A to T. If set at load induced pressure, the proportional valve controls the cylinder as if there were no load since the counterbalance valve holds the load at its pressure setting. The counterbalance valve is difficult to adjust properly, and introduces the possibility of rod end pressure intensification. This possibility can be eliminated if the counterbalance valve were to be externally drained. To clearly demonstrate this point we will consider a condition that has the following parameters. A double rod cylinder has an area of 10 in², and an overhung load of 45,000 lbs (P_p = 5000 PSI).

The actual setting of the counterbalance valve normally would be slightly more than 4500 PSI. (Chapter 2).

Because this is an equal area cylinder and valve, the pressure

Figure 11

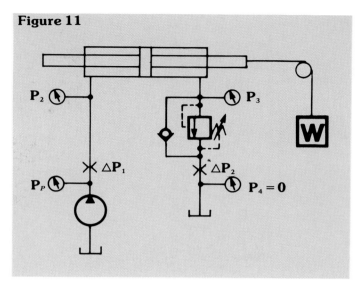

drop across the valve from P to A and B to T will be shared equally. Also, since the counterbalance valve's setting influences this condition as if there were no load, by summing forces the pressure drop on both sides of the valve will be 2500 PSI. The forces will balance such that the pressure on the load side of the cylinder will be 2500 PSI and 4500 PSI, which equals 7000 PSI. Likewise, the pressure at the opposite end will be 2500 PSI. 7000 PSI pressure at the load end is obviously quite high and cannot be tolerated. In actual applications if counterbalancing were used this way, depending on the load conditions, and the setting of the counterbalance valve the pressure at the rod end would not be as high. The problem still exists, however, and one must be aware of what can happen. A more acceptable way of counterbalancing can be seen in Figure 12.

By using a check valve and connecting the tank port of the counterbalance valve directly back to the tank, the propor-

Figure 12

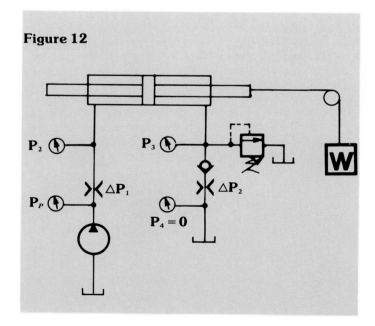

Figure 13

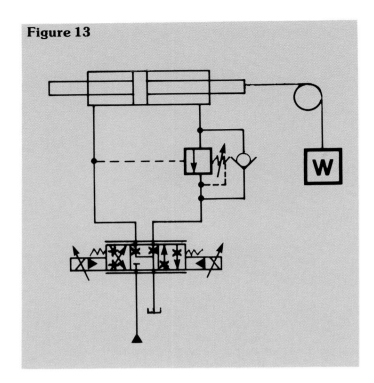

Figure 14

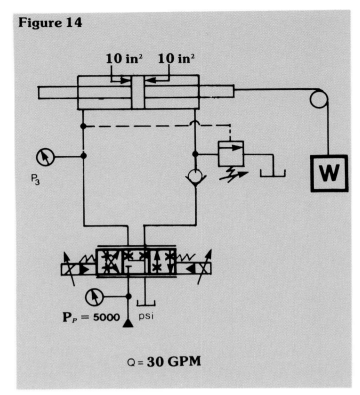

$Q = 30$ GPM

tional valve no longer influences the setting of the valve. Speed control can still be set electronically controlled since the proportional valve still will be metering-in when lowering the load. This also prevents damage to the cylinder if the proportional valve quickly closes due to a power loss, since the counterbalance also functions as a port relief valve.

When holding a load with a remote pilot operated counterbalance valve, it is more desirable to run the tank port of the valve directly back to the tank (Figure 14), as in the case of placing the valve directly between the valve and actuator (Figure 13) where there are two restrictions in series. Once again, as with the direct operated counterbalance valve, the pressure at the load side of the cylinder can become higher than expected due to the pressure felt at the spring chamber of the counterbalance valve unless the valve is externally drained. One should also remember that the setting of the counterbalance valve must also be higher than the pressure at the no load side of the cylinder P_3 (Figure 14). In this case as the load is being pulled up it acts as a resistive load. Since the proportional valve adds resistance to flow at the no load side of the cylinder, pressure at the no load side may be higher than the setting of the counterbalance valve when the load is being moved up. This could cause erratic movement of the load; therefore, the counterbalance valve must be set

higher than the pressure at the no load side of the cylinder. To calculate the pressure at P_3 for this condition, the equation for a 1:1 valve can be used. (See chart of equations on Pages 9-20.) The pressure at the no load side would be 250 PSI; therefore, the counterbalance valve would have to be set slightly higher than 250 PSI.

$$P_3 = \frac{P_P - \dfrac{F}{A_r}}{\left[\dfrac{Q_1}{Q_2}\right]^2 + \dfrac{A_h}{A_r}}$$

$$P_3 = \frac{5000 \text{ PSI} - 45{,}000 \text{ lbs} / 10 \text{ in}^2}{\left[\dfrac{30 \text{ GPM}}{30 \text{ GPM}}\right]^2 + \dfrac{10 \text{ in}^2}{10 \text{ in}^2}}$$

$$P_3 = 250 \text{ PSI}$$

APPLICATION	OVERRUNNING LOAD 2:1 VALVE	
DIRECTION	P_2 P_p $\triangle P_1$ Q_1 Q_2 P_3 $P_4 = 0$ W	W P_2 P_p $\triangle P_1$ Q_1 P_3 $P_4 = 0$ $\triangle P_2$ Q_2
PRESSURE AT P_2	$P_2 = \dfrac{P_p \dfrac{(2 \times Q_2)^2}{Q_1{}^2} - \dfrac{F}{A_r}}{\dfrac{A_b}{A_r} + \dfrac{2 \times Q_2{}^2}{Q_1{}^2}}$	$P_2 = \dfrac{P_p \dfrac{Q_2{}^2}{(2 \times Q_1)^2} - \dfrac{F}{A_b}}{\dfrac{A_r}{A_b} + \dfrac{Q_2{}^2}{(2 \times Q_1)^2}}$
PRESSURE AT P_3	$P_3 = \dfrac{F + P_2 A_b}{A_r}$	$P_3 = \dfrac{F + P_2 A_r}{A_b}$
PRESSURE DROP ACROSS VALVE	$\triangle P_1 = P_p - P_2$ $\triangle P_2 = P_3$ $\triangle P_t = \triangle P_1 + \triangle P_2$	$\triangle P_1 = P_p - P_2$ $\triangle P_2 = P_3$ $\triangle P_t = \triangle P_1 + \triangle P_2$

APPLICATION	OVERRUNNING LOAD 1:1 VALVE	
DIRECTION		
PRESSURE AT P_2	$$P_2 = \dfrac{P_p \dfrac{Q_2{}^2}{Q_1{}^2} - \dfrac{F}{A_r}}{\dfrac{A_b}{A_r} + \dfrac{Q_2{}^2}{Q_1{}^2}}$$	$$P_2 = \dfrac{P_p \dfrac{Q_2{}^2}{Q_1{}^2} - \dfrac{F}{A_b}}{\dfrac{A_r}{A_b} + \dfrac{Q_2{}^2}{Q_1{}^2}}$$
PRESSURE AT P_3	$$P_3 = \dfrac{F + P_2 A_b}{A_r}$$	$$P_3 = \dfrac{F + P_2 A_r}{A_b}$$
PRESSURE DROP ACROSS VALVE	$\triangle P_1 = P_p - P_2$ $\triangle P_2 = P_3$ $\triangle P_t = \triangle P_1 + \triangle P_2$	$\triangle P_1 = P_p - P_2$ $\triangle P_2 = P_3$ $\triangle P_t = \triangle P_1 + \triangle P_2$

APPLICATION	RESISTIVE LOAD 2:1 VALVE	
DIRECTION	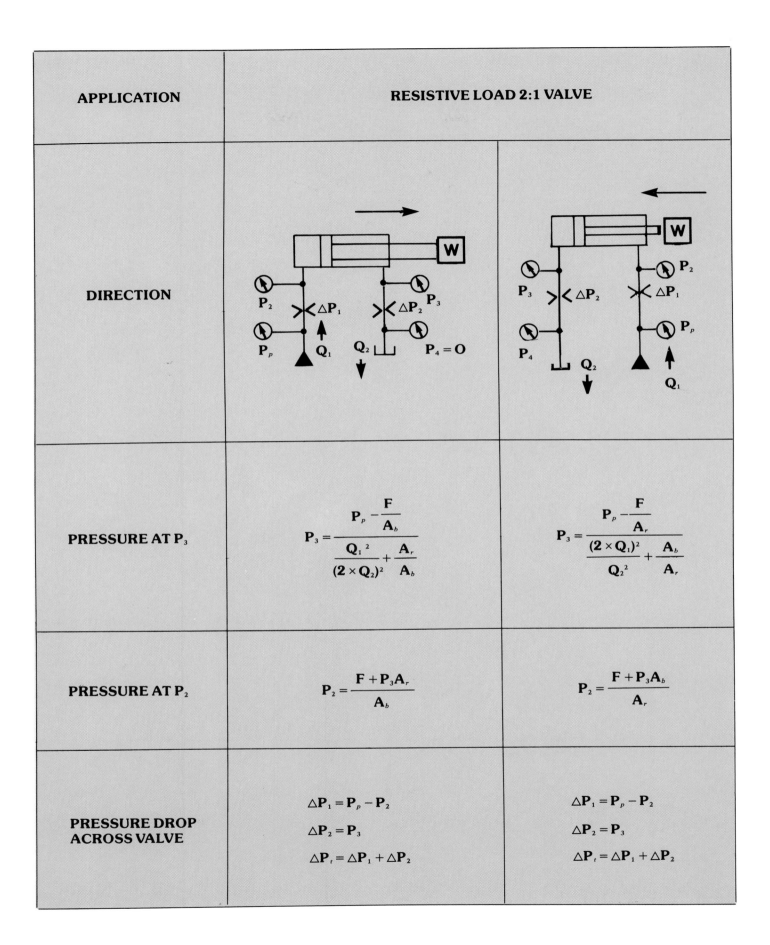	
PRESSURE AT P_3	$$P_3 = \dfrac{P_p - \dfrac{F}{A_b}}{\dfrac{Q_1{}^2}{(2 \times Q_2)^2} + \dfrac{A_r}{A_b}}$$	$$P_3 = \dfrac{P_p - \dfrac{F}{A_r}}{\dfrac{(2 \times Q_1)^2}{Q_2{}^2} + \dfrac{A_b}{A_r}}$$
PRESSURE AT P_2	$$P_2 = \dfrac{F + P_3 A_r}{A_b}$$	$$P_2 = \dfrac{F + P_3 A_b}{A_r}$$
PRESSURE DROP ACROSS VALVE	$\triangle P_1 = P_p - P_2$ $\triangle P_2 = P_3$ $\triangle P_t = \triangle P_1 + \triangle P_2$	$\triangle P_1 = P_p - P_2$ $\triangle P_2 = P_3$ $\triangle P_t = \triangle P_1 + \triangle P_2$

APPLICATION	RESISTIVE LOAD 1:1 VALVE	
DIRECTION		
PRESSURE AT P_3	$$P_3 = \dfrac{P_p - \dfrac{F}{A_b}}{\dfrac{Q_1{}^2}{Q_2{}^2} + \dfrac{A_r}{A_b}}$$	$$P_3 = \dfrac{P_p - \dfrac{F}{A_r}}{\dfrac{Q_1{}^2}{Q_2{}^2} + \dfrac{A_b}{A_r}}$$
PRESSURE AT P_2	$$P_2 = \dfrac{F + P_3 A_r}{A_b}$$	$$P_2 = \dfrac{F + P_3 A_b}{A_r}$$
PRESSURE DROP ACROSS VALVE	$\triangle P_1 = P_p - P_2$ $\triangle P_2 = P_3$ $\triangle P_t = \triangle P_1 + \triangle P_2$	$\triangle P_1 = P_p - P_2$ $\triangle P_2 = P_3$ $\triangle P_t = \triangle P_1 + \triangle P_2$

CHAPTER 10
ACCESSORIES

Today, hydraulic systems play a vital role in keeping industry in production. Unfortunately, there are many hydraulic systems now in operation which do not have the accessory equipment necessary to provide for easy maintenance and trouble-shooting. These "no frills" systems are a product of cost cutting system design, which excludes *extra cost* items that have no apparent influence on the operation of the system. However, the hydraulic system must be dependable and this can only be achieved by designing into the system components which will provide for better serviceability, easier troubleshooting, and longer system life.

After much experience with hydraulic applications, we have concluded that only two types of hydraulic systems exist: those which have been designed with the proper accessories, and those to which the necessary accessory components have been added in the field. Once we accept the fact that accessory items are mandatory for proper operation, we must also accept the fact that it is less expensive to include these items in the design stage than to add them on later. In addition, we will be able to enhance both the appearance and serviceability of the system if we integrate these components in the overall design stage.

This chapter is intended to familiarize you with some of the more popular accessories. We will discuss pressure switches, pressure gauges, gauge protectors, modular manifolds, accumulators, and filters.

In modern day hydraulics, safety and automation have made the pressure switch a very important system component. Classical applications include: pressure dependent sequential interlocks, high/low pressure unloading, audio or visual warning systems, and all types of safety interlocks. Pressure switches not only protect expensive components and machinery, but they also provide for operator safety. By nature of their application, extreme operating conditions must be considered in their design and use so that dependable operation is guaranteed. Typical operating conditions include:

— Long periods of pressurization
— High cycle frequency
— High pressure peaks
— Thermal shock
— Mechanical vibration
— Hydraulic pulsations
— Silting by contaminated fluids

Basically, there are two different pressure switch designs to meet the needs of various operating requirements. They are the piston and the Bourdon tube pressure switches.

THE PISTON DESIGN PRESSURE SWITCH

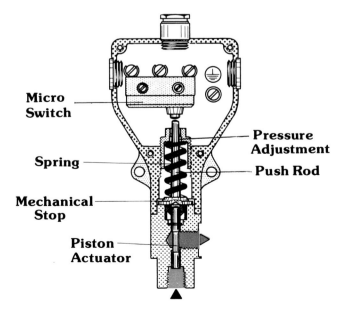

PRESSURE SWITCHES

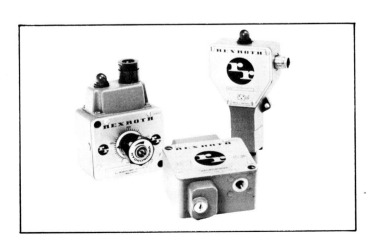

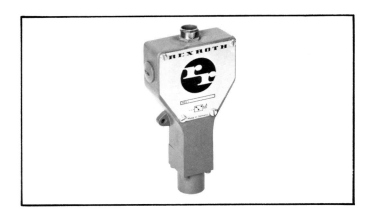

cycles/minute), high repeatability (± 1.5% of set pressure), small pressure differential between on and off positions (a deadband within 5% of set pressure), and extremely long life expectancy (10^7 cycles).

The cross-sectional illustration shows the basic design of this piston actuator. The bottom area of the spool is exposed to system pressure, while leakage past the spool is drained through the "L" port. The housing of the switch is sealed from leakage oil by the low pressure, low friction seal located above the "L" port. The seal in this design seals only leakage oil. Since it is not designed for exposure to high system pressures, the maximum allowable pressure on port "L" is 30 PSIG.

The piston design pressure switch should be selected for use in systems with high switching frequencies or in those which have strong mechanical vibration and/or hydraulic pulsation. The basic design incorporates a die cast aluminum housing which includes the spring chamber, pressure adjustment, micro switch, and wiring box. Attached to the bottom of this aluminum housing is a piston actuator assembly. Depending on the intended use, the piston actuator can be ordered with or without a leakage port connection. In either design the operating principle is identical. The valve actuates when a system pressure, working on the area of the piston actuator, overcomes the spring force. This causes a slight upward motion of the push rod, which, in turn, causes the micro switch to become activated. The mechanical stop prevents overloading of the spring, and limits the travel of the push rod so that the micro switch is not damaged.

Before discussing the merits of the various pressure switch designs it is important that we define two terms used to describe the performance capability of these pressure switches. The first term, *deadband*, describes the pressure differential between the rising pressure which activates the switch and the falling pressure which deactivates the switch. In general, if a switch is set to actuate at some particular set pressure, then each time *pressure increases* to this point the micro switch is activated. Deactivation, on the other hand, does not normally occur at this same set pressure. Because of static friction, we find that a typical pressure switch generally deactivates at a pressure which is slightly lower than the pressure which originally actuated the switch. *Repeatability* is the second term used to define the performance capability of any pressure switch. Simply stated, repeatability is the accuracy with which the switch actuates on consecutive pressure cycles. Let us now look at the various designs and their intended applications.

PISTON ACTUATED SWITCHES WITH LEAKAGE CONNECTIONS

The piston design pressure switch with leakage connection provides for a low friction piston actuator because it eliminates the pressure loaded dynamic sealing. This feature is particularly suited for high cycle frequency (up to 200

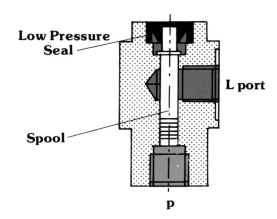

The actuator housing is made of gray cast iron with a hardened steel spool. The clearance between the spool and housing is between 8 to 12 microns (see Chapter 5), which allows a maximum leakage of .18 in³/min at maximum operating pressure. Although this limits the use of the switch in small accumulator circuits, spool clearance and low pressure sealing provide the highest possible accuracy at all operating pressures because friction does not increase with system pressure. This feature is not possible in models with pressure load seals.

As with any direct spring operated component, the spring constant (Chapter 2) can influence the operating characteristics of the pressure switch. However, since the switch does not have to handle varying flow rates, it is not influenced by pressure override (Chapter 2). For this reason, only three different springs are necessary to provide adequate adjustment sensitivity in the pressure range from 70 to 7250 PSI. The built-in mechanical stop (shown in the first cross section) protects the micro switch from damage and allows peak pressures of up to 8700 PSI.

THE PISTON ACTUATED PRESSURE SWITCH WITHOUT LEAKAGE CONNECTION

The piston design pressure switch without leakage connection is particularly suited for operating conditions which include high levels of mechanical and/or hydraulic oscillation, contaminated oil, and long periods of pressurization. In this design, the piston actuator uses a U-cup seal on the pressurized side of the spool. At 5000 PSI the seal has a life expectancy of 5×10^6 cycles, with a proportional increase in life expectancy as operating pressure decreases. Since the seal is a normal wearing item, the piston actuator is designed for easy seal replacement.

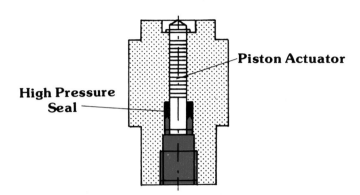

High Pressure Version

As shown in the cross-sectional illustration, the location of the seal not only protects against leakage, but it also prevents contamination from entering the close tolerance fit between the piston and its housing. Consequently, jamming of the spool because of silting during long periods of pressurization is not a problem with this design.

Pressure loading of the seal forces it against the spool, thus increasing friction. This high friction serves as a dampener for mechanical and hydraulic pulsations, but it also has an influence on the operating characteristic of the switch. The deadband with this design is pressure dependent with the average deadband being approximately 15% of set pressure. The average repeatability is within ± 2% of the pressure setting.

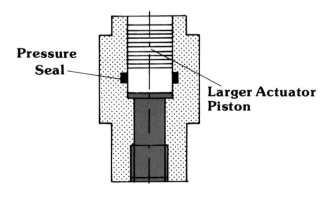

Low Pressure Version

As shown in the cross-sectional illustration, the low pressure version of this design incorporates a larger piston than do the higher pressure models. On this model, the seal's friction characteristics become a lower percentage of the shifting force (larger area means higher force), and, consequently, they provide more favorable characteristics. In this model the average deadband drops from 15 to 9% of set pressure, with an average repeatability of 1.5% of set pressure.

To obtain suitable life expectancy for the high pressure seal, the maximum cycle frequency should be kept below 50 cycles per minute. The high pressure seal limits the maximum pressure, so excessive pressure spikes should be avoided.

PISTON ACTUATED PRESSURE SWITCHES WITH DIFFERENT MOUNTING STYLES

Up to this point, we have shown only line mounted pressure switches which must be "teed" into the plumbing of the hydraulic system. The cross sectional illustration shows a more compact design piston actuated pressure switch, which can be easily adapted for line mounting, subplate mounting, or sandwich mounting between the directional control valve and its subplate. The sandwich mounted version can be supplied with one or two switch assemblies attached to the adaptor plate. Adaptor plates are available with passages which allow the switch(es) to sense pressure in either the P, A, or B ports of the directional control.

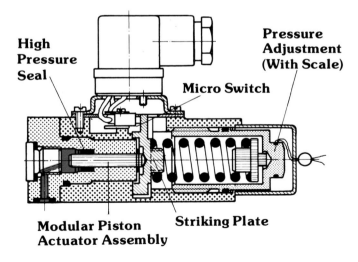

Pressure Switch For Subplate (Manifold) Mounting

The cross-sectional illustration shows a piston actuated pressure switch which operates in a slightly different manner from the one discussed up to this point. In this design, the spring holds the striking plate in a position which actuates the single pole double throw micro switch. As pressure increases in the piston actuator assembly, the spring collapses and allows the striking plate to move away from the micro switch. When the switch *deactivates*, the electrical path through the switch is changed. As you can see in the cross section, the movement of the striking plate is limited to prevent overstressing of the spring when system pressure goes higher than the switch setting. Because of the compact design, this switch is only available with a high pressure seal on the piston actuator. Consequently, a model with a leakage port is not available.

Piston Actuator Module With Threaded Port.

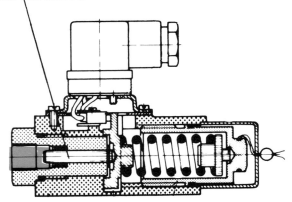

Line Mounted Version

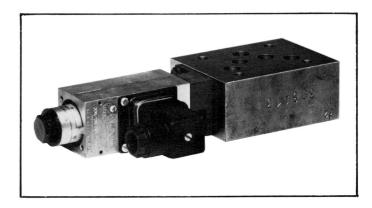

Sandwich Mounted Version

BOURDON TUBE PRESSURE SWITCHES

The Bourdon tube pressure switch is available in two different designs. One design offers a key locked pressure setting which is read directly from the pressure scale. The second design offers two independently adjustable micro switches which allow for an infinitely adjustable deadband. Let us now take a closer look at the operating principle of the Bourdon tube design pressure switch.

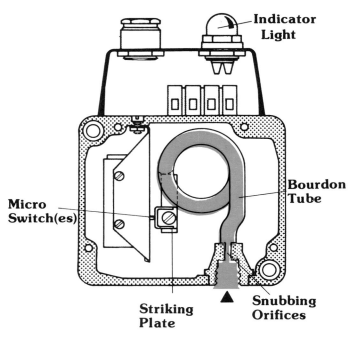

Bourdon Tube Pressure Switch

The cross-sectional illustration shows the general arrangement of the Bourdon tube, micro switch(es), and striking plate. The Bourdon tube is a helical wound tube which is connected to system pressure at one end and sealed at the other end. When the tube is pressurized, it tends to straighten. The expansion of the helical coil causes the free end of the tube to move proportionately to the pressure applied internally. The pressure adjustment is made simply by changing the position of the micro switch with respect to the striking plate on the free end of the tube. The micro switches are spring loaded so that they are not damaged by further tube expansion when system pressure goes beyond the pressure setting of the switch.

The special advantages of the Bourdon tube design are:
— Extreme accuracy
— Small pressure differential
— No seal or leakage problems
— Insensitive to contamination
— Assured of functioning even after long periods (years) of pressurization
— Can be used with gases as well as liquids

The sensitivity of the Bourdon tube is a desireable feature of this type of switch. However, in designing a system with a Bourdon tube pressure switch, you must be aware that the pressure setting will be quite inaccurate if the pressure switch is subjected to mechanical vibration or hydraulic pulsations.

With respect to mechanical vibration we must remember that the helical coil of tube is suspended in free air, and is supported only at one end. If the housing of the switch is rigidly mounted to a vibrating member of the machine's frame, the vibration will be transmitted to the tube. The spring action of the tube will amplify this mechanical vibration, which, in turn, will cause erratic and unwanted activation of the micro switch. To avoid transmitting this mechanical vibration to the Bourdon tube, the switch housing frequently must be mounted on resilient rubber shock mounts with the pressure connection being made of a short piece of hose.

With very little mass and virtually no sliding friction the Bourdon tube responds quickly to changes in system pressure. In fact, it is quite possible that the Bourdon tube will sense the pulsation in system pressure as created by the pump. To help alleviate this potential problem, the standard switch is supplied with an orificed inlet to the tube. Nevertheless, additional orificing or the use of a sintered metal gauge snubber may be required. By using a coil of hose for the pressure connection, the capacitance of the hose will help dampen the hydraulic pulsations.

THE BOURDON TUBE PRESSURE SWITCH WITH FIXED PRESSURE DEADBAND

The photograph shows a typical Bourdon tube pressure switch with a fixed pressure deadband. This design incorporates one single pole double throw micro switch, which is activated by the positioning of the Bourdon tube under pressure. The lockable hand knob positions the micro switch by means of a mechanical cam, and has a pressure scale for setting the actuating pressure. The accuracy of the pressure scale is ±2% of the maximum pressure rating. Since the pressure rating of the switch is based on the strength of the Bourdon tube, five different tubes are available to cover the 20 to 6000 PSI pressure range. Repeatability of the Bourdon tube design is better than ± 1% of set pressure.

**Fixed Deadband
Bourdon Tube Pressure Switch**

The life expectancy of the Bourdon tube design is directly influenced by the mechanical integrity of the tube and the pressure at which the switch operates. To prevent premature damage due to overstressing of the tube (by overpressurization) a mechanical stop is provided in the switch housing. Likewise, for maximum life, it is recommended that the cycle frequency be kept below 30 cycles per minute.

THE BOURDON TUBE PRESSURE SWITCH WITH AN ADJUSTABLE PRESSURE DIFFERENTIAL

This model is identical in operation to the model previously discussed except for the fact that this switch contains two micro-switches with a different means of independantly adjusting their position. When used in conjunction with an electrical relay, the pressure differential is infinitely variable between maximum and minimum values. Let us now take a look at a typical application of this switch.

The accumulator unloading circuit is a classical application for a pressure switch with an adjustable pressure differential (deadband). When used with a normally open solenoid vented relief, the switch offers precision control of the maximum and minimum pressure limits of the accumulator. The pressure switch with solenoid vented relief is sometimes preferred over the accumulator unloading valve (Chapter 2) simply because the pressure differential can be set at the value necessary to meet the requirements of the system. Remember that with the accumulator unloading valve the pressure differential is established only by the area differential in the pilot valve. Of course, this area differential is not adjustable. The following electrical diagram shows the typical wiring of a switch for this application.

The electrical schematic shows the pressure switch with adjustable pressure differential, a double pole double throw coil relay (use of only the normally open contacts is indicated), the solenoid on the solenoid vented relief, and two indicator lights. Initially, upon start-up of the system, the coil relay is energized through the normally closed contact of the low pressure micro switch. This causes CR-A and CR-B to close. The solenoid is energized (which loads the relief valve) through CR-B.

As system pressure increases to the low pressure setting, the low pressure micro switch is activated, which causes the "Low Pressure Exceeded" indicator light to function. At this point, the coil relay is still "latched" in by the electrical connection through the normally closed contacts of the high pressure micro switch and the now closed CR-A contacts.

The third part of the cycle functions when system pressure reaches the high pressure setting of the second micro switch. Activation of this switch causes illumination of the "High Pressure" indicator light, and, at the same time, "drops out" the coil relay. This, in turn, causes CR-A and CR-B to open. Opening of CR-B causes de-energization of the solenoid and vents the pump to tank. Opening of CR-A "resets" the system. Once CR-A opens, the coil relay can only be reactivated if system pressure drops below the setting of the low pressure switch.

PRESSURE GAUGES

Obviously, pressure gauges indicate the operating pressure in the part of the system to which they are connected. Once the pressure is known, the output force or torque fo the actuator can be calculated precisely. Pressure gauge indications are also necessary when you are adjusting a pressure control or setting the pressure adjustment on a variable displacement pump control. However, in addition to these more obvious uses, pressure gauges play an even more important role in the operation of the hydraulic system.

The pressure gauge is probably the most important tool available to the person who must trouble shoot a hydraulic system. By studying a circuit schematic we can determine the pressure level that is supposed to exist in a given part of the circuit, but, without the aid of a pressure gauge, we have

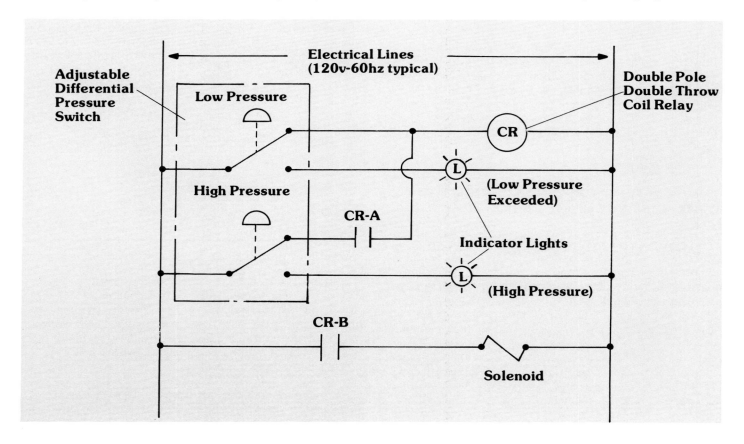

no means of *seeing* if this pressure really exists. For instance, pressure gauges are instrumental in determining if a directional valve has shifted, in ascertaining whether or not the sequence valve has opened, in tracing hydraulic lines, etc. For these reasons, an adequate number of pressure gauges must be provided in the design stage so that the pressure in each portion of the circuit can easily be determined once the system is actually functioning. If a system requires so many gauges that its construction would not be feasible or economical, plugged gauge port connections should be provided in the plumbing. In this way, the *troubleshooter* can more easily install the required gauges in order to determine the pressure levels in different portions of the circuit.

PRESSURE GAUGE OPERATION

The operating principle of the pressure gauge is similar to that of the Bourdon tube pressure switch. As shown in the cross-sectional illustration, the Bourdon tube is connected via mechanical linkage to the pointer's gear drive. As the pressurized tube expands, the gearing is repositioned, and it moves the pointer so that the pressure can be read directly from the pressure scale.

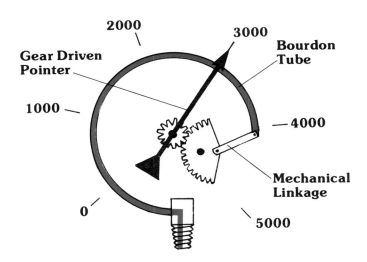

GAUGE INSTALLATION

The Bourdon tube design allows extreme gauge accuracy at a nominal cost. Production gauges typically display an accuracy of better than 2% of the full scale pressure. Nevertheless, these gauges are no more accurate than the Bourdon pressure switch if they are subject to mechanical or hydraulic pulsation. When you are selecting a gauge for permanent mounting in the hydraulic system, remember that the full scale pressure should be 1½ to 2 times the maximum operating pressure of the system. This prolongs the life of the gauge by preventing an overstress of the Bourdon tube.

When you are installing the gauge, we recommend that you use a gauge shut-off or a *gauge isolator valve*. This will isolate the gauge from the system until a pressure reading is required. The simplest form of shut-off valve is a ¼" needle valve, while the more sophisticated gauge isolator valve is designed specifically for this purpose.

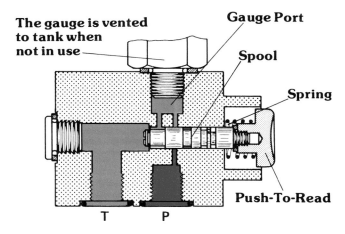

Gauge Isolator Valve

The cross-sectional illustration shows a typical push-to-read gauge isolator valve. This valve is similar in function to a manually operated 3-way spool type directional control. In the spring offset position, pressure is blocked and the gauge is vented to tank. Pushing the button blocks the tank connection and exposes the gauge to system pressure. The major advantage of the gauge isolator valve is that it prevents an improper interpretation of the actual pressure in the system. A needle valve, if shut off under pressure, can actually capture pressurized fluid in the gauge. If this occurs, the gauge can read full system pressure even if there is no pressure in the system. Consequently, the gauge isolator valve offers the convenience of isolating the gauge even during operation of the system.

The gauge isolator valve, as shown in the illustration, connects pressure to the gauge port through small diameter passages in the valve body. This restricted flow area provides an orifice effect which dampens out the hydraulic pulsations, helping to avoid inaccurate pressure reading (needle flutter). Although this orificing is sufficient for most applications, it is sometimes necessary to use a *gauge snubber* to dampen out all the hydraulic pulsations.

Gauge snubbers come in a variety of designs and models, but their sole purpose is to prevent hydraulic pulsation from reaching the pressure gauge. The cross-sectional illustration shows a sintered metal snubber, which is commonly used in hydraulic systems.

The sintered metal snubber is nothing more than a ¼" NPT fitting which incorporates a sintered metal insert. The sin-

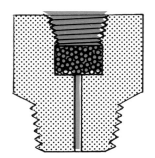

**Sintered
Metal
Insert**

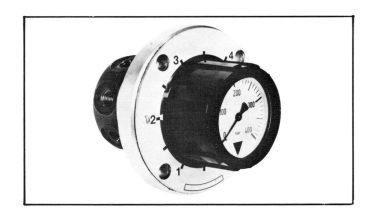

tered metal is porous, and it allows fluid to reach the gauge only after passing through many small passages. This provides good gauge stability by isolating the gauge from hydraulic pulsations. Typical sintered metal gauge snubbers come in a variety of porosities for use with fluids of different viscosities. The porosity of the element is selected to give favorable gauge response while at the same time preventing needle flutter.

Finally, when mounting the gauge, remember to isolate the gauge from mechanical vibration. This is most easily accomplished by remotely mounting the gauge and using a length of hose to make the pressure connection. For installation convenience, pressure gauges are offered in a variety of pressure ranges with several different mounting styles. The two most popular are the ¼" NPT lower male connection and the ¼" NPT center back male connection with face flange for panel mounting.

GLYCERIN FILLED GAUGES

The glycerin filled gauge, although slightly more expensive, is far superior to the dry gauge for use on hydraulic systems. The glycerin filled gauge is similar to the dry gauge in operation, except for the fact that the gauge housing is sealed, and then filled with a viscous clear liquid, *glycerin*. The glycerin lubricates the gauge mechanism and the high viscosity dampens the vibration of the needle created by either mechanical or hydraulic pulsations. However, there are two precautions concerning the use of glycerin filled gauges. First, the gauge must be mounted vertically with the case vent at the top. This, of course, will prevent leakage of the glycerin from the gauge housing. Second, glycerin has the tendency to "*yellow*" when exposed to direct sunlight. This can make the pressure scale difficult to read.

THE MULTI-CIRCUIT GAUGE ISOLATOR

The multi-circuit gauge isolator is a convenience item which allows the operator to check the operating pressure at as many as six points in the circuit directly at the control con-

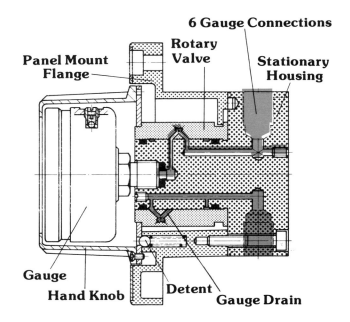

Multi-Circuit Gauge Isolator

sole. As shown in the cross-sectional illustration, the multi-circuit gauge isolator consists of six radially arranged gauge ports, a tank connection, and a separate master gauge port (not shown).

The rotary hand knob turns the valving mechanism, and, when properly positioned, it connects one of the six gauge ports to the pressure gauge. Between each of the six radially arranged gauge ports, there is a gauge drain passage (shown in blue) which vents the gauge to a common tank port. As shown in the photograph, the rotary hand knob has a pointer and a scale which indicate which pressure connection is being read. The zeros indicate that the gauge is isolated from the circuit.

MODULAR MANIFOLDS

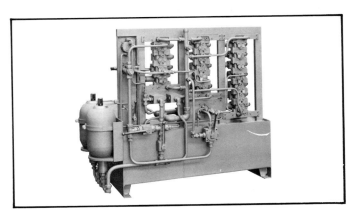

Because of the complexity of today's hydraulic systems, many hydraulic equipment suppliers have sought new ways of piping the many valves needed for such sophisticated circuitry. Within the past several years, the modular manifold has become the logical answer for piping the multitude of valves needed in today's complicated circuits. Consequently, modular manifolds are growing in popularity, not only to OEM's, but also to the end user market.

There are many reasons for this increased interest in modular manifold units. One advantage for OEM's is that the units can be received from the factory ready to install on their equipment, thus greatly reducing costly labor involved in piping. Furthermore, their final piece of machinery is neat in appearance and easy to service, since hundreds of feet of pipe have been eliminated. It no longer looks like a plumber's nightmare. Likewise, the end user can cut costs and give his equipment a finished look, while retaining the flexibility for future re-design or disassemblement and re-use of the modular manifolds in other designs. The information which follows is intended to show the general processes to be followed in building a modular unit in the most economical way. If your interest is aroused by modular manifolds, you need only let this information kindle your imagination, for the

combinations available from the items now on the market are unlimited.

In a general sense, a modular manifold is made up of modules, pieces of standard size, which are fitted together in a variety of ways to comprise the desired manifold. That is, the modular subplate is manufactured in such a way that the subplate of one control valve can be combined in the manifold with the subplate of any other control valve. For complete versatility, such subplates are manufactured for any one of the multitude of valves needed in today's sophisticated circuits.

A modular subplate for a 4-way directional control valve is a good example to use to further explain the modular method for reduction of interconnecting piping. Basically, a modular subplate consists of a valve mounting face, external connections for A & B Ports, and a series of standardized through ports which allow any combination of connections with other control valves. A typical modular subplate for a directional control valve may be described as one with a standard ANSI/NFPA mounting face for the valve, three pipe tap plugs on the opposite side to allow for pressure connection for the entire system, connections for the A & B Ports as required, with five through ports to interconnect the 4-way valve with other valves in the manifold. In a usual modular manifold system, external piping is reduced by reserving the center passage for system pressure and the two inner passages to connect the A & B Ports with other parts of the system, thus reserving the two outer most passages for tank connections, external pilots, or diverted oil flows from other passages in the manifold.

Modular Subplate for ANSI DO2 Directional Valve

Although subplates of all control valves are designed for their most probable usage, (for instance a pressure reducing valve would be connected to the pressure passage in the center and the "A" passage to one side), it sometimes becomes necessary to change the flow from one passage to another. This can be accomplished by the use of an *interconnecting plate*, which is bolted between the subplates of two different valves. Interconnecting plates are designed so that any number of ports can be connected or diverted into another passage. Likewise, interconnecting plates are usually supplied with plugged piped ports on the back side so that hydraulic oil can be diverted into or out of any one or more of the passages within the modular system. Consequently, interconnecting plates combined with *divider plates*, greatly add to the versatility of the modular manifold.

End plates, the finishing touch to a modular system, mount against the two end subplates of the module, needing only O-rings for an oil tight seal. Like inter-connecting plates, end plates add to the versatility of the modular manifold since they are available with pipe connections for oil passages within the manifold. Being the last component of a modular system, end plates not only terminate internal oil passage, but they are also drilled to allow mounting of the complete system to the machinery.

Interconnecting Plate

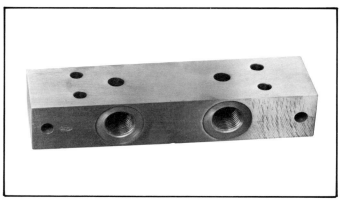

End Plate

Divider plates serve two purposes within a modular manifold system. Available in many different patterns, a divider plate is basically a flat piece of steel which is either drilled to allow the flow to continue from one subplate to another, or not drilled to block the flow of oil. Apart from controlling flow within the modular manifold, divider plates have a second function. That is, divider plates are used as O-ring seats, allowing a leak proof connection between the modular subplates. Therefore, divider plates are normally a necessity in making connection within the modular manifold. However, they are not required when mounting the "end plates."

In review, we now have *modular subplates* for use with almost any hydraulic control valve, each having standardized oil passages which allow the valves to be connected in an undetermined number of ways. Moreover, we have further methods of controlling the direction of oil flow with *interconnecting* and *dividing plates*, and with *end plates* to finish the unit and allow us to mount the entire system.

BUILDING THE MODULAR MANIFOLD

In order to have a common basis, we must discuss the special modular symbols used in conjunction with the ANSI/NFPA standard symbols for describing segments of a module unit. Basically, all the valving of a modular manifold system is depicted by standard symbols. However, to describe oil passages and connections within the manifold, a special set of symbols becomes necessary. Usually, a subplate is denoted by horizontal lines showing the internal oil passages, as viewed from the valve mounting face. Likewise, all pipe ports on the back of manifold segments, along with other connections, are viewed from the valve mounting face as described in the following table.

Since module subplates of a particular type of valve are quite similar, combinations of NFPA symbols and special modular symbols form what can be called a group symbol.

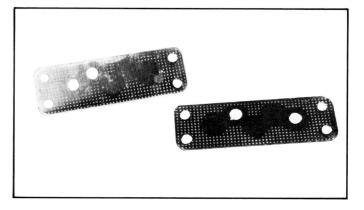

Divider Plates

——	**Main oil passages**		**Connection porting to the valve mounting face, and plugged threaded port on the line connection side**
- - - - -	**Pilot oil passages**		**Connection porting to the valve mounting face, and open threaded port on the line connection side**
· · · · · · ·	**Drain oil passages**		
	Connection porting to the valve mounting face of a subplate	—‖—	**Passage between two adjoining sub-plates or inter-connecting plates blocked, using "blank" dividing plate**
	Connection porting in an inter-connecting plate	—‖—	**Passage between two adjoining sub-plates or inter-connecting plates continued, using drilled dividing plate**
	Plugged threaded port on line connection side		
	Open threaded port on line connection side		**Passage between sub-plate and valve blocked**

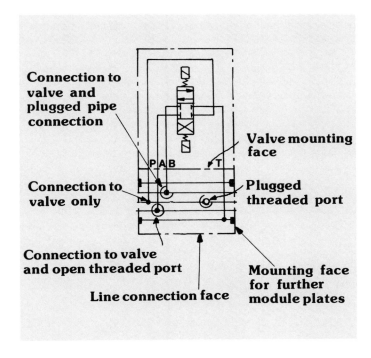

Group Symbol

Connection to valve and plugged pipe connection

Valve mounting face

Connection to valve only

Plugged threaded port

Connection to valve and open threaded port

Mounting face for further module plates

Line connection face

Valve port letters are given on the dividing line between the valve and the module subplate. Consequently, the special module symbols, along with standard NFPA valve symbols, must be kept in mind as we design a module circuit.

In order to design a module unit economically, and to avoid confusion, you should first draw a working conventional circuit. For purposes of this discussion, we have chosen a two legged circuit. The circuit, which operates from one pump, operates two cylinders which are controlled by two directional control valves. One leg of the circuit contains a pressure compensated flow control for meter out speed control of the cylinder, while the other leg of the circuit has a fine throttle valve and a pressure reducing valve for speed and pressure control of the cylinder. The entire system is protected by a pressure relief valve. The installation of a modular manifold can eliminate virtually all interconnecting piping in this circuit, reducing construction costs and giving a neater appearance.

Because modular manifold systems offer complete versatility, the designer should first draw a conventional circuit, then consider the many possibilities, and, finally, conceive the module from the best of his ideas. Indeed, planning ahead at this early stage will prove to be of economic value in the actual assembly of the modular manifold.

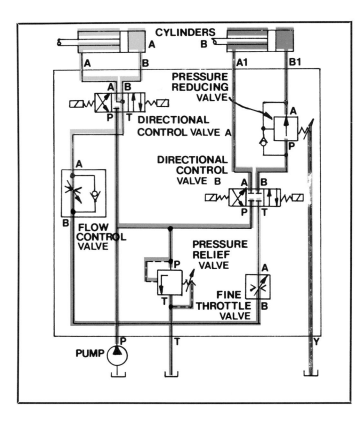

Conventional Circuit Schematic

Since the module unit we are to design has two separate circuits with a relief valve common to both legs, it is probably most advantageous to start our module with the subplate of the relief. Therefore, the first decision is to make a pump connection to the center (pressure) passage of the relief valved module subplate. Having chosen this common starting point, you must remember that there are now two ports in use, pressure (center) and tank (outside).

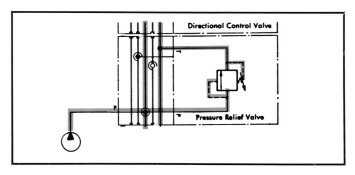

Pressure Relief Valve Module

At this time, a decision should be made to work one leg of the circuit, saving the second leg for later on. To avoid confusion, we have chosen the left leg of the conventional circuit, electing to finish the leg with the 4-way directional control and the pressure compensated flow control first. The

other leg of the circuit will be connected to the remaining side of the pressure relief subplate at a later time.

Having made this decision, we must consider the use of a dividing plate before connecting the directional control valve module subplate to the unit. The divider plate is necessary not only to make a positive O'ring seal between the two subplates, but also to allow only the needed passages to be open.

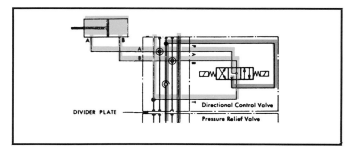

Directional Control Module

Since the left leg of the circuit will receive pressure from the center passage and utilize an outside passage for a tank connection, the remaining ports should be blocked, thus isolating them for future use if necessary. Consequently, the subplate for the directional control valve may now be bolted with O'rings and the divider plate to the subplate of the relief valve. No interconnecting plates are required since the center passage of the directional control is connected to the pressure port of the valve. It should be noted, at this point, that the subplate of the directional valve is turned end for end (another versatile feature of the module system), so that the tank port of the directional control valve is isolated from that of the relief valve, since this line must be directed through a pressure compensated flow control (the next valve to be mounted). Having connected this valve as described, an account of our oil passages shows that there are external connections for A & B ports on the back side of the subplate, and two tank line passages. That is: the tank line from the relief passes undisturbed through the subplate, and the tank line from the directional control which is to be connected to the flow control.

Once again taking account of all oil passages we must choose a suitable dividing plate. In this situation, we would choose a dividing plate which would allow the two outside (tank) lines to flow into the next module component, blocking off the three center passages, since the pressure passage (center) must only be connected to the directional control, while the A & B connections (inner passages) must be externally connected to the cylinder.

A close look at the subplate for the pressure compensated flow control will show that the A & B ports of this valve are connected to passages other than those which have been established so far. Since the A port of the flow control is connected to the center passage, while the B port is connected to one of the inner passages, we must choose the correct interconnecting plate. This plate would be one which diverts one of the outermost passages to the center passage, and also diverts the other outside passage to one inside. It is shown in the following diagram.

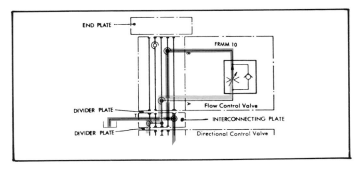

Interconnecting Plate & Flow Control Module

In review, oil flows from the tank port of the directional control valve to the outside passage in the subplate. The flow of oil then passes through the inter-connecting plate, being switched into the center passage of the flow control subplate. The oil, which is routed through the valve, exits through the B port (inner passage) and again enters the interconnecting plate, where it is diverted to the tank line passage. Consequently, this leg, with the addition of an end plate which blocks off all passages, is now complete. Thus, a divider plate with a center and one inner passage open is all that is needed to bolt the pressure compensated flow control to the unit. A pipe connection is provided on the back side of the interconnecting plate for an external connection to the tank.

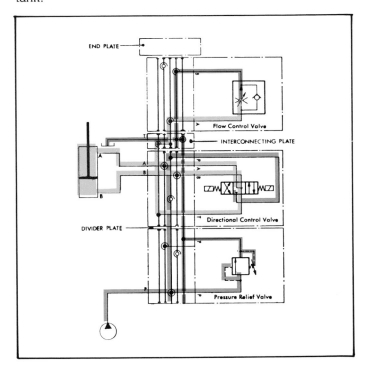

Having finished the left leg of the module circuit on one side of the pressure relief valve, we can now complete the modular manifold by isolating the right leg on the opposite side. A review of the conventional circuit will show that

system pressure enters a 4-way directional control which has its A port connected directly to the cylinder, while the pressure from the B port is controlled by a pressure reducing valve. The speed of the cylinder is controlled by metering the oil from the directional valve's tank port through a fine throttle (needle) valve. Knowing the particular control valves needed, we can now build the final leg of the circuit.

Since system pressure first enters the directional control valve through the center passage, we must choose a suitable dividing plate. Because the tank line is already externally connected, we should connect this passage with the left leg of the module. Accordingly, the correct choice of an interconnecting plate would be one with center (pressure) and one of the outermost passages (tank) open.

After adding the four way directional control valve to the module manifold, we must now consider the following passages. First of all, the A port of the valve enters one of the inner passages, which must be blocked on both ends because this port is externally connected to the cylinder. Secondly, the pressure passage must be blocked from any additional valving, since system pressure will be distributed by the directional control, thus terminating the pressure passage in this subplate. Furthermore, as with the module subplate of the left leg, this one is also rotated 180°, thus isolating the tank line passage of the 4-way valve so that the control of flow through the existing system tank line passage will be directed, undisturbed, through the subplate for future use with additional valves. Consequently, we must choose a divider plate which will block only the A (inner) and pressure (center) passages, allowing the others to flow into the additional valves in the system.

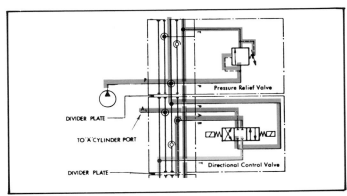

Directional Control Valve Module

There are now only two remaining valves to be added to the system to complete our module unit. Accordingly, it is most suitable to add the fine throttle valve next, as we did the flow control in the left leg, since the external pilot drain connection needed for the pressure reducing valve (final valve) can be made easily through the end plate.

Having added the fine throttle valve, we can readily see the need for an interconnecting plate to connect the existing passages with the correct ones in the subplate of the fine throttle valve. Since the A port of the fine throttle valve is connected with an inner passage, while the B port is connected to the center passage, the isolated tank line of the 4-way valve must be diverted to an inner passage. Likewise, the existing system tank line must be directed into the center passage to be connected to the fine throttle valve. The B port of the directional control valve is connected with a passage that will flow through the interconnecting plate and the subplate of the fine throttle valve undisturbed. The addition of the fine throttle valve along with the correct interconnecting and dividing plate is shown as follows.

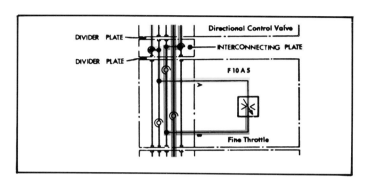

Fine Throttle Valve Module

To complete the system only the B port passage from the 4-way directional control must be controlled by the pressure reducing valve. Since the inner passage from the 4-way valve allows oil to flow into the correct passage (P connection) of the pressure reducing valve subplate, a divider plate must be chosen to block all passages allowing only an inner passage open for the straight line flow of oil from the B Port of the directional valve. The valve with the correct dividing plate is connected as shown, with an external pipe connection to the B port of the cylinder made on the back side of the modular assembly.

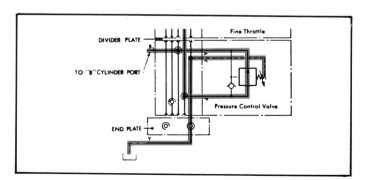

Pressure Reducing Valve Module

The modular manifold is now complete, using only the number of pipe runs necessary to make connections to the cylin-

ders, pump, and reservoir. The modular conversion requires some careful planning, but in the long run, the time the engineer spends at this will be far less than the assembly time required to pipe the components individually. The actual hardware of the module as described is shown in the two photographs. The compactness of this design is readily apparent considering the fact that 6 valves are mounted on a manifold which is just slightly over two feet in length. The back side of the modular unit shows the pipe connects to the remote parts of this hydraulic system.

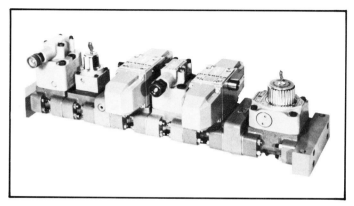

Module Unit as Described in the Text

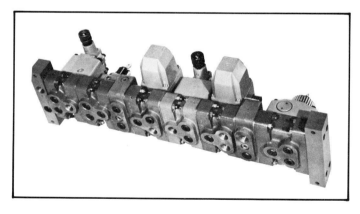

Back Side of Module Shows Pipe Connections

Modular manifolds not only reduce piping and provide answers to design problems, but they also serve as a form of preventive maintenance. That is, any complex hydraulic unit that is to be piped by the conventional method not only requires an undesirable amount of assembly time, but it also creates hidden problems as the number of pipes and fittings increases. All too often it is found that a valve entangled in a cage of pipes is virtually inaccessible when the time comes for service or replacement. This is not true with a modular manifold, since all piping is done from the back of the unit, placing all the valves within easy access of the repairmen. Another advantage which results from the reduction of

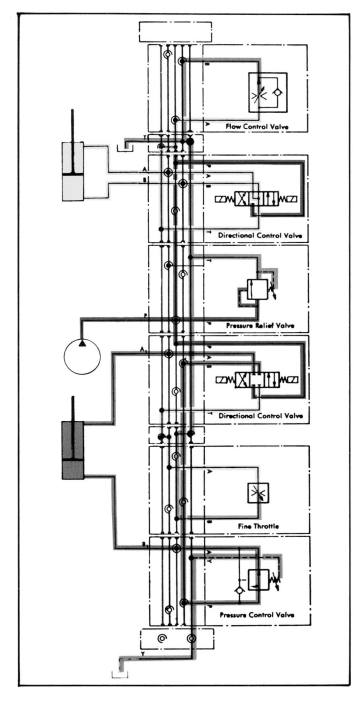

Complete Modular Schematic for System as Described in the Text

Merely adding, rearranging, or eliminating module components allows flexibility for modification virtually impossible with a drilled type manifold.

Although the module system, as described, deals with mounting single components on a particular module subplate, sandwich mounted valves, as discussed in other chapters can be used to add to the versatility of the system.

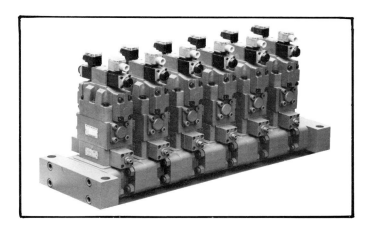

Modular unit mounting a total of 18 different valves. Sandwich mounted double pilot operated check valves and sandwich mounted dual flow controls are used with each of the six 50 GPM directional controls.

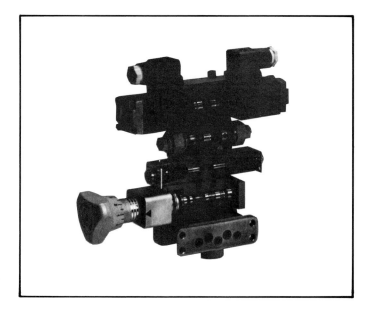

Directional valve with sandwich mounted dual pilot operated check, dual flow control, and pressure reducing valve all mounted on a modular subplate.

piping is the elimination of the leakage that is so common in a system with numerous fittings.

Off-the-shelf module components make the modular method for reducing piping the most flexible system available. Modular manifolds, unlike cross drilled manifolds, never become obsolete. That is, if a circuit needs to be modified or discontinued, module components permit field changes.

ACCUMULATORS

Today there are three types of accumulators which can be used in a hydraulic system: the weight loaded, the spring loaded, and the gas charged. The first two consist basically of a hydraulic cylinder which has a force exerted on one side of its piston by either a vertically acting weight or a heavy spring. Hydraulic fluid then enters the opposite side of the cylinder, and, as pressure rises, lifts the weight or compresses the spring. The fluid is then stored in the housing of the cylinder, until system pressure drops to the point at which the weight or the spring can *push* oil back into the hydraulic system. With the weight loaded accumulator, system pressure will remain constant as fluid discharges from the accumulator because the weight exerts a constant force. The spring loaded accumulator, on the other hand, causes a decay in system pressure as the accumulator discharges. This happens because the spring force relaxes as the spring becomes longer, during discharge.

Although the weight loaded and spring loaded accumulators can be used successfully, they are usually home made devices, incorporating standard hydraulic cylinders. The gas charged accumulator, on the other hand, is a very popular accessory which can be used to perform many different functions. Since gas charged accumulators are by far the most popular, this section will be devoted to the design, application, and installation of these components.

OPERATION OF GAS CHARGED ACCUMULATORS

A gas charged accumulator stores a non-compressible fluid, under pressure, by compressing an inert gas (nitrogen). When the accumulator is empty of oil, the gas chamber is *precharged* to a predetermined *precharge pressure* with nitrogen gas. Then, as oil enters the accumulator, the gas is compressed. The pressure at the accumulator's oil port is proportional to the amount of fluid *stored* in the accumulator. This pressure increases as oil is pumped into the accumulator, and it decreases as the accumulator discharges. Today, there are two popular variations of the basic gas charged accumulator. They are the piston accumulator and the bladder type accumulator. Let us now take a look at each design.

THE PISTON TYPE ACCUMULATOR

The cross-sectional illustration shows the operating principle of a typical piston type accumulator. In this design, a sealed but movable piston isolates the gas chamber from the oil chamber. The accumulator is precharged with nitrogen gas to a level dictated by the system requirement. During operation, when system pressure exceeds the gas precharge pressure, oil enters the accumulator and forces the piston up-

(Courtesy of Greer Hydraulics, Inc.)

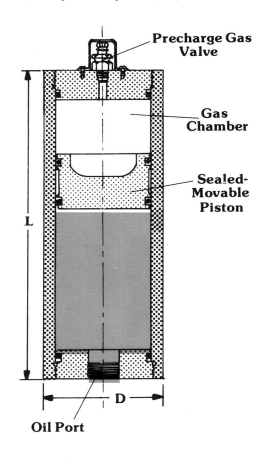

Precharge Gas Valve

Gas Chamber

Sealed-Movable Piston

Oil Port

Piston Type Accumulator
(Courtesy of Greer Hydraulics, Inc.)

ward. This compresses the gas, which increases the pressure in the accumulator.

A major advantage offered by the piston type accumulator is that it can operate with an infinite gas compression ratio. In addition, the piston accumulator can be fully discharged during the operating cycle without fear of damage. Conversely, the disadvantage of this design is that the friction caused by the piston seals, and the inertial mass of the piston tend to slow the accumulator's response characteristics. Also, the piston seals are subject to wear, and eventually to leakage of the precharge. For this reason, the piston type accumulator generally requires a more frequent check on the precharge pressure.

BLADDER ACCUMULATORS

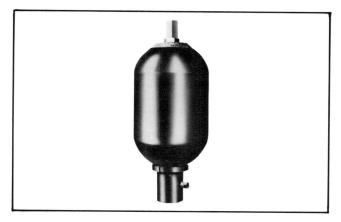

(Courtesy of Greer Hydraulics, Inc.)

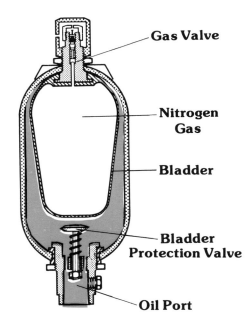

Gas Valve

Nitrogen Gas

Bladder

Bladder Protection Valve

Oil Port

Basic Bladder Accumulator

Accumulators with the bladder design are probably used more frequently than the others. As shown in the cross-sectional illustration, the bladder accumulator has a steel outer wall which contains the operating pressure of the system. A rubber bladder serves as the separating barrier between the gas chamber and the oil chamber. Initially, the oil port is vented to atmospheric pressure, and the rubber bladder is precharged with nitrogen gas through the gas valve. Precharging the bladder causes it to stretch until it comes completely in contact with the retaining walls of the vessel. During precharging, the mushroom shaped bladder protection valve closes, which prevents the bladder from extruding through the oil connection port.

During operation of the hydraulic system, once system pressure exceeds the precharge pressure, oil enters the accumulator and compresses the rubber bladder and the gas it contains. Needless to say, the more the gas is compressed, the higher the system pressure must be. Likewise, as system pressure decays from maximum to minimum, the gas expands and forces an oil flow from the accumulator.

Because the bladder of the accumulator has very little mass and virtually no friction, this design responds to changes in pressure almost instantaneously. In fact, the bladder type accumulator reacts to changes in system pressure faster than any other type of hydraulic system component.

There are two precautions concerning the selection of a bladder type accumulator which are worthy of mention at this point. First, to avoid damage to either the bladder or the bladder protection valve, the accumulator must be sized large enough so that it will not close the anti-extrusion valve during normal system operation. As will be shown, this protection can also be accomplished through the selection of the proper precharge pressure. Second, it is detrimental to the life expectancy of the rubber bladder to compress it too much. To avoid excessive bladder deformation when the accumulator is fully charged, there is a defined gas compression ratio which must not be exceeded.

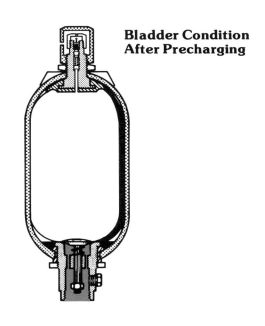

Bladder Condition After Precharging

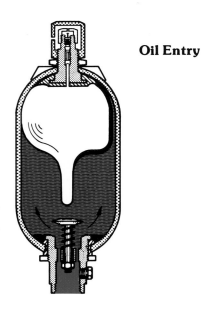

Oil Entry

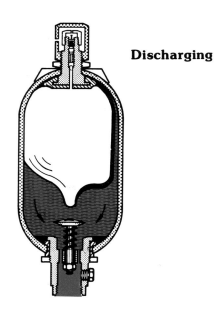

Discharging

CALCULATIONS FOR GAS CHARGED ACCUMULATORS

We have shown that the gas charged accumulator is a pressure storage vessel, which stores the potential energy of an incompressible fluid against the compressible force of an inert gas. For this reason, the amount of energy stored by an accumulator is influenced by the pressure and volume conditions of the *gas*. The calculations for determining the pressure and volume conditions are summarized by the mathematical relationship known as Boyle's Law.

Simply stated:

$$P_1V_1 = P_2V_2 = \textbf{Constant}$$
(with constant gas temperature)

Where: P_1 = initial gas pressure (PSIA)

V_1 = initial gas volume (in³)

P_2 = final gas pressure (PSIA)

V_2 = Final gas volume (in³)

This formula implies that if we have a volume of gas (V_1) stored at a pressure (P_1), an increase or decrease of the volume will also change the pressure. You will notice that if V_2 is larger than V_1, then P_2 must be smaller than P_1. Likewise, if V_2 is smaller than V_1, then P_2 is greater than P_1. It is important to remember that a gas completely fills its containing vessel. Therefore, the volume of the gas is determined by the volume of its container. A ten gallon accumulator, when precharged, holds a *gas volume* of ten gallons. *It does not mean that this same accumulator will store 10 gallons of pressurized fluid.* Before examining the following example, it is important for you to note that the pressure must always be represented as absolute pressure (Chapter 1) when using Boyle's Law.

Example: A 5 gallon accumulator is precharged with nitrogen to 1500 PSI. What would the volume of oil be if the gas pressure increased to 3000 PSI?

$$P_1V_1 = P_2V_2$$

P_1 = Absolute pre-charge pressure =
   1500 PSIG + 14.7 PSI = 1514.7 PSIA

V_1 = Initial gas volume = 5 gallon $\times \dfrac{231 \text{ in}^3}{\text{gallon}}$ = 1155 in³

P_2 = Final pressure (absolute) = 3000 PSIG + 14.7 PSI = 3014.7 PSIA

V_2 = Final *gas* volume (in³)

solving for V_2 we can write:

$$V_2 = \frac{P_1}{P_2} V_1$$

$$V_2 = \frac{1514.7 \times 1155}{3014.7}$$

$$V_2 = .502 \times 1155$$

$$V_2 = 580 \text{ in}^3$$

Since V_2 = final *gas* volume the oil volume would be the initial gas volume minus the final gas volume or

$$V_{oil} = V_1 - V_2 = 1155 - 580 = 574 \text{ in}^3.$$

There is sometimes a problem when using Boyle's Law to calculate the expected volume and pressure conditions. The problem is that the formula is accurate only when the temperature of the gas remains constant, while the pressure and volume conditions change. Unfortunately a gas increases in temperature when it is compressed, and it cools as it expands. This means that the formula would be accurate only if sufficient time were available for the accumulator to stabilize at room temperature after a change in volume of the gas occurred. This *isothermal change* of pressure and volume would only be applicable when the duty cycle of the accumulator was quite slow.

THE ADIABATIC CHANGE

The *adiabatic* change of pressure and volume condition is one in which the process of change in volume and pressure occurs so quickly that *no heat* can transfer into or out of the gas. This means that if the gas is being compressed, the heat given off during compression would warm up the gas and increase its pressure to a point higher than would be indicated by the simple relationship of Boyle's Law. Also, during discharge of fluid from the accumulator, the gas cools as it expands. Since the temperature would be somewhat lower than room temperature, the final pressure in the gas would be lower than that calculated by using the formula of Boyle's Law. The relationship between an isothermal process and an adiabatic process is shown in the graph.

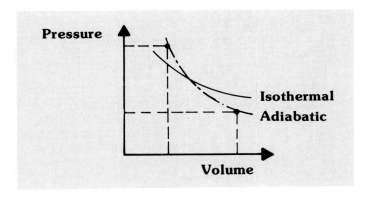

Comparison of Isothermal and Adiabatic Volume Change of Pressure and

Although the formula which expresses the adiabatic change of pressure and volume condition is similar in appearance to Boyle's formula, mathematically it is somewhat more difficult to use. Let us now state this formula, and then we will attempt to explain its use in simple terms:

$$P_1 V_1^n = P_2 V_2^n = \text{Constant}$$

In this formula "n" is the molar specific heat ratio of the gas.

It is beyond the scope of this text to fully explain what is meant by the term molar specific heat of a gas. Fortunately, if we accept the fact that the molar specific heat ratio for nitrogen is 1.4, the understanding of this term is not essential to our calculating pressure and volume conditions of an accumulator which undergoes an adiabatic change of condition. The following example explains the mathematics involved in working with this formula. You will notice that it is necessary to work with logarithms. This will require the use of log tables, a slide rule or a pocket calculator with a log function.

Example: A 5 gallon accumulator is pre-charged with nitrogen to a pressure of 1500 PSI.

1. What volume of oil will the accumulator store when rapid oil entry increases the gas pressure to 3000 PSI. 2. How much oil will be discharged if the system pressure then drops quickly to 2250 PSI?

1. Solution:

$$P_1 V_1^n = P_2 V_2^n$$

P_1 = absolute pre-charge pressure =
    1500 PSI G + 14.7 PSI = 1514.7 PSIA

V_1 = Initial gas volume = $\dfrac{5 \text{ gallon} \times 231 \text{ in}^3}{\text{gallon}}$ = 1155 in^3

P_2 = maximum pressure (absolute) =
    3000 PSI + 14.7 PSI = 3014.7 PSIA

V_2 = final gas volume (in^3)

$n = 1.4$

Since we must first solve for V_2:

$$V_2^n = \frac{P_1}{P_2} V_1^n \quad \text{or} \quad V_2 = \sqrt[n]{\frac{P_1}{P_2}} \; V_1$$

$$V_2 = \left[\sqrt[1.4]{\frac{1514.7}{3014.7}} \right] \times 1155$$

$$V_2 = \sqrt[1.4]{.502} \times 1155$$

$$V_2 = \text{anti-log} \left[\frac{\log(.502)}{1.4} \right] \times 1155$$

$$V_2 = \text{anti-log} \left[\frac{.299}{1.4} \right] \times 1155$$

$$V_2 = .611 \times 1155$$

$$V_2 = 706 \text{ in}^3 \text{ (gas volume)}$$

Since V_2=final *gas* volume the oil volume would be the initial gas volume minus the final gas volume:

$$V_{oil}=V_1 - V_2$$

$$V_{oil}=1155-706$$

$$V_{oil}=449 \text{ in}^3 \text{ (oil volume in storage)}$$

2. Solution:

$$P_1 V_1^n = P_2 V_2^n$$

P_1=Initial gas pressure (absolute) =
3000 PSIG + 14.7 PSI= 3014.7 PSIA

V_1=Initial gas volume = 706 in³ (from # 1)

P_2=Final gas pressure = 2250 PSIG + 14.7 PSI = 2264.7 PSIA

V_2=Final gas volume

n=1.4

$$V_2 = \sqrt[1.4]{\frac{P_1}{P_2}}\ V_1$$

$$V_2 = \sqrt[1.4]{\frac{3014.7}{2264.7}} \times 706$$

$$V_2 = \sqrt[1.4]{1.33} \times 706$$

$$V_2 = \text{antilog} \left[\frac{\log 1.33}{1.4}\right] \times 706$$

$$V_2 = \text{antilog} \left[\frac{.124}{1.4}\right] \times 706$$

$$V_2 = 1.23 \times 706$$

$$V_2 = 866 \text{ in}^3 \text{(gas volume)}$$

The oil volume stored at this pressure (2250 PSI) would be the total gas volume of the accumulator minus the final gas volume or:

$$V_{oil} = 1155 \text{ in}^3 - 866 \text{ in}^3 = 289 \text{ in}^3$$

Consequently, the oil discharged would be found by subtracting the final oil volume from the initial oil volume:

$$\triangle V = 449 - 289 = 160 \text{ in}^3 \text{ (oil discharged)}$$

If we compare the oil volumes as calculated in the isothermal and adiabatic examples, we find that the isothermal change stores 125 in³ (574-449=125 in³) more oil than the adiabatic change, given an equivalent pressure change. Since this extra 1/2 gallon of fluid can influence the proper operation of the hydraulic system, we must consider the conditions under which the oil enters and leaves the accumulator. Our example has shown that moments after the adiabatic charging of the accumulator with oil, the gas volume would be 706 in³. However, if the same accumulator were given enough time, the temperature of the gas would equalize at room temperature. As the gas cools, its internal pressure decreases. This allows more oil to enter the accumulator as the gas volume drops to the isothermal level (580 in³).

USING ACCUMULATOR CURVES

In actual application, the pressure and volume conditions more closely approximate the adiabatic change of state than the isothermal change. To avoid the somewhat complicated mathematics, accumulator manufacturers publish curves from which the volume of oil available can be determined directly, assuming that the precharge pressure and operating pressure are known. The graphs are usually corrected so that the precharge pressure and the operating system pressure are represented directly in gauge pressure (PSIG). Normally, two curves are given for each accumulator. One represents the simple isothermal relationship, while the second represents the more complicated adiabatic change. The graphs which follow are typical examples.

When using the graph, there is certain information which must be determined from the operating condition of the circuit in which the accumulator will be used. If a bladder type accumulator is to be used, there are specific limits which must be placed on the precharge pressure and the gas compression ratio. A logical selection process would include the following steps.

Step 1: Determine the minimum operating pressure.
With any circuit design, it is imperative to determine the minimum operating pressure which will produce the required thrust or torque at the work output. When working with accumulators, it is important to size the actuator so that the operating pressure will be well below the maximum pressure rating of the pump and other system components. In this way the accumulator can be charged with pressurized fluid whenever system pressure exceeds the minimum operating pressure limit. For the purpose of this explanation, let us assume that our minimum operating pressure is 1500 PSI.

Step 2: Determine the maximum system pressure.

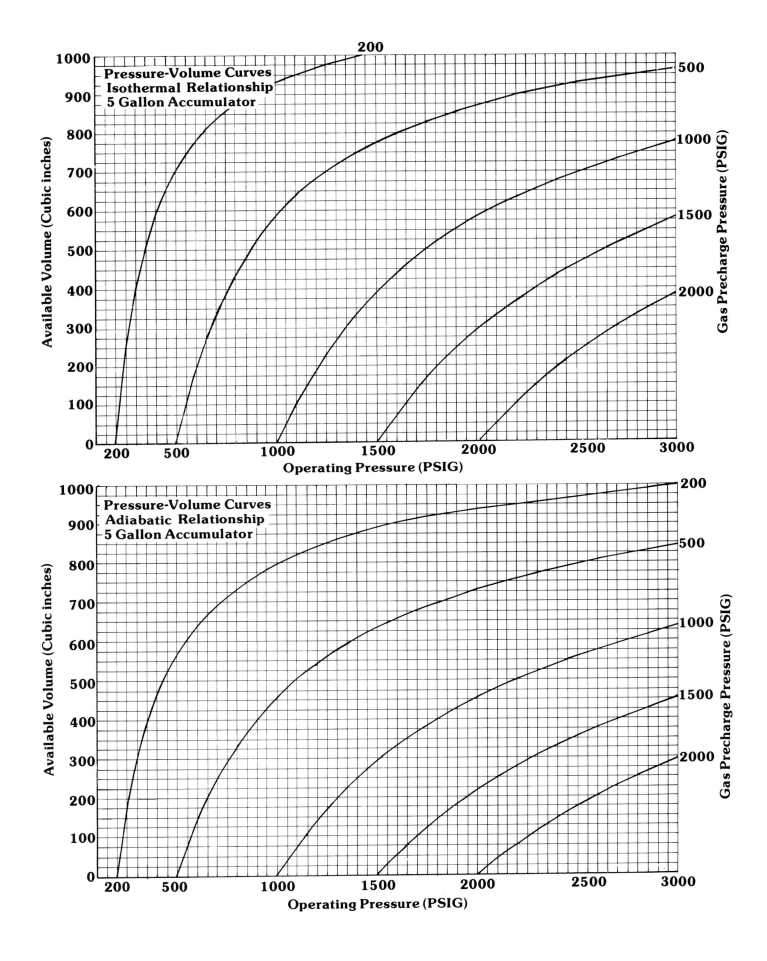

Generally speaking, the maximum system pressure is determined either by the pressure rating of the pump or the accumulator. You will find that most accumulators are rated for a maximum operating pressure of 3000 PSI. Higher pressure versions (up to 6000 PSI) are available. However, they cost considerably more than the 3000 PSI units. It is important to fix the maximum pressure limit as high as feasibly possible. In this way the maximum storage capability of the accumulator can be utilized. Let us assume that our maximum operating pressure will be 3000 PSI.

NOTE: As previously mentioned, when selecting a bladder type accumulator, we must limit the maximum gas compression ratio to prevent overflexing of the bladder. To prevent overflexing of the bladder, the maximum system pressure should not exceed three times the minimum operating pressure. If, for example, the minimum operating pressure were 500 PSI, then the maximum operating pressure should not exceed 1500 PSI.

STEP 3: Determine the precharge pressure.

With a gas charged accumulator, the lower the precharge pressure, the more oil the accumulator will store at maximum operating pressure. Likewise, the lower the precharge pressure, the lower the minimum operating pressure can be before the accumulator completely empties its oil charge. Actually, the precharge pressure is best determined by studying the accumulator pressure volume curves, and comparing the performance with the result you expect to obtain for your system. Nevertheless, there are some guidelines to follow for determining the proper precharge pressure *range*. Although these guidelines specifically set the limits of precharge pressure for bladder type accumulators, they can also be applied to piston designs.

With bladder type accumulators, we must prevent overstressing the bladder when it is fully compressed at maximum operating pressure. To prevent excessive deformation at high pressure, the precharge pressure should never drop below 25% of the maximum operating pressure. This means that with a maximum pressure of 3000 PSI, the minimum precharge pressure should not be less than 750 PSI.

On the other hand, we usually do not want to precharge the accumulator to a level higher than the minimum operating pressure. If this were the case, the precharge would have enough force to empty the accumulator completely. This would cause the bladder protection valve to close during normal operation of the system. For mechanical reasons, this is not recommended.

One way to assure that the bladder protection valve will always remain open is to limit the maximum precharge to 90% of the minimum operating pressure. In this way, the actuator will stall, from lack of pressure force, before the accumulator fully discharges. With this method the maximum precharge for a system which must operate with at least 1500 PSI would be determined as follows:

$$1500 \text{ PSI} \times .9 - 1350 \text{ PSI}$$

This means that the acceptable precharge for the example we are developing would be somewhere between 1350 PSI and 750 PSI.

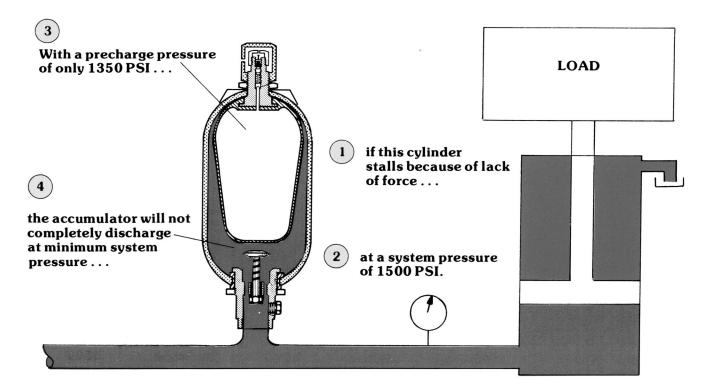

3 With a precharge pressure of only 1350 PSI . . .

4 the accumulator will not completely discharge at minimum system pressure . . .

1 if this cylinder stalls because of lack of force . . .

2 at a system pressure of 1500 PSI.

LOAD

Although the above guideline provides satisfactory operation for many hydraulic circuits, it may not be desirable to have the load stall at some minimum operating pressure.

For instance, in applications with varying loads, we would have to precharge the accumulator based on the minimum pressure required to move the heaviest load. You can see that there would be no safeguard against emptying the accumulator if the cylinder were to be extended with no load.

For this reason, it is sometimes better to assure that the accumulator will not fully discharge simply by oversizing the accumulator. In this way the precharge is not limited to some maximum level for a mechanical reason. With this design perspective, the only limiting factor on maximum precharge is how much oil you expect the accumulator to store. As shown in the example, a flow control is usually required to control the speed of the actuator because the pressure of the accumulator, being higher than the pressure required to do the work, can cause an undesirably high flow rate.

STEP 4: Determine the size of the accumulator.
In general, it will be necessary to determine how much fluid must be displaced to do the required work. Once we determine the amount of oil required, we simply choose an accumulator from the graphs that will supply the working volume as pressure drops from maximum to minimum values. If, for instance, we require 300 in³ of working volume, and the maximum pressure is 3000 PSI, the minimum pressure 1500 PSI, and the accumulator is precharged to 1000 PSI, the graphic solution would indicate that a 5 gallon accumulator is required. We have assumed that the adiabatic relationship applies to this circuit requirement.

It is important to note that we size the accumulator by the oil it *displaces* rather than by a *flow rate*. The flow rate of an accumulator is determined solely by the prevailing pressure conditions. High pressure at the accumulator means high potential energy. If the accumulator were discharged into a system with little resistance to flow, the flow rate through the oil port of the accumulator could be quite high. Although this high flow rate is short lived, it is not impossible to achieve instantaneous flow rates of over 500 GPM from a one gallon accumulator.

Consequently, the flow rate from an accumulator is determined solely by the time allotted for it to discharge. Normally, flow controls (Chapter 3) are required to control the rate of discharge from the accumulator.

ACCUMULATOR APPLICATIONS

In many hydraulic systems, it would be convenient if we could somehow store hydraulic energy during one portion of the cycle, and then use this energy later in the cycle, to perform the required work function. However, hydraulic fluid is only slightly compressible, which eliminates the possibility of storing high levels of energy directly. To store this energy in the system, it then becomes necessary to make use of an oil accumulator. Nevertheless, because of lack of application experience, and because of the misconception that the accumulator is both expensive and a service problem, this device is often omitted from the hydraulic system design. Rather than engineer the hydraulic circuit to include an ac-

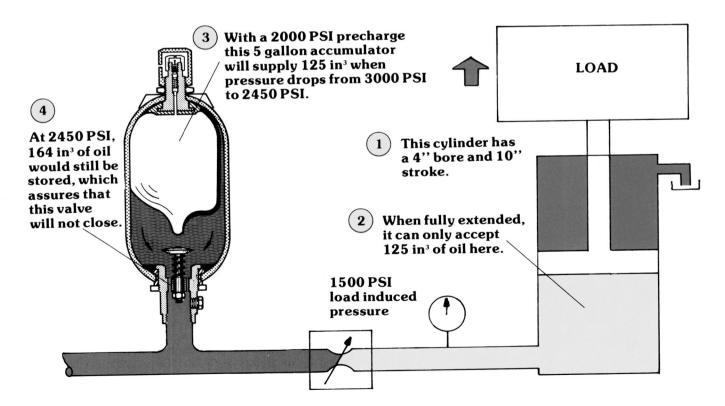

③ With a 2000 PSI precharge this 5 gallon accumulator will supply 125 in³ when pressure drops from 3000 PSI to 2450 PSI.

④ At 2450 PSI, 164 in³ of oil would still be stored, which assures that this valve will not close.

① This cylinder has a 4" bore and 10" stroke.

② When fully extended, it can only accept 125 in³ of oil here.

1500 PSI load induced pressure

LOAD

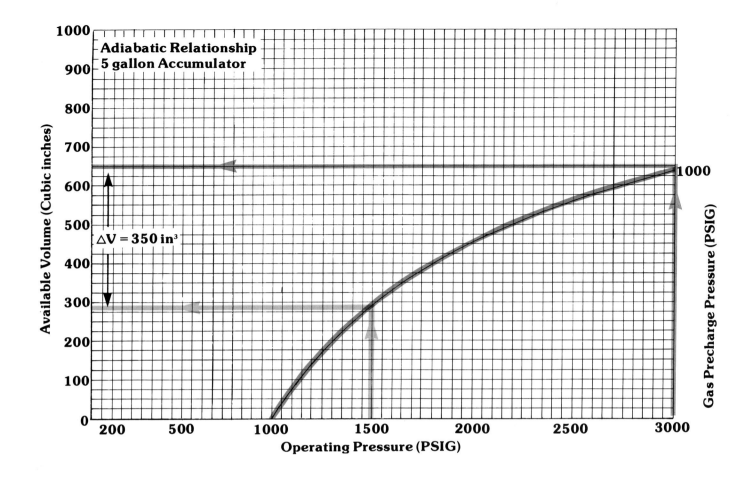

Adiabatic Relationship
5 gallon Accumulator

$\Delta V = 350$ in³

Available Volume (Cubic inches)

Operating Pressure (PSIG)

Gas Precharge Pressure (PSIG)

cumulator, the designer simply provides a circuit in which the pump can produce instantaneously the hydraulic energy which is required to do the work. Nevertheless there are many circuit designs which could be enhanced by the use of an accumulator. Let us now mention a few examples.

ENERGY STORAGE

In any circuit which has an intermittent duty cycle, there is a potential use for the accumulator. Likewise, circuits which are continuously operating can make good use of an accumulator, if during a portion of their cycles, a high flow rate is required for a short period of time. The design theory is that large hydraulic pumps (which also require large prime movers) which operate intermittently, are replaced by smaller pumps which operate a greater percentage of the time. If we look at the overall duty cycle, we are putting the same level of energy into our system by either method. The difference is that the accumulator circuit more continuously supplies this energy at a lower power level. For those of you who are familiar with electric motors and the industrial *power factor* the efficiency of the accumulator circuit is readily apparent.

ENERGY RESERVE

In critical application when it would be dangerous to stop the

system function at some midpoint in the duty cycle, the accumulator can be used to store an *emergency supply* of energy. If there is a pump or power failure, this stored energy can be used to complete the cycle and return the machinery to safe condition. In this type of application, the accumulator must be large enough to supply enough oil to run the machinery through at least one complete cycle.

LEAKAGE COMPENSATION

In many hydraulic circuits it is often necessary for the actuator to provide a holding force without any motion. Hydraulically, this requires pressure with no flow. We have shown in Chapter 6 how this problem can be solved by using a pressure compensated pump. However, the accumulator offers the designer a viable alternative. In machine tool circuits, for instance, the accumulator will exert pressure on the clamping cylinders for extended periods of time. The oil stored in the accumulator will supply the relatively small oil flow which is required to replace the oil lost by internal leakage of spool type directional controls (for example) and possible leakage by the piston seals. When leakage losses allow the accumulator to drop below the minimum clamping pressure, the pump will be turned on momentarily to recharge the accumulator. This can be an automatic function if the circuit incorporates an accumulator charging valve

(Chapter 2) or a pressure switch with an adjustable pressure differential (Chapter 8).

THERMAL COMPENSATOR

We have shown in Chapter 2 how a *port relief* can be used to protect the system from overpressure due to thermal expansion of the fluid. However, this method provides no means of maintaining pressure if the oil cools. In static closed systems that are subject to varying temperatures, the accumulator will compensate for the expansion and contraction of the fluid, and maintain system pressure within safe limits.

HYDRAULIC SHOCK ABSORBER

The bladder type accumulator, because of its extremely low inertia, can be used to dampen pressure pulsations in the hydraulic system. These pulsations can be high frequency, such as those generated by the individual pumping chambers within a pump, or they can be low frequency, such as would be produced by precompression/decompression shocks experienced during shifting of a directional valve. Whatever the source, a high percentage of the pulsations can be removed by a bladder accumulator located close to it. For pulsation dampening, the precharge is normally established at 80% of the maximum operating pressure. Then, by experimentation, the precharge can be adjusted higher or lower until the most favorable results are obtained.

ENERGY RECOVERY

In systems in which large masses must be decelerated, it is possible to use the accumulator to recover most of the energy that was originally required to put the load in motion. When the load *overruns* the actuator, load induced pressure will force oil out of the actuator. If this flow of fluid is directed into an adequately sized accumulator, the precharge pressure will offer resistance to this flow. Then, as the accumulator becomes more fully charge, the back pressure on the actuator will cause the load to decelerate. When accumulator pressure rises to meet the load induced pressure, the motion of the load will stop. By altering the precharge of the accumulator, the deceleration rate can be adjusted. The recovered potential energy now stored by the accumulator can then be used to assist in restarting the system.

INSTALLATION PRECAUTIONS FOR GAS CHARGED ACCUMULATORS

The accumulator offers many advantages to the hydraulic system design because of its ability to store *potential energy*. It is important, however, for those who work with accumulators to respect this high energy level. Irresponsible tinkering with a charged accumulator can be as lethal as the release of the energy stored in several sticks of dynamite.

Whenever an accumulator is to be precharged, it is imperative that the oil side of the accumulator be vented to atmosphere. Also, before attempting to remove an accumulator from the system (for repair or replacement), it is mandatory that the oil port be at zero pressure. A charged accumulator which is not mechanically restrained will propel itself through the air like a rocket once it is unthreaded from the plumbing. For these reasons, proper valving (gate valves, ball valve and/or needle valves) must be incorporated on the oil side of the accumulator. One valve (usually a ball valve) is required for the initial isolation of the accumulator form the rest of the hydraulic system. The second valve (usually a small needle valve) is teed into the line between the isolating valve and the accumulator so that the oil charge can be bled to the reservoir.

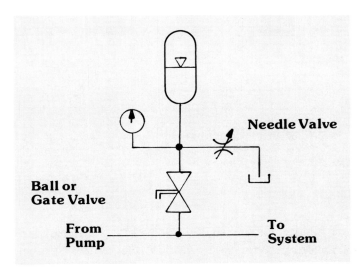

Minimum Valving Needed to Isolate the Accumulator

CHECKING THE PRECHARGE PRESSURE

One of the easiest ways to check the precharge pressure on an inservice accumulator is to close the isolating valve when there is an oil charge in the accumulator. When it is closed, the needle valve can be opened to bleed the oil charge in the accumulator slowly to tank. By carefully watching the pressure gauge, you will first see a gradual decay in pressure as the oil charge empties through the partially open needle valve. However, the moment the accumulator rids itself of all the oil the needle on the pressure gauge will immediately drop to zero. The pressure from which the needle drops quickly to zero is the precharge pressure in the accumulator.

NOTES ON PRECHARGING

The most important point to remember is that *an accumulator should be precharged only with "oil pumped" or "dry" nitrogen.* Never consider using compressed air or oxygen for precharging accumulator, since oxygen has a tendency to explode if mixed with oil under compression.

Nitrogen is a commercially available bottled gas. A fully charged nitrogen bottle is normally supplied with an internal pressure of approximately 2500 PSI, which is usually adequate for precharging most accumulators. As with any pressure vessel designed for transporting high pressure gases, the shutoff valve on top of the bottle is protected with a metal cover which is threaded to the bottle. This cover protects the valve from being broken if the nitrogen bottle were to be inadvertantly dropped. It is important to remember that this protective cover should never be removed unless the bottle is firmly supported. In addition, the cover should be immediately replaced upon completion of the precharging, and before attempting to move the bottle.

In order to precharge the accumulator, it will be necessary to purchase an accumulator charging assembly from the accumulator manufacturer. This assembly consists of a length of hose, a pressure gauge, a bleeder valve, a check valve, and the necessary fittings for connecting to both the accumulator gas valve and the nitrogen bottle. (The standard thread connection for an American nitrogen bottle is a 29/32-14 left hand thread gland nut). Although the procedure is different for different charging assemblies, a general procedure would be as follows:
— Connect the charging assembly first to the nitrogen bottle and then to the accumulator, carefully making sure that all fittings are tightened.
— Operate the mechanism of the charging assembly which opens the gas valve on the accumulator.
— Begin inflating the accumulator by slowly opening and then closing the valve on the nitrogen bottle. Remember, the adiabatic expansion of the nitrogen as it is transferred from the bottle to the accumulator will cause the gas to cool.
— When the required precharge pressure has been reached, allow time for the temperature of the gas to equalize. Then check the pressure on the gauge. Bleed off any excess pressure and/or add nitrogen as required.
— When satisfied with the *isothermal* precharge pressure, operate the mechanism to close the gas valve on the accumulator.
— Open bleeder valve to vent residual pressure from the hose and charging assembly.
— Remove charging assembly from the gas valve on the accumulator.
— Check gas valve with soapy water for gas leak.
— Remove charging assembly from nitrogen bottle, and replace protective covers on both the nitrogen bottle and the accumulator.

Once the accumulator is put into operation, check the precharge when the system is at operating temperature. If the accumulator was precharged at room temperature, and is then heated by the hydraulic system, the precharge pressure could become higher than desired. After putting the accumulator into service, it is good practice to check its precharge pressure periodically. We recommend checking the precharge after one week of service. If no loss of precharge is indicated, the precharge should be checked on increasing time intervals of one month, six months, and then yearly. In order to prevent excessive wear of the gas valve and unnecessary loss of precharge pressure, do not continuously (daily) check the precharge pressure by using the gas valve.

FILTRATION

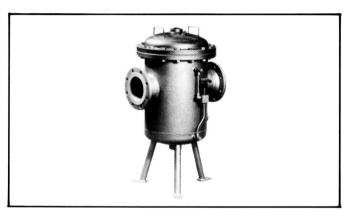

1800 GPM Return Line Filter
(Courtesy of The Hycon Corp.)

There is nothing more frustrating than to see a well designed system, which uses the best hydraulic components, fail, simply because of dirt. Nevertheless, studies have shown that over 60% of all hydraulic systems down time can be attributed to untidy maintenance, and lack of proper filtration. In Chapter 5, we have discussed the *micron* and its relationship to the close tolerance manufacturing of the directional control valve. If we consider any of the other hydraulic system components covered in other chapters, we can see that close tolerance oil sealing also plays a very important role in obtaining the proper valve function. Consequently, anyone who is responsible for the design and/or maintenance of a hydraulic system must consider the *precision* with which hydraulic system components are manufactured. Let us now take a practical look at how dirt affects the performance of the hydraulic system, and what you can do to preserve the life of the system's components.

THE CONTAMINANT

The American National Standard Glossary of Terms for

Fluid Power (ANSI B93.2-1971) as published by The NFPA, (The National Fluid Power Association, 3333 North Mayfair Road, Milwaukee, Wisconsin 53222) defines contaminant as, ". . . any *material*, or substance which is unwanted or adversely affects the fluid power system or components, or both."

The material or substance they define can have many origins. First, there are the huge amounts of dirt present in the hydraulic system when newly fabricated. When it is first started, a properly filtered system is probably the dirtiest it ever will be. The fact is that during the fabrication stage the reservoir is open for abuse. A newly fabricated reservoir, if not used immediately, often becomes the shops garbage can. During this time it collects cigarette butts, lunch bags, apple cores, soda cans, packing materials, and other large objects. These large objects, though, are usually not harmful to the system, since they will be removed prior to assembly and *cleaning* of the reservoir. The harmful dirt which is built into the system has much smaller dimensions. The new system, which looks clean, is actually contaminated by millions of invisible contaminants.

It is difficult, if not impossible, to remove the invisible contaminants in a new system by washing with solvents and then wiping with rags. Likewise, after the assembly, much of the contamination becomes inaccessable to standard cleaning processes. Harmful, built-in contaminants include rust, paint chips, paint over-spray, shop dust, teflon tape and other sealing compounds, metal chips from bolt threads and pipe fittings, coring sand from cast housings, lint from "cleaning rags", welding slag, etc.

The second source of contamination is the dirty environment in which the system must operate. During normal operation, the oil level in the reservoir is constantly changing. For instance, during extension of a cylinder the oil level drops, and the reservoir inhales polluted dust and water vapor laden air from its surroundings. The dust mixes with the oil and enters the hydraulic system. After shutdown of the system, the moisture which has entered condenses on the walls of the reservoir as the system cools. This not only dilutes the oil but also causes formation of rust particles. Although most air is filtered by the breather element, some air is drawn into the reservoir through other openings. These openings include improperly fitted suction and return line flanges, shaft seals of pumps and motors, and rod seals of cylinder actuators.

A third source for contamination is that generated by the system during normal operation. As the system operates friction in pumps, valves, cylinders and motors causes normal wearing of the sliding surfaces. Likewise, high oil velocities can cause erosion of these metal surfaces. In either case, microscopic particles enter the system with an abrasive effect. These particles in turn accelerate wear which further increases the contamination level in the system.

Another source for contamination which is also generated during normal operation of the system is oil oxidation. This formation of solid carbon particles has been discussed in Chapter 7.

THE EFFECTS OF CONTAMINATION

Now that we have discussed some of the possible causes of contamination, it is important to understand the effect this contamination has on the hydraulic system. Basically, there are two types of failures that can be attributed to contamination in the system. They are degradation failure and catastrophic failure. Degradation failure is probably the most costly contamination-caused failure because it degrades the performance characteristics of virtually every component in the system. During degradation failure of a component, the abrasiveness of minute particles causes accelerated wearing of the close tolerance, sealing surfaces. This increases internal leakage and reduces the performance capability of the component. Unfortunately, degradation failure is a relatively slow process, which camouflages the loss of performance on a day to day basis.

Degradation failure spreads throughout the hydraulic system like cancer, and is usually not detected until the damage is irreversible. Indications that degradation failure has occurred include sluggish system responses, loss of speed adjustment accuracy (Chapter 3), inability of the system to build full tonnage, and/or overheating. To safeguard against this type of premature failure, it is imperative that adequate filtration be provided for the system.

Catastrophic failure, on the other hand, is the immediate failure of a system component. Although this type of failure is not always related to contamination, contaminants are the most probable cause. In catastrophic failure, large particles (usually visable contaminants) cause moving parts to jam or stick. With pumps the contaminants can gather in a location which blocks critical lubrication passages. Without proper lubrication, immediate failure is sure to follow.

Finally, dirt can collect in orifices which supply oil to the pilot circuit of pilot operated relief valves, pressure compensated flow controls, and various variable displacement pump controls to name just a few. If, for example, we consider the pilot operated relief valve as discussed in Chapter 2, it is easy to see that if dirt plugs any one of the pilot supply orifices, oil can no longer enter the area above the main poppet. In this example, the relief valve would not build pressure since there would be no hydraulic force holding the main poppet closed. Although this type of malfunction is easily corrected by disassembling and cleaning, it should still be classified as catastrophic. Even though the component itself is not physically damaged, money is wasted because of downtime and loss of production.

Considering the fact that contaminants cause failure, we must take positive steps to minimize the level of contamination in the hydraulic system. Common sense precautions will prevent many of the contaminants from entering the system, but there is no way to totally eliminate the source of contamination. So that we can keep the number of contaminants, and their size, within tolerable limits, we must provide the system with adequate filtration.

Particle Size (μ)	Particle Count For 100 mL of Fluid						
	Class 0	Class 1	Class 2	Class 3	Class 4	Class 5	Class 6
5-10	2700	4600	9700	24,000	32,000	87,000	128,000
10-25	670	1340	2680	5360	10,700	21,400	42,000
25-50	93	210	380	780	1510	3130	6500
50-100	16	28	56	110	225	430	1000
100+	1	3	5	11	21	41	92

In consideration of the number of contaminants there is an SAE standard which specifies seven levels of cleanliness. The classifications range from Class 0, the cleanest, to Class 6, the dirtiest. The levels of cleanliness, according to the SAE standard, are defined in the chart.

A new drum of hydraulic oil, as received from the refinery, typically falls into Class 6. This means that *new oil is not satisfactorily clean,* for use in most hydraulic systems. To determine the level of cleanliness in your hydraulic system, oil companies and some hydraulic equipment suppliers provide an oil analysis service. As a guideline, we recommend that servo systems be provided with filtration sufficient to achieve Class 0 or Class 1 specifications. For hydraulic systems which must function dependably, or where extended service life of the components is required, the level of cleanliness should fall in the Class 2 to Class 4 category. Finally, hydraulic systems which are used on an infrequent basis, or those which do not require an extreme level of dependability, can operate with fluid in the Class 4 to Class 6 range.

To achieve a specific level of cleanliness, we must of course select the proper filtration for the system. Unfortunately, the degree of filtration required can only be estimated. The level of cleanliness must be then checked by taking test samples of fluid from the system. From experience we have found that the nominal filter rating as listed in the chart below normally achieves the specified levels of cleanliness.

Let us now look at the types of filtering medias available and some of the considerations which affect the performance of the filter.

Degree of Filtration	Level of Cleanliness Generally Achieved	Application
1-5μ	Class 0 to Class 1	Servo System
10μ	Class 2 to Class 4	Hydraulic system with piston pumps, piston motors, flow controls, reducing valves. (Extended service life for any type component)
20-25μ	Class 4 to Class 5	Hydraulic system with gear or vane pumps
40μ	Class 6	Hydraulic system with infrequent duty cycle, and non critical components

THE FILTERING MEDIA

The purpose of a filter is to remove contaminants from the hydraulic system. This is achieved by forcing the hydraulic fluid to pass through a *filtering media*. The filtering media is made of a porous substance which allows oil to pass through microscopic openings, but catches the dirt particles which are larger than the pores. In principle the operation of a filter is similar to a screen on a window. The screen allows air to enter but it filters out insects which are larger than the openings in the screen.

Today filter elements are constructed with various types of filtering medias. These include porous paper, wire cloth, nylon cloth, sintered (bonded by a heating process) metal fiber and polyester fleece. These filtering medias are pleated and encased to form a filter element. The type of filtering medias can be broken down into two general classifications; surface type and depth type elements. Let us now take a closer look at these two media types.

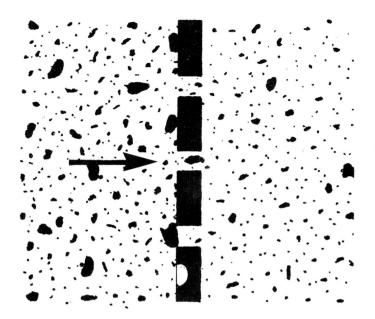

Surface Type Filtering Principle

Typical Filter Elements
(Pleating increases surface area of the media)

(Courtesy of The Hycon Corp.)

SURFACE TYPE FILTERS

A surface filter, as the name implies, filters the hydraulic fluid by collecting the contaminants on the surface of the filtering media. The filtering media is a single layer of precisely *woven* strands of either stainless steel wire or nylon filament. The pore size of these elements is determined by the diameter of the individual strands and the number of strands woven into each inch of the material. A *100 mesh* element, for instance, has 100 strands per inch (length and width) of the filtering media. This means that one square inch of this material would have approximately 10,000 square openings. Each of the square openings in a 100 mesh element, has a length and width dimension of 149 microns. Some of the other mesh numbers commonly used in hydraulic systems are listed in the chart.

Mesh No.	Opening Size (Microns)
60	238
100	149
200	74
325	44

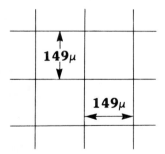

100 Mesh Opening Size

The advantage of the relatively expensive weaving process used in the construction of a surface type filtering media, is the precision control over the pore size in the final product. For this reason surface type filters are normally given an *absolute* rating. An absolute rating of 149 microns, for instance, means none of the holes in the filtering media will be larger than 149 microns. An absolute rating *does not mean* that the filter absolutely will not pass particles larger than its largest pore.

There are several reasons why particles larger than the absolute rating can migrate through the filtering media. First, the openings formed by the weaving process are not perfectly rigid. If, for example, a 160 micron particle were to be lodged in the center of a 149 micron opening, the pressure differential from inlet to outlet of the filter could create enough force on the particle to deform the previously square opening, allowing this particle to pass through the media. Second, the contaminant itself may not be perfectly rigid. The force due to the pressure differential can easily extrude O-ring fragments, and other similar substances, through the smaller openings. Finally, we must consider the fact that all particles are not perfectly dimensioned. A steel splinter, for example may be many times larger in length than the absolute rating of the filtering media. However, this same splinter can also be so narrow that it can penetrate the filtering media without even touching the wire mesh. It is then free to pass through the system, causing damage because of its larger dimension.

DEPTH TYPE FILTERING MEDIA

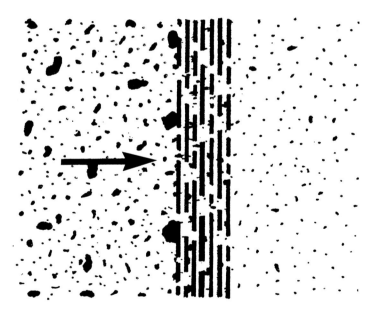

Depth Type Filtering Principle

Today most filter elements below the 40 micron rating use a depth type filtering media. This media captures the contaminants within the media structure by causing the oil to flow through a maze of passages. The filtering media is composed of a relatively thick mat of stainless steel wire, paper fibers or synthetic fibers arranged in a random pattern. The fibers are then bonded to each other to form a highly porous media. Generally speaking, the pore size is regulated by controlling the compaction of the fibers prior to the bonding process. However, since the individual pore sizes cannot be as accurately controlled as they are in the weaving process for surface filtering medias, depth filters are normally given a *nominal* rating. A nominal rating of 10 microns simply means that the largest percentage of the pores in the element has a dimension of 10 microns or less. Such an element will remove most of the particles 10 microns or larger, while at the same time allowing a few of these larger particles to pass through. On the other hand, it will also remove many particles smaller than 10 microns. Today depth type elements are readily available with nominal ratings in the range of 1 to 25 microns, with the most common being the 10 micron element.

The depth filter offers two major advantages. First, the element has a higher dirt retention capability because it captures particles in a *volume* of filtering media, rather than on a surface *area*. Generally, this results in depth elements having a longer service life. The second major advantage offered by depth filtration is that these elements, when bonded correctly, are mechanically stronger. They can withstand a higher pressure differential before they collapse or rupture. This also increases the service life since full flow can be forced through a partially clogged element, as long as the pressure differential is high enough. For the most part, the construction material determines the maximum pressure differential the element can withstand. The chart indicates the maximum practical pressure differential for various filtering medias.

Depth Filter Media	Maximum Pressure Differential
paper	150 PSI
polyester fleece	3000 PSI
stainless steel fiber	4500 PSI

FILTER LOCATION IN THE HYDRAULIC SYSTEM

There are two ways to approach the problem as to where the filter should be located in the hydraulic system. The first avenue of thinking is based on the assumption that dirt is constantly being generated and ingested by the hydraulic system. By placing a filter downstream of the source we can keep the entire system clean, or at least within acceptable limits of cleanliness. The second way to approach the problem is based on the assumption that contamination is always present in the hydraulic system. If we make this assumption, then the logical place for the filter's location is before the oil enters the critical component or components. In this way the filter acts as a barrier between the damaging contamination and the precision component(s).

Locating the filter in your hydraulic system requires a clear understanding of all factors. Let us now consider the advantages and disadvantages of suction, pressure and return line filtration.

SUCTION FILTRATION

Suction filtration is achieved by locating a filtering media between the reservoir and the hydraulic pump. The most common practice involves immersing a *"suction strainer"* in the hydraulic reservoir which is threaded onto the end of the suction line. Generally, the strainer is oriented horizontally, well below the minimum oil level in the reservoir. It is also good practice to orient the suction strainer a minimum of three inches from the bottom of the reservoir to avoid the possibility of picking up contamination which has settled out of the hydraulic fluid. A typical suction strainer is shown in the illustration.

Threaded Connection

Filtering Media

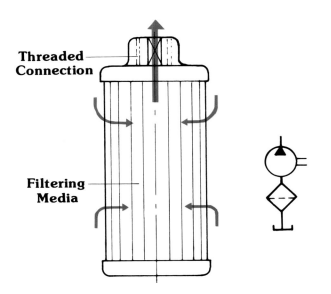

Typical Suction Strainer
(Courtesy of The Hycon Corp.)

ADVANTAGES

The suction strainer, from a filtration standpoint, places the filtering media in an ideal location. Both fluid velocity and pressure differential across the element are, out of necessity, extremely low at this point. This increases the filter's efficiency since high fluid velocities are not present to disturb the collected particles, and there is very little pressure force to cause particle migration through the media. Also, the filter is in an ideal location for preventing contamination within the reservoir from entering the system where it can cause damage to critical clearances in pumps, valves and actuators.

DISADVANTAGES

The advantages of suction filtration are strongly outweighed by the disadvantage of the pressure drop created by the element. We have shown in Chapter 1 the extreme precautions which must be observed when determining the suction conditions for the hydraulic pump. Any benefit the suction filter offers by keeping contamination out of the pump, is offset by the possibility of damaging the pump because of cavitation. The low pressure differential, which may be sufficient to push oil through a clean element, is not always adequate to supply the required flow when the element becomes partially clogged. To provide an adequate service life, the suction filter must be grossly oversized and maintained on a more frequent basis.

Another major disadvantage of the suction strainer is that it is located inside the oil reservoir which makes it inconvenient to service. It is for this reason many suction strainers in industrial hydraulic systems go unserviced until they starve the pump and cause cavitation damage.

Due to these disadvantages, a fine degree of filtration at the inlet of the pump is *specifically not recommended*. It is possible to install a course filtering media at this location simply to prevent large objects, (nuts, bolts, etc.) from causing catastrophic pump failure. However, even this type of filtration requires definite precautions.

When electing to use a suction strainer it is advisable to select the most coarse mesh available. We recommend nothing finer than 100 mesh or preferably 60 mesh screen. This strainer should be adequately oversized so that the pressure versus flow characteristics are negligable. Second, the suction strainer should be provided with a safety by-pass check valve. It is important to check the pressure override characteristics of this bypass check valve. This valve must be able to pass the full flow without causing a pressure differential that exceeds the vacuum capabilities of the pump. Also, a vacuum gauge should be located at the *pump's* inlet port so that the vacuum conditions can be continuously monitored during operation. This, of course, indicates the condition of the suction strainer. One final recommendation is that the suction strainer should be made as easy to service as possible. This can be accomplished by locating a gasketed access cover on the top plate of the reservoir, directly above the suction strainer. This allows removal of the strainer without draining oil from the reservoir. The cover should be clearly labeled as to its purpose. One last precaution is that the element should be contained in a plastic bag before it is removed from the suction line. This prevents the collected contamination from falling into the reservoir when the element is removed.

PRESSURE FILTERS

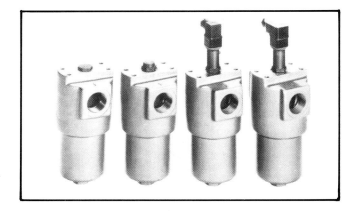

Typical Pressure Filters
(Courtesy of The Hycon Corp.)

A pressure filter is nothing more than a filter element contained in a housing which can withstand full system pressure. Generally speaking, a pressure filter can be located in any of the pressure lines downstream of the pump. It provides maximum protection for the component located directly downstream of the filter's outlet. Pressure filters are commonly used to protect high precision equipment such as electronic servo valves and piston type hydraulic motors. A typical filter is shown in the cross-sectional illustration.

ADVANTAGES

Probably the most favorable aspect of a pressure filter is that it can operate with very find filtration rates (1 micron nominal) and still have an acceptable life expectancy for the element. This is due to the fact that there is ample pressure available to force an oil flow through the minute passages in the filtering media.

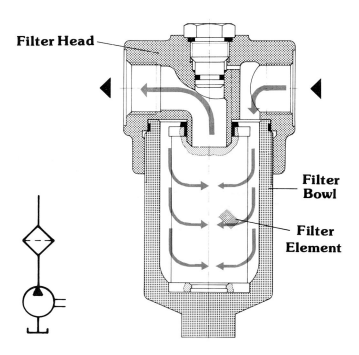

Pressure Filter Cross Section
(Courtesy of The Hycon Corp.)

DISADVANTAGES

The major disadvantage of pressure filtration is that both the housing and the element itself must be designed to withstand not only high system pressure but also the pressure spikes which occur during operation. To meet such pressure requirements the filter is somewhat more expensive both in initial cost and future element replacement. This is why pressure filtration is normally reserved for servo systems and other components which have a low dirt tolerance. A pressure filter can, however, be used in any system which requires a high degree of reliability, or where extended life expectancy of standard components is desired.

A technical disadvantage of pressure filtration is that pressure transients and high flow velocities tend to continually disturb the contaminants which are collected by the filtering media. The high pressure forces and the continuous motion of particles allow more contaminants to pass through the filtering media than would be common with other types of filtration. This, of course, has a tendancy to reduce the efficiency of the filtering media.

APPLICATION NOTES FOR PRESSURE FILTERS

The most important criteria when selecting a pressure filter for your application is the operating system pressure and the collapse pressure rating of the element. The fact is, that pressure at the filter's inlet is governed by the pressure setting of the main relief valve while pressure at the filter's outlet is determined solely by the load conditions. With little or no load induced pressure, it is possible to develop a considerable pressure drop across the element. This is particularly true during cold start-ups or for elements which have been in service for some time and have many pores plugged with contamination. Unless the element can withstand this high pressure differential, it is susceptible to rupture. Of course, if this is allowed to happen the filter immediately dumps a high concentration of contamination directly into the component it was supposed to protect.

A common practice used to prevent an element from rupturing is the use of a by-pass check valve in the head of the filter. As the filter becomes more and more clogged with contamination the pressure drop across the element increases until the cracking pressure of the by-pass check valve (Chapter 4) is reached. Once the by-pass opens, oil passes directly through the filter head, without being filtered. Unfortunately, if the filter is allowed to continue operating in the by-pass condition, it no longer provides the intended protection for the system or system components.

Today, fail-safe filtration is possible because filter elements are now available that can withstand full system pressure without collapsing. This type of element allows the media to become so clogged with contamination that the filter will cause a flow control function before the element will rupture. This means contamination will not be able to pass into the critical parts of the system. The system has fail-safe filtration because without a by-pass, the end actuator will stall due to the lack of oil rather than damage the filter element.

RETURN LINE FILTERS

Return Line Filters
(Courtesy of The Hycon Corp.)

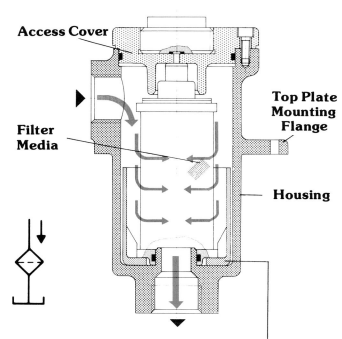

This basket prevents the collected contaminants from entering the reservoir when the element is removed.

Return Line Filter
(Courtesy of The Hycon Corp.)

Return line filtration is based on the assumption that a clean hydraulic system will remain clean if the contamination is filtered out of the fluid soon after it is ingested or created by the system. If the reservoir is properly designed and gasketed, return line filtration is the ideal choice for the majority of *standard* hydraulic systems.

ADVANTAGES

By locating a filter in the return line connection to the reservoir we can take advantage of three ideal conditions. First, there is sufficient pressure available to force an oil flow through a fine filtering media. This not only allows micronic filtration (typically 10 microns) but provides favorable life expectancy for the filtering elements. Although pressure is available, it is not high enough to complicate the design of the filter housing or element. The second advantage then, is that a high degree of filtering efficiency can be achieved with a less expensive element design. Since return line elements do not require high collapse pressure ratings, return line filtration is far more economical than is pressure filtration. The third advantage is related to the fact that a properly designed system has relatively low return line flow velocities. Such a flow allows efficient filtering since collected contaminants are not disturbed.

DISADVANTAGES

A disadvantage of return line filtration is that if contamination exists in the reservoir, then it must pass through every system component before being removed by the filter. Second, some components cannot withstand the varying, flow related, back pressure created by the return line filter. Case drain lines on pumps and motors, for instance, must be connected directly to the reservoir without passing through the filter. This allows a percentage of the flow to return to the reservoir without being filtered. Also, return line filtration has limited application possibilities in systems which must be decompressed (Chapter 4) rapidly.

APPLICATION NOTES ON RETURN LINE FILTRATION

Return line filtration is a logical solution to contamination related problems, only if we make the assumption that the reservoir, and the oil it contains, is clean. Of course, this is possible only if proper maintenance procedures are adhered to. Such procedures should include:

— Filling the reservoir only with properly filtered oil (newly refined oil is not clean by hydraulic standards).
— Whenever a component is temporarily removed from the system, the opening(s) should be covered or capped with plastic plugs. Remember, most harmful contamination cannot be seen.
— Before removing a component, thoroughly clean the immediate area with a degreasing solvent.
— Do not run the system without the return line filter element in place.
— Be sure all gaskets on suction and return line flanges, and access covers are properly fitted.
— Never weld on the reservoir or plumbing if the system is in service.

Another consideration when electing to use return line filtration is the important role the filler/breather cap plays in keeping ambient dirt out of the fluid. Unfortunately, many of the filler/breather caps available do not provide adequate filtration of the air drawn into the reservoir. Ideally, the filtration rate of the filler/breather should be identical to that of the return line filter. This can only be accomplished by specifying a high quality filler/breather for the reservoir. Likewise, the filler cap should be maintained on a regular basis.

Finally, when considering a return line filter, remember the return line flow rate can be higher than the flow produced by the pump. If, for example, a cylinder with a 2:1 area ratio is being used, we must consider the flow intensification this type of actuator creates. When sizing the filter, the maximum return flow valve must be used even if this flow rate exists only for a small portion of the total cycle.

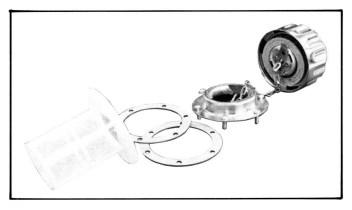

(Courtesy of The Hycon Corp.)

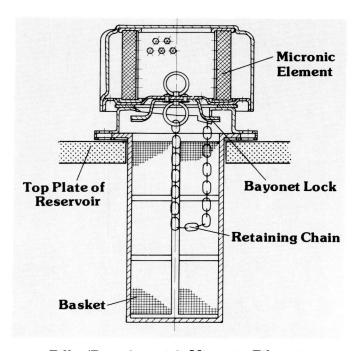

Filler/Breather with Micronic Filtration

(Courtesy of The Hycon Corp.)

SELECTION OF THE PROPER FILTER SIZE

Independant of the type of application and the location of the filter, we must size this component so that it will be capable of handling the maximum flow potential with a relatively low pressure drop. In addition, it is important to keep in mind the fact that the pressure drop through the filter will increase as the element becomes more and more clogged with contamination. For this reason, it is important to select a filter which has a negligible pressure drop when passing the required flow rate through a clean element.

Second, it is of the utmost importance that the designer size the filter so that it will operate correctly during cold start-up when the fluid is at its highest viscosity (Chapter 1). Since the oil must pass through microscopic pores in the filtering media, it is easy to understand why the filter is more susceptable to high pressure drops during cold start-up than is any other system component. A filter element which collapses and ruptures, or a by-pass valve which opens during cold start-up, provides little protection for the system. This pressure drop information for viscous fluids is not generally published and must be requested from the filter manufacturer.

FILTER MAINTENANCE

The best filter in the best possible location, will not be able to perform its required function if it is not maintained properly. Unfortunately, there is no rule of thumb, for recommending a time interval for filter inspection and/or element replacement. Therefore, it is the responsibility of maintenance personnel to develop a maintenance schedule, and then follow the schedule faithfully. Guidelines in establishing this schedule are given in the chart.

Inspection of the Filter's Condition
— Hourly during initial start-up
— Daily during first week of operation
— Weekly when daily inspection is found to be unnecessary
— Monthly after the first 100 hours of operation

CLOGGING INDICATORS

When checking the condition of a filter, do not rely solely on the *clogging indicator* if the filter is so equipped. A clogging indicator gives a visual or electrical indication of the pressure differential required to force a fluid flow through the filtering media. For example, with return line filters we can assume the pressure at the filter's outlet is zero (atmospheric). Therefore, with this type of filter, the indicator is simply a pressure gauge or pressure switch which senses the pressure at the filter's inlet. Visual indicators may be calibrated in PSI, however, they are more often color coded to indicate the filter's condition. For example, green indicates the filter is clean, yellow indicates the filter is clogging but satisfactory for continued use, and red indicates servicing is needed immediately. The problem encountered when relying solely on the indicator is that the devise has no way of determining if the element is clean, or whether the element has ruptured. For this reason we suggest that the element be removed and visually inspected on a regular basis.

It is important to note that the aforementioned inspection applies to all filter types. The clogging indicator for a pressure filter operates slightly differently since it must sense the pressure drop across the element. As shown in the cross section it does this by subtracting the effects of the outlet pressure from that at the inlet. However, if the element ruptures, the indicator will sense a low pressure differential and give the indication that the element is clean.

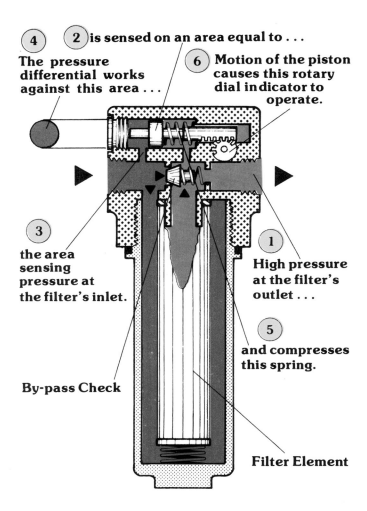

④ ② is sensed on an area equal to . . .

The pressure differential works against this area . . .

⑥ Motion of the piston causes this rotary dial indicator to operate.

③ the area sensing pressure at the filter's inlet.

① High pressure at the filter's outlet . . .

⑤ and compresses this spring.

By-pass Check

Filter Element

SYMBOLS

As shown in the following chart, accessory items can be represented in symbol form to aid in circuit design. You will notice that the chart does not list the symbols for modular manifolds since this topic was described adequately in the text. We have also included symbols for some other accessory items which were not covered in this chapter.

Symbol	Description
	Pressure switch with fixed pressure differential
	Pressure switch with fixed pressure differential and leakage port
	Pressure switch with adjustable pressure differential
	Pressure gauge
	Pressure gauge with snubber
	Pressure gauge with gauge isolator valve
	Pressure gauge with gauge shut off (needle valve)
	Multi-circuit gauge isolator valve

	Gas charged accumulator
	Filter or suction strainer
	Filter with built-in by-pass check valve
	Filter with mechanical indicator and by-pass valve
	Filter with electrical indicator and by-pass valve
	Filter with pressure gauge indicator and by-pass valve

	Pressure filter with pressure differential mechanical indicator and by-pass valve
	Air/oil heat exchanger
	Water/oil heat exchanger
	Immersion heater
	Flow meter
	Thermometer

CONCLUSION

This chapter has been devoted to a study of the more popular accessory items which are available for use with industrial hydraulic systems. These items included pressure switches, pressure gauges, gauge protectors, modular manifolds, accumulators and filters. Although these different product groups have very little in common on a functional basis, they all play an important role in proper operation, easier maintenance and trouble free life of the hydraulic system.

In consideration of pressure switches we have attempted to relate the operational characteristics of the different designs (piston and Bourdon tube) to the intended application. We have also compared operation of the Bourdon tube pressure switch with that of the pressure gauge and have indicated some of the installation precautions common to these two devices.

The modular manifold has been presented as a viable means to provide better serviceability, and reduce the amount of leakage in the hydraulic system. Although the discussion was limited to the design concept of one particular type of manifolding system, the designer should be aware that the modular concept has a much broader significance. Today's more specialized modules are reducing leakage, providing easier serviceability, and allowing a more compact design. The machine tool and press industries are but two examples where specialized modular componentry is rapidly gaining popularity. We have asked, however, that the interested reader look into these specialized modules individually.

The gas charged accumulator has been introduced as a component with many application possibilities. This single item can reduce pump size and installed horsepower, compensate for leakage, provide an emergency energy reserve, recover energy which would otherwise be wasted, compensate for thermal changes, reduce noise, and dampen pressure surges in the hydraulic system. The application information for accumulators included a discussion of Boyle's Law, adiabatic and isothermal pressure volume relationships, calculation of the available volume of oil which is stored in the accumulator, and determination of the precharge pressure limits.

The final component discussed was the hydraulic oil filter. By selecting this item as the last component covered in this chapter, we hope to leave you with the impression that this single item is a manditory accessory for all hydraulic systems. It is impossible to achieve a satisfactory life expectancy for any high performance system or component unless the control of contamination is dealt with properly. To aid the designer in selecting a proper filtration system, we have discussed the different types of filtering media. We have also listed the advantages and disadvantages offered by each possible filter location. These included suction, pressure and return line filters.

INDEX